SI Units and Their U.S. Customary Equiv

Quantity	SI Unit	U.S. Customary Unit
Acceleration	m/s^2	$3.281 \ ft/s^2$
Angular acceleration	rad/s^2	rad/s^2
Angular velocity	rad/s	rad/s
Area	m^2	$10.764 \ ft^2$
Energy	J (Joule)	0.7375 lb · ft
Force	N	0.22482 lb
	kN	0.22482 kip
Impulse	N · s	0.22482 lb · s
Length	m	3.281 ft
	km	0.6215 mi
Mass	kg	0.06854 slug
Moment	N · m	0.7375 lb · ft
Moment of inertia of an area	m^4	$8.63 \times 10^{-3} \ ft^4$
Moment of inertia of a mass	$kg \cdot m^2$	0.7375 lb · ft · s^2
Power	W	0.7375 lb · ft/s
Pressure	Pa	$1.45 \times 10^{-4} lb/in^2$
Velocity	m/s	$3.281 \ ft/s$
Volume (liquid)	L	0.2642 gal
Volume (solid)	m^3	$35.311 \ ft^3$
	cm^3	$0.061 \ in^3$
Work	J	0.7375 lb · ft

ENGINEERING MECHANICS

DYNAMICS

ENGINEERING MECHANICS

DYNAMICS

Braja M. Das
Aslam Kassimali
Sedat Sami

Department of Civil Engineering and Mechanics

Southern Illinois University at Carbondale

IRWIN

Burr Ridge, Illinois
Boston, Massachusetts
Sydney, Australia

© Richard D. Irwin, Inc., 1994

Cover photo by:	Paul Rung
Associate editor:	Kelley Butcher
Marketing manager:	Robb Linsky
Project editor:	Jess Ann Ramirez
Production manager:	Ann Cassady
Art manager:	Kim Meriwether
Compositor:	CRWaldman Graphic Communications
Typeface:	10/12 Times Roman
Printer:	R.R. Donnelley & Sons Company

Library of Congress Cataloging-in-Publication Data

Das, Braja M., date
    Engineering mechanics : dynamics / Braja M. Das, Aslam Kassimali,
Sedat Sami.
      p.   cm.
    Includes index.
    ISBN 0-256-11450-1
    1. Mechanics, Applied.   2. Dynamics.   I. Kassimali, Aslam.
II. Sami, Sedat.   III. Title.
TA352.D37   1994
620.1′04—dc20   92–36127

Printed in the United States of America

2 3 4 5 6 7 8 9 0 DOC 0 9 8 7 6 5 4

PREFACE

Engineering mechanics, which is concerned with the study of equilibrium and motion of rigid and elastic bodies, has always been regarded as essential to the basic education of an engineer. Since the problems confronted by today's engineers are seldom restricted to one's own particular specialization, it is imperative that the engineering student become thoroughly grounded in the fundamental principles of mechanics so necessary for the solution of many problems. Therefore, a major objective of the authors in writing the two volumes of this book has been to present, in a coherent and systematic fashion and by emphasizing the useful application, a fundamental treatment of the principles of mechanics. It was indeed particularly important to illustrate the application of these principles to problems encountered in various fields of engineering endeavor.

The authors have made a special effort to attain a degree of clarity that should be within the grasp of an average sophomore with prior knowledge of algebra, geometry, trigonometry, and calculus. The illustrative examples offered in the book are representative applications of the fundamental principles developed previously. As for the problems, they have been designed, for the most part, with the goals of familiarizing the student with real-life problems and developing in the student an appreciation for his or her own power of analysis and the effective use of mathematical modeling.

This volume, the subject of which is *dynamics* (the motion of bodies), is divided into 10 chapters and an appendix. As in Volume 1, the organization of subject matter adopted throughout the text may be considered somewhat unconventional. In order to avoid repetitious and redundant derivations, the laws governing the kinematics of rigid bodies have been developed without the artificial differentiation between two- and three-dimensional bodies. Furthermore, the introduction of dynamics moves from the study of the motion of a particle to that of a system of particles and eventually to the development of the essential arguments and equations governing the dynamics of rigid bodies. The authors hope that this approach will make the student more fully appreciative of the common and unifying themes constituting the foundations of all engineering mechanics. Throughout the volume a consistent emphasis on the use of vectors will be apparent; consequently, the student is expected to be familiar with vector algebra.

In order to provide the student with a solid understanding of the applied nature of engineering mechanics and the physical nature of the problems he or she may confront, the book contains a large number of illustrative examples. The problems accompanying each chapter have also been designed with the same objective; they are problems with a clear engineering purpose. The International System of Units (SI) and U.S. customary units have both been used throughout the text and at the end of each chapter. Not all 10 chapters of this book need be covered in a three-semester-hour course. However, certain sections within the first eight chapters and all of the final two chapters, Chapter 9 on Spatial Dynamics and Chapter 10 on Vibrations, could be omitted without any loss of continuity, and are all indicated with an asterisk(*).

Each chapter has a brief chapter outline and introduction, many illustrations, and a summary section. To illustrate the application of methods and equations developed in the text, there is an abundance of worked examples in each chapter (over 115 total). Example solutions are detailed and clearly explained for maximum understanding. Homework problems appear at the end of each chapter. These problem sets represent a wide range of applications and progress from simple to more complex. There are approximately 700 homework problems in all.

The solutions to all of the examples and homework problems have been double checked by two independent accuracy checkers. We have taken every effort to provide you with an error-free book. Any remaining errors can be brought to the attention of the authors for correction in future editions. Special thanks to James Matthews and Charles Atz for their diligent efforts at finding errors.

The Instructor's Manual, available from the publisher to adopters of the text, contains complete typeset solutions to the homework problems. Transparency masters of important figures and examples are also available from the publisher.

It is almost impossible to list and give proper credit to all those who have aided in the preparation of this book. However, the authors are especially indebted to Janice Das and Maureen Kassimali for their tireless efforts in preparing the manuscript for publication. Thanks are due to our former editor, Bill Stenquist, and Kelley Butcher, associate editor, of Richard D. Irwin, Inc., for their constant help and support during the period of the development of the manuscript. The authors are indebted to

Ken Oster
University of Missouri at Rolla

Ron Roth
California State Polytechnic University at Pomona

John Kennedy
Clemson University

Kwan Rim
University of Iowa

Dr. Williams
University of Houston

Allen Cogley
Kansas State University

Robert Ward
Ohio Northern University

Donald A. Grant
University of Maine

William L. Bingham
North Carolina State University

Robert D. Tzou
University of New Mexico

G. H. Nazari
North Dakota State University

Uei-Jiun Fan
California State Polytechnic University at Pomona

William M. Lee
US Naval Academy

Charles Evces
University of Alabama

Katherine Hunter-Zaworski
Oregon State University

Charles Smith
Oregon State University

Ralph E. Flori
University of Missouri at Rolla

Karim Nohra
University of South Florida

Fay Salmon
Tennessee Technological University

for their helpful comments, suggestions, and critical reviews of the manuscript.

Braja M. Das
Aslam Kassimali
Sedat Sami

CONTENTS

SYMBOLS

$\mathbf{a}$	Acceleration vector	F	Magnitude of force vector
a	Magnitude of the acceleration vector; distance; semimajor axis of ellipse	F_D	Drag force magnitude
		F_s	Spring force magnitude
$\mathbf{a}_c$	Acceleration of mass center	F_μ	Friction force magnitude
$\mathbf{a}_{B/A}$	Acceleration of B with respect to a frame at A in translation	g	Gravitational acceleration
		$\mathbf{G}$	Linear momentum vector
$\mathbf{a}_{\text{Cor}}$	Coriolis acceleration	$\dot{\mathbf{G}}$	Time rate of change of linear momentum
$\mathbf{A,B,C}$	Vectors; reactions at supports A,B,C	G	Universal constant of gravitation; magnitude of linear momentum
A,B,C	Points in space		
A	Planar area; amplitude of vibration	h	Height
b	Width; distance; semiminor axis of ellipse	$\mathbf{H}_C$	Angular momentum vector about mass center C
c	Distance; coefficient of viscous damping	$\mathbf{H}_O$	Angular momentum vector about point O
C	Constant of integration; path of particle; center of mass; constant of proportionality	$\dot{\mathbf{H}}_O$	Time rate of change of angular momentum about point O with respect to the fixed frame of reference XYZ
d	Distance; diameter		
e	Coefficient of restitution; eccentricity; natural logarithm base	$(\dot{\mathbf{H}}_O)_{xyz}$	Time rate of change of angular momentum about point O with respect to the rotating frame of reference xyz
f	Frequency		
f_n	Natural frequency	$\mathbf{i,j,k}$	Unit vectors in the rectangular coordinate system along axes x,y,z, respectively
$\mathbf{F}$	Force vector		

IC	Instantaneous center of zero velocity (instantaneous center of rotation)	r	Radial coordinate; radius
I_C	Centroidal mass moment of inertia	$\mathbf{r}_x, \mathbf{r}_y, \mathbf{r}_z$	Rectangular components of the position vector $\mathbf{r}$
$I_{x,y,z}$	Mass moment of inertia about the coordinate axes x,y,z, respectively	$\mathbf{R}$	Resultant force vector; reaction force vector
$I_{x',y',z'}$	Principal centroidal moments of inertia	R	Radius of the earth
I_{xy}, I_{yz}, I_{zx}	Mass products of inertia	s	Curvilinear coordinate; curve length
J	Polar moment of inertia	t	Time; thickness
k	Constant; radius of gyration; spring stiffness	T	Kinetic energy, $mv^2/2$; tension; thrust; periodic time
k_s	Spring constant	T_n	Natural period
k_C	Radius of gyration about mass center C	$\mathbf{u}$	Velocity; unit vector
k_O	Radius of gyration about point O	$\mathbf{u}_n, \mathbf{u}_t$	Unit vectors in the normal and tangential directions respectively
k_x, k_y, k_z	Radius of gyration with respect to the axes x,y,z, respectively	$\mathbf{u}_r, \mathbf{u}_\theta$	Unit vectors in the radial and transverse directions respectively
K	Constant	U	Work
l	Length	$U_{A \to B}$	Work done between positions A and B
l,m,n	Direction cosines	$U_{1 \to 2}$	Work done between positions 1 and 2
L	Length	$\mathbf{v}$	Velocity vector
m	mass	$\mathbf{v}_{B/A}$	Velocity of B with respect to A
$\mathbf{M}$	Moment or couple vector	$\mathbf{v}_C$	Velocity of mass center C
M	Total mass (Σm_1); mass of earth; magnitude of moment	$\mathbf{v}_e$	Escape velocity
$\mathbf{M}_{AB}$	Moment vector about axis AB	$\mathbf{v}_i$	Injection velocity
$\mathbf{M}_O$	Moment vector about point O	$\mathbf{v}_r, \mathbf{v}_\theta$	Radial and transverse components of the velocity vector
$\mathbf{n}$	Unit normal vector	v	Speed
N	Magnitude of a force normal to a surface	V	Potential energy
O	Origin of coordinate system	V_e	Elastic potential energy
p	Pressure; distance from origin to center of percussion	V_g	Gravitational potential energy
P	Particle; point in space	w	Weight per unit length
Q	Flow rate	$\mathbf{W}$	Weight vector
$\mathbf{r}$	Position vector	W	Weight
$\mathbf{r}_C$	Position vector of mass center C	x,y,z	Rectangular coordinates in the frame of reference xyz; distances
$\mathbf{r}_A$	Position vector of point A	x',y',z'	Principal axes of inertia
$\mathbf{r}_{A/C}$	Position vector of point A with respect to mass center C	X,Y,Z	Rectangular coordinates in the fixed reference frame XYZ

α (alpha)	Angular acceleration vector	μ (mu)	Coefficient of friction
α	Magnitude of the angular acceleration vector; angle	μ_k	Coefficient of kinetic friction
β (beta)	Angle	μ_s	Coefficient of static friction
γ (gamma)	Specific weight; angle; Eulerian angle of spin	ρ (rho)	Mass density; radius of curvature
$\dot{\gamma}$	Rate of spin	φ (phi)	Angle; Eulerian angle of precession; phase angle
δ (delta)	Change in length; angle	$\dot{\phi}$	Angular speed; rate of precession
Δ (delta)	Change in a geometric or kinematic property	ω (omega)	Angular velocity of rigid body
η (eta)	Efficiency; property N of a system per unit mass, N/m	ω	Angular speed
		ω_n	Natural circular frequency
θ (theta)	angular coordinate; angle; Eulerian angle of nutation	ω_d	Damped natural frequency
		ω	Circular frequency of excitation
θ_O	Phase angle	Ω (omega)	Angular velocity of rotating coordinate system
$\dot{\theta}$	Angular speed; rate of nutation	Ω	Angular speed; forcing frequency
λ (lambda)	Constant		

KINEMATICS OF PARTICLES

1.1 INTRODUCTION

Dynamics is the branch of engineering mechanics that is concerned with bodies in motion under the action of forces. The principles of dynamics play an important role in many diverse engineering applications of the modern world, such as the design of cars, airplanes, spacecraft, and various types of machines for manufacturing processes. Galileo Galilei (1564–1642) made a significant early contribution to the field of dynamics when he studied the motions of the pendulum and of falling bodies. However, the most important contribution to this field came from Sir Isaac Newton (1642–1727), who developed the laws of motion and the law of gravitational attraction between bodies.

Dynamics may be subdivided into the following areas of study: (*a*) *kinematics*, which deals with only the geometrical aspects of motion without considering the forces that cause the motion, and (*b*) *kinetics*, which considers the effects of forces on the motion of bodies.

In Chapters 1 to 5, we will focus our attention on the *dynamics of particles*. The concepts developed in these chapters are applicable not only to particles of negligible dimensions, but also to bodies of finite or definite sizes, provided that they do not rotate about their mass centers, or that such rotations can be neglected. For example, flight paths and trajectories of airplanes, spacecraft, and satellites, which are usually described by the motions of their mass centers, can be analyzed by the principles of particle dynamics.

In many engineering applications, however, the rotation of a body about its mass center cannot be neglected; consequently, the dimensions of the body must be considered in the analysis. Such bodies are treated as rigid bodies in this textbook, and the *dynamics of rigid bodies* is developed in Chapters 6 to 9. Lastly, Chapter 10 contains the analysis of vibrating (oscillating) motion.

The objective of this chapter is to define the basic concepts of *position, velocity*, and *acceleration*, and to illustrate their use in studying the motions of particles with respect to both fixed and translating (moving) coordinate systems.

In Sections 1.2 to 1.4, we consider the basic concepts of the position, velocity, and acceleration of a particle as it moves along a straight line. We then proceed to the description of the motion of a particle along a curved path using various types of coordinate systems (Sections 1.5 to 1.8). The analysis of motion of a particle relative to another particle, also in motion, follows in Section 1.9. Finally, in Section 1.10 we consider the motions of systems of particles connected together by inextensible cables.

1.2 RECTILINEAR KINEMATICS: POSITION, VELOCITY, AND ACCELERATION

If a particle moves along a straight line, its motion is called *rectilinear motion*. An example of rectilinear motion of a particle is shown in Figure 1.1. The particle is at point A at time t_0. It moves to the right along a straight line until it reaches point B at time t_2, where it reverses direction and moves to the left

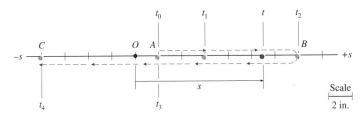

Figure 1.1

along the same straight line. During its motion to the left, the particle passes point A at time t_3, and continues moving to the left until it reaches point C at time t_4.

Position

The *position* of the particle at any instant of time t may be defined by its coordinate on a coordinate axis s along the path of the particle (see Figure 1.1). The origin O of the s axis may be fixed at any convenient location on the straight-line path, and its positive direction may be chosen arbitrarily. The position of the particle is then completely defined by its distance s from the origin O with the appropriate plus or minus sign according to whether the particle is on the positive or the negative side of the origin. The position of a particle is also referred to as its *position coordinate*.

For the example shown in Figure 1.1, using the given scale (1 division $=$ 2 in.), the positions of the particle at various times are the following:

$$
\begin{aligned}
\text{at time } t_0, \quad & s_0 = \quad +2 \ \text{in.} \\
\text{at time } t_1, \quad & s_1 = \quad +6 \ \text{in.} \\
\text{at time } t_2, \quad & s_2 = +14 \ \text{in.} \\
\text{at time } t_3, \quad & s_3 = \quad +2 \ \text{in.} \\
\text{at time } t_4, \quad & s_4 = \quad -8 \ \text{in.}
\end{aligned}
$$

The change in position of the particle during a time interval is called its *displacement*. The displacement is considered positive if the position coordinate of the particle at the end of the time interval is greater than its position coordinate at the beginning of the time interval. Conversely, if the position coordinate at the end of the time interval is less than that at the beginning of the time interval, the displacement is negative. For example, the displacement of the particle in Figure 1.1 during the time interval from t_1 to t_2 is

$$\Delta s_{1 \to 2} = s_2 - s_1 = 14 - 6 = 8 \ \text{in.}$$

Similarly, for the time interval from t_1 to t_4, the displacement of the particle is

$$\Delta s_{1 \to 4} = s_4 - s_1 = -8 - 6 = -14 \ \text{in.}$$

The displacement depends only on the positions of the particle at the beginning and the end of the time interval. This is not necessarily equal to the distance traveled by the particle during the interval. For example, the displacement of the particle in Figure 1.1 during the time interval from t_0 to t_3 is zero although the particle has traveled from point A to point B, and back to A, during this interval.

The *distance traveled* by the particle during a time interval is equal to the total length (considering the direction reversals) of the path traveled by the particle during the interval. For example, the distance traveled by the particle of Figure 1.1 during the time interval from t_0 to t_4 is equal to the sum of distances AB and BC; that is, $d_{0 \rightarrow 4} = 12 + 22 = 34$ in.

In many cases of practical interest, the relationship between the position s of a particle in motion and time t can be expressed in the form of an equation. Occasionally, however, such a mathematical equation may not be available, and the position s is known at a number of discrete instants of time t (experimental or field data are often determined in the discrete form). In order to gain a better understanding of the motion, the variation of s with t may be described graphically. Such a position-versus-time graph (s-t graph) for a motion represented by the equation $s = 2 + 6t - 2t^3/9$, during the interval from $t = 0$ to $t = 6$ seconds, is shown in Figure 1.2. As the graph indicates, the initial position of the particle at time $t = 0$ is 2 in. The particle moves in the positive direction until it reaches a distance of 14 in. from the origin at time $t = 3$ seconds where it reverses direction. For $t > 3$ seconds, the particle moves in the negative direction.

Keep in mind that the particle does not move along the curve of the s-t graph; it is moving along a straight line as shown previously (Figure 1.1). The s-t graphs describe the position of the particle continuously for every instant of time. Such a complete description of the motion is not possible on a one-dimensional diagram of the type shown in Figure 1.1.

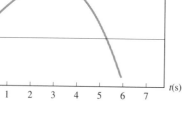

Figure 1.2

Velocity

Consider a particle moving along a straight line as shown in Figure 1.3. The positions of the particle at times t and $t + \Delta t$ are s and $s + \Delta s$, respectively, as shown. Again, Δs represents the displacement of the particle during the time interval Δt. The ratio of the displacement Δs to the time interval Δt is

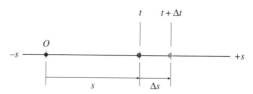

Figure 1.3

called the *average velocity* of the particle during the interval Δt. Thus

$$v_{\text{avg}} = \frac{\Delta s}{\Delta t} \tag{1.1}$$

The *instantaneous velocity* of the particle at time t is defined as the *time rate of change of position* at time t. The expression for instantaneous velocity can be obtained from Equation (1.1) by letting Δt approach zero in the limit:

$$v = \lim_{\Delta t \to 0} \frac{\Delta s}{\Delta t} = \frac{ds}{dt} = \dot{s} \tag{1.2}$$

in which a dot (˙) denotes a differentiation with respect to t.

The velocity is expressed in the units of length divided by time. The commonly used units are feet per second (ft/s) or inches per second (in./s) in the U.S. Customary System, and meters per second (m/s) in the International System of units (SI). A *positive* velocity indicates that the particle is moving in the positive direction at that time. A *negative* velocity indicates that the particle is moving in the negative direction. The magnitude or the absolute value of velocity, $|v|$, is called the *speed* of the particle.

As Equation (1.2) indicates, the velocity at a time t is equal to the slope of the tangent to the s-t curve at time t. When the equation of the position s as a function of time t is known, the expression for velocity v can be obtained by differentiating the equation of s with respect to t. As an example, if the position of a particle in motion is represented by the equation

$$s = 2 + 6t - \frac{2}{9}t^3$$

then the equation of the velocity v is given by

$$v = \frac{ds}{dt} = 6 - \frac{2}{9}(3t^2) = 6 - \frac{2}{3}t^2$$

The position-versus-time and the velocity-versus-time graphs for this motion are shown in Figure 1.4. As the v-t graph indicates, the initial velocity of the particle at $t = 0$ is 6 in./s, and it decreases with increasing t. Note that at the time $t = 3$ seconds, when the position coordinate s reaches the maximum value, the velocity of the particle is zero. This is because the velocity is equal to the slope of the s-t curve, which becomes zero whenever s attains a maximum (or a minimum) value.

When the motion of a particle cannot be expressed in the form of an equation, but the s-t graph of the motion is available, then the v-t graph can be constructed by measuring the slopes of the s-t graph at various instants of time and plotting the measured values of slopes, which are equal to velocities, against time.

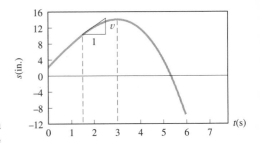

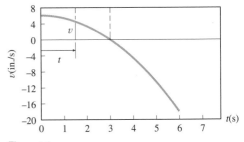

Figure 1.4

Acceleration

If the velocities of a particle at times t and $t + \Delta t$ are v and $v + \Delta v$, respectively, then the ratio of the change in velocity Δv to the time interval Δt is called the *average* **acceleration** of the particle during the interval Δt. Thus,

$$a_{\text{avg}} = \frac{\Delta v}{\Delta t} \tag{1.3}$$

The *instantaneous acceleration* of the particle at time t is defined as the *time rate of change of velocity*. The expression for instantaneous acceleration can be obtained from Equation (1.3) by letting Δt approach zero in the limit:

$$a = \lim_{\Delta t \to 0} \frac{\Delta v}{\Delta t} = \frac{dv}{dt} = \dot{v} \tag{1.4}$$

Substituting $v = ds/dt$ from Equation (1.2) into Equation (1.4), we obtain

$$a = \frac{dv}{dt} = \frac{d^2 s}{dt^2} = \ddot{s} \tag{1.5}$$

As Equations (1.4) and (1.5) indicate, each dot (˙) on a variable denotes one differentiation with respect to time; thus, $\ddot{s}$ represents the second derivative of s with respect to t.

The acceleration is expressed in the units of length divided by time squared. The commonly used units are ft/s^2 or in./s^2 in the U.S. Customary System, and m/s^2 in the International System of units (SI). A *positive* acceleration indicates that the velocity of the particle is increasing; a *negative* acceleration indicates that the velocity is decreasing. If the velocity and the acceleration of a particle at a time t are both positive, the particle is moving faster in the positive direction. Conversely, if the velocity and the acceleration are both negative, the particle is moving faster in the negative direction. A positive velocity with negative acceleration indicates that the particle is moving in the positive direction but it is slowing down; a negative velocity with positive acceleration indicates that the particle is moving in the negative direction and it is slowing down. The particle is said to be *decelerating* when it is slowing down. The particle is said to be *decelerating* when it is slowing down.

As Equation (1.5) indicates, the acceleration a at a time t is equal to the slope of the tangent to the v-t curve at time t. When the equation of the velocity v as a function of time t is known, the expression for acceleration a can be obtained by differentiating the equation of v with respect to t. For example, for the particle in motion considered previously (Figure 1.4), with velocity

$$v = 6 - \frac{2}{3}t^2$$

we obtain the expression for the acceleration by differentiation as

$$a = -\frac{2}{3}(2t) = -\frac{4}{3}t$$

The velocity-versus-time and the acceleration-versus-time graphs for this motion are shown in Figure 1.5. As the *a-t* graph indicates, the initial acceleration of the particle at $t = 0$ is zero, and it decreases linearly with increasing t. The acceleration a at any time t is equal to the slope of the *v-t* curve at that time.

When the motion cannot be expressed in the form of an equation, but the *v-t* graph is available, then the *a-t* graph can be constructed by measuring the slopes of the *v-t* graph at various instants of time and plotting the measured values of the slopes, which are equal to accelerations, against time.

Equations (1.2) and (1.5) are called the *differential equations for the rectilinear motion of a particle.* Another useful differential expression relating position, velocity, and acceleration can be obtained by eliminating the time differential dt from Equations (1.2) and (1.5). By applying the chain rule, we write

$$a = \frac{dv}{dt} = \frac{dv}{ds}\frac{ds}{dt} = \frac{dv}{ds}v$$

Thus,

$$a = v\frac{dv}{ds} \tag{1.6}$$

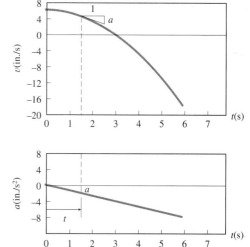

Figure 1.5

which indicates that the acceleration a at a time t is equal to the product of the velocity v at time t and the slope of the velocity-versus-position (*v-s*) curve at time t.

It should be realized that although the position, velocity, and acceleration of a particle have been treated here as scalar quantities, they are actually vectors in the sense that they possess magnitudes and directions, and obey the parallelogram law of addition. However, in the case of rectilinear motion being considered here, the directions of the position, velocity, and acceleration of the particle do not change but remain along the straight-line path of the motion. It is, therefore, convenient to treat them as scalars when the motion is rectilinear. In the general case of the motion of a particle along a curved path, which we will consider in Section 1.5, the position, velocity, and acceleration will be reintroduced as vectors.

EXAMPLE 1.1

The position of a particle moving in a straight line is given by the equation $s = 4(1 + t) - t^2/4$ where s is in feet and t in seconds. Determine (a) the equations of the velocity and the acceleration of the particle; (b) the position of the particle when $t = 12$ s; (c) the time when the velocity will be zero; (d) the position and the acceleration of the particle at that time; and (e) the displacement and the distance traveled by the particle during the time interval from $t = 5$ s to $t = 19$ s. Also, plot the s-t, v-t, and a-t graphs of the motion of the particle during the interval from $t = 0$ to $t = 20$ s.

Solution

a. *Equations of velocity and acceleration.* The equation of the position of the particle is given as

$$s = 4(1 + t) - \frac{t^2}{4} \text{ ft}$$

The equation of the velocity is obtained by differentiating s with respect to t. Thus

$$v = \frac{ds}{dt} = 4 - \frac{1}{4}(2t)$$

$$v = 4 - \frac{t}{2} \text{ ft/s} \blacktriangleleft$$

The equation of the acceleration is determined by differentiating v with respect to t:

$$a = -\frac{1}{2} \text{ ft/s}^2 \blacktriangleleft$$

b. *Position when $t = 12$ seconds.* Substituting $t = 12$ s into the equation for s, we have

$$s = 4(1 + 12) - \frac{(12)^2}{4} \qquad s = 16 \text{ ft} \blacktriangleleft$$

c. *Time when $v = 0$.* Setting $v = 0$ in the equation of v, we obtain

$$0 = 4 - \frac{t}{2} \qquad t = 8 \text{ s} \blacktriangleleft$$

d. *Position and acceleration when $v = 0$.* Substituting $t = 8$ s in the equation for s:

$$s = 4(1 + 8) - \frac{(8)^2}{4} \qquad s = 20 \text{ ft} \blacktriangleleft$$

The equation for a indicates that the acceleration is constant for all values of t. Thus, for $t = 8$ s,

$$a = -\frac{1}{2} \text{ ft/s}^2 \blacktriangleleft$$

e. *Displacement and distance traveled from $t = 5$ seconds to $t = 19$ seconds.* Substituting $t = 5$ s in the equation of s, we obtain the position of the particle at time $t = 5$ s as

$$s_5 = 4(1 + 5) - \frac{(5)^2}{4} = 17.75 \text{ ft}$$

Similarly, at $t = 19$ s the position of the particle is

$$s_{19} = 4(1 + 19) - \frac{(19)^2}{4} = -10.25 \text{ ft}$$

Therefore, the displacement of the particle is

$$\Delta s = s_{19} - s_5 = -10.25 - 17.75$$

$$\Delta s = -28 \text{ ft} \blacktriangleleft$$

The negative sign of Δs indicates that the displacement is in the negative direction.

Since the particle is traveling in the positive direction from $t = 5$ s to $t = 8$ s (at which time $v = 0$ and the particle reverses direction), and in the negative direction from $t = 8$ s to $t = 19$ s, the total distance traveled is equal to the sum of the absolute values of the distances traveled during each of these time intervals. As we have found, the positions of the particle at $t = 5$ s and $t = 8$ s are

$$s_5 = 17.75 \text{ ft} \qquad \text{and} \qquad s_8 = 20 \text{ ft}$$

Therefore, the distance traveled from $t = 5$ s to $t = 8$ s is

$$s_8 - s_5 = 20 - 17.75 = 2.25 \text{ ft}$$

(*continued*)

EXAMPLE 1.1 *(concluded)*

The position at $t = 19$ s is

$$s_{19} = -10.25 \text{ ft}$$

and the distance traveled from $t = 8$ s to $t = 19$ s is

$$s_{19} - s_8 = -10.25 - 20 = -30.25 \text{ ft}$$

Therefore, the total distance traveled from $t = 5$ s to $t = 19$ s is

$$|2.25| + |-30.25| = 32.5 \text{ ft} \blacktriangleleft$$

The *s-t*, *v-t*, and *a-t* graphs are shown.

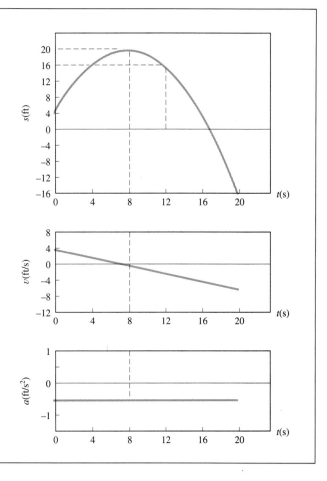

1.3 ANALYSIS OF RECTILINEAR MOTION FROM KNOWN VELOCITY OR ACCELERATION

In the preceding section, we defined the three basic kinematic characteristics—position, velocity, and acceleration—of the rectilinear motion of a particle. It was shown that if the position s of the particle is known as a function of time t, then the velocity v and the acceleration a can be determined by successive differentiation of s with respect to t. However, in many engineering applications, the motion is specified in terms of the velocity of the particle, or its acceleration, rather than its position. In such cases, the position of the particle is obtained by integration of the differential equations. In this section, we will discuss how to determine the relationship between the position of a particle and time, when its velocity or acceleration may be known in various forms.

Constant Velocity (Uniform Motion)

When the velocity v of a particle in rectilinear motion is constant, $v = v_c$, then the motion is called the *uniform motion*. The position s of a particle in uniform motion can be determined by integrating Equation (1.2) with $v = v_c$. Rearranging Equation (1.2) and substituting $v = v_c$, we write

$$ds = v\, dt = v_c\, dt$$

Integrating both sides, and using the initial condition that the position of the particle is $s = s_0$ at time $t = 0$, we obtain

$$\int_{s_0}^{s} ds = v_c \int_{0}^{t} dt \tag{1.7}$$

and from this,

$$s - s_0 = v_c t$$

or

$$s = s_0 + v_c t \tag{1.8}$$

which gives the position s at time t. It is important to realize that the velocity by itself is not sufficient to uniquely define the motion of the particle. Additional information about the motion, or a *condition*, must be known in order to uniquely define the motion. In Equations (1.7) and (1.8), it has been assumed for simplicity that the initial position s_0 of the particle at time $t = 0$ is known. However, instead of this initial condition, if the position s_1 is known at a nonzero time t_1, then the values of s_1 and t_1 should be used as the integration limits in Equation (1.7).

Substituting $v = v_c$ into Equation (1.5) and differentiating it with respect to t, we obtain

$$a = \frac{dv}{dt} = \frac{dv_c}{dt} = 0 \tag{1.9}$$

which shows that the acceleration of a particle in uniform motion is zero.

Velocity Known as a Function of Time

If the velocity of a particle in motion is known as a function of time, $v = f(t)$, then the position can be determined by substituting $v = f(t)$ into Equation (1.2) and integrating the equation. Thus, for the initial condition $s = s_0$ at $t = 0$, we obtain

$$\int_{s_0}^{s} ds = \int_{0}^{t} v\, dt = \int_{0}^{t} f(t)\, dt$$

or

$$s = s_0 + \int_{0}^{t} f(t)\, dt \tag{1.10}$$

The acceleration a of the particle can be determined by differentiating the velocity with respect to time, thus

$$a = \frac{dv}{dt} = \frac{d\,f(t)}{dt} \tag{1.11}$$

Velocity Known as a Function of Position

Occasionally, the velocity may be known as a function of the position of a particle in motion, $v = f(s)$. In such a case, the relationship between the position s and time t can be obtained by rearranging Equation (1.2) to separate the variables s and t as

$$dt = \frac{ds}{v} = \frac{ds}{f(s)}$$

and integrating both sides. Using the initial condition $s = s_0$ at $t = 0$, we obtain

$$\int_0^t dt = \int_{s_0}^s \frac{ds}{f(s)}$$

or

$$t = \int_{s_0}^s \frac{ds}{f(s)} \tag{1.12}$$

Note that Equation (1.12) yields t as a function of s and, therefore, must be solved for s as a function of t.

The acceleration a in terms of s can be determined by substituting $v = f(s)$ into Equation (1.6). Thus,

$$a = v\frac{dv}{ds} = f(s)\frac{df(s)}{ds} \tag{1.13}$$

The expression for the acceleration a in terms of time t can be determined either by substituting s as a function of t, obtained by solving Equation (1.12), into the expression of a in terms of s; or by successively differentiating s with respect to t according to Equation (1.5).

Constant Acceleration (Uniformly Accelerated Motion)

When the acceleration a of a particle in rectilinear motion is constant, $a = a_c$, then the motion is referred to as the *uniformly accelerated motion*. The velocity v of a particle in uniformly accelerated motion can be determined by integrating Equation (1.5) with $a = a_c$. Rearranging Equation (1.5) and substituting $a = a_c$, we write

$$dv = a\,dt = a_c\,dt$$

Integrating both sides, and using the initial condition that the velocity of the particle is $v = v_0$ at time $t = 0$, we obtain

$$\int_{v_0}^{v} dv = a_c \int_{0}^{t} dt$$

or

$$v = v_0 + a_c t \tag{1.14}$$

which gives the velocity v at time t.

We can now determine the position s by substituting Equation (1.14) into Equation (1.2) and integrating it. Thus, for the initial condition $s = s_0$ at $t = 0$, we obtain

$$\int_{s_0}^{s} ds = \int_{0}^{t} v\, dt = \int_{0}^{t} (v_0 + a_c t)\, dt$$

or

$$s = s_0 + v_0 t + \frac{1}{2} a_c t^2 \tag{1.15}$$

The relationship between the velocity v and the position s, without direct reference to time t, can be obtained by rearranging Equation (1.6) as

$$a\, ds = a_c\, ds = v\, dv$$

and integrating as

$$a_c \int_{s_0}^{s} ds = \int_{v_0}^{v} v\, dv$$

$$a_c(s - s_0) = \frac{1}{2}(v^2 - v_0^2)$$

or

$$v^2 = v_0^2 + 2a_c(s - s_0) \tag{1.16}$$

Equations (1.14) to (1.16) can be used to determine the motion of a particle provided that the two initial conditions of the particle at time $t = 0$, are known; that is, the position s_0 and the velocity v_0.

Acceleration Known as a Function of Time

If the acceleration of a particle in motion is known as a function of time, $a = g(t)$, then the velocity can be determined by substituting $a = g(t)$ into Equation (1.5) and integrating the equation. Thus

$$\int_{v_0}^{v} dv = \int_{0}^{t} a \, dt = \int_{0}^{t} g(t) \, dt$$

or

$$v = v_0 + \int_{0}^{t} g(t) \tag{1.17}$$

Now we can determine the position s by substituting v as a function of t, as obtained from Equation (1.17), into Equation (1.2) and integrating. Thus

$$s = s_0 + \int_{0}^{t} v \, dt \tag{1.18}$$

Acceleration Known as a Function of Position

Occasionally, the acceleration may be known as a function of the position of a particle in motion, $a = g(s)$. In such a case, the velocity can be obtained by integration from Equation (1.6). Rearranging Equation (1.6) and integrating, we obtain

$$\int_{v_0}^{v} v \, dv = \int_{s_0}^{s} a \, ds = \int_{s_0}^{s} g(s) \, ds$$

$$\frac{1}{2}(v^2 - v_0^2) = \int_{s_0}^{s} g(s) \, ds$$

$$v^2 = v_0^2 + 2 \int_{s_0}^{s} g(s) \, ds \tag{1.19}$$

Equation (1.19) expresses v in terms of s. We can then find the relationship between s and t by substituting v in terms of s, as obtained from Equation (1.19), into Equation (1.2) and integrating. Thus,

$$\int_{0}^{t} dt = \int_{s_0}^{s} \frac{ds}{v}$$

$$t = \int_{s_0}^{s} \frac{ds}{v} \tag{1.20}$$

Equation (1.20) yields t as a function of s and it must be solved to obtain s as a function of t.

Acceleration Known as a Function of Velocity

If the acceleration is known as a function of velocity, $a = g(v)$, then the velocity can be determined by integrating Equation (1.5) after separating the variables v and t. Thus,

$$\int_0^t dt = \int_{v_0}^v \frac{dv}{a} = \int_{v_0}^v \frac{dv}{g(v)}$$

$$t = \int_{v_0}^v \frac{dv}{g(v)} \tag{1.21}$$

Equation (1.21) is solved for v as a function of t, and the resulting expression is substituted into Equation (1.2), which is then integrated to yield s as a function of t.

The direct relationship between v and s, without the variable t, can be obtained by separating the terms containing v and s in Equation (1.6) and integrating it as

$$\int_{s_0}^s ds = \int_{v_0}^v v\,\frac{dv}{a} = \int_{v_0}^v v\,\frac{dv}{g(v)}$$

$$s = s_0 + \int_{v_0}^v v\,\frac{dv}{g(v)} \tag{1.22}$$

Graphical Integration

When the velocity or the acceleration of a motion can be expressed in the form of a simple mathematical equation such as a polynomial, a trigonometric, or an exponential function, the motion can be analyzed by integrating the known function using calculus. However, if the velocity or the acceleration is in the form of a complicated function that cannot be integrated analytically; or if the values of v or a are known at a number of discrete instants of time t, as is often the case with experimental data, the integration must be performed by graphical methods or numerical techniques.

Consider again the two basic differential equations $v = ds/dt$ and $a = dv/dt$. Integrating these equations between the limits t_1 to t_2, we obtain

$$s_2 - s_1 = \int_{t_1}^{t_2} v\,dt \tag{1.23}$$

and

$$v_2 - v_1 = \int_{t_1}^{t_2} a\,dt \tag{1.24}$$

Equation (1.23) indicates that the displacement, or the change in position $(s_2 - s_1)$ of a particle during a time interval from t_1 to t_2, is equal to the area under the v-t curve during the same time interval (see Figure 1.6). Similarly, as indicated by Equation (1.24), the change in the velocity of a particle during

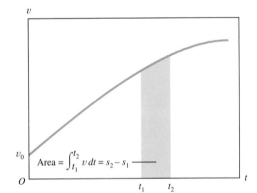

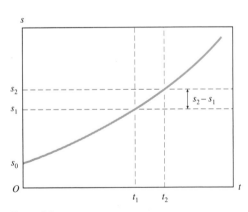

Figure 1.6

a time interval is equal to the area under the a-t curve during the same interval of time (Figure 1.7).

When the v-t graph of a motion is known, the corresponding s-t graph can be constructed by measuring the area under the v-t curve and using Equation (1.23). Starting with the known initial position s_0 at time $t = 0$, the position s_1 at time t_1 is computed from the relationship

$$s_1 = s_0 + (\text{area under } v\text{-}t \text{ curve between } t = 0 \text{ and } t = t_1)$$

Next, the position s_2 at time t_2 is computed by algebraically adding to s_1 the area under the v-t curve between t_1 and t_2. This procedure may be repeated using the general relationship

$$s_{i+1} = s_i + (\text{area under } v\text{-}t \text{ curve between } t_i \text{ and } t_{i+1})$$

until all the desired values of s have been determined.

When the a-t graph and the initial velocity v_0 are known, the v-t graph can be constructed by using a procedure similar to the one described in the preceding paragraph. The v-t graph thus obtained can then be used to determine the s-t graph of the motion.

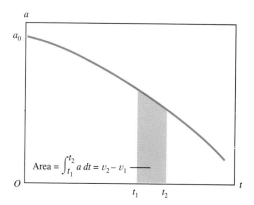

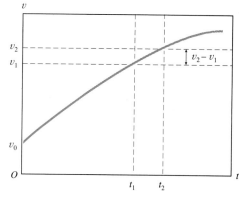

Figure 1.7

1.4 RECTILINEAR MOTION: PROCEDURE FOR ANALYSIS

The objective of the kinematic analysis is to determine the position, velocity, and acceleration of a particle, at any or all times of interest, using the available information about the motion. The following summarizes the step-by-step procedures that may be used for this analysis.

1.   Select the origin and the positive direction of the position coordinate. The origin may be chosen at any point along the path of the motion. However, it is usually convenient to locate it at the position of the particle at the beginning of the duration of interest (at time $t = 0$).

2.   Identify all known quantities by carefully reading the problem statement. In order to proceed with the analysis, it is necessary that a relationship between any two of the four variables, s, v, a, and t, be known throughout the duration of interest of the motion. If such a relationship is not explicitly given in the problem statement, establish one by using the information provided. Moreover, in the problems involving known velocity, it is necessary to know the initial position of the particle; and in the problems with known acceleration, both the initial position and initial velocity should be known.

3.   Knowing one of the three characteristics (position, velocity, or acceleration) of the motion, determine the remaining two as follows:

   a.   If the position is known, determine the velocity and the acceleration by successively differentiating the expression for the position with respect to time ($v = ds/dt$ and $a = dv/dt$).

b. If the velocity and the initial position are known, determine the position by substituting the expression for velocity into the differential equation $v = ds/dt$, and integrating the equation. [See Equations (1.8), (1.10), and (1.12).] Determine the acceleration by substituting the expression for velocity into the appropriate differential equation, $a = dv/dt$ or $a = v \, dv/ds$, depending on the particular form of the acceleration function desired, and performing the necessary differentiation. [See Equations (1.9), (1.11), and (1.13).]

c. If the acceleration, the initial position, and the initial velocity are known, determine first the velocity by integrating the appropriate differential equation, $a = dv/dt$ or $a = v \, dv/ds$, depending on the particular form of the acceleration function. [See Equations (1.14), (1.17), (1.19), and (1.21).] Then, substitute the expression for velocity into the differential equation, $v = ds/dt$, and integrate the equation to obtain the relationship between the position and time. [See Equations (1.15), (1.18), (1.20), and (1.22).]

4. Using the expressions of the position, velocity, and acceleration, compute the numerical values of these quantities at any desired instants of time.

EXAMPLE 1.2

The velocity of a particle in rectilinear motion is given by the equation $v = 7 - (t^2/10)$, where v is in m/s. If the initial position of the particle is $s_0 = 0$ when $t_0 = 0$, determine (*a*) the equations of the position and the acceleration of the particle; and (*b*) its position, velocity, and acceleration when $t = 8$ s. Also, plot the *s-t*, *v-t*, and *a-t* graphs for the motion during the interval from $t = 0$ to $t = 8$ s.

Solution The equation for the velocity of the particle, $v = 7 - (t^2/10)$, and its initial position, $s_0 = 0$ at $t = 0$, are known. As this initial condition indicates, the origin of the position coordinate s is located at the initial position of the particle.

a. Equations of position and acceleration. The equation of the position s is obtained by integrating the differential equation $v = ds/dt$. Thus,

$$\int_0^s ds = \int_0^t v \, dt = \int_0^t \left(7 - \frac{t^2}{10}\right) dt$$

$$s = 7t - \frac{t^3}{30} \text{ m} \blacktriangleleft$$

The equation of the acceleration is determined by differentiating v with respect to t. Thus,

$$a = \frac{dv}{dt} = -\frac{t}{5} \text{ m/s}^2 \blacktriangleleft$$

b. Position, velocity, and acceleration when $t = 8$ seconds. Substituting $t = 8$ s into the equations of s, v, and a, we obtain

$$s = 7(8) - \frac{(8)^3}{30} \qquad s = 38.9 \text{ m} \blacktriangleleft$$

$$v = 7 - \frac{(8)^2}{10} \qquad v = 0.6 \text{ m/s} \blacktriangleleft$$

$$a = -\frac{8}{5} \qquad a = -1.6 \text{ m/s}^2 \blacktriangleleft$$

(*continued*)

EXAMPLE 1.2 (*concluded*)

The *s-t*, *v-t*, and *a-t* graphs are shown.

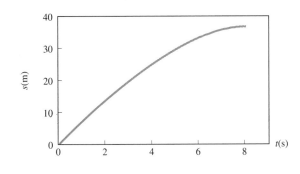

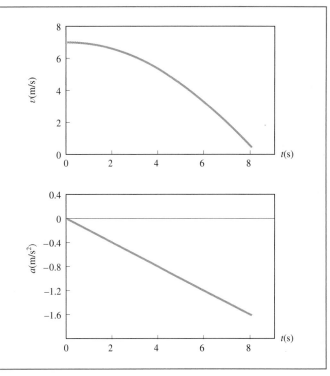

EXAMPLE 1.3

A car starts from rest with an acceleration of 1300 mi/h^2, which remains constant until its velocity reaches 65 mph. Thereafter, the car maintains this velocity. Determine the distance traveled by the car during the first 10 minutes of motion.

Solution The position coordinate *s* is chosen to be positive to the right, with the origin *O* at the initial position of the car at $t = 0$, as shown. The initial conditions are $s_0 = 0$ and $v_0 = 0$ at time $t = 0$.

Acceleration. The motion of the car can be divided into two time intervals: one from $t = 0$ to $t = t_1$, where t_1 represents the yet unknown time at which the velocity of the car reaches 65 mph; and another, when *t* is greater than t_1. The acceleration

(*continued*)

EXAMPLE   1.3   *(concluded)*

of the car is known throughout the duration of the motion, and is given by

$0 \leq t \leq t_1$: $a = 1300 \text{ mi/h}^2$

$t > t_1$: $a = 0$

Note that for $t > t_1$, the acceleration is zero because the velocity remains constant after it reaches 65 mph.

Velocity. The velocity is determined by integrating the differential equation, $a = dv/dt$. Thus,

$0 \leq t \leq t_1$:

$$\int_0^v dv = \int_0^t a\,dt = 1300 \int_0^t dt$$

$$v = 1300t \text{ mi/h} \qquad\qquad \text{(a)}$$

$t \geq t_1$:

$$\int_0^v dv = \int_0^{t_1} a\,dt + \int_{t_1}^t a\,dt$$

$$v = 1300 \int_0^{t_1} dt + 0 = 1300t_1 \text{ mi/h}$$

Time when $v = 65$ mph. Setting $v = 65$ mph and $t = t_1$ into Equation (a), we obtain $65 = 1300t_1$ or $t_1 = 0.05 \text{ h} = 3 \text{ min}$.
   Therefore, the velocity of the car is given by

$0 \leq t \leq 0.05$ h: $v = 1300t \text{ mi/h}$

$t \geq 0.05$ h: $v = 65 \text{ mi/h}$

Position.   The position is obtained by integrating the differential equation $v = ds/dt$. Thus,

$0 \leq t \leq 0.05$ h:

$$\int_0^s ds = \int_0^t v\,dt = 1300 \int_0^t t\,dt$$

$$s = 1300 \left(\frac{t^2}{2} \right) = 650\,t^2 \text{ mi}$$

$t \geq 0.05$ h:

$$s = 1300 \int_0^{0.05} t\,dt + 65 \int_{0.05}^t dt$$

$$s = 1.625 + 65(t - 0.05) \text{ mi}$$

Position when $t = 10 \text{ min} = 0.167$ h. As the specified time $t = 10 \text{ min} = 0.167$ h is greater than $t_1 = 3 \text{ min} = 0.05$ h, we substitute $t = 0.167$ h into the second equation of s (for $t \geq t_1$) to compute the distance traveled. Thus,

$$s = 1.625 + 65(0.167 - 0.05) = 9.23 \text{ mi}$$

Therefore, the distance traveled by the car during the first 10 minutes of motion is

$$s = 9.23 \text{ mi} \blacktriangleleft$$

EXAMPLE   1.4

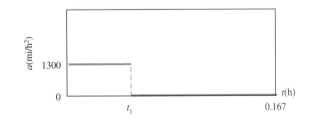

Solve Example 1.3 by graphically integrating the *a-t* graph for the motion of the car.

Solution The *a-t* graph for the motion of the car during the interval $0 \leq t \leq 0.167$ h (i.e., $0 \leq t \leq 10$ min) is shown. This graph indicates that during the time interval $0 \leq t \leq t_1$, the acceleration is 1300 mi/h^2; whereas, when $t > t_1$, it is zero.

(continued)

EXAMPLE 1.4 (*concluded*)

Time when v = 65 mi/h. The value of t_1, at which the velocity reaches 65 mi/h, can be determined from this relationship:

$$\left.\begin{array}{l}\text{Change in velocity during}\\ \text{interval from}\\ t = 0 \text{ to } t_1\end{array}\right\} = \left\{\begin{array}{l}\text{Area under } a\text{-}t\\ \text{curve during}\\ \text{interval from}\\ t = 0 \text{ to } t_1\end{array}\right.$$

In this case,

$$65 - 0 = 1300t_1 \qquad \text{or} \qquad t_1 = 0.05 \text{ h} = 3 \text{ min}$$

For $t > t_1$, since the area under the *a-t* curve is zero, the velocity will not change; it will remain constant at 65 mi/h. The *v-t* graph is shown. Note that since the acceleration is a positive constant from $t = 0$ to $t = 0.05$ h, the slope of the *v-t* curve is also positive and constant; that is, the velocity increases linearly during this interval. Then, for $t > 0.05$ h, the acceleration is zero; therefore, the slope of the *v-t* graph is also zero.

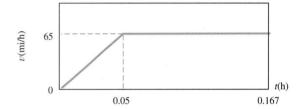

Position when t = 10 min = 0.167 h. The position of the car at $t = 0.167$ h can be determined from this relationship:

$$\left.\begin{array}{l}\text{Change in position}\\ \text{during interval}\\ \text{from } t = 0\\ \text{to } t = 0.167 \text{ h}\end{array}\right\} = \left\{\begin{array}{l}\text{Area under } v\text{-}t\\ \text{curve during}\\ \text{interval from}\\ t = 0 \text{ to } t = 0.167 \text{ h}\end{array}\right.$$

So we may write that

$$s - 0 = \frac{1}{2}(65)(0.05) + 65(0.167 - 0.05) = 9.23 \text{ mi}$$

Thus, the distance traveled by the car during the first 10 minutes of motion is

$$s = 9.23 \text{ mi} \blacktriangleleft$$

The *s-t* graph is shown. The graph consists of two segments: For $0 \le t \le 0.05$ h, the shape of the *s-t* curve is parabolic, whereas for $t > 0.05$ h, *s* increases linearly with *t*. The position at $t = 0.05$ h can be obtained by evaluating the triangular area under the *v-t* curve from $t = 0$ to $t = 0.05$ h; that is,

$$s = \frac{1}{2}(65)(0.05) = 1.625 \text{ mi}$$

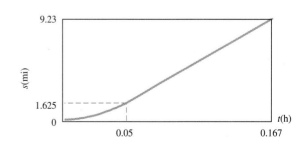

EXAMPLE 1.5

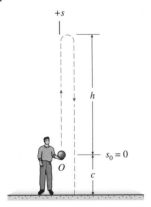

A ball is thrown vertically upward with a velocity v_0 from a distance c above the ground, as shown. Derive the expressions for (a) the maximum height h to which the ball could rise and (b) the velocity v_c of the ball when it hits the ground. The ball has a constant downward acceleration g due to gravity, and the air resistance is neglected. Also, determine the numerical values of h and v_c, if $v_0 = 45$ ft/s, $c = 5$ ft, and $g = 32.2$ ft/s^2.

Solution   The position coordinate s is chosen to be positive upward with origin O at the initial position of the ball (at distance c above the ground) as shown.

Acceleration.   The acceleration of the ball is known throughout the duration of the motion and is given by $a = -g$.

Velocity.   The expression for the velocity is obtained by integrating the differential equation, $a = dv/dt$. Thus,

$$\int_{v_0}^{v} dv = -g \int_{0}^{t} dt \qquad v = v_0 - gt \qquad \text{(a)}$$

Position.   The equation of the position as a function of time is determined by integrating the equation $v = ds/dt$, with the initial condition $s_0 = 0$, at $t = 0$. Thus,

$$\int_{0}^{s} ds = \int_{0}^{t} v \, dt = \int_{0}^{t} (v_0 - gt) \, dt$$

$$s = v_0 t - \frac{1}{2} gt^2 \qquad \text{(b)}$$

Since the acceleration of the ball is constant through the entire duration of the motion, the motion is classified as uniformly accelerated; therefore, the above equations of velocity and position could have been obtained directly by substituting $a_c = -g$ and $s_0 = 0$ into Equations (1.14) and (1.15), respectively.

Height.   The velocity of the ball is zero when it reaches the maximum height h. Setting $v = 0$ in the equation of v [Equation (a)], we determine the time at which s is maximum. Thus,

$$0 = v_0 - gt \qquad t = \frac{v_0}{g}$$

(continued)

EXAMPLE 1.5 (concluded)

Next, substituting $t = v_0/g$ into the equation of s [Equation (b)], we determine the maximum height h to be

$$h = v_0\left(\frac{v_0}{g}\right) - \frac{1}{2}g\left(\frac{v_0}{g}\right)^2 \qquad h = \frac{v_0^2}{2g} \blacktriangleleft$$

Velocity v_c at the ground. When the ball hits the ground, its position coordinate is $s = -c$. The velocity v_c can be determined by setting $s = -c$ in Equation (b) to obtain the time at which the ball hits the ground, and then substituting that time into Equation (a) to obtain v_c. However, since in this problem we are asked to determine only the velocity, but not the time, when the ball hits the ground, we can use Equation (1.16)—the direct relationship between v and s, without reference to t, established previously by integrating the differential equation $a = v\,dv/ds$. Substituting $s = -c$, $s_0 = 0$, $a_c = -g$, and $v = v_c$ into Equation (1.16), we have

$$v_c^2 = v_0^2 + 2gc$$
$$v_c = \pm\sqrt{v_0^2 + 2gc}$$

As the particle is moving in the negative direction (downward), its velocity is negative. Therefore,

$$v_c = -\sqrt{v_0^2 + 2gc} \blacktriangleleft$$

Numerical results. Substituting numerical values $v_0 = 45$ ft/s, $c = 5$ ft, and $g = 32.2$ ft/s^2 into the expressions for h and v_c, we obtain

$$h = \frac{v_0^2}{2g} = \frac{(45)^2}{2(32.2)} \qquad h = 31.4 \text{ ft} \blacktriangleleft$$

and

$$v_c = -\sqrt{v_0^2 + 2gc} = -\sqrt{(45)^2 + 2(32.2)(5)} = -48.4 \text{ ft/s}$$
$$v_c = 48.4 \text{ ft/s} \downarrow \blacktriangleleft$$

EXAMPLE 1.6

An airplane lands on a straight runway with the touchdown speed of 200 km/h, whereupon the brakes are applied causing a deceleration proportional to the velocity of the plane, $a = -105v$. Determine the time required for the plane to reduce its velocity to 20 km/h after touchdown, and the distance traveled during that interval.

Solution The position coordinate s is chosen to be positive in the direction of the motion of the plane, with the origin O at the point where the plane makes contact with the runway. The initial conditions are $s_0 = 0$ and $v_0 = 200$ km/h at $t = 0$. The deceleration of the plane is given by $a = -105v$. The expression for the velocity is obtained by integrating equation $a = dv/dt$; thus,

$$\int_0^t dt = -\frac{1}{105}\int_{200}^v \frac{dv}{v}$$

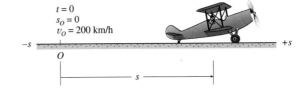

$t = 0$
$s_0 = 0$
$v_0 = 200$ km/h

$-s$ $\qquad$ $+s$

O

s

(continued)

EXAMPLE 1.6   (*concluded*)

Upon integration, we obtain

$$t = -\frac{1}{105}[\ln(v) - \ln(200)] = -\frac{1}{105}\ln\left(\frac{v}{200}\right) \qquad (a)$$

in hours, or

$$v = 200e^{-105t} \text{ km/h} \qquad (b)$$

Time when v = 20 km/h. Setting $v = 20$ km/h into Equation (a), we obtain

$$t = -\frac{1}{105}\ln\left(\frac{20}{200}\right) = 0.022 \text{ h}$$

$$t = 1.32 \text{ min} \blacktriangleleft$$

Position. The position is obtained by integrating the equation $v = ds/dt$. Thus,

$$\int_0^s ds = 200\int_0^t e^{-105t}\,dt$$

$$s = -\frac{200}{105}(e^{-105t} - 1) = 1.9(1 - e^{-105t}) \text{ km} \qquad (c)$$

Substituting $t = 0.022$ h into Equation (c), we obtain the distance traveled by the plane as

$$s = 1.9[1 - e^{-105(0.022)}]$$

$$s = 1.71 \text{ km} \blacktriangleleft$$

Relationship between v and s. The position s of the plane when $v = 20$ km/h can also be determined by establishing a direct relationship between v and s (without reference to t) by integrating the differential equation $a = v\,dv/ds$. Substituting $a = -105v$ into this equation, we have

$$-105v = v\frac{dv}{ds} \qquad \text{or} \qquad -105ds = dv$$

Integrating both sides, we obtain

$$-105\int_0^s ds = \int_{200}^v dv \qquad -105s = v - 200$$

$$v = 200 - 105s$$

Substituting $v = 20$ km/h into the above equation, we obtain

$$s = 1.71 \text{ km} \qquad\qquad checks$$

1.5 CURVILINEAR KINEMATICS:
POSITION, VELOCITY, AND ACCELERATION

When a particle moves along a curved path, its motion is called *curvilinear motion*. If the motion takes place in a single plane, it is referred to as the *plane curvilinear motion*; a motion in three dimensions is usually called the *space curvilinear motion*. In this section, we will discuss the basic concepts of position, velocity, and acceleration of a particle as it moves along a curved path.

Position

Consider a particle moving along a curved path as shown in Figure 1.8. The position A of the particle at any time t may be defined by a *position vector* $\mathbf{r}(t)$, from an arbitrarily chosen fixed origin O, to A. The position vector is a function of time and, in general, may change in magnitude and direction as the particle moves.

The vector change in position of the particle during a time interval is called its *displacement vector*. If the position vectors of a particle at times t_1 and t_2 are $\mathbf{r}(t_1) = \mathbf{r}_1$ and $\mathbf{r}(t_2) = \mathbf{r}_2$, respectively, then the displacement of the particle during the time interval from t_1 to t_2 is given by the vector $\Delta\mathbf{r} = \mathbf{r}_2 - \mathbf{r}_1$ (Figure 1.8). Note that, although the position vectors $\mathbf{r}_1$ and $\mathbf{r}_2$ depend on the location of the fixed origin O, the displacement $\Delta\mathbf{r}$ is independent of the choice of origin—it will remain the same regardless of where the origin O is located.

The distance traveled by the particle during a time interval is equal to the total length of the curved path traveled by the particle during the interval. It is a scalar quantity.

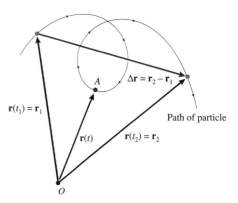

Figure 1.8

Velocity

Consider a particle moving along a curved path as shown in Figure 1.9a. The positions of the particle with respect to a fixed origin O, at times t and $t + \Delta t$, are given by the vectors $\mathbf{r}(t) = \mathbf{r}$ and $\mathbf{r}(t + \Delta t) = \mathbf{r} + \Delta\mathbf{r}$, respectively. As discussed, $\Delta\mathbf{r}$ represents the displacement of the particle during the time interval Δt. The average velocity of the particle during the time interval Δt is defined as

$$\mathbf{v}_{avg} = \frac{\Delta\mathbf{r}}{\Delta t} \tag{1.25}$$

As Δt is a scalar, the average velocity $\mathbf{v}_{avg}$ is a vector, and has the same direction as the displacement vector $\Delta\mathbf{r}$. The *instantaneous velocity vector* of the particle at time t is defined as the time rate of change of position vector at time t. By letting Δt approach zero in the limit in Equation (1.25), we obtain

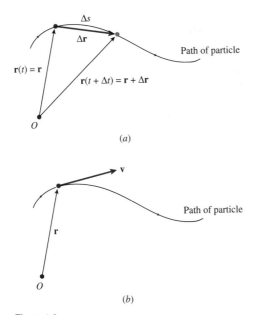

Figure 1.9

the instantaneous velocity **v** as

$$\mathbf{v} = \lim_{\Delta t \to 0} \frac{\Delta \mathbf{r}}{\Delta t} = \frac{d\mathbf{r}}{dt} = \dot{\mathbf{r}} \tag{1.26}$$

From Figure 1.9*a* we see that as Δt approaches zero, the direction of $\Delta \mathbf{r}$ approaches the tangent to the path at position $\mathbf{r}(t)$, and the magnitude of $\Delta \mathbf{r}$ approaches the arc length Δs. Hence, the velocity vector **v** is always tangent to the path as shown in Figure 1.9*b*; and its magnitude, which is usually called the *speed*, can be expressed as

$$v = |\mathbf{v}| = \left| \frac{d\mathbf{r}}{dt} \right| = \frac{ds}{dt} = \dot{s} \tag{1.27}$$

Like the position vector, the velocity vector is a function of time and, in general, may change in magnitude and direction with time.

Acceleration

Let the velocities of a particle at times t and $t + \Delta t$ be $\mathbf{v}(t) = \mathbf{v}$ and $\mathbf{v}(t + \Delta t) = \mathbf{v} + \Delta \mathbf{v}$, respectively, as shown in Figure 1.10*a*. Figure 1.10*b* shows the same two velocity vectors drawn from an arbitrary fixed reference point A. The dashed curve shown in this figure is not the path of the particle, but the locus of the tips (arrowheads) of the velocity vectors at various instants of time. This curve is called the **hodograph** of the motion.

The ratio of the change in velocity $\Delta \mathbf{v}$ to the time interval Δt is called the *average acceleration* during the interval Δt, and is given as

$$\mathbf{a}_{avg} = \frac{\Delta \mathbf{v}}{\Delta t} \tag{1.28}$$

Note that the average acceleration $\mathbf{a}_{avg}$ is a vector, and has the same direction as $\Delta \mathbf{v}$. The *instantaneous acceleration vector* of the particle at time t is defined as the time rate of change of velocity vector at time t; we obtain it from Equation (1.28) by letting Δt approach zero in the limit. Thus,

$$\mathbf{a} = \lim_{\Delta t \to 0} \frac{\Delta \mathbf{v}}{\Delta t} = \frac{d\mathbf{v}}{dt} = \dot{\mathbf{v}} \tag{1.29}$$

Substituting $\mathbf{v} = \dot{\mathbf{r}}$ from Equation (1.26) into Equation (1.29), we obtain

$$\mathbf{a} = \dot{\mathbf{v}} = \ddot{\mathbf{r}} \tag{1.30}$$

From Figure 1.10*b* we can see that as Δt approaches zero, the direction of $\Delta \mathbf{v}$ approaches the tangent to the hodograph at velocity $\mathbf{v}(t)$. Hence, the acceler-

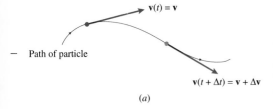

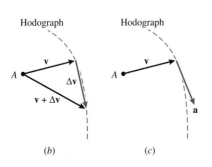

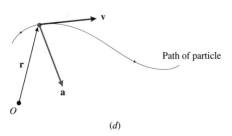

Figure 1.10

ation vector **a** is always tangent to the hodograph as shown in Figure 1.10*c*. But realize that the acceleration vector in general is *not* tangent to the path of motion (Figure 1.10*d*). Like position and velocity vectors, the acceleration vector is a function of time, and may change in magnitude and direction with time.

In our discussion thus far, we have not referred to any coordinate system to describe the position, velocity, and acceleration of motion of a particle. The following sections present the description of curvilinear motion in three commonly used types of coordinate systems. For each type of coordinate system, the case of planar motion is considered first, followed by the general case of motion in three-dimensional space.

1.6 CURVILINEAR MOTION: RECTANGULAR COORDINATES

Planar Motion

As shown in Figure 1.11*a*, the position vector of a particle moving in the *x*-*y* plane can be expressed in terms of its **rectangular components**, in the directions of the fixed *x* and *y* axes, as

$$\mathbf{r} = x\mathbf{i} + y\mathbf{j} \tag{1.31}$$

in which **i** and **j** are the unit vectors along the *x* and *y* axes, respectively. It should be realized that since the particle is in motion, its two coordinates, *x* and *y*, are functions of time *t*. However, the unit vectors **i** and **j** do not vary with time as their magnitudes and directions remain constant.

By successively differentiating Equation (1.31) twice with respect to *t*, we obtain the velocity vector and the acceleration vector in terms of their rectangular components as

$$\mathbf{v} = \dot{\mathbf{r}} = \dot{x}\mathbf{i} + \dot{y}\mathbf{j} \tag{1.32}$$

and

$$\mathbf{a} = \dot{\mathbf{v}} = \ddot{\mathbf{r}} = \ddot{x}\mathbf{i} + \ddot{y}\mathbf{j} \tag{1.33}$$

As Equation (1.32) indicates, the magnitudes of the rectangular components of the velocity vector (Figure 1.11*b*) are given by

$$v_x = \dot{x} \qquad v_y = \dot{y} \tag{1.34}$$

Similarly, from Equation (1.33), we obtain the magnitudes of the rectangular components of the acceleration vector (Figure 1.11*c*) as

$$a_x = \dot{v}_x = \ddot{x} \qquad a_y = \dot{v}_y = \ddot{y} \tag{1.35}$$

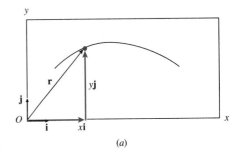

(*a*)

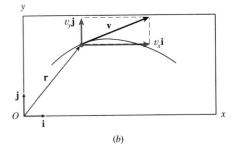

(*b*)

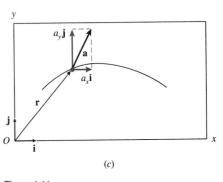

(*c*)

Figure 1.11

The magnitudes of the position, velocity, and acceleration vectors are given by

$$r = \sqrt{x^2 + y^2} \qquad v = \sqrt{v_x^2 + v_y^2} \qquad a = \sqrt{a_x^2 + a_y^2} \qquad (1.36)$$

It is important to recognize that any plane curvilinear motion of a particle may be considered to be the vector sum of the two rectilinear motions occurring simultaneously in the x and y directions. Therefore, the characteristics of the motion (i.e., position, velocity, and acceleration components) in each of the two directions may be determined by using the procedure for analysis of rectilinear motion outlined in Section 1.4. The resultant motion is then obtained by vectorially adding the two component motions.

Projectile Motion

A special case of plane curvilinear motion, which is of considerable practical interest, is the motion of a *projectile*, such as a missile, bullet, ball, or any other freely flying object. Let us examine the motion of a projectile fired from an initial position $\mathbf{r}_0 = x_0\mathbf{i} + y_0\mathbf{j}$, with an initial velocity $\mathbf{v}_0 = v_{x0}\mathbf{i} + v_{y0}\mathbf{j}$ (Figure 1.12). If the air resistance is neglected, then the projectile is subjected to a constant downward acceleration g due to gravity. Thus, the acceleration of the projectile is known and can be written as

$$\mathbf{a} = a_x\mathbf{i} + a_y\mathbf{j} = -g\mathbf{j} \qquad (1.37)$$

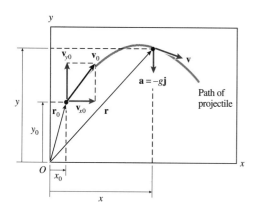

Figure 1.12

The x and y components of the velocity and the position vectors of the projectile at a time t are obtained by integration from the corresponding components of the acceleration vector, which are known. Since $a_x = 0$, the x component of the velocity is obtained by integrating the differential equation $a_x = \dot{v}_x$ as

$$\int_{v_{x0}}^{v_x} dv_x = \int_0^t a_x\, dt = 0$$

$$v_x = v_{x0} \qquad (1.38)$$

which indicates that the velocity in the x direction remains constant. The x coordinate of the projectile at time t is determined by integrating the differential equation $v_x = \dot{x}$ as

$$\int_{x_0}^{x} dx = \int_0^t v_x\, dt = v_{x0} \int_0^t dt$$

$$x = x_0 + v_{x0}t \qquad (1.39)$$

Similarly, the y component of velocity vectors is determined by integration of $a_y = -g = \dot{v}_y$. Thus,

$$\int_{v_{y0}}^{v_y} dv_y = \int_0^t a_y\, dt = -g \int_0^t dt$$

$$v_y = v_{y0} - gt \qquad (1.40)$$

and the y coordinate is obtained by integrating the equation $v_y = \dot{y}$ as

$$\int_{y_0}^{y} dy = \int_{0}^{t} v_y \, dt = \int_{0}^{t} (v_{y0} - gt) \, dt$$

$$y = y_0 + v_{y0}t - \frac{1}{2}gt^2 \qquad (1.41)$$

The equation of the path, or the *trajectory*, of the projectile is obtained by eliminating t from the equations of x and y [Equations (1.39) and (1.41)], and is given by

$$y = y_0 + \frac{v_{y0}}{v_{x0}}(x - x_0) - \frac{g}{2v_{x0}^2}(x - x_0)^2 \qquad (1.42)$$

which indicates that the trajectory of a projectile has a parabolic shape.

The resultant motion of the projectile is obtained by the vector sum of its motions in the x and y directions. Thus, the position vector at a time t is given by

$$\mathbf{r} = (x_0 + v_{x0}t)\mathbf{i} + \left(y_0 + v_{y0}t - \frac{1}{2}gt^2\right)\mathbf{j} \qquad (1.43)$$

and the velocity vector by

$$\mathbf{v} = v_{x0}\mathbf{i} + (v_{y0} - gt)\mathbf{j} \qquad (1.44)$$

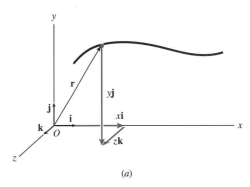

(a)

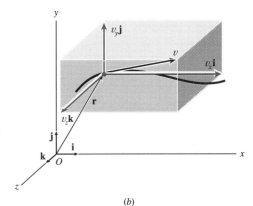

(b)

Spatial Motion

When the motion of a particle takes place along a three-dimensional space curve as shown in Figure 1.13a, then the position, velocity, and acceleration vectors of the particle, at any time, can be expressed in terms of their rectangular components, as

$$\begin{aligned}
\mathbf{r} &= x\mathbf{i} + y\mathbf{j} + z\mathbf{k} \\
\mathbf{v} &= \dot{x}\mathbf{i} + \dot{y}\mathbf{j} + \dot{z}\mathbf{k} \\
\mathbf{a} &= \ddot{x}\mathbf{i} + \ddot{y}\mathbf{j} + \ddot{z}\mathbf{k}
\end{aligned} \qquad (1.45)$$

The magnitudes of the x, y, and z components of the velocity and the acceleration vectors (Figures 1.13b and c) are given by

$$v_x = \dot{x} \qquad v_y = \dot{y} \qquad v_z = \dot{z} \qquad (1.46)$$

$$a_x = \dot{v}_x = \ddot{x} \qquad a_y = \dot{v}_y = \ddot{y} \qquad a_z = \dot{v}_z = \ddot{z} \qquad (1.47)$$

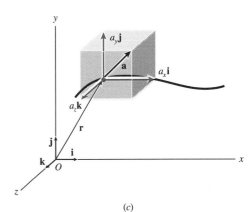

(c)

Figure 1.13

and the magnitudes of the position, velocity, and acceleration vectors can be written as

$$
\left.\begin{array}{l}
r = \sqrt{x^2 + y^2 + z^2} \\[4pt]
v = \sqrt{v_x^2 + v_y^2 + v_z^2} \\[4pt]
a = \sqrt{a_x^2 + a_y^2 + a_z^2}
\end{array}\right\}
\tag{1.48}
$$

EXAMPLE   1.7

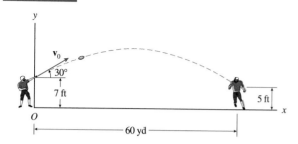

A football quarterback throws a 60-yd pass from 7 ft above the ground to a receiver, who catches the ball at 5 ft above the ground. Determine the initial velocity of the ball if it is thrown at an angle of 30° with the horizontal. Also, determine the time it takes for the ball to reach the receiver, and the maximum height above the ground reached by the ball. Neglect air resistance. Let $g = 32.2$ ft/s^2.

Solution   Since throughout its motion the ball is subjected to only the downward acceleration due to gravity ($g = 32.2$ ft/s^2), we solve this problem directly by using the equations of the projectile motion [Equations (1.37) to (1.44)] derived previously.

The origin of the x-y coordinate system is chosen at point O on the ground (see the figure), so that the initial position of the ball is $x_0 = 0$ and $y_0 = 7$ ft.

Initial velocity.   If $\mathbf{v}_0$ is the yet unknown initial velocity of the ball, then its components in the x and y directions are $v_{x0} = v_0 \cos 30° = 0.866 v_0$, and $v_{y0} = v_0 \sin 30° = 0.5 v_0$, respectively. Since the initial and final positions of the ball are known, the solution for v_0 can be obtained using Equation (1.42):

$$
y = y_0 + \frac{v_{y0}}{v_{x0}}(x - x_0) - \frac{g}{2 v_{x0}^2}(x - x_0)^2
$$

$$
5 = 7 + \frac{0.5 v_0}{0.866 v_0}[60(3) - 0] - \frac{32.2}{2(0.866 v_0)^2}[60(3) - 0]^2
$$

$$
v_0 = 81.0 \text{ ft/s} \blacktriangleleft
$$

The initial velocity can also now be expressed in the vector form as

$$
\mathbf{v}_0 = 70.2\mathbf{i} + 40.5\mathbf{j} \text{ (ft/s)} \blacktriangleleft
$$

(continued)

EXAMPLE 1.7   (*concluded*)

Flight time.   The time it takes for the ball to reach the receiver can be computed by using either Equation (1.39) or Equation (1.41). Using Equation (1.39), we write

$$x = x_0 + v_{x0}t \qquad 180 = 0 + 70.2t$$

$$t = 2.56 \text{ s} \blacktriangleleft$$

Maximum height.   At maximum height, the velocity component v_y is zero. Setting $v_y = 0$ in Equation (1.40), we obtain the time to reach the maximum height as

$$v_y = v_{y0} - gt \qquad 0 = 40.5 - 32.2t \qquad t = 1.26 \text{ s}$$

By substituting $t = 1.26$ s into the equation for y [Equation (1.41)], we determine the maximum height as

$$y = y_0 + v_{y0}t - \frac{1}{2}gt^2$$

$$y = 7 + 40.5(1.26) - \frac{1}{2}(32.2)(1.26)^2 = 32.5 \text{ ft}$$

$$\text{Maximum height} = 32.5 \text{ ft} \blacktriangleleft$$

EXAMPLE 1.8

A self-propelled rocket is fired from an airplane flying at an altitude of 500 m to hit a target on the ground. The velocity of the rocket at release is the same as that of the airplane, which is 720 km/h in the horizontal direction. The acceleration of the rocket is 1.5 m/s^2 in the horizontal direction, and 9.81 m/s^2 downward due to gravity. Determine the horizontal distance from the point where the rocket is fired, to the target.

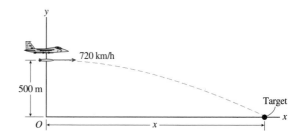

Solution   The origin of the x-y coordinate system is chosen at point O on the ground directly under the point of release of the rocket, as shown in the figure. Thus, the coordinates of the initial position of the rocket at time $t = 0$ are $x_0 = 0$ and $y_0 = 500$ m. The rectangular components of the initial velocity of the rocket are given as $v_{x0} = 720$ km/h $= 200$ m/s and $v_{y0} = 0$. The components of the acceleration in the horizontal and the vertical directions, respectively, are known as $a_x = 1.5$ m/s^2 and $a_y = -9.81$ m/s^2.

Motion in horizontal direction.   We obtain the velocity in the horizontal direction by integrating the differential equation $a_x = \dot{v}_x$. Thus,

$$\int_{200}^{v_x} dv_x = 1.5 \int_0^t dt \qquad v_x = 200 + 1.5t$$

We determine the horizontal distance x by integrating the equation $v_x = \dot{x}$ as

$$\int_0^x dx = \int_0^t (200 + 1.5t)\, dt \qquad x = 200t + 0.75t^2 \qquad \text{(a)}$$

(*continued*)

EXAMPLE 1.8 *(concluded)*

Motion in vertical direction. We obtain the velocity in the vertical direction by integrating the equation $a_y = \dot{v}_y$. Thus,

$$\int_0^{v_y} dv_y = -9.81 \int_0^t dt \qquad v_y = -9.81t$$

For the vertical distance y, we integrate the equation $v_y = \dot{y}$ as

$$\int_{500}^y dy = -9.81 \int_0^t t\, dt \qquad y = 500 - 4.91t^2 \qquad \text{(b)}$$

Time when $y = 0$. When the rocket hits the target on the ground, $y = 0$. Setting $y = 0$ in Equation (b), we write

$$0 = 500 - 4.91t^2$$

from which $t = \pm 10.1$ s. As the negative root, $t = -10.1$ s, describes a time before the initiation of motion, the desired time is $t = +10.1$ s.

Horizontal distance to target. Substituting $t = 10.1$ s into Equation (a), we obtain the horizontal distance from the origin O to the target:

$$x = 200(10.1) + 0.75(10.1)^2$$

$$x = 2100 \text{ m} \quad \blacktriangleleft$$

1.7 CURVILINEAR MOTION: TANGENTIAL AND NORMAL COORDINATES

In many practical applications, the curved path of the motion of a particle is specified. In these cases, it is usually convenient to express the acceleration vector in terms of components directed along the tangent and the normal to the curved path. (Recall from Section 1.5 that the velocity vector is always directed along the tangent to the path.)

Planar Motion

Consider a particle moving along a curved path as shown in Figure 1.14. The position A of the particle at any time t is defined by the distance s measured along the path from an arbitrarily chosen fixed origin O, to A. The origin of the *tangential* and *normal* (*t-n*) *coordinate* system is considered to be located on, and moving with, the particle—with the t axis always tangent to the path, and the n axis perpendicular to the t axis. The positive senses of these axes are defined by the unit vectors $\mathbf{n}_t$ and $\mathbf{n}_n$, directed along, and pointing in the positive directions of, the t and n axes, respectively. As shown in Figure 1.14, the unit vector $\mathbf{n}_t$ (or the t axis) is considered positive toward the direction of motion, that is, in the direction of positive s; and the unit vector $\mathbf{n}_n$ (or the n axis) is positive toward the center of curvature C of the path. As the particle moves along the curved path from position A to another position B, the orientation of the *t-n* coordinate system changes so that $\mathbf{n}_t$ always remains tangent to the path, pointing in the direction of motion; and $\mathbf{n}_n$ always points toward the center of curvature of the path. Note that during the motion, while the directions of $\mathbf{n}_t$ and $\mathbf{n}_n$ change, the magnitudes of these unit vectors do not change but remain constant at one.

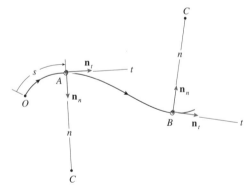

Figure 1.14

As discussed in Section 1.5, the velocity vector of the particle is always tangent to the path; therefore, it can be expressed in the *t-n* coordinate system as

$$\mathbf{v} = v\mathbf{n}_t = \dot{s}\mathbf{n}_t \qquad (1.49)$$

A positive velocity **v** indicates that the particle is moving in the positive *s* direction at that time. Conversely, a negative velocity indicates that it is moving in the negative *s* direction.

To determine the expression for acceleration in terms of components along the tangential and normal directions, we differentiate Equation (1.49) with respect to time *t* to obtain

$$\mathbf{a} = \dot{\mathbf{v}} = \dot{v}\mathbf{n}_t + v\dot{\mathbf{n}}_t = \ddot{s}\mathbf{n}_t + \dot{s}\dot{\mathbf{n}}_t \qquad (1.50)$$

Note that in this equation, the derivative $\dot{\mathbf{n}}_t = d\mathbf{n}_t/dt$ represents the change in the direction of the tangential unit vector $\mathbf{n}_t$. As stated previously, the magnitude of $\mathbf{n}_t$ remains constant.

The derivative $\dot{\mathbf{n}}_t$ can be written as

$$\dot{\mathbf{n}}_t = \frac{d\mathbf{n}_t}{dt} = \frac{d\mathbf{n}_t}{ds}\frac{ds}{dt} = \frac{d\mathbf{n}_t}{ds}\dot{s} = \frac{d\mathbf{n}_t}{ds}v \qquad (1.51)$$

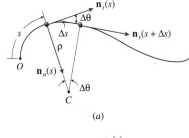

(a)

Substituting Equation (1.51) into Equation (1.50), we obtain

$$\mathbf{a} = \dot{\mathbf{v}} = \dot{v}\mathbf{n}_t + v^2\frac{d\mathbf{n}_t}{ds} = \ddot{s}\mathbf{n}_t + \dot{s}^2\frac{d\mathbf{n}_t}{ds} \qquad (1.52)$$

To evaluate the derivative $d\mathbf{n}_t/ds$, consider the motion of a particle shown in Figure 1.15*a*. Let $\mathbf{n}_t(s)$ and $\mathbf{n}_t(s + \Delta s)$ be the tangential unit vectors corresponding to the positions *s* and *s* + Δ*s* of the particle, respectively. The derivative $d\mathbf{n}_t/ds$ is defined as

$$\frac{d\mathbf{n}_t}{ds} = \lim_{\Delta s \to 0}\frac{\mathbf{n}_t(s + \Delta s) - \mathbf{n}_t(s)}{\Delta s} = \lim_{\Delta s \to 0}\frac{\Delta \mathbf{n}_t}{\Delta s} \qquad (1.53)$$

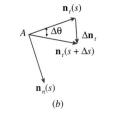

(b)

where $\Delta \mathbf{n}_t$ represents the change in $\mathbf{n}_t$. In Figure 1.15*b*, the two unit vectors $\mathbf{n}_t(s)$ and $\mathbf{n}_t(s + \Delta s)$ are drawn from a common origin *A*. As $\mathbf{n}_t(s)$ and $\mathbf{n}_t(s + \Delta s)$ both have unit magnitudes, their tips (arrowheads) lie on a circle of unit radius with center at *A*. As Δ*s* approaches zero in the limit, the direction of $\Delta \mathbf{n}_t$ approaches the tangent to this circle of unit radius in the direction of the normal unit vector $\mathbf{n}_n(s)$. Also, as Δ*s* approaches zero, the magnitude of $\Delta \mathbf{n}_t$ approaches the arc length (1)Δθ = Δθ on the circle of unit radius. From Figure 1.15*a*, we observe that the angle Δθ approaches Δ*s*/ρ in the limit, where ρ is the radius of curvature of the path at position *s*. Thus, the magnitude of $\Delta \mathbf{n}_t$ approaches Δ*s*/ρ as Δ*s* approaches zero in the limit. The derivative $d\mathbf{n}_t/ds$

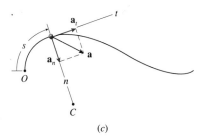

(c)

Figure 1.15

[Equation (1.53)] can now be evaluated as

$$\frac{d\mathbf{n}_t}{ds} = \lim_{\Delta s \to 0} \frac{\Delta \mathbf{n}_t}{\Delta s} = \lim_{\Delta s \to 0} \left(\frac{\Delta s/\rho}{\Delta s} \right) \mathbf{n}_n = \frac{1}{\rho} \mathbf{n}_n \tag{1.54}$$

Substituting Equation (1.54) into Equation (1.52), we obtain the expression for acceleration in terms of components along the tangential and normal directions as

$$\mathbf{a} = \dot{v}\mathbf{n}_t + \frac{v^2}{\rho}\mathbf{n}_n = \ddot{s}\mathbf{n}_t + \frac{\dot{s}^2}{\rho}\mathbf{n}_n \tag{1.55}$$

As Equation (1.55) indicates, the magnitudes of the acceleration components in the tangential and normal directions (Figure 1.15c) are

$$a_t = \dot{v} = \ddot{s} \qquad a_n = \frac{v^2}{\rho} = \frac{\dot{s}^2}{\rho} \tag{1.56}$$

and the magnitude of the acceleration vector is given by

$$a = \sqrt{a_t^2 + a_n^2} \tag{1.57}$$

It is important to realize that the tangential component of the acceleration $\mathbf{a}_t$ of a particle measures the rate of change of the magnitude of its velocity; whereas, the normal component $\mathbf{a}_n$ measures the rate of change of the direction of the velocity vector. The direction of the normal component is always toward the center of curvature of the path. A positive tangential component $\mathbf{a}_t$ indicates that the magnitude of the velocity of the particle is increasing, and a negative tangential component indicates that the magnitude of the velocity is decreasing. From Equation (1.55), we can see that the resultant acceleration $\mathbf{a}$ is zero only when both tangential and normal components are zero. For example, in the case of a particle moving along a circular path with constant speed, the tangential component $\mathbf{a}_t$ will be zero; but the normal component $\mathbf{a}_n$ will not be zero and, hence, the resultant acceleration $\mathbf{a}$ will not be zero. The rectilinear motion of a particle, studied previously in Sections 1.2 to 1.4, may be considered as a special case of the plane curvilinear motion by recognizing that since the radius of curvature ρ of a straight-line path is infinite, the magnitude of the normal component $a_n = v^2/\rho$ is zero and, therefore, the resultant acceleration is equal to the time rate of change of the magnitude of velocity ($\mathbf{a} = \mathbf{a}_t$).

Procedure for Analysis From Equations (1.49) and (1.56), we can see that the relationships between the position s, the velocity $v = \dot{s}$, and the tangential component of acceleration $a_t = \dot{v} = \ddot{s}$, for a particle in plane curvilinear motion, are the same as those for the case of rectilinear motion. Therefore, if one of these three characteristics is known, the remaining two can be determined by using the procedure for analysis of rectilinear motion outlined in Section 1.4. The normal component of acceleration is then obtained from the relationship $a_n = v^2/\rho$, provided that the radius of curvature of the path ρ is known.

In some problems of practical interest, the path or trajectory of motion of the particle may be specified using rectangular $(x$-$y)$ coordinates. In these cases, the radius of curvature can be calculated by using the relation from elementary calculus,

$$\rho = \left| \frac{[1 + (dy/dx)^2]^{3/2}}{d^2y/dx^2} \right| \qquad (1.58)$$

Spatial Motion

Equations (1.49) to (1.57) derived previously for the planar motion remain valid in the case of motion along a three-dimensional space curve, provided the normal (n) axis at a point on a three-dimensional path is defined in the direction perpendicular to the tangent to the path, and in the direction of the center of curvature of the path at that point (Figure 1.16). This strict definition of the normal axis is necessary because there are an infinite number of axes perpendicular to the tangential axis at a point on a space curve. The plane containing the tangential and normal axes at a point on a space curve is referred to as the *osculating plane*.

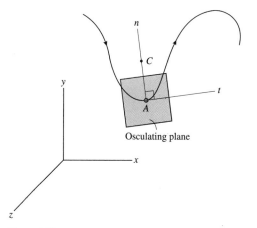

Figure 1.16

EXAMPLE 1.9

A car starts from rest on a curved path of 1000-ft radius with a constant tangential acceleration of 4 ft/s². If the acceleration in the normal direction cannot exceed $0.3g$ without the car sliding, determine (*a*) the maximum safe speed of the car; (*b*) the time required to reach the maximum speed; and (*c*) the distance traveled during this interval.

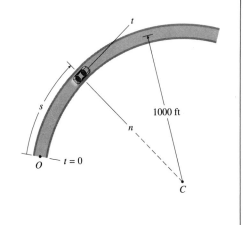

Solution The origin O of the position coordinate s is chosen at the initial position of the car at $t = 0$ as shown. The initial conditions are $s_0 = 0$ and $v_0 = 0$.

Maximum speed. The maximum speed the car can achieve without sliding is computed by substituting $a_n = 0.3g = 0.3(32.2) = 9.66$ ft/s² and $\rho = 1000$ ft into the equation for

(*continued*)

EXAMPLE 1.9 (*concluded*)

the normal component of acceleration; thus,

$$a_n = \frac{v^2}{\rho} \qquad v^2 = a_n\rho = 9.66(1000)$$

$$v = 98.3 \text{ ft/s} = 67 \text{ mph} \blacktriangleleft$$

Time when $v = 98.3$ ft/s. As the tangential component of the acceleration is known, $a_t = 4$ ft/s^2, we first determine the expression for velocity by integrating the differential equation $a_t = \dot{v}$. Thus,

$$\int_0^v dv = \int_0^t a_t dt = 4 \int_0^t dt \qquad v = 4t \text{ ft/s}$$

Setting $v = 98.3$ ft/s into the expression for velocity, we obtain the time required:

$$98.3 = 4t \qquad\qquad t = 24.6 \text{ s} \blacktriangleleft$$

Distance traveled in $t = 24.6$ s. The equation of the position is obtained by integrating the equation $v = \dot{s}$. Thus,

$$\int_0^s ds = \int_0^t v\, dt = 4 \int_0^t t\, dt \qquad s = 2t^2$$

Substituting $t = 24.6$ s into the above equation, we find the distance traveled to be

$$s = 2(24.6)^2 \qquad\qquad s = 1210 \text{ ft} \blacktriangleleft$$

EXAMPLE 1.10

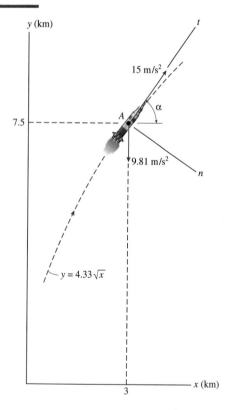

During a phase of its flight, the trajectory of a rocket is described by the equation $y = 4.33\sqrt{x}$, where x and y are in km. At the position shown, the rocket is subjected to an acceleration of 15 m/s^2 tangent to its trajectory due to thrust, in addition to the downward acceleration of 9.81 m/s^2 due to gravity. Determine the velocity and the acceleration of the rocket at this position.

Solution The origin of the t-n coordinate system is located at the position A of the rocket as shown in the figure. We can determine the angle α between the t axis and the x axis by evaluating the derivative of the path equation at the position of the rocket. Thus, at $x = 3$ km,

$$\frac{dy}{dx} = 2.17x^{-1/2} \quad \tan \alpha = 2.17(3)^{-1/2} = 1.25 \quad \alpha = 51.34°$$

Acceleration. The tangential and normal components of acceleration are given by

$$a_t = 15 - 9.81 \sin 51.34° = 7.34 \text{ m/s}^2$$
$$a_n = 9.81 \cos 51.34° = 6.13 \text{ m/s}^2$$

Therefore, the acceleration vector can be written as

$$\mathbf{a} = 7.34\mathbf{n}_t + 6.13\mathbf{n}_n \text{ (m/s}^2)$$

(continued)

EXAMPLE 1.10 (*concluded*)

The magnitude of the acceleration vector is

$$a = \sqrt{a_t^2 + a_n^2} = \sqrt{(7.34)^2 + (6.13)^2} = 9.56 \text{ m/s}^2$$

The direction of **a** with respect to the *t* axis is determined by using the relationship

$$\tan \theta = \frac{a_n}{a_t} = \frac{6.13}{7.34} = 0.84 \qquad \theta = 39.87°$$

Therefore, the direction of the acceleration vector with respect to the *x* axis is

$$51.34 - 39.87 = 11.47°$$

$$a = 9.56 \text{ m/s}^2 \text{ at } \triangle 11.47° \blacktriangleleft$$

Radius of curvature.   The second derivative of *y* with respect to *x* is

$$\frac{d^2y}{dx^2} = -1.09 \, x^{-3/2}$$

We then compute the radius of curvature by using Equation (1.58) as

$$\rho = \left| \frac{[1 + (dy/dx)^2]^{3/2}}{d^2y/dx^2} \right| = \left| \frac{[1 + (2.17x^{-1/2})^2]^{3/2}}{-1.09x^{-3/2}} \right|$$

Substituting *x* = 3 km into the above equation, we find the radius of curvature of the path at the position of the rocket as

$$\rho = \left| \frac{[1 + (1.25)^2]^{3/2}}{-0.21} \right| = 19.53 \text{ km} = 19,530 \text{ m}$$

Velocity.   The velocity vector is directed tangent to the path. We determine its magnitude from the equation

$$a_n = \frac{v^2}{\rho} \qquad 6.13 = \frac{v^2}{19,530}$$

$$v = 346 \text{ m/s at } \triangle 51.34° \blacktriangleleft$$

1.8 CURVILINEAR MOTION: CYLINDRICAL COORDINATES

Planar Motion: Polar Coordinates

In problems involving rotation of a particle about an axis, it is usually convenient to analyze the motion using *polar coordinates*. In this method, the position *A* of a particle moving along a plane curvilinear path (Figure 1.17*a*) is defined by its distance *r* from a fixed origin or pole *O*, and the angle θ, which the line *OA* makes with a fixed reference line. The line *OA* is called the *radial* axis (*r* axis) and its positive sense is defined by the unit vector $\mathbf{n}_r$ directed from origin *O* toward the position *A* of the particle. The direction perpendicular to the radial direction is referred to as the *transverse* direction, and the positive sense of the transverse axis (θ axis) is established by the unit vector $\mathbf{n}_\theta$ pointing in the direction of increasing θ. The position vector **r** of the particle at any time *t* can be expressed as

$$\mathbf{r} = r\mathbf{n}_r \tag{1.59}$$

As the particle moves along the curved path, both the magnitude *r* and the direction θ of the position vector **r** change. The change in angle θ causes the mutually perpendicular *r* and θ axes, and the corresponding unit vectors $\mathbf{n}_r$ and $\mathbf{n}_\theta$, to rotate about the origin *O*. Realize that while the directions of $\mathbf{n}_r$ and $\mathbf{n}_\theta$ change during the motion, their magnitudes remain constant at one.

To obtain the expression for velocity vector **v** in terms of its components

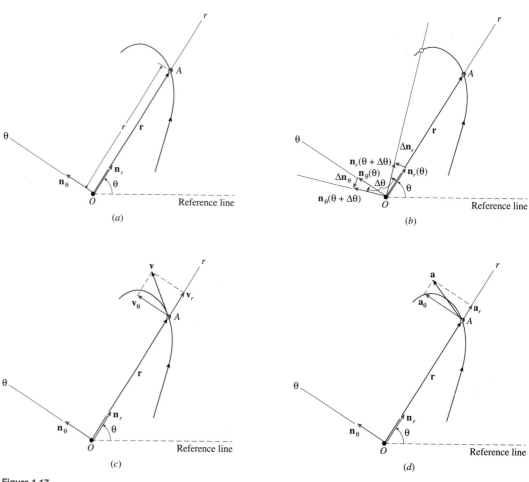

Figure 1.17

in the radial and transverse directions, we differentiate Equation (1.59) with respect to time t. Thus,

$$\mathbf{v} = \dot{\mathbf{r}} = \dot{r}\mathbf{n}_r + r\dot{\mathbf{n}}_r \tag{1.60}$$

Writing $\dot{\mathbf{n}}_r$ as

$$\dot{\mathbf{n}}_r = \frac{d\mathbf{n}_r}{dt} = \frac{d\mathbf{n}_r}{d\theta}\frac{d\theta}{dt} = \frac{d\mathbf{n}_r}{d\theta}\dot{\theta} \tag{1.61}$$

and substituting Equation (1.61) into Equation (1.60), we obtain

$$\mathbf{v} = \dot{\mathbf{r}} = \dot{r}\mathbf{n}_r + r\dot{\theta}\frac{d\mathbf{n}_r}{d\theta} \tag{1.62}$$

in which $d\mathbf{n}_r/d\theta$ represents the change in the direction of the radial unit vector

$\mathbf{n}_r$ due to the change in θ. To evaluate this derivative, consider the motion of a particle during a time interval Δt. As shown in Figure 1.17b, during this interval the direction of the position vector $\mathbf{r}$ changes from θ to $\theta + \Delta\theta$, causing the unit vectors $\mathbf{n}_r$ and $\mathbf{n}_\theta$ to rotate by angle $\Delta\theta$. The changes in $\mathbf{n}_r$ and $\mathbf{n}_\theta$ are denoted by $\Delta\mathbf{n}_r$ and $\Delta\mathbf{n}_\theta$, respectively. Since the unit vectors maintain their magnitudes at unity, we can see from Figure 1.17b that, as $\Delta\theta$ approaches zero in the limit, the magnitudes of $\Delta\mathbf{n}_r$ and $\Delta\mathbf{n}_\theta$ approach the arc lengths $1(\Delta\theta) = \Delta\theta$. Also, as $\Delta\theta$ approaches zero, the direction of $\Delta\mathbf{n}_r$ approaches that of $\mathbf{n}_\theta$, whereas the direction of $\Delta\mathbf{n}_\theta$ approaches that of $-\mathbf{n}_r$. Thus,

$$\frac{d\mathbf{n}_r}{d\theta} = \lim_{\Delta\theta\to 0} \frac{\Delta\mathbf{n}_r}{\Delta\theta} = \lim_{\Delta\theta\to 0} \frac{\Delta\theta\mathbf{n}_\theta}{\Delta\theta} = \mathbf{n}_\theta \tag{1.63}$$

$$\frac{d\mathbf{n}_\theta}{d\theta} = \lim_{\Delta\theta\to 0} \frac{\Delta\mathbf{n}_\theta}{\Delta\theta} = \lim_{\Delta\theta\to 0} -\frac{\Delta\theta\mathbf{n}_r}{\Delta\theta} = -\mathbf{n}_r \tag{1.64}$$

Substituting Equation (1.63) into Equation (1.62), we obtain the expression for velocity in terms of components along the radial and transverse directions as

$$\mathbf{v} = \dot{r}\mathbf{n}_r + r\dot{\theta}\mathbf{n}_\theta \tag{1.65}$$

As Equation (1.65) indicates, the magnitudes of the velocity components in the radial and transverse directions (Figure 1.17c) are

$$v_r = \dot{r} \qquad v_\theta = r\dot{\theta} \tag{1.66}$$

The quantity $\dot{\theta}$, which is the time rate of change of the angle θ, is expressed in units of rad/s. The magnitude of the velocity vector is given by

$$v = \sqrt{v_r^2 + v_\theta^2} \tag{1.67}$$

By differentiating Equation (1.65) with respect to time, we obtain the acceleration vector in terms of radial and transverse components. Thus,

$$\mathbf{a} = \dot{\mathbf{v}} = \ddot{r}\mathbf{n}_r + \dot{r}\dot{\mathbf{n}}_r + \dot{r}\dot{\theta}\mathbf{n}_\theta + r\ddot{\theta}\mathbf{n}_\theta + r\dot{\theta}\dot{\mathbf{n}}_\theta \tag{1.68}$$

By using Equations (1.63) and (1.64), we can write $\dot{\mathbf{n}}_r$ and $\dot{\mathbf{n}}_\theta$ as

$$\left. \begin{array}{l} \dot{\mathbf{n}}_r = \dfrac{d\mathbf{n}_r}{dt} = \dfrac{d\mathbf{n}_r}{d\theta}\dot{\theta} = \dot{\theta}\mathbf{n}_\theta \\[3mm] \dot{\mathbf{n}}_\theta = \dfrac{d\mathbf{n}_\theta}{dt} = \dfrac{d\mathbf{n}_\theta}{d\theta}\dot{\theta} = -\dot{\theta}\mathbf{n}_r \end{array} \right\} \tag{1.69}$$

Substituting Equations (1.69) into Equation (1.68), we obtain the expression for acceleration in terms of components in the radial and transverse directions as

$$\mathbf{a} = \ddot{r}\mathbf{n}_r + \dot{r}\dot{\theta}\mathbf{n}_\theta + \dot{r}\dot{\theta}\mathbf{n}_\theta + r\ddot{\theta}\mathbf{n}_\theta - r\dot{\theta}^2\mathbf{n}_r$$
$$\mathbf{a} = (\ddot{r} - r\dot{\theta}^2)\mathbf{n}_r + (r\ddot{\theta} + 2\dot{r}\dot{\theta})\mathbf{n}_\theta \tag{1.70}$$

Therefore, the magnitudes of the acceleration components in the radial and transverse directions (Figure 1.17d) are

$$a_r = \ddot{r} - r\dot{\theta}^2 \qquad a_\theta = r\ddot{\theta} + 2\dot{r}\dot{\theta} \tag{1.71}$$

in which $\ddot{\theta}$ is expressed in the units of rad/s^2. The magnitude of the acceleration vector is given by

$$a = \sqrt{a_r^2 + a_\theta^2} \tag{1.72}$$

Circular Motion   A special case of plane curvilinear motion that is of practical interest is the motion of a particle moving along a circular path of radius r and center O. As the radius r is constant, $\dot{r} = \ddot{r} = 0$, and therefore, the expressions for velocity [Equation (1.65)] and acceleration [Equation (1.70)] can be simplified as

$$\boxed{\begin{aligned} \mathbf{v} &= r\dot{\theta}\mathbf{n}_\theta \\ \mathbf{a} &= -r\dot{\theta}^2\mathbf{n}_r + r\ddot{\theta}\mathbf{n}_\theta \end{aligned}} \tag{1.73}$$

Spatial Motion: Cylindrical Coordinates

In the case of the motion of a particle along a three-dimensional space curve, the position of the particle may be defined by the three *cylindrical coordinates* R, θ, and z. As shown in Figure 1.18, the z axis is perpendicular to the plane containing the R and θ axes, and its positive sense is specified by the unit vector $\mathbf{k}$. The position vector $\mathbf{r}$ of the particle at any time t can be expressed as

$$\mathbf{r} = R\mathbf{n}_R + z\mathbf{k} \tag{1.74}$$

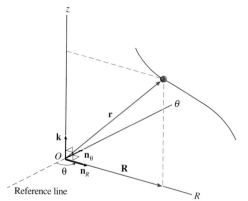

Figure 1.18

Since $\mathbf{k}$ remains constant in both magnitude and direction during the motion of the particle, its derivatives with respect to time are zero. Therefore, the expressions for velocity and acceleration vectors in cylindrical coordinates are obtained by replacing r with R in Equations (1.65) and (1.70), and by adding the first and second time derivatives of the z coordinate to these equations, respectively; thus,

$$\boxed{\mathbf{v} = \dot{R}\mathbf{n}_R + R\dot{\theta}\mathbf{n}_\theta + \dot{z}\mathbf{k}} \tag{1.75}$$

$$\boxed{\mathbf{a} = (\ddot{R} - R\dot{\theta}^2)\mathbf{n}_R + (R\ddot{\theta} + 2\dot{R}\dot{\theta})\mathbf{n}_\theta + \ddot{z}\mathbf{k}} \tag{1.76}$$

EXAMPLE 1.11

The position of a collar that is sliding along a rod as it rotates about O is given by the equation $r = 6 + 12t - 2t^2$. If the rotation of the rod is described by the equation $\theta = 0.5t^2 + 0.1t^3$, determine the velocity and acceleration of the collar when $t = 1.25$ s. In the given equations, r is in in., θ is in radians, and t is in s.

Solution Before we can use Equations (1.65) and (1.70) to determine the velocity and acceleration of the collar, we need to evaluate the first and second time derivative of r and θ at $t = 1.25$ s. Thus,

$$r = 6 + 12t - 2t^2 = 17.88 \text{ in.}$$
$$\dot{r} = 12 - 4t = 7 \text{ in./s}$$
$$\ddot{r} = -4 \text{ in./s}^2$$
$$\theta = 0.5t^2 + 0.1t^3 = 0.98 \text{ rad} = 56.15°$$
$$\dot{\theta} = t + 0.3t^2 = 1.72 \text{ rad/s}$$
$$\ddot{\theta} = 1 + 0.6t = 1.75 \text{ rad/s}^2$$

Velocity. The velocity components in the radial and transverse directions are

$$v_r = \dot{r} = 7 \text{ in./s}$$
$$v_\theta = r\dot{\theta} = (17.88)(1.72) = 30.75 \text{ in./s}$$

The magnitude of the velocity is

$$v = \sqrt{v_r^2 + v_\theta^2} = \sqrt{(7)^2 + (30.75)^2}$$
$$v = 31.5 \text{ in./s} \blacktriangleleft$$

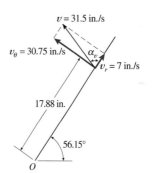

The direction of **v** with respect to the rod can be determined as

$$\alpha_v = \tan^{-1}\left(\frac{30.75}{7}\right) \qquad \alpha_v = 77.2° \blacktriangleleft$$

The velocity vector is shown.

Acceleration. The acceleration components in the radial and transverse directions are

$$a_r = \ddot{r} - r\dot{\theta}^2 = -4 - (17.88)(1.72)^2 = -56.9 \text{ in./s}^2$$
$$a_\theta = r\ddot{\theta} + 2\dot{r}\dot{\theta} = 17.88(1.75) + 2(7)(1.72) = 55.37 \text{ in./s}^2$$

(continued)

EXAMPLE   1.11   (*concluded*)

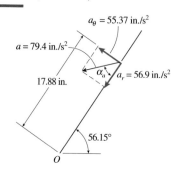

The magnitude of the acceleration is

$$a = \sqrt{a_r^2 + a_\theta^2} = \sqrt{(-56.9)^2 + (55.37)^2}$$

$$a = 79.4 \text{ in./s}^2 \blacktriangleleft$$

The direction of **a** with respect to the rod is

$$\alpha_a = \tan^{-1}\left(\frac{55.37}{56.9}\right) \qquad \alpha_a = 44.2° \blacktriangleleft$$

The acceleration vector is shown.

EXAMPLE   1.12

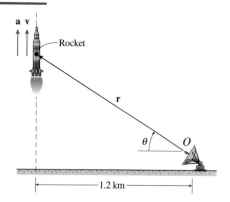

A rocket launched vertically upward is being monitored by a radar located at a distance of 1.2 km from the launch pad. The tracking data show that $\dot{\theta} = 0.2$ rad/s and $\ddot{\theta} = 0.1$ rad/s² when $\theta = 45°$. Determine the velocity and acceleration of the rocket at this position.

Solution   From the figure, we can see that the relationship between the coordinates r and θ is given by

$$r \cos \theta = 1.2 \text{ km} = 1200 \text{ m}$$

$$r = 1200 \sec \theta \qquad (a)$$

The first time derivative of r can be written as

$$\dot{r} = \frac{dr}{d\theta}\dot{\theta} = 1200(\tan \theta)(\sec \theta)\dot{\theta} \qquad (b)$$

Differentiating the above expression for $\dot{r}$ with respect to t, we obtain

$$\ddot{r} = 1200[(\sec^2 \theta)\dot{\theta}(\sec \theta)\dot{\theta} + (\tan \theta)(\tan \theta \sec \theta)\dot{\theta}^2$$
$$+ (\tan \theta)(\sec \theta)\ddot{\theta}]$$

$$\ddot{r} = 1200[(\sec^3 \theta + \tan^2 \theta \sec \theta)\dot{\theta}^2 + (\tan \theta \sec \theta)\ddot{\theta}] \qquad (c)$$

Substituting the numerical values $\theta = 45°$, $\dot{\theta} = 0.2$ rad/s, and $\ddot{\theta} = 0.1$ rad/s² into Equations (a) to (c), we obtain

$$r = 1697.06 \text{ m}$$

$$\dot{r} = 339.41 \text{ m/s}$$

$$\ddot{r} = 373.35 \text{ m/s}^2$$

(*continued*)

EXAMPLE 1.12 (*concluded*)

Velocity. The velocity components in the radial and transverse directions are

$$v_r = \dot{r} = 339.41 \text{ m/s}$$

$$v_\theta = r\dot{\theta} = (1697.06)(0.2) = 339.41 \text{ m/s}$$

The magnitude of velocity is, then,

$$v = \sqrt{v_r^2 + v_\theta^2} = \sqrt{(339.41)^2 + (339.41)^2}$$

$$v = 480 \text{ m/s} \blacktriangleleft$$

Acceleration. The components of acceleration in the radial and transverse directions are

$$a_r = \ddot{r} - r\dot{\theta}^2 = 373.35 - (1697.06)(0.2)^2 = 305.47 \text{ m/s}^2$$

$$a_\theta = r\ddot{\theta} + 2\dot{r}\dot{\theta} = (1697.06)(0.1) + 2(339.41)(0.2)$$

$$= 305.47 \text{ m/s}^2$$

Thus, the magnitude of acceleration is

$$a = \sqrt{a_r^2 + a_\theta^2} = \sqrt{(305.47)^2 + (305.47)^2}$$

$$a = 432 \text{ m/s}^2 \blacktriangleleft$$

1.9 RELATIVE MOTION

When a particle's motion is described with respect to a fixed coordinate system, it is called the *absolute motion* of the particle. In Newtonian mechanics, a fixed coordinate system is defined as one that does not move in space; in a majority of engineering applications, a coordinate system attached to the surface of earth may be considered as fixed, without causing appreciable error in the analysis due to earth's movement. In analyses involving motions of space vehicles and planets, however, the coordinate system must be fixed in outer space, that is, on a distant star.

In many problems of practical interest, one must determine the motion of a particle with respect to another particle that is also moving. When the motion of a particle B is described with respect to a coordinate system attached to, and moving with, another particle A, it is referred to as the ***relative motion*** of B with respect to A. In this section, we will describe the relative motion of a particle using a moving coordinate system with nonrotating axes. The description of relative motion in terms of rotating coordinate systems will be presented in Chapter 5.

Let us consider the motions of particles A and B along two different curvilinear paths as shown in Figure 1.19. At any instant of time t, the positions of these particles, with respect to the origin O of the fixed x-y-z coordinate system, are defined by the vectors $\mathbf{r}_A$ and $\mathbf{r}_B$. As shown in this figure, we attach a *translating* coordinate system to particle A, so that the origin of the x_A-y_A-z_A coordinate system translates (moves) with A, with the directions of the x_A, y_A, and z_A axes always remaining parallel to the fixed x, y, and z axes, respectively. The position of particle B relative to the x_A-y_A-z_A coordinate system at time t is defined by the vector $\mathbf{r}_{B/A}$ from A to B. From Figure 1.19, we see that the

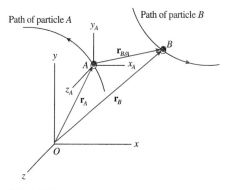

Figure 1.19

absolute position vector $\mathbf{r}_B$ of particle B can be determined by vectorially adding the relative position vector $\mathbf{r}_{B/A}$ to the absolute position vector $\mathbf{r}_A$ of particle A:

$$\mathbf{r}_B = \mathbf{r}_A + \mathbf{r}_{B/A} \tag{1.77}$$

By successively differentiating Equation (1.77) twice with respect to time t, we obtain the relationships between the velocities and the accelerations of particles A and B as

$$\mathbf{v}_B = \mathbf{v}_A + \mathbf{v}_{B/A} \tag{1.78}$$

and

$$\mathbf{a}_B = \mathbf{a}_A + \mathbf{a}_{B/A} \tag{1.79}$$

In Equation (1.78), $\mathbf{v}_A = \dot{\mathbf{r}}_A$ and $\mathbf{v}_B = \dot{\mathbf{r}}_B$ represent the absolute velocities of particles A and B, respectively; and $\mathbf{v}_{B/A} = \dot{\mathbf{r}}_{B/A}$ defines the velocity of particle B relative to the x_A-y_A-z_A coordinate system attached to particle A. Similarly, in Equation (1.79), $\mathbf{a}_A = \dot{\mathbf{v}}_A = \ddot{\mathbf{r}}_A$ and $\mathbf{a}_B = \dot{\mathbf{v}}_B = \ddot{\mathbf{r}}_B$ represent the absolute accelerations of A and B, respectively; and $\mathbf{a}_{B/A} = \dot{\mathbf{v}}_{B/A} = \ddot{\mathbf{r}}_{B/A}$ defines the acceleration of B with respect to the coordinate system attached to A.

Procedure for Analysis   The procedure for solution of relative motion problems essentially consists of identification of the known and unknown quantities, and determination of the unknowns using Equations (1.77) to (1.79). The translating coordinate system is usually attached to the particle whose absolute motion is known. Each of the three vector equations—Equations (1.77) to (1.79)—represents a vector triangle, and can be solved by using trigonometric relations, by expressing the vectors in terms of their rectangular components, or graphically. It should be realized that no more than two scalar unknowns can be determined from each of these equations.

EXAMPLE 1.13

Boat A is moving along a straight path with a speed of 40 mph as shown in the figure. When observed from boat A, another boat B appears to be moving in the direction perpendicular to the path of A with a speed of 30 mph. Determine the true (absolute) velocity of boat B at this instant.

Solution The moving coordinate system is attached to boat A as shown. The absolute velocity of A, and the velocity of B relative to A, are known as

$$\mathbf{v}_A = 40\mathbf{i} \text{ mph} \qquad \mathbf{v}_{B/A} = 30\mathbf{j} \text{ mph}$$

We can determine the absolute velocity of boat B from the vector equation $\mathbf{v}_B = \mathbf{v}_A + \mathbf{v}_{B/A}$. The triangle of velocity vectors is shown, from which we obtain the magnitude of $\mathbf{v}_B$ as

$$v_B = \sqrt{(40)^2 + (30)^2} = 50 \text{ mph}$$

The direction of $\mathbf{v}_B$ with respect to $\mathbf{v}_A$ is

$$\tan \alpha = \frac{30}{40} \qquad \alpha = 36.87°$$

Therefore, the true (absolute) velocity of boat B is

$$v_B = 50 \text{ mph at } \angle 36.87° \blacktriangleleft$$

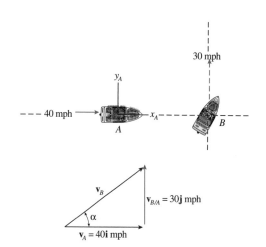

EXAMPLE 1.14

The positions of cars A and B on a race track at an instant of time are shown in the figure. Car A has a speed of 80 km/h, and is accelerating at a rate of 25 km/h², while car B has a speed of 20 km/h, which is decreasing at a rate of 30 km/h². Determine the position, velocity, and acceleration of car B relative to car A at this instant.

Solution The absolute $(x$-$y)$ coordinate system is located at point O. We attach the moving coordinate system $(x_A$-$y_A)$ to car A.

Relative position. The absolute position vectors of cars A and B at the instant of interest are

$$\mathbf{r}_A = 4.5\mathbf{i} + 4\mathbf{j} \text{ (km)} \qquad \text{and} \qquad \mathbf{r}_B = 12\mathbf{i} \text{ (km)}$$

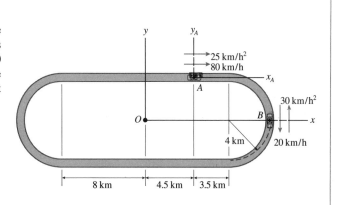

(*continued*)

EXAMPLE   1.14   *(continued)*

The position of B relative to A is given by the equation

$$\mathbf{r}_B = \mathbf{r}_A + \mathbf{r}_{B/A}$$

$$\mathbf{r}_{B/A} = \mathbf{r}_B - \mathbf{r}_A = 12\mathbf{i} - (4.5\mathbf{i} + 4\mathbf{j}) = 7.5\mathbf{i} - 4\mathbf{j} \text{ (km)}$$

The magnitude of $\mathbf{r}_{B/A}$ is

$$r_{B/A} = \sqrt{(7.5)^2 + (-4)^2} = 8.5 \text{ km}$$

and the direction with respect to the x axis is

$$\tan \alpha_r = \frac{4}{7.5} \qquad \alpha_r = 28.07°$$

Therefore, the position of B relative to A is

$$r_{B/A} = 8.5 \text{ km at } \diagdown 28.07° \blacktriangleleft$$

The triangle of position vectors is shown. Note that $\mathbf{r}_{B/A}$ can also be obtained from this triangle by using the law of cosines and the law of sines.

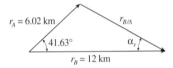

$r_A = 6.02$ km $r_{B/A}$

41.63° α_r

$r_B = 12$ km

Relative velocity.   The velocities of cars A and B are given as $\mathbf{v}_A = 80\mathbf{i}$ (km/h) and $\mathbf{v}_B = -20\mathbf{j}$ (km/h). The velocity of B relative to A is obtained from the equation

$$\mathbf{v}_{B/A} = \mathbf{v}_B - \mathbf{v}_A = -20\mathbf{j} - 80\mathbf{i} \text{ (km/h)}$$

For the magnitude and the direction of $\mathbf{v}_{B/A}$,

$$v_{B/A} = \sqrt{(-80)^2 + (-20)^2} = 82.5 \text{ km/h}$$

and

$$\tan \alpha_v = \frac{20}{80} \qquad \alpha_v = 14.04°$$

Therefore, the velocity of B relative to A is

$$v_{B/A} = 82.5 \text{ km/h at } 14.04° \triangledown \blacktriangleleft$$

The triangle of velocity vectors is shown; use it to check the above results.

$v_A = 80$ km/h

$v_B = 20$ km/h α_v

$v_{B/A}$

Relative acceleration.   Car A is moving along the straight path with acceleration $\mathbf{a}_A = 25\mathbf{i}$ (km/h²). Car B is moving on the curved path of radius $\rho = 4$ km. The magnitude of acceleration component in the tangential direction is given as $a_t = 30$ km/h². The magnitude of the normal component of the acceleration of B is $a_n = v^2/\rho = (20)^2/4 = 100$ km/h². The acceleration of car B can therefore be expressed in terms of components along the x and y directions as

$$\mathbf{a}_B = -100\mathbf{i} + 30\mathbf{j} \text{ (km/h}^2)$$

The acceleration of B relative to A is

$$\mathbf{a}_{B/A} = \mathbf{a}_B - \mathbf{a}_A = (-100\mathbf{i} + 30\mathbf{j}) - 25\mathbf{i}$$

$$= -125\mathbf{i} + 30\mathbf{j} \text{ (km/h}^2)$$

The magnitude of $\mathbf{a}_{B/A}$ is

$$a_{B/A} = \sqrt{(-125)^2 + (30)^2} = 128.5 \text{ km/h}^2$$

and its direction with respect to the x axis is

$$\tan \alpha_a = \frac{30}{125} \qquad \alpha_a = 13.5°$$

Therefore, the acceleration of B relative to A is

$$a_{B/A} = 128.5 \text{ km/h}^2 \text{ at } 13.5° \triangle \blacktriangleleft$$

The triangle of acceleration vectors is shown; use it to verify the above results.

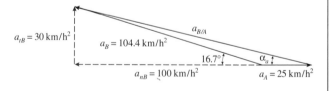

$a_{tB} = 30$ km/h²

$a_B = 104.4$ km/h² $a_{B/A}$

16.7° α_a

$a_{nB} = 100$ km/h² $a_A = 25$ km/h²

1.10 DEPENDENT MOTION

When two or more particles are connected together by means of inextensible cables, ropes, or bars, the motion of each particle depends on that of the others. This is called **dependent motion**.

Figure 1.20 shows two particles A and B connected by a cable passing over frictionless pulleys C and D. The positions of particles A and B at time t are defined by the coordinates s_A and s_B, respectively, measured from the fixed center O of pulley C. Note that, since the motion of particle A is the same as the center of pulley D, the coordinate s_A is measured from origin O to the center of pulley D. The positive senses of s_A and s_B are shown in the figure. We can establish the relationship between s_A and s_B by realizing that the total length L of the cable remains constant during the motion, and can be written as

$$L = 2s_A + s_B + \text{(lengths of cable passing over pulleys } C \text{ and } D) \quad (1.80)$$

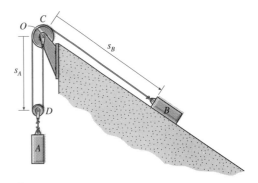

Figure 1.20

As the lengths of the portions of cable passing over the two pulleys are also constant, we can express the relationship between the positions of particles A and B as

$$2s_A + s_B = \text{constant}$$

By successively differentiating the above equation twice with respect to time, we obtain the relationships between the velocities and the accelerations of particles A and B as

$$2\dot{s}_A + \dot{s}_B = 0 \qquad \text{or} \qquad 2v_A + v_B = 0$$

and

$$2\ddot{s}_A + \ddot{s}_B = 0 \qquad \text{or} \qquad 2a_A + a_B = 0$$

Thus, if the motion of one of the particles is known, the motion of the other can be determined. It should be realized that, although the positions of particles A and B in Figure 1.20 are defined from a common origin O, it is not necessary that the position coordinates of all the particles of a system have the same origin. The position of each particle may be defined from any convenient fixed origin with the coordinate axis in the direction of the path of the particle.

The number of independent position coordinates necessary to specify the positions of all the particles of a system is referred to as the *degree of freedom* of the system. Thus, the system shown in Figure 1.20 is considered to be a *single degree of freedom system* because only one position coordinate (s_A or s_B) is necessary to specify the positions of both of its particles, A and B. In other words, if the position of one of the particles is known, the position of the other can be determined using Equation (1.80).

EXAMPLE   1.15

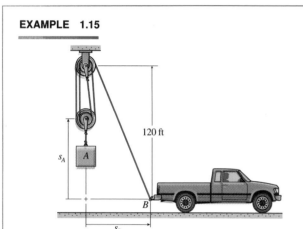

120 ft

A pickup truck initially at rest under the hoist starts moving forward with a constant acceleration of 0.4 ft/s², thereby lifting the crate A. Determine the velocity of the crate when time $t = 20$ s.

Solution   The positions of the crate A and the truck B are defined by the coordinates s_A and s_B, directed along the paths of the crate and the truck, respectively.

Motion of truck.   The acceleration of the truck is constant and is given as $a_B = 0.4$ ft/s². Therefore, the equation for the velocity of the truck is $v_B = 0.4t$ ft/s, and the position of the truck can be expressed as $s_B = 0.2t^2$ ft. At $t = 20$ s,

$$v_B = 0.4(20) = 8 \text{ ft/s} \qquad s_B = 0.2(20)^2 = 80 \text{ ft}$$

Motion of crate.   The total length of the cable can be written as

$$L = 4(120 - s_A) + \sqrt{s_B^2 + (120)^2}$$
$$+ \text{ (lengths of cable passing over pulleys)}$$

As the total length L as well as the lengths of the portions of cable passing over the pulleys are constant, we can express the relationship between the positions of crate A and truck B as

$$4(120 - s_A) + \sqrt{s_B^2 + (120)^2} = \text{constant}$$

Differentiating this expression with respect to t, we obtain velocity v_A as

$$-4v_A + \frac{s_B v_B}{\sqrt{s_B^2 + (120)^2}} = 0 \qquad v_A = \frac{s_B v_B}{4\sqrt{s_B^2 + (120)^2}}$$

Substituting the numerical values of $s_B = 80$ ft and $v_B = 8$ ft/s into the equation for v_A, we obtain the velocity of the crate when $t = 20$ s:

$$v_A = \frac{80(8)}{4\sqrt{(80)^2 + (120)^2}}$$

$$v_A = 1.11 \text{ ft/s} \, (\uparrow) \; \blacktriangleleft$$

EXAMPLE 1.16

Determine the relationship between the velocities, and between the accelerations, of blocks A, B, and C shown in the figure.

Solution From the figure, we see that the given system contains two cables, which are connected at pulley D. The position coordinates of the three blocks and pulley D are defined from a fixed reference line as shown. As the length of each cable remains constant during the motion, we can write

$$2s_A + 2s_D = \text{constant}$$

$$(s_B - s_D) + s_B + s_C = \text{constant}$$

By eliminating s_D from these equations, we obtain

$$s_A + 2s_B + s_C = \text{constant}$$

Differentiating with respect to t, we obtain the relationship between the velocities of blocks A, B, and C as

$$\dot{s}_A + 2\dot{s}_B + \dot{s}_C = 0$$

$$v_A + 2v_B + v_C = 0 \quad \blacktriangleleft$$

Differentiating once more, we obtain the relationship between the accelerations of the blocks:

$$\ddot{s}_A + 2\ddot{s}_B + \ddot{s}_C = 0$$

$$a_A + 2a_B + a_C = 0 \quad \blacktriangleleft$$

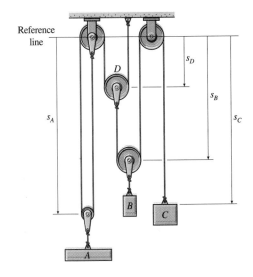

1.11 SUMMARY

In this chapter, we have learned the following:

1. If a particle moves along a straight-line path, its motion is called rectilinear motion. The velocity v of the particle is defined as the time rate of change of position,

$$v = \dot{s} \tag{1.2}$$

and the acceleration a is defined as the time rate of change of velocity,

$$a = \dot{v} = \ddot{s} \tag{1.5}$$

Another useful differential expression relating position, velocity, and acceleration is

$$a = v\frac{dv}{ds} \tag{1.6}$$

When one of the three kinematic characteristics—position, velocity, or acceleration—of the motion is known, then the remaining two are determined by differentiation and/or integration from the known characteristic, according to Equations (1.2), (1.5), and (1.6).

2. If a particle moves along a curved path, its motion is called curvilinear motion. The velocity vector $\mathbf{v}$ of the particle is defined as the time rate of change of position vector,

$$\mathbf{v} = \dot{\mathbf{r}} \tag{1.26}$$

and the acceleration vector $\mathbf{a}$ is defined as the time rate of change of velocity vector,

$$\mathbf{a} = \dot{\mathbf{v}} = \ddot{\mathbf{r}} \tag{1.30}$$

3. In terms of rectangular coordinates, the velocity and acceleration of a particle in curvilinear motion can be expressed as

$$\begin{aligned} \mathbf{v} &= \dot{x}\mathbf{i} + \dot{y}\mathbf{j} + \dot{z}\mathbf{k} \\ \mathbf{a} &= \ddot{x}\mathbf{i} + \ddot{y}\mathbf{j} + \ddot{z}\mathbf{k} \end{aligned} \tag{1.45}$$

4. In terms of coordinates directed along the tangent and the normal to the curved path of a particle, the velocity and acceleration can be expressed as

$$\mathbf{v} = v\mathbf{n}_t = \dot{s}\mathbf{n}_t \tag{1.49}$$

$$\mathbf{a} = \dot{v}\mathbf{n}_t + \frac{v^2}{\rho}\mathbf{n}_n = \ddot{s}\mathbf{n}_t + \frac{\dot{s}^2}{\rho}\mathbf{n}_n \tag{1.55}$$

5. The expressions for the velocity and acceleration in terms of polar coordinates (in the radial and transverse directions) are

$$\mathbf{v} = \dot{r}\mathbf{n}_r + r\dot{\theta}\mathbf{n}_\theta \tag{1.65}$$

$$\mathbf{a} = (\ddot{r} - r\dot{\theta}^2)\mathbf{n}_r + (r\ddot{\theta} + 2\dot{r}\dot{\theta})\mathbf{n}_\theta \tag{1.70}$$

6. The expressions for the velocity and acceleration of a particle along a space curve, in terms of cylindrical coordinates R, θ, and z, are given in Section 1.8, Equations (1.75) and (1.76).

7. The motion of a particle B relative to another particle A can be determined from the equations

$$\mathbf{r}_B = \mathbf{r}_A + \mathbf{r}_{B/A} \tag{1.77}$$

$$\mathbf{v}_B = \mathbf{v}_A + \mathbf{v}_{B/A} \tag{1.78}$$

$$\mathbf{a}_B = \mathbf{a}_A + \mathbf{a}_{B/A} \tag{1.79}$$

8. The relationship between the position coordinates of particles connected by inextensible cables can be established by using the condition that the lengths of cables remain constant during the motion. The velocity and acceleration equations are then obtained by successively differentiating the position coordinate equation with respect to time.

KEY TERMS

acceleration *6*

circular motion *38*

curvilinear motion *22*

cylindrical coordinates *38*

dependent motion *45*

displacement *3*

dynamics *2*

hodograph *24*

kinematics *2*

kinetics *2*

particle *2*

polar coordinates *35*

position *3*

projectile *26*

rectangular coordinates *25*

rectilinear motion *2*

relative motion *41*

speed *5*

tangential and normal coordinates *30*

velocity *5*

PROBLEMS

SECTION 1.2

1.1 The position of a particle moving in a straight line is given by the equation $s = 5t$, where s is in inches and t in seconds. Determine (*a*) the velocity when $t = 2.5$ s, and (*b*) the displacement of the particle during the interval from $t = 2$ s to $t = 3$ s. Also, plot the *s-t* and *v-t* graphs of the motion of the particle from $t = 0$ to $t = 4$ s.

1.2 The position of a car traveling along a straight road is given by the equation $s = 10 + 40t$, where s is in km and t in hours. Determine (a) the velocity of the car when $t = 0.5$ h, and (b) the distance traveled by the car in one hour. Also, plot the s-t and v-t graphs of the motion of the car from $t = 0$ to $t = 2$ h.

1.3 The motion of a particle along a straight line is described by the equation $s = 11 + 9t - 6t^2$, where s is in mm and t in seconds. Determine (a) the position, velocity, acceleration, and the distance traveled by the particle, when $t = 2.5$ s, and (b) the position and acceleration of the particle when the velocity is zero. Also, plot the s-t, v-t, and a-t graphs of the motion of the particle from $t = 0$ to $t = 3$ s.

1.4 The motion of a train along a straight track is described by the equation $s = 25 - 7t + (t^2/120)$; where s is in ft and t in seconds. Determine (a) the position, velocity, and acceleration of the train when $t = 30$ min, and (b) the position and acceleration of the train when the velocity is zero. Also, plot the s-t, v-t, and a-t graphs of the motion of the train from $t = 0$ to $t = 15$ min.

1.5 The position of a particle moving in a straight line is given by the equation $s = 12 - 5t - 9t^2 + 2t^3$, where s is in meters and t in seconds. Determine (a) the position, velocity, and acceleration of the particle when $t = 4$ s; (b) the position and velocity of the particle when the acceleration is zero; and (c) the position and acceleration of the particle when the velocity is zero.

1.6 The position of a particle in rectilinear motion is given by the equation $s = 9t^2 - t^3$, where s is in in. and t in seconds. Determine (a) the position, velocity, and acceleration of the particle when $t = 2$ s, and (b) the position and velocity of the particle when the acceleration is zero. Also, plot the s-t, v-t, and a-t graphs of the motion of the particle from $t = 0$ to $t = 4$ s.

1.7 The position of a particle in rectilinear motion is given by the equation $s = -126 + 80t^2 - 3t^4$, where s is in mm and t in seconds. Determine (a) the position, velocity, and acceleration of the particle when $t = 1$ s, and (b) the position and velocity of the particle when the acceleration is zero.

1.8 The equation of position of a particle in rectilinear motion has the form of $s = -bt^2 + ct^4$. If the positions of the particle at times $t_1 = 3$ s and $t_2 = 4$ s are -27 mm and 176 mm, respectively, determine the position, velocity, and acceleration of the particle when $t = 3.5$ s.

SECTIONS 1.3 AND 1.4

1.9 The velocity of a particle in rectilinear motion is given by the equation $v = -15 + 7t$, where v is in in./s. If the initial position of the particle is $s_0 = 9$ in. when $t = 0$, determine the equations of the position and the acceleration of the particle; and the position and acceleration of the particle when the velocity is zero.

1.10 Determine the displacement of the particle in Problem 1.9, from $t = 1.5$ s to $t = 4$ s, by graphically integrating the v-t graph for the motion.

1.11 The motion of a car traveling along a straight road is described by the equation $v = -1 - 2t + 3t^2$, where v is in km/h. The initial position of the car is

$s_0 = 0$ when $t = 0$. Determine (*a*) the position, velocity, acceleration, and the distance traveled by the car, when $t = 2$ h; (*b*) the position and velocity of the car when the acceleration is zero; and (*c*) the position and acceleration of the car when the velocity is zero.

1.12 An airplane lands on a straight runway with the touchdown speed of 100 mph, whereupon the brakes are applied causing its velocity to decrease with increased position coordinate according to the equation $v = 200/(2 + s)$. Determine (*a*) the acceleration of the plane at touchdown, and (*b*) the time required for the airplane to reduce its velocity to 40 mph after touchdown, and the distance traveled during that interval.

1.13 The velocity of a bullet fired into a resisting material decreases linearly with increased position coordinate. If $v = 50$ m/s when $s = 0$, and $v = 10$ m/s when $s = 8$ m, determine the acceleration of the bullet when $s = 0$.

1.14 Determine the position, velocity, and acceleration of the bullet in Problem 1.13, when $t = 0.25$ s. The initial position of the bullet is $s_0 = 0$ when $t = 0$.

1.15 A car starts from rest on a straight road with a constant acceleration of 0.4 ft/s². Determine (*a*) the distance traveled by the car during the first 3 min of motion, and (*b*) the velocity when $t = 3$ min.

1.16 Solve Problem 1.15 by graphically integrating the *a-t* graph for the motion of the car.

1.17 A stone dropped from the edge of a building reaches the ground in 2 seconds. Determine the height of the building, and the velocity of the stone when it hits the ground. The downward acceleration due to gravity is 9.81 m/s². Neglect air resistance.

1.18 Solve Problem 1.17 by graphically integrating the *a-t* curve for the motion of the stone.

1.19 A stone is thrown vertically downward with a velocity of 1.5 ft/s from the edge of a cliff 300 ft above ground level. Determine the time it takes the stone to hit the ground, and at what velocity. Neglect air resistance. The acceleration due to gravity is 32.2 ft/s².

1.20 Solve Problem 1.19 by graphically integrating the *a-t* curve for the motion of the stone.

1.21 A projectile fired vertically upward reaches a maximum height of 61 m before returning to the ground. Determine the initial velocity, and the time it takes the projectile to return to the ground. Neglect air resistance. The acceleration due to gravity is 9.81 m/s².

1.22 Solve Problem 1.21 by graphically integrating the *a-t* curve for the motion of the projectile.

1.23 A train is moving with a velocity of 25 mph along a straight track, when it is accelerated at a constant rate to increase its velocity to 60 mph in 30 seconds. Determine the distance traveled during this interval, and the acceleration.

1.24 An airplane lands on a straight runway with the touchdown speed of 150 km/h. After a reaction time of 2 seconds, the pilot applies the brakes causing the speed to reduce at a constant rate. If the time required to stop the plane is 58 seconds after touchdown, determine the deceleration and the distance traveled on the runway.

1.25 A ball thrown vertically upward returns to the ground in 5 seconds. Determine the maximum height reached by the ball, and its initial velocity. Neglect air resistance. The acceleration due to gravity is 32.2 ft/s^2.

1.26 A stone is thrown vertically upward with a velocity of 9 m/s from the edge of a cliff 150 m above ground level. Determine the time it takes the stone to hit the ground, and at what velocity it hits the ground. Neglect air resistance. The acceleration due to gravity is 9.81 m/s^2.

1.27 A projectile fired vertically upward from the edge of a cliff 400 ft above ground level hits the ground after 7 seconds. Determine the initial velocity of the projectile, and the velocity with which it hits the ground. Neglect air resistance, and use $g = 32.2$ ft/s^2.

1.28 A truck starts from rest and travels on a straight highway with constant acceleration of 2000 km/h^2 until its speed reaches 100 km/h. The truck maintains this speed for a certain time interval; then the brakes are applied to reduce the speed at a constant rate of 1500 km/h^2 to stop. If the total time of travel is 20 minutes, determine the total distance traveled by the truck.

1.29 Solve Problem 1.28 by graphically integrating the a-t and v-t curves for the motion of the truck.

1.30 Car A crosses intersection O while moving at a constant speed of 30 mph. Car B crosses the same intersection 10 s later, moving at a constant speed of 50 mph. Determine the time it takes car B to pass car A, after B crosses the intersection.

1.31 Car A crosses intersection O with a speed of 80 km/h, which is decreasing at a constant rate of 7 km/h^2. Car B crosses the same intersection 15 s later with a speed of 50 km/h, which is increasing at a constant rate of 10 km/h^2. Determine the time it takes car B to pass car A, after B crosses the intersection.

1.32 and 1.33 The a-t curve for the motion of a car starting from rest is shown. Determine the v-t and s-t curves for the motion by graphical integration.

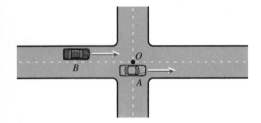

Figure P1.30 and P1.31

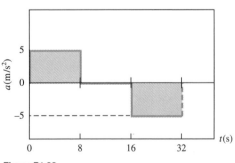

Figure P1.32

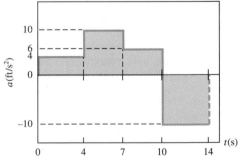

Figure P1.33 and P1.34

1.34 Solve Problem 1.33, if the initial position and the initial velocity of the car are 30 ft and 15 ft/s, respectively.

1.35 The *a-t* curve for the motion of a particle is shown. If the initial velocity of the particle is 125 mm/s, determine its velocity when $t = 17$ s by graphical integration.

1.36 Truck *B* and car *A* are traveling on a straight highway at a constant speed of 65 mph. The distance between the two vehicles is 45 ft, when the truck driver starts to decelerate truck *B* at a constant rate of 10 ft/s². If it takes 2 s for the driver of car *A* to react, determine the constant rate at which she must decelerate car *A* to avoid a collision.

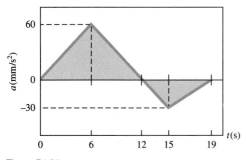

Figure P1.35

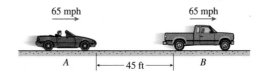

Figure P1.36

1.37 A train is approaching a station with a constant velocity of 73.5 ft/s, when the brakes are applied causing a deceleration proportional to time, $a = -0.2t$ ft/s². Determine the time required for the train to stop, and the distance traveled while it is decelerating.

1.38 The acceleration of a particle in rectilinear motion is given by the equation $a = 15 - 4s$, where *a* is in mm/sec² and *s* in mm. If $s_0 = 0$ and $v_0 = 0$, determine (*a*) the position *s* where the velocity is maximum, and (*b*) the velocity when $s = 7.5$ mm.

1.39 In a test drive, a motorcycle is started from rest and accelerated according to the equation $a = 0.02t$ m/s², until the maximum velocity of 40 m/s is reached. Then, the acceleration is decreased linearly with time until the motorcycle stops. If the total time required for the test drive is 180 s, determine (*a*) the total distance traveled, and (*b*) the position, velocity, and acceleration of the motorcycle when $t = 120$ s.

1.40 The acceleration of a particle is given by the equation $a = -cv^2$, where *c* is a constant. Derive the expressions for the position, velocity, and acceleration, as functions of time.

1.41 The acceleration of a particle in rectilinear motion is given by the equation $a = -0.15v^2$ in./s². If $s_0 = 0$ and $v_0 = 36$ in./s when $t = 0$, determine the position, velocity, and acceleration of the particle when $t = 5$ s.

1.42 The acceleration of a bullet fired into a resisting material decreases according to the equation $a = -cv^2$, where c is a constant. If the initial position and the initial velocity are $s_0 = 0$ and $v_0 = 40$ m/s, respectively, when $t = 0$, and if the bullet travels 2.5 m into the material in 4 seconds, determine the constant c.

1.43 The acceleration of a rocket during a short interval is given by the equation $a = 45 - 3t + 2t^2$ ft/s². At the beginning of the interval, the position and the velocity of the rocket are 275 ft and 110 ft/s, respectively. Determine the position, velocity, and acceleration of the rocket when $t = 4$ s.

1.44 The acceleration of a particle is given by the equation $a = 4 - 3s^2$, where a is in m/s² and s in m. If $s_0 = 0$ and $v_0 = 0$ when $t = 0$, determine (a) the position s where the velocity is maximum and (b) the velocity when $s = 2$ m.

1.45 The acceleration of a particle is given by the equation $a = 12\sqrt{s}$, where a is in in./s² and s in inches. If $s_0 = 0$ and $v_0 = 0$ when $t = 0$, determine the position, velocity, and acceleration of the particle when $t = 8$ s.

1.46 The acceleration of a piston, moving against oil pressure in a cylinder, is expressed by equation $a = 64 \sin\pi t$ in./s². If $s_0 = 0$ and $v_0 = 0$ when $t = 0$, determine (a) the maximum velocity, and (b) the position, velocity, and acceleration when $t = 2.5$ s.

1.47 The acceleration of a vibrating particle is given by the equation $a = -20 \sin(\pi t/2)$ in./s². If $s_0 = 5$ in. and $v_0 = 10$ in./s when $t = 0$, determine the position, velocity, and acceleration of the particle when $t = 1.33$ s.

1.48 The acceleration of a body moving through a fluid is given by the equation $a = cv^3$, where c is a constant. Derive the expressions for the position, velocity, and acceleration as functions of time.

1.49 The acceleration in the downward direction of a particle falling through a fluid can be expressed as $a = g - kv^2$, where g is the gravitational acceleration and k is a constant. Derive the expression for the velocity as a function of time. Use $v_0 = 0$ when $t = 0$.

1.50 A body is dropped from an altitude of $h = 200$ km above the earth. If the acceleration due to gravity at higher altitudes is given by the equation $g = -9.81[(636 \times 10^4)^2/(636 \times 10^4 + h)^2]$ m/s², determine the velocity with which the body will hit the earth.

SECTION 1.6

1.51 The curvilinear motion of a particle is described by the equations $x = 2 - 7t^2$ and $y = -4t + 5t^3$, where x and y are in ft and t in s. Determine the magnitudes and directions of the position, velocity, and acceleration vectors when $t = 4$ s.

1.52 The position vector of a particle in curvilinear motion is given by $\mathbf{r} = (10t^2 - 3t^3)\mathbf{i} + (5 + 3t)\mathbf{j}$ (ft), where t is in s. Determine the magnitudes and directions of the velocity and acceleration vectors when $t = 2.5$ s.

1.53 The curvilinear motion of a particle is described by the equations $v_x = -5t$ and $v_y = 2 - 9t^2$, where v_x and v_y are in m/s and t in s. If $x_0 = 0$ and $y_0 = 0$ when $t = 0$, determine the magnitudes and directions of the position, velocity, and acceleration vectors when $t = 1$ s.

1.54 The velocity of a particle in curvilinear motion is expressed by the equation $\mathbf{v} = (-9 + 5t)\mathbf{i} - (13 - 2t)\mathbf{j}$ (in./s). If the initial position of the particle is given by the vector $\mathbf{r}_0 = 3\mathbf{i} + 4\mathbf{j}$ (in.), determine the magnitudes and directions of the position, velocity, and acceleration vectors when $t = 4$ s.

1.55 The acceleration of a particle in curvilinear motion is given by the equations $a_x = 5 - 6t$ and $a_y = -8$, where a_x and a_y are in m/s^2 and t in s. If $x_0 = 0.5$ m, $y_0 = 2$ m, $v_{x0} = 0$, and $v_{y0} = 0$ when $t = 0$, determine the magnitudes and directions of the position, velocity, and acceleration vectors when $t = 2$ s.

1.56 The acceleration vector of a particle in curvilinear motion is expressed by the equation $\mathbf{a} = 7\mathbf{i} - 9t\mathbf{j}$ (ft/s^2). If $\mathbf{r}_0 = \mathbf{i} - 2\mathbf{j}$ (ft), and $\mathbf{v}_0 = -3\mathbf{i} + 5\mathbf{j}$ (ft/s), determine the magnitudes and directions of the position, velocity, and acceleration vectors when $t = 5$ s.

1.57 The curvilinear motion of a particle is described by the equations $x = 24t - 3t^3$ mm and $v_y = 3 - (t/2)$ mm/s. If $y_0 = 5$ mm when $t = 0$, determine the magnitudes and directions of the position, velocity, and acceleration vectors when the x coordinate is maximum.

1.58 The curvilinear motion of a particle is described by the equations $v_x = 15 - 7t$ ft/s and $a_y = -32.2$ ft/s^2. If $x_0 = 0$, $y_0 = 0$, and $v_y = 10$ ft/s when $t = 0$, determine the magnitudes and directions of the position, velocity, and acceleration vectors when $t = 3$ s.

1.59 The motion of a particle along a circular path is described by the equation $\mathbf{r} = 8\cos(\pi t/5)\mathbf{i} + 8\sin(\pi t/5)\mathbf{j}$ (mm), where t is in s. Show that the magnitudes of the velocity and acceleration vectors are constant, and determine the magnitudes and directions of the position, velocity, and acceleration vectors when $t = 1$ s.

1.60 The motion of a particle along an elliptic path is described by the equation $\mathbf{r} = 2\cos(\pi t/4)\mathbf{i} + 3\sin(\pi t/4)\mathbf{j}$ (ft), where t is in s. Determine the magnitudes and directions of the position, velocity, and acceleration vectors when $t = 3$ s.

1.61 A soccer player kicks a ball with a velocity v_0 at an angle α with the horizontal. If $v_0 = 9$ m/s and $\alpha = 30°$, determine (*a*) the time it takes the ball to fall back to the ground; (*b*) the distance to the point where the ball hits the ground; and (*c*) the maximum height reached by the ball. Neglect air resistance. Let $g = 9.81$ m/s^2.

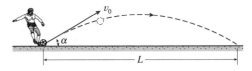

Figure P1.61, P1.62, and P1.63

1.62 Solve Problem 1.61 if $\alpha = 60°$.

1.63 Solve Problem 1.61 if $v_0 = 15$ m/s.

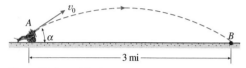

Figure P1.64 and P1.65

1.64 A projectile is fired with a velocity v_0 at an angle α, at a target B located at a distance of 3 mi from the gun A. If $\alpha = 20°$, determine the initial velocity with which the projectile must be fired to reach the target B. Neglect air resistance. Let $g = 32.2$ ft/s^2.

1.65 If the firing velocity of the projectile in Problem 1.64 is 735 ft/s, determine the two values of the angle α with which the projectile may be fired to reach the target. Also, determine the flight times of the projectile corresponding to the two values of α.

1.66 An airplane flying at an altitude of 600 m with a velocity of 750 km/h in the horizontal direction releases a bomb to hit a target B on the ground. Determine the horizontal distance L from the point where the bomb is released to the target. Neglect air resistance. Let $g = 9.81$ m/s^2.

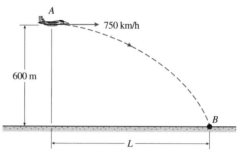

Figure P1.66

1.67 Solve Problem 1.66 if the plane is climbing upward at an angle of 20° with the horizontal at the instant the bomb is released.

1.68 A projectile fired horizontally with a velocity of 350 ft/s from point A on a cliff, hits a target B in 12 s. Determine (a) the height h of the cliff, and (b) the horizontal distance L from point A to the target B. Neglect air resistance. Let $g = 32.2$ ft/s^2.

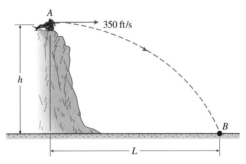

Figure P1.68

1.69 A projectile is fired with a velocity v_0, at an angle α with the horizontal, from point A on a cliff of height h. If $h = 70$ m, $v_0 = 100$ m/s, and $\alpha = 60°$, determine (a) the time it takes the projectile to hit the ground; (b) the horizontal distance L to point B where the projectile hits the ground; and (c) the maximum height above the ground reached by the projectile. Neglect air resistance. Let $g = 9.81$ m/s^2.

1.70 Solve Problem 1.69 if $h = 100$ m.

1.71 Solve Problem 1.69 if $v_0 = 150$ m/s.

1.72 Solve Problem 1.69 if $\alpha = 20°$.

1.73 A person throws a ball with velocity v_0 at an angle α from a point A, to hit a target B on the wall, as shown in the figure. If $\alpha = 65°$, determine the value of v_0 for which the ball will hit the target. Neglect air resistance. Let $g = 32.2$ ft/s^2.

1.74 In Problem 1.73, if the ball is thrown with a velocity $v_0 = 60$ ft/s, determine the two values of the angle α for which the ball will hit the target. Also, determine the flight times of the ball corresponding to the two values of α.

1.75 A projectile is fired from point A on a surface inclined at an angle of 20° with the horizontal. If the firing angle $\alpha = 50°$ with respect to the surface, determine the initial velocity v_0 for which the projectile will hit target B. Neglect air resistance. Let $g = 9.81$ m/s^2.

1.76 Solve Problem 1.75 if $\alpha = 90°$.

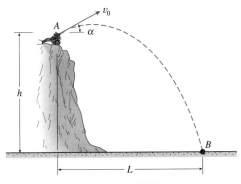

Figure P1.69, P1.70, P1.71, and P1.72

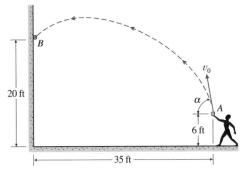

Figure P1.73 and P1.74

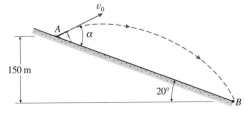

Figure P1.75 and P1.76

1.77 Small blocks are being dropped into a 3-foot-wide chute by means of a conveyor belt from a height h as shown in the figure. If $h = 6$ ft, determine the range of the velocity v_0 of the conveyor belt for which the blocks will fall into the chute. Neglect air resistance. Let $g = 32.2$ ft/s^2.

1.78 If the conveyor belt in Problem 1.77 is moving at a velocity of 20 ft/s, determine the range of the height h of the conveyor belt for which the blocks will fall into the chute.

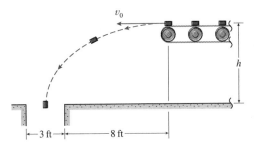

Figure P1.77 and P1.78

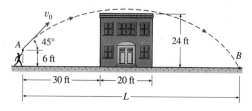

Figure P1.79

1.79 A person throws a ball at an angle of 45° toward a building as shown in the figure. Determine the minimum initial velocity v_0 for which the ball will go over the building. Also, determine the horizontal distance L to point B where the ball hits the ground. Neglect air resistance. Let $g = 32.2$ ft/s².

1.80 The curvilinear motion of a particle is described by the equation $\mathbf{r} = (5 - t^2)\mathbf{i} + (3 - 2t + t^3)\mathbf{j} - (6 + 2t - 5t^5)\mathbf{k}$ (ft), where t is in s. Determine the position, velocity, and acceleration vectors when $t = 1$ s.

1.81 The acceleration of a particle in curvilinear motion is expressed by the equation $\mathbf{a} = 5t\mathbf{i} - 9\mathbf{j} - 3t^2\mathbf{k}$ (m/s²). If $\mathbf{r}_0 = -3\mathbf{i} + 2\mathbf{j} + \mathbf{k}$ (m), and $\mathbf{v}_0 = -4\mathbf{i} + 5\mathbf{j} + 7\mathbf{k}$ (m/s) when $t = 0$, determine the position, velocity, and acceleration vectors when $t = 5$ s.

1.82 The curvilinear motion of a body along a cylindrical helix is described by the equation $\mathbf{r} = 8\cos(\pi t/5)\mathbf{i} + 8\sin(\pi t/5)\mathbf{j} + 4t\mathbf{k}$ (ft), where t is in s. Determine the position, velocity, and acceleration vectors when $t = 1$ s.

1.83 Determine the altitude h and the velocity v_0 of an airplane flying east if a missile released from it strikes a ship, sailing north with a constant speed of 125 km/h, as it reaches point B. The position of the ship at the instant the missile is released is given in the figure.

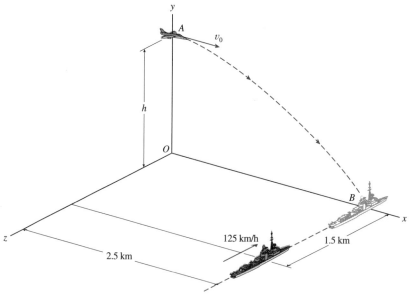

Figure P1.83

SECTION 1.7

1.84 A car is moving along a curve of 800-ft radius with a constant speed of 40 mph. Determine the magnitude of the acceleration of the car.

1.85 A motorcycle is traveling along a curve of 150-m radius. If the acceleration in the normal direction cannot exceed $0.4g$ without the motorcycle sliding, determine the maximum safe speed of the motorcycle.

1.86 At an instant, the speed of a car moving along a curvilinear path is 24 m/s, which is decreasing at a rate of 2 m/s^2. If the magnitude of the total acceleration of the car is 3.5 m/s^2, determine the radius of curvature of the path at that instant.

1.87 The position of a car along a circular path is described by the equation $s = 2t^2 + (t^3/3)$ where s is in ft, and t in s. If the magnitude of the total acceleration of the car is 18 ft/s^2 when $t = 6$ s, determine the radius of the path.

1.88 A truck starts from rest on a circular path of 500-ft radius with a constant tangential acceleration of 4 ft/s^2. Determine the magnitude of total acceleration of the truck when $t = 10$ s.

1.89 A car is traveling on a circular path of 200-m radius with a velocity of 35 m/s when the brakes are applied, causing its speed to decrease according to the equation $a_t = -3t - 2t^2$ m/s^2. Determine the magnitude of total acceleration of the car 2 seconds after the brakes are applied.

1.90 A race car is moving at a constant speed of 45 mph on an S-shaped track, composed of two semicircles of 800-ft and 600-ft radii, as shown. Determine the acceleration of the car at positions B, C, and D.

1.91 The car in Problem 1.90 starts from rest at A with a constant tangential acceleration of 2 ft/s^2. Determine the velocity and total acceleration of the car at positions B, C, and D.

1.92 The position of the car in Problem 1.90 is described by the equation $s = t^3/180$ ft, where s is measured from A and t is in s. Determine the velocity and the total acceleration of the car at positions B, C, and D.

1.93 The electric hoist shown in the figure raises a block W at a constant speed v of 2 m/s. Determine the magnitudes of the total acceleration of the portions of the cable in contact with frictionless pulleys A, B, and C.

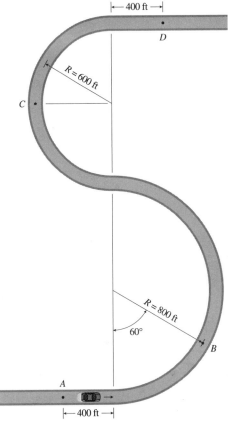

Figure P1.90, P1.91, and P1.92

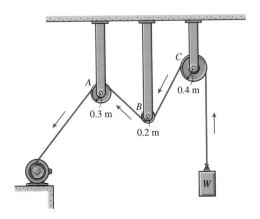

Figure P1.93, P1.94, and P1.95

1.94 Solve Problem 1.93 if, at the instant of interest, the speed of the block W is 3 m/s and it is decreasing at a constant rate of 10 m/s^2.

1.95 At a particular instant, a point of the cable in Problem 1.93 in contact with pulley B has a total acceleration of magnitude 18 m/s^2, with a tangential component of magnitude 15 m/s^2. Determine the magnitudes of the total accelerations of the portions of the cable in contact with pulleys A and C and the velocity and the acceleration of the block W at that instant.

1.96 During a phase of its flight, the trajectory of an airplane is described by the equation $y = 9 - (x/2)^2$, where x and y are in miles. At the position shown, the plane is subjected to an acceleration of 25 ft/s^2 tangent to its trajectory due to thrust, in addition to the downward acceleration of 32.2 ft/s^2 due to gravity. Determine the velocity and the acceleration of the airplane at this position.

1.97 Solve Problem 1.96 if the acceleration due to thrust is zero.

1.98 A projectile is fired with a velocity $v_0 = 115$ m/s at an angle $\alpha = 70°$ with the horizontal. Determine the radius of curvature of the path of the projectile just after it is fired, and at its maximum height.

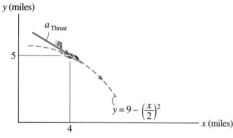

Figure P1.96 and P1.97

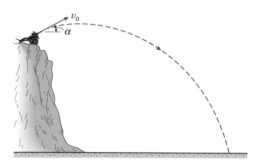

Figure P1.98 and P1.99

1.99 Solve Problem 1.98 if $v_0 = 150$ m/s and $\alpha = 20°$.

SECTION 1.8

1.100 A car is traveling on a circular path of 500-ft radius with a constant velocity of 55 mph. Determine the value of $\dot{\theta}$ for the car, and the magnitudes of the radial and transverse components of its acceleration.

1.101 The position of a particle moving along a circular path of 800-mm radius is described by the equation $\theta = t^3 - 2t$, where θ is in radians and t in s. Determine the magnitudes of the velocity and acceleration of the particle when $t = 2$ s.

1.102 At a certain instant, the speed of a truck traveling on a circular path of 200-m radius is 16 m/s and decreasing at a rate of 2 m/s^2. Determine the magnitude of the total acceleration of the truck at this instant.

1.103 A motorcycle is traveling along a circular path of 150-m radius with a constant speed. If the acceleration in the radial direction cannot exceed $0.4g$ without the motorcycle sliding, determine the maximum safe speed of the motorcycle. Let $g = 9.81$ m/s^2.

1.104 A particle is moving along a circular path of 8-in. radius. If at an instant $\dot{\theta} = 0.17$ rad/s and $\ddot{\theta} = 0.12$ rad/s^2, determine the magnitudes of the velocity and acceleration of the particle at this instant.

1.105 The position of a collar that slides along a rod as it rotates about O is given by the equation $r = 10 - 2t + 3t^3$. If the rotation of the rod is described by the equation $\theta = 0.2t + 0.05t^2$, determine the magnitudes of the velocity and acceleration of the collar when $t = 2$ s. In the given equations, r is in mm, θ is in radians, and t is in s.

1.106 The rod in Problem 1.105 is rotating with a constant angular velocity $\dot{\theta} = 5$ rad/s, while the collar is moving along the rod at a constant rate $\dot{r} = 12$ in./s. If at this instant $r = 6$ in., determine the magnitudes of the velocity and acceleration of the collar.

1.107 At a certain instant, the rod in Problem 1.105 has an angular velocity $\dot{\theta} = 2$ rad/s, which is increasing at a rate $\ddot{\theta} = 0.8$ rad/s^2. The collar is moving along the rod with a velocity $\dot{r} = 0.5$ ft/s, decreasing at a rate $\ddot{r} = -0.3$ ft/s^2. If $r = 1$ ft at this instant, determine the magnitudes of the velocity and acceleration of the collar.

1.108 The curvilinear motion of a particle is described by the equations $r = 3 \sin(\pi t/2)$ and $\theta = 2 \cos(\pi t/5)$, where r is in in., θ is in radians, and t is in s. Determine the magnitudes of the velocity and acceleration of the particle when $t = 1.5$ s.

1.109 The curvilinear motion of a particle is described by the equations $r = 15e^{0.5t}$ mm and $\dot{\theta} = -1$ rad/s. Determine the magnitudes of the velocity and acceleration of the particle when $t = 1$ s.

1.110 The motion of an airplane is being monitored by radar as shown. If, at an instant, $\dot{\theta} = 0.04$ rad/s, $\ddot{\theta} = 0.002$ rad/s^2, $r = 21,000$ ft, $\dot{r} = 1000$ ft/s, and $\ddot{r} = -40$ ft/s^2, determine the magnitudes of the velocity and acceleration of the airplane at this instant.

Figure P1.105, P1.106, and P1.107

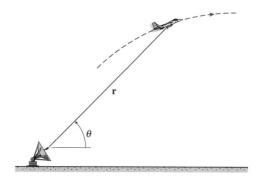

Figure P1.110, P1.111, and P1.112

1.111 For the airplane in Problem 1.110, if at an instant, $\dot{\theta} = 0.05$ rad/s, $\ddot{\theta} = -0.007$ rad/s^2, $r = 8000$ m, $\dot{r} = 350$ m/s, and $\ddot{r} = 10$ m/s^2, determine the magnitudes of the velocity and acceleration of the airplane.

1.112 At an instant, the airplane in Problem 1.110 is flying with a speed of 120 mph, and has a total acceleration of magnitude 55 ft/s^2, with a radial component of magnitude 45 ft/s^2. If $\dot{\theta} = 0.1$ rad/s and $\ddot{\theta} = 0$, determine r, $\dot{r}$, and $\ddot{r}$.

1.113 A rocket launched vertically upward is being monitored by radar located at a distance $c = 1.5$ miles from the launch pad. The tracking data show that $\dot{\theta} = 0.3$ rad/s and $\ddot{\theta} = 0.05$ rad/s^2 when $\theta = 60°$. Determine the velocity and acceleration of the rocket at this position.

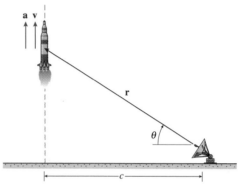

Figure P1.113, P1.114, and P1.115

1.114 For the rocket in Problem 1.113, if $\dot{r} = 800$ ft/s and $\ddot{r} = 0$ when $r = 4$ miles, determine the velocity and acceleration of the rocket.

1.115 For the rocket in Problem 1.113, if the distance $c = 0.75$ km, $\dot{r} = 200$ m/s, and $\ddot{r} = 125$ m/s^2 when $\theta = 30°$, determine the velocity and acceleration of the rocket.

1.116 A helicopter flying in the horizontal direction at an altitude $c = 5$ miles is being monitored by radar on the ground as shown. The tracking data show that $\dot{r} = -300$ ft/s when $\theta = 40°$. Determine the velocity of the helicopter at this position.

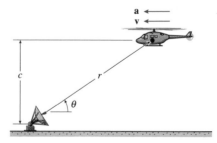

Figure P1.116, P1.117, and P1.118

1.117   For the helicopter in Problem 1.116, if $\dot\theta = 0.007$ rad/s when $\theta = 30°$, determine the velocity of the helicopter.

1.118   For the helicopter in Problem 1.116, if $\dot\theta = 0.005$ rad/s and $\ddot\theta = -0.04$ rad/s^2 when $\theta = 50°$, determine the velocity and acceleration of the helicopter.

1.119   The pin A slides along the fixed vertical guide as the arm OB rotates about O. If $\dot\theta = 0.7$ rad/s and $\ddot\theta = -0.3$ rad/s^2 when $\theta = 60°$, determine the velocity and acceleration of the pin A at this instant. Use $d = 150$ in.

1.120   If the pin in Problem 1.119 is moving downward with a constant velocity of 7 in/s, determine $\dot\theta$ and $\ddot\theta$ when $\theta = 40°$.

1.121   The collar A moves along a circular guide of radius e as the arm OB rotates about O. Derive the expressions for the magnitudes of the velocity and acceleration of the collar A in terms of θ, $\dot\theta$, $\ddot\theta$, and e.

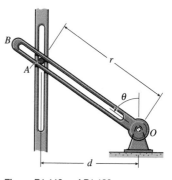

Figure P1.119 and P1.120

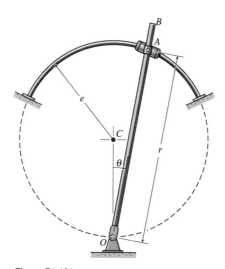

Figure P1.121

1.122   The arm OB rotates counterclockwise with a constant angular velocity $\dot\theta$, causing the collar A to slide on a fixed horizontal guide as shown. Determine the expression for the magnitude of the velocity of collar A.

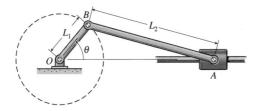

Figure P1.122

Figure P1.123 and P1.124

1.123 The base shaft of a telescoping arm rotates counterclockwise about the fixed vertical axis (z axis) at a constant rate $\dot{\theta} = 10$ revolutions/min, while the arm OAB is being raised upward at a constant rate $\dot{z} = 2$ in./s. Determine the magnitudes of the velocity and acceleration of the end B of the arm.

1.124 The rotating arm in Problem 1.123 is being lowered, and at an instant $\dot{\theta} = -1.6$ rad/s, $\ddot{\theta} = -0.3$ rad/s^2, $\dot{z} = -3$ in./s, and $\ddot{z} = -0.5$ in./s^2. Determine the magnitudes of the velocity and acceleration of the end B of the arm at this instant.

1.125 During a ride at an amusement park, the motion of car A is described by the equations $z = 7 + 3 \sin(\pi t/15)$ m and $\theta = \pi t/60$ rad. Determine the magnitudes of the velocity and acceleration of car A when $t = 21$ s.

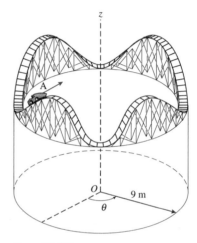

Figure P1.125

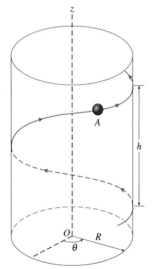

Figure P1.126 and P1.127

1.126 The motion of particle A along a cylindrical helix is described by the equations $z = ht/n$ and $\theta = 2\pi t/n$, where n is a constant. Derive the expressions for the magnitudes of the velocity and acceleration of the particle.

1.127 The motion of particle A along a cylindrical helix is described by the equations $\theta = ct^2$ and $z = cht^2/2\pi$, where c is a constant. Derive the expressions for the magnitudes of the velocity and acceleration of the particle.

SECTION 1.9

1.128 Cars A and B are traveling in the same direction with constant speeds of 45 mph and 60 mph respectively. Determine (a) the velocity of B relative to A, and (b) the velocity of A relative to B.

1.129 Cars A and B are traveling toward each other as shown with constant speeds of 80 km/h and 35 km/h, respectively. If the distance between the cars is $d = 23$ km, determine (a) the velocity of car B relative to car A; (b) the velocity of car A relative to car B; and (c) when the cars will pass each other.

1.130 At an instant, the distance between cars A and B traveling in the same direction is $d = 0.5$ km. Car A has a velocity of 90 km/h, which is decreasing at a constant rate of 5 km/h². Car B has a velocity of 75 km/h, which is increasing at a constant rate of 10 km/h². Determine (a) the position, velocity, and acceleration of car B relative to car A; (b) the position, velocity, and acceleration of car A relative to car B; and (c) when and where car B will pass car A.

1.131 At an instant, the distance between cars A and B traveling toward each other is 0.75 mi. Car A has a velocity of 30 mph, which is decreasing at a constant rate of 2 mi/h². Car B has a velocity of 45 mph, which is increasing at a constant rate of 3 mi/h². Determine (a) the position, velocity, and acceleration of car B relative to car A; (b) the position, velocity, and acceleration of car A relative to car B; and (c) when and where the cars will pass each other.

1.132 Car A is traveling along a straight road as shown in the figure with a speed of 22 m/s, which is increasing at a constant rate of 9 m/s². Car B is traveling in the perpendicular direction with a speed of 13 m/s, which is decreasing at a constant rate of 2 m/s². Determine the velocity and acceleration of car B relative to car A.

1.133 Boats A and B are traveling along the straight-line paths as shown. Boat A has a velocity of 40 ft/s, which is decreasing at a constant rate of 6 ft/s². Boat B has a velocity of 55 ft/s increasing at a constant rate of 8 ft/s². Determine the velocity and acceleration of boat A relative to boat B.

1.134 Car B is traveling along a straight road as shown in the figure, with a constant speed of 100 km/h. When observed from B, car A appears to be moving at an angle of 30° with respect to the path of B. Determine (a) the absolute velocity of car A, and (b) the velocity that car A appears to have when observed from car B.

1.135 Boat A is moving along a straight path with a constant speed of 60 ft/s. When observed from A, boat B appears to be moving at an angle of 20° with respect to the path of A. Determine (a) the absolute velocity of boat B, and (b) the velocity that boat B appears to have when observed from boat A.

1.136 Boats A and B are traveling along straight intersecting paths as shown, with constant speeds of 70 km/h and 40 km/h, respectively. If at an instant, the distance between them is $d = 2$ km, determine (a) the distance between boats A and B after 1 minute and (b) when the two boats will be 1 km apart.

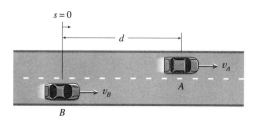

Figure P1.128 and P1.130

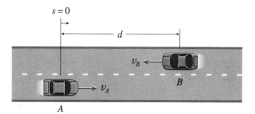

Figure P1.129 and P1.131

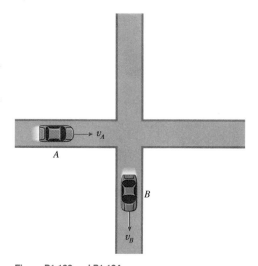

Figure P1.132 and P1.134

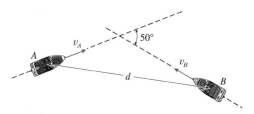

Figure P1.133, P1.135, and P1.136

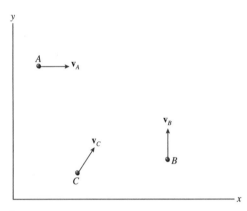

Figure P1.137 and P1.138

1.137   The velocities of two particles A and B are 3 in./s $\ominus$ and 4 in./s $\uparrow$, respectively. If the velocity of A relative to a third particle C is 2 in./s 30° $\searrow$, determine (*a*) the absolute velocity of C and (*b*) the velocity of C relative to B.

1.138   If particles A, B, and C are moving in a common plane, show that $\mathbf{a}_{A/C} = \mathbf{a}_{A/B} + \mathbf{a}_{B/C}$.

1.139   Motorcycles A and B are moving along two circular tracks with constant speeds of 30 mph and 50 mph, respectively, as shown. Determine the velocity and acceleration of motorcycle B relative to motorcycle A.

1.140   If at an instant, motorcycle A has a speed of 40 mph decreasing at a rate of 10 mi/h², and motorcycle B has a speed of 25 mph increasing at a rate of 20 mi/h², determine the velocity and acceleration of motorcycle B relative to motorcycle A.

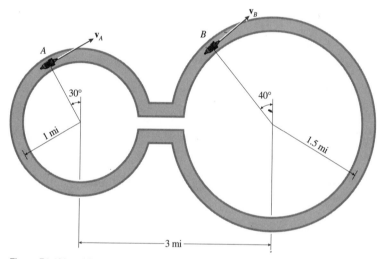

Figure P1.139 and P1.140

1.141   Awaiting clearance to land at a busy airport, airplanes A and B are flying at altitudes of 15,000 ft and 10,000 ft, respectively, along circular paths as shown. The velocities of the two planes are constant, at $v_A = 300$ mph and $v_B = 200$ mph. Determine (*a*) the velocity and acceleration of airplane B relative to airplane A, and (*b*) the velocity of airplane A relative to airplane B.

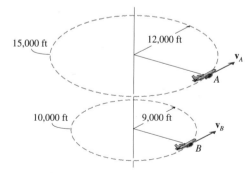

Figure P1.141

SECTION 1.10

1.142 Block A is moving downward with a constant velocity of 10 in./s. Determine (*a*) the velocity of block B, and (*b*) the velocity of block B relative to block A.

1.143 If block A is moving up the incline at a constant velocity of 15 m/s, determine the speed with which the electric hoist B is wrapping the cable around its drum.

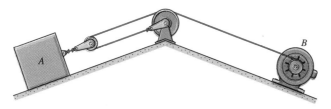

Figure P1.143

Figure P1.142 and P1.144

1.144 Block B starts from rest and moves downward with a constant acceleration of 10 m/s². Determine the distance traveled by block A in 0.6 s.

1.145 A pickup truck initially at rest under pulley C starts moving forward with a constant acceleration of 0.75 ft/s². Determine the velocity of weight B when $t = 5$ s.

1.146 Determine the acceleration of the weight B in Problem 1.145 when $t = 5$ s.

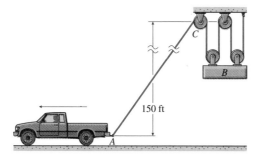

Figure P1.145 and P1.146

1.147 Determine the relationships between the velocities, and the accelerations, of blocks A, B, and C.

Figure P1.147

1.148 and 1.149 Block *A* is moving downward with a velocity of 7 m/s, which is increasing at a rate of 2 m/s², while block *C* is moving upward with a velocity of 9 m/s, which is decreasing at a rate of 3 m/s². Determine the velocity and acceleration of block *B* at this instant.

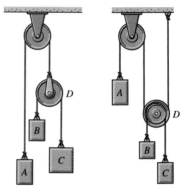

Figure P1.148   **Figure P1.149**

KINETICS OF PARTICLES: NEWTON'S SECOND LAW OF MOTION

2

OUTLINE

2.1 INTRODUCTION

In Chapter 1, we studied the geometry of the motion of a particle without any consideration of the forces causing the motion. In this chapter, we will consider the effects of forces on the motions of particles. We will establish the relationship between the forces acting on a particle and the resulting change in the particle's motion by the direct application of Newton's second law of motion. Newton's second law, which we will review in the following section, will be used to relate external forces acting on a particle to its mass and acceleration. This relationship, called the *equation of motion*, will be expressed in terms of three types of coordinate systems commonly encountered in engineering applications: rectangular coordinates, tangential and normal coordinates, and cylindrical coordinates. The velocity and the position of the particle can be related to the external forces by integrating the equation of motion according to the kinematic expressions described in Chapter 1.

The objective of this chapter is to develop the analysis of motion of a particle subjected to a system of forces, by the direct application of Newton's second law. Newton's second law of motion is discussed in detail in Section 2.2. The equation of motion of a particle subjected to a system of forces is developed in Section 2.3, where a general procedure for the kinetic analysis is presented. The expressions of the equation of motion in terms of components of forces and accelerations in rectangular, tangential and normal, and cylindrical coordinates are then developed in Sections 2.4, 2.5, and 2.6, respectively, and are applied to solve problems involving kinetics of particles.

2.2 NEWTON'S SECOND LAW OF MOTION

It may be recalled from Section 1.4 of the statics volume that *Newton's second law of motion* can be stated as:

A particle acted upon by an unbalanced force experiences an acceleration that is directly proportional to the force and has the same direction as the force.

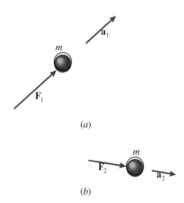

(a)

(b)

Figure 2.1

Although this law cannot be proven mathematically, it has been verified by numerous experiments, and forms the basis for most of the kinetic analysis of particles and rigid bodies. Consider as an example a particle of mass m shown in Figure 2.1. According to Newton's second law, if the particle is subjected to a force $\mathbf{F}_1$, it will experience an acceleration $\mathbf{a}_1$ in the direction of $\mathbf{F}_1$ as shown in Figure 2.1a. If instead of $\mathbf{F}_1$, the particle is subjected to another force $\mathbf{F}_2$ of a different magnitude and/or direction, it will experience an acceleration

a_2 in the direction of $\mathbf{F}_2$ (Figure 2.1*b*). Moreover, since in accordance with Newton's second law the magnitude of acceleration will be directly proportional to the magnitude of the force, the ratios of the magnitudes F_1/a_1 and F_2/a_2 will be the same, or

$$\frac{F_1}{a_1} = \frac{F_2}{a_2} = \cdots = c$$

in which the constant of proportionality c is a property, called the **inertia**, of the particle. The inertia is defined as the particle's resistance to change of velocity. A particle of a small inertia will accelerate more under a given force, as compared to a particle of a larger inertia subjected to the same force. Provided consistent units are employed, the constant c (or inertia) can be taken as equal to the **mass** *m* of the particle. Thus, Newton's second law of motion can be mathematically expressed as

$$\mathbf{F} = m\mathbf{a} \qquad (2.1)$$

where $\mathbf{F}$ is the unbalanced force acting on a particle of mass *m*, and $\mathbf{a}$ is the resulting acceleration of the particle (Figure 2.2).

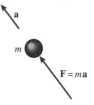

Newton's first law of motion, given in the statics volume, may be considered as a special case of the second law. When a particle is not subjected to an unbalanced (or resultant) force, it does not accelerate. Therefore, if initially at rest, the particle remains at rest; or if initially in motion, the particle continues its motion along a straight line with a constant velocity.

Figure 2.2

For measurements of accelerations, Newton's laws of motion are based on coordinate systems that do not rotate in space and are either fixed in space or translate with constant velocities. Such coordinate systems are called **Newtonian** or **inertial frames of reference**. The motion measured with respect to a Newtonian reference frame is referred to as the **absolute motion**. The earth is not truly an inertial reference frame, because it rotates and accelerates with respect to the sun. However, for most engineering problems near or on the surface of the earth, the rotation and acceleration of the earth are negligible, and a coordinate system attached to the earth can be used for measurements of acceleration and the application of Newton's laws. But in analyses involving motions of space vehicles and planets, a Newtonian reference frame fixed in outer space (such as on a distant star) should be used.

Units

When applying the equation $\mathbf{F} = m\mathbf{a}$ to solve problems, it is essential that consistent units of force, mass, and acceleration be used. Of the four quantities involved—force, mass, length, and time—the units for three may be chosen arbitrarily, and the unit of the fourth quantity is derived by satisfying the equation $\mathbf{F} = m\mathbf{a}$. Such a system of units is referred to as a *kinetic* system.

As discussed in *Statics*, Section 1.6, in the International System of units (SI) the base units are *meter* (m) for length, *kilogram* (kg) for mass, and *second* (s) for time. The unit of force is called *newton* (N), and is derived from the units of mass (kg) and acceleration (m/s²) by satisfying the equation $\mathbf{F} = m\mathbf{a}$ as

$$1\ \text{N} = (1\ \text{kg})(1\ \text{m/s}^2) = 1\ \text{kg} \cdot \text{m/s}^2$$

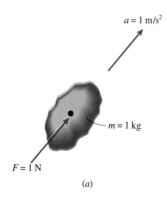

$a = 1\ \text{m/s}^2$

$m = 1\ \text{kg}$

$F = 1\ \text{N}$

(a)

Thus, 1 newton is defined as the force required to give an acceleration of 1 m/s² to a mass of 1 kg (Figure 2.3*a*). The weight of a body, which is the force of gravitational attraction, can be determined by writing Equation (2.1) as (Figure 2.3*b*)

$$W\,(\text{N}) = m\,(\text{kg}) \times g\,(\text{m/s}^2) \tag{2.2}$$

where m is the mass of the body, and g is the acceleration of gravity. While the magnitude of g varies slightly at different positions on the surface of the earth, the standard value of $g = 9.81$ m/s² is commonly used in engineering computations. Thus, the weight of a body of 1-kg mass is

$$W = (1\ \text{kg})(9.81\ \text{m/s}^2) = 9.81\ \text{kg} \cdot \text{m/s}^2 = 9.81\ \text{N}$$

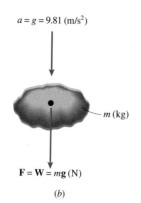

$a = g = 9.81\ (\text{m/s}^2)$

$m\,(\text{kg})$

$F = W = m\mathbf{g}\,(\text{N})$

(b)

Figure 2.3

In U.S. Customary units, the base units are *foot* (ft) for length, *pound* (lb) for force, and *second* (s) for time. The unit of mass is called *slug*, and is derived from the units of force (lb) and acceleration (ft/s²) by satisfying the equation $\mathbf{F} = m\mathbf{a}$ as

$$1\ \text{lb} = (1\ \text{slug})(1\ \text{ft/s}^2)$$

or

$$1\ \text{slug} = \frac{(1\ \text{lb})}{(1\ \text{ft/s}^2)} = 1\ \text{lb} \cdot \text{s}^2/\text{ft}$$

Thus, 1 slug is defined as the mass that is accelerated at a rate of 1 ft/s² when subjected to a force of 1 lb (Figure 2.4*a*). When the weight of a body is known, its mass can be obtained from the equation (Figure 2.4*b*).

$$m\,(\text{slug}) = \frac{W\,(\text{lb})}{g\,(\text{ft/s}^2)} \tag{2.3}$$

The standard value of g is 32.2 ft/s². Therefore, the mass of a body weighing 1 lb is

$$m = \frac{(1\ \text{lb})}{(32.2\ \text{ft/s}^2)} = \frac{1}{32.2}\ \text{lb} \cdot \text{s}^2/\text{ft}$$

$$= \frac{1}{32.2}\ \text{slug}$$

and the weight of a body of 1-slug mass is

$$W = (1\ \text{slug})(32.2\ \text{ft/s}^2) = 32.2\ \text{lb}$$

2.3 EQUATION OF MOTION: PROCEDURE FOR ANALYSIS

Consider a particle of mass m subjected to a system of concurrent forces $\mathbf{F}_1$, $\mathbf{F}_2$, $\mathbf{F}_3$, ... as shown in Figure 2.5. Since the forces $\mathbf{F}_1$, $\mathbf{F}_2$, $\mathbf{F}_3$, ... can be replaced by the single resultant $\mathbf{R} = \Sigma\mathbf{F}$, which will produce the same effect on the particle, we can express Equation (2.1) as

$$\mathbf{R} = m\mathbf{a}$$

or

$$\Sigma\mathbf{F} = m\mathbf{a} \qquad (2.4)$$

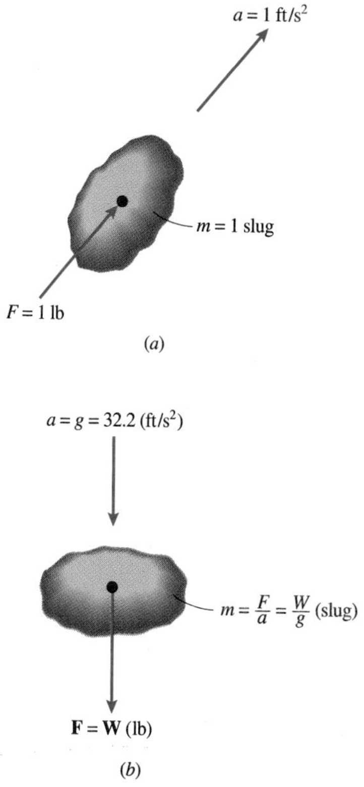

Thus, when a particle is subjected to a system of concurrent forces, it will experience acceleration in the direction of the resultant of the force system, with the magnitude of acceleration proportional to the magnitude of the resultant, in accordance with Equation (2.4). Equation (2.4), called the **equation of motion**, forms the basis of the kinetic analysis presented in this chapter. Expressions of this equation in terms of force and acceleration components in three commonly used types of coordinate systems will be presented in the following sections. These scalar components of Equation (2.4) are usually referred to as the equations of motion of particles.

The analysis based on Equation (2.4) is applicable not only to particles of negligible dimensions, but also to the motions of the mass centers of bodies of finite or definite sizes, provided the forces acting on the body are concurrent at its center of mass, or the rotation of the body about its mass center can be neglected.

D'Alembert's Principle

In 1743, the French mathematician J. d'Alembert presented an alternative interpretation of Equation (2.4). In this approach, commonly referred to as **d'Alembert's principle**, the equation of motion is rewritten in the form

$$\Sigma\mathbf{F} - m\mathbf{a} = \mathbf{0}$$

and the quantity $-m\mathbf{a}$ is treated as a fictitious *inertia force* acting on the particle in the direction opposite to that of the acceleration. Thus, the particle can be considered to be in a state of (fictitious) **dynamic equilibrium** at any instant of time under the action of actual forces $\mathbf{F}$ and the inertia force $-m\mathbf{a}$. This approach allows the solution of dynamics problems by the methods developed in statics. One should realize that to an observer located at, and moving with, the particle, the particle would indeed appear to be in equilibrium. Furthermore, the observer would feel pushed in the direction opposite to that of the particle's acceleration by the fictitious inertia force.

As d'Alembert's principle offers no advantage over the direct application of Newton's second law in the solution of problems considered in this introductory text, we will not pursue it any further. All examples presented herein

$a = 1 \text{ ft/s}^2$

$m = 1 \text{ slug}$

$F = 1 \text{ lb}$

(a)

$a = g = 32.2 \ (\text{ft/s}^2)$

$m = \dfrac{F}{a} = \dfrac{W}{g} \ (\text{slug})$

$\mathbf{F} = \mathbf{W} \ (\text{lb})$

(b)

Figure 2.4

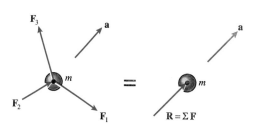

Figure 2.5

have been solved by the direct application of Newton's second law of motion, Equation (2.4).

Procedure for Analysis   The following step-by-step procedure can be used to solve problems involving kinetics of particles by the application of Newton's second law of motion.

1.   Select an inertial coordinate system for specifying the motion of the particle. The particular type of coordinate system to use in a given problem usually depends on the conditions of the problem, the form in which the data are provided, and the type of solution desired. For example, if the curved path of the motion of a particle is specified, it is usually convenient to use tangential and normal coordinates; or if the planar motion of a particle is specified by its position along a radial line and the orientation of the line, it will be convenient to use polar coordinates. Recall that for most engineering problems, a coordinate system attached to the surface of the earth can be considered an inertial coordinate system.

2.   Draw a free-body diagram of the particle (or the body) showing all the forces acting on it. This is perhaps the most crucial step in the analysis. To draw the correct free-body diagram:

   a.   Identify the particle (body) to be isolated.

   b.   Detach the particle (body) from its supports and disconnect it from any other bodies to which it is connected. Draw the outline of this isolated particle (body).

   c.   Show each known force on the diagram by an arrow indicating its direction and sense. Write the magnitude of each known force in a consistent kinetic unit (N or lb) next to its arrow.

   d.   Show each unknown force component on the free-body diagram by an arrow in the direction of its line of action. The senses of these forces may not be known but can be arbitrarily assumed. It is usually convenient to assume the senses of unknown force components in the positive directions of the coordinate axes. Show these assumed senses on the free-body diagram. It should be realized that the actual senses of these forces will be known only after we have determined their magnitudes by solving the equations of motion. A positive magnitude for a force will indicate that the assumed sense was correct, whereas a negative value will imply a sense opposite to the one assumed. The magnitude of each unknown force should be denoted by an appropriate letter symbol on the free-body diagram.

   If the problem involves dependent motion of two or more particles (bodies), draw a free-body diagram of each particle (body).

3.   If the weight of the particle is given rather than its mass, determine the mass from the relationship $m = W/g$. Express the mass in a consistent kinetic unit (kg or slug).

4.   Draw a diagram of the particle (body) showing the components of the $m\mathbf{a}$ vector (i.e., the product of the mass m and the acceleration vector $\mathbf{a}$) in the directions of the coordinate axes. Show each known component of $m\mathbf{a}$ by an

arrow indicating its direction and sense. Write the magnitude of each known component next to its arrow. If instead of acceleration, the velocity or position of the particle is specified, determine the acceleration by differentiating the known quantity according to the kinematic relationships described in Chapter 1. Represent each unknown component of $m\mathbf{a}$ by an arrow in the direction of its line of action. Again, it is usually convenient to assume the senses of unknown components in the positive directions of the coordinate axes. A graphical representation of the equations of motion can now be obtained by equating the diagram showing the $m\mathbf{a}$ components to the free-body diagram depicting the forces (from Step 2).

5.   If the forces acting on the particle are constant, or if the particle's acceleration is known, determine the unknown acceleration and/or force components, or other unknowns, by solving the equations of motion in the component form for the coordinate system selected. Sections 2.4, 2.5, and 2.6 give the equations of motion in the component form for the rectangular, the tangential and normal, and the cylindrical coordinate systems, respectively. Realize that the number of unknown quantities that can be determined from the equations of motion cannot exceed the total number of independent equations. In problems involving planar motions, each free-body diagram provides two equations of motion; in the case of space motions, each free-body diagram provides three equations of motion.

If the velocity and position of the particle are desired, they can now be determined by integrating the acceleration in accordance with the kinematic equations of Chapter 1.

6.   If the forces acting on the particle are functions of time, position, velocity, or acceleration, first determine the expressions for the unknown acceleration components as functions of time, position, or velocity (depending on the particular form of force function) by solving the equations of motion. Then, integrate these expressions using the procedure outlined in Section 1.3 to obtain the equations of position and velocity; from these, determine the desired quantities.

2.4 RECTANGULAR COORDINATES

Planar Motion

When the forces and the acceleration of a particle in planar motion are expressed in rectangular coordinates (see Section 1.6), the equation of motion $\Sigma \mathbf{F} = m\mathbf{a}$ can be written as

$$\Sigma F_x \mathbf{i} + \Sigma F_y \mathbf{j} = m(a_x \mathbf{i} + a_y \mathbf{j})$$

from which we obtain the equations of motion in scalar form in terms of rectangular components as (Figure 2.6)

$$\Sigma F_x = ma_x = m\ddot{x} \qquad \Sigma F_y = ma_y = m\ddot{y} \qquad (2.5)$$

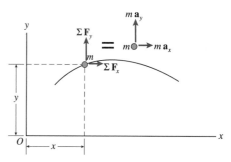

Figure 2.6

Spatial Motion

When the motion of a particle takes place along a three-dimensional space curve (Figure 2.7), the equation of motion $\Sigma\mathbf{F} = m\mathbf{a}$ can be expressed in terms of rectangular components as

$$\Sigma F_x = ma_x = m\ddot{x} \qquad \Sigma F_y = ma_y = m\ddot{y} \qquad \Sigma F_z = ma_z = m\ddot{z} \qquad (2.6)$$

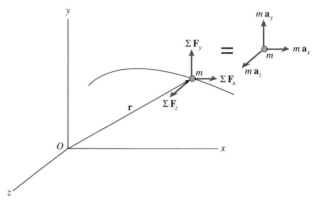

Figure 2.7

EXAMPLE 2.1

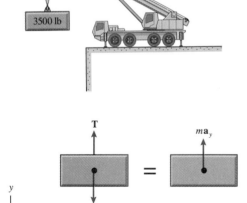

A 3500-lb crate is being moved by a crane as shown. Determine the tension in the hoisting cable when (*a*) the crate is being lifted with an upward acceleration of 10 ft/s², and (*b*) the crate is being lowered with a downward acceleration of 10 ft/s².

Solution   The free-body diagram of the crate shows the known weight, $W = 3500$ lb, of the crate, and the unknown cable tension T, which is assumed to be positive upward (in the positive y direction).

The mass of the crate is

$$m = \frac{W}{g} = \frac{3500}{32.2} = 108.7 \text{ lb} \cdot \text{s}^2/\text{ft} = 108.7 \text{ slug}$$

Applying the equation of motion

$$\textcircled{\uparrow}\,\Sigma F_y = ma_y \qquad T - 3500 = 108.7a_y$$

$$T = 108.7a_y + 3500 \qquad\qquad\qquad (a)$$

(*a*)   *Upward acceleration* $a_y = 10$ ft/s². Substituting $a_y = 10$ ft/s² into Equation (a), we obtain

$$T = 108.7(10) + 3500 = 4590 \text{ lb}$$

$$T = 4590 \text{ lb} \blacktriangleleft$$

(*continued*)

EXAMPLE 2.1 (*concluded*)

(b) Downward acceleration $a_y = -10$ ft/s². Substituting $a_y = -10$ ft/s² into Equation (a), we obtain

$$T = 108.7(-10) + 3500 = 2410 \text{ lb}$$

$$T = 2410 \text{ lb} \blacktriangleleft$$

It is of interest to note from Equation (a) that if there is no acceleration (i.e., if the crate is either moving with a constant velocity, or is at rest), the tension in the cable is equal to the weight of the crate.

EXAMPLE 2.2

A 2000-kg airplane lands on a runway with 9 percent grade with a touchdown speed of 130 km/h, whereupon the brakes are applied causing a constant braking force of 12 kN to be exerted on the airplane. Neglecting air resistance, determine the distance traveled by the airplane before it stops.

Solution The free-body diagram of the plane shows the two known forces: the weight of the airplane $W = mg = 2000(9.81) = 19,620$ N inclined at an angle $\alpha = \tan^{-1}(9/100) = 5.14°$ with respect to the y axis, and the braking force of 12,000 N. It also shows the unknown reaction N being exerted by the ground on the plane. The unknown acceleration a_x is assumed to be positive in the positive x direction. Note that the x and y axes are oriented along and perpendicular to, respectively, the inclined path of the plane. For this orientation of coordinate axes, each of the two equations of motion contains only one unknown quantity (a_x or N) that can be determined directly.

Note that the choice of x and y axes as horizontal and vertical would result in each equation of motion containing two unknowns, and determining the unknowns would involve the solution of two simultaneous equations.

Equations of motion. Since there is no acceleration in the y direction, the equation of equilibrium $\Sigma F_y = 0$ can be used to determine the ground reaction N if desired. Applying the equation of motion in the x direction,

④ $\Sigma F_x = ma_x$

$$-19,620(\sin 5.14°) - 12,000 = 2000a_x$$

$$a_x = -6.88 \text{ m/s}^2$$

Distance traveled before the airplane stops. The distance x traveled by the plane before it stops can be determined by integrating the kinematic relationship $a_x = v_x \, dv_x/dx$ with the initial conditions, $x_0 = 0$ and $v_{x0} = 130$ km/h $= 36.11$ m/s

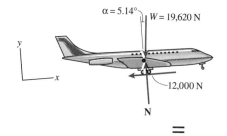

when $t = 0$, and the condition that $v_x = 0$ when the airplane stops. Thus,

$$a_x \, dx = v_x \, dv_x$$

$$-6.88 \int_0^x dx = \int_{36.11}^0 v_x \, dv_x$$

$$-6.88x = \frac{-(36.11)^2}{2}$$

$$x = 94.8 \text{ m} \blacktriangleleft$$

EXAMPLE 2.3

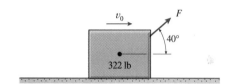

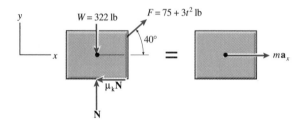

A block weighing 322 lb is sliding on the horizontal surface under the action of a force $F = 75 + 3t^2$ lb, where t is in seconds. If the initial velocity of the block is 1.8 ft/s when $t = 0$, determine its velocity when $t = 3$ s, and the distance traveled during that interval. The coefficient of kinetic friction between the block and the surface is 0.2.

Solution The free-body diagram of the block is shown. Note that the frictional force has the magnitude of $\mu_k N$, and it acts in the direction opposite to that of the motion.

The mass of the block is

$$m = \frac{W}{g} = \frac{322}{32.2} = 10 \text{ lb} \cdot \text{s}^2/\text{ft} = 10 \text{ slug}$$

Applying the equations of motion in the x and y directions, respectively, we obtain

$$\xrightarrow{+} \Sigma F_x = ma_x$$

$$-0.2N + (75 + 3t^2)\cos 40° = 10a_x$$

$$10a_x + 0.2N = 57.45 + 2.3t^2 \tag{a}$$

$$\xuparrow{+} \Sigma F_y = ma_y$$

$$-322 + (75 + 3t^2)\sin 40° + N = 0$$

$$N = 273.75 - 1.93t^2 \tag{b}$$

Substituting Equation (b) into Equation (a), we obtain the expression for a_x in terms of time t. Thus,

$$10a_x + 0.2(273.75 - 1.93t^2) = 57.45 + 2.3t^2$$

$$a_x = 0.27(1 + t^2) \text{ ft/s}^2$$

Velocity when $t = 3$ s. The expression for velocity is determined by integrating the kinematic relationship $a_x = dv_x/dt$ with the initial condition $v_{x0} = 1.8$ ft/s when $t = 0$. Thus,

$$dv_x = a_x \, dt \qquad \int_{1.8}^{v_x} dv_x = \int_0^t 0.27(1 + t^2) \, dt$$

$$v_x = 1.8 + 0.27\left(t + \frac{t^3}{3}\right)$$

When $t = 3$ s, $\qquad\qquad\qquad\qquad v_x = 5.04 \text{ ft/s} \circlearrowright$ ◄

Distance traveled during 3 s. Integrating the kinematic relationship $v_x = dx/dt$, with the initial condition $x_0 = 0$ when $t = 0$, we obtain

$$dx = v_x \, dt \qquad \int_0^x dx = \int_0^t 1.8 + 0.27\left(t + \frac{t^3}{3}\right) dt$$

$$x = 1.8t + 0.27\left(\frac{t^2}{2} + \frac{t^4}{12}\right)$$

Thus, when $t = 3$ s, $\qquad\qquad\qquad\qquad x = 8.44 \text{ ft}$ ◄

EXAMPLE 2.4

Blocks A and B of masses 200 kg and 300 kg, respectively, are released from rest simultaneously. If the coefficient of kinetic friction between block B and the inclined plane is 0.3, determine the tension in the cable and the accelerations of the blocks. Neglect the masses of the pulleys and the cable, and assume that the pulleys are frictionless.

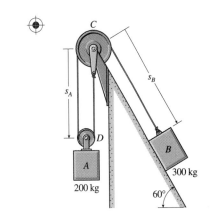

Solution   The relationship between the motions of blocks A and B can be established by realizing that the total length of the cable is constant; that is, $2s_A + s_B = $ constant. By differentiating this expression twice with respect to time, we obtain the relationship between the accelerations of blocks A and B as

$$2a_A + a_B = 0 \qquad (a)$$

The free-body diagrams of the two blocks and pulley D are shown. Note that the positive senses of the accelerations a_A and a_B on the free-body diagrams (assumed to be in the positive x directions) are consistent with those of s_A and s_B used to derive the kinematic equation of dependent motion, Equation (a). Also, since the mass of the pulley D is assumed to be negligible, the forces acting on it must satisfy the force and moment equilibrium equations.

Applying the equation of motion for block A,

$\downarrow \Sigma F_x = m_A a_A$

$$-2T + 1962 = 200a_A$$

$$2T + 200a_A = 1962 \qquad (b)$$

For block B,

$\oplus \Sigma F_x = m_B a_B$

$$-T - 0.3N + 2943 \sin 60° = 300a_B$$

$$-T - 0.3N + 2548.71 = 300a_B \qquad (c)$$

$\oplus \Sigma F_y = 0$

$$N - 2943 \cos 60° = 0$$

$$N = 1471.5 \text{ N}$$

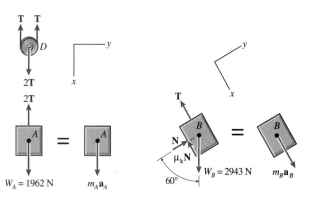

Substituting $N = 1471.5$ N and $a_B = -2a_A$ from Equation (a) into Equation (c), we write

$$T = 2107.26 + 600a_A \qquad (d)$$

Substituting Equation (d) into Equation (b), we obtain

$$2(2107.26 + 600a_A) + 200a_A = 1962$$

$$a_A = -1.61 \text{ m/s}^2$$

$$a_A = 1.61 \text{ m/s}^2 \uparrow \blacktriangleleft$$

Substituting the numerical value of a_A into Equations (a) and (d), we obtain

$$a_B = -2a_A = -2(-1.61)$$

$$a_B = 3.22 \text{ m/s}^2$$

$$a_B = 3.22 \text{ m/s}^2 \searrow 60° \blacktriangleleft$$

$$T = 2107.26 + 600(-1.61) = 1140 \text{ N}$$

$$T = 1140 \text{ N} \blacktriangleleft$$

2.5 TANGENTIAL AND NORMAL COORDINATES

If the curvilinear path of the motion of a particle is specified, it is usually convenient to use the tangential and normal coordinates defined in Section 1.7. The equation of motion $\Sigma\mathbf{F} = m\mathbf{a}$ can be written in terms of the components of forces and acceleration, which are directed along the tangent and the normal to the curved path (Figure 2.8) as

$$\Sigma F_t\mathbf{n}_t + \Sigma F_n\mathbf{n}_n = m(a_t\mathbf{n}_t + a_n\mathbf{n}_n)$$

from which we obtain the equations of motion in scalar form in terms of tangential and normal components as

$$\Sigma F_t = ma_t = m\dot{v} = m\ddot{s}$$
$$\Sigma F_n = ma_n = m\frac{v^2}{\rho} = m\frac{\dot{s}^2}{\rho} \tag{2.7}$$

As shown in Figure 2.8, the positive t direction is always in the direction of the motion; hence, a tangential force component $\mathbf{F}_t$ is considered positive if it is acting in the positive t direction. Similarly, a normal force component $\mathbf{F}_n$ is considered positive if it is acting in the positive n direction, which is always toward the center of curvature C of the path. The normal force is sometimes referred to as **centripetal force**.

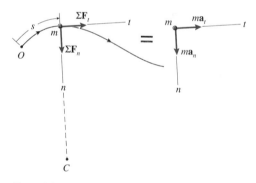

Figure 2.8

EXAMPLE   2.5

Determine the maximum safe speed at which a vehicle can travel on a highway curve of 800-ft radius without sliding sideways, if the coefficient of static friction between the tires and asphalt surface is 0.6.

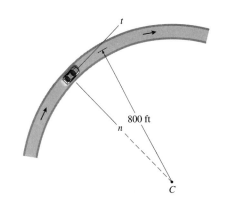

Solution   The free-body diagram of the vehicle is shown. Note that the normal component of acceleration is directed toward the center of curvature C.

Applying the equations of motion in the y and n directions, we obtain

$$(\updownarrow)\,\Sigma F_y = 0$$

$$-N + mg = 0 \qquad N = mg = 32.2m$$

$$(\to)\,\Sigma F_n = ma_n = m\frac{v^2}{\rho}$$

$$0.6N = m\frac{v^2}{800}$$

Substituting $N = 32.2m$ into the above equation, we obtain

$$0.6(32.2m) = m\frac{v^2}{800}$$

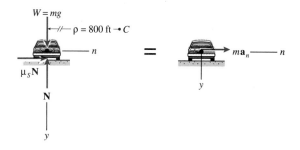

Therefore, the maximum speed the vehicle can achieve without sliding is

$$v = 124.32 \text{ ft/s} = 84.6 \text{ mph} \blacktriangleleft$$

EXAMPLE 2.6

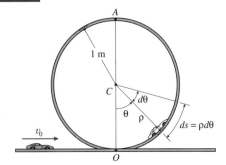

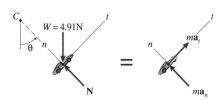

Determine the minimum initial velocity with which a 0.5-kg toy car should be propelled so that it makes a complete circuit around the vertical loop. Neglect friction and the dimensions of the car.

Solution The free-body diagram of the car in a general position θ is shown.

We can write the equations of motion in the tangential and normal directions as

$$\stackrel{\curvearrowright}{\textcircled{+}}\, \Sigma F_t = ma_t$$

$$-4.91 \sin \theta = 0.5a_t \qquad a_t = -9.82 \sin \theta \qquad \text{(a)}$$

$$\stackrel{\nwarrow}{\textcircled{+}}\, \Sigma F_n = ma_n = m\frac{v^2}{\rho}$$

$$N - 4.91 \cos \theta = \frac{0.5v^2}{1} \qquad N = 0.5v^2 + 4.91 \cos \theta \qquad \text{(b)}$$

Velocity. We determine the expression for velocity in terms of θ by integrating the kinematic relationship

$$a_t = v\frac{dv}{ds}$$

As shown in the figure, $ds = \rho\, d\theta = (1)\, d\theta$. Thus,

$$v\, dv = a_t\, d\theta$$

Substituting Equation (a) and integrating, we find

$$\int_{v_0}^{v} v\, dv = -9.82 \int_0^{\theta} \sin \theta\, d\theta$$

$$\frac{1}{2}(v^2 - v_0^2) = 9.82(\cos \theta - 1)$$

$$v^2 = v_0^2 - 19.64(1 - \cos \theta) \qquad \text{(c)}$$

Minimum velocity. Equation (c) indicates that the velocity of the car decreases from its initial value v_0 as it moves up the side of the loop from position O at the bottom, to position A at the top. Thereafter, the velocity increases as the car moves down the other side of the loop. The velocity at the top is obtained by setting $\theta = 180° = \pi$ rad in Equation (c):

$$v_A^2 = v_0^2 - 39.28 \qquad \text{(d)}$$

Next, turning our attention to the normal force N from Equation (b), we can see that the normal force depends on the velocity.

(continued)

EXAMPLE   2.6   (*concluded*)

The car will stay on the circular path as long as there is a normal force between the loop and the car. When the velocity becomes small enough to reduce the normal force to zero, the car will not follow the loop and will fall off. Substituting Equation (d) into Equation (b) and setting $\theta = 180° = \pi$ rad, we obtain the normal force at the top A as

$$N_A = 0.5(v_0^2 - 39.28) - 4.91$$
$$N_A = 0.5v_0^2 - 24.55$$

and by setting $N_A = 0$ in the above equation, we obtain the minimum velocity,

$$v_0 = 7.01 \text{ m/s} \circlearrowright \quad \blacktriangleleft$$

Thus, the car must be propelled with a minimum velocity of 7.01 m/s in order to make it around the loop.

2.6 CYLINDRICAL COORDINATES

Planar Motion: Polar Coordinates

When the forces and the acceleration of a particle in planar motion are expressed in polar coordinates (see Section 1.8), the equation of motion $\Sigma \mathbf{F} = m\mathbf{a}$ can be written as (Figure 2.9)

$$\Sigma F_r \mathbf{n}_r + \Sigma F_\theta \mathbf{n}_\theta = m(a_r \mathbf{n}_r + a_\theta \mathbf{n}_\theta)$$

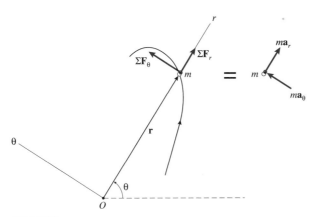

Figure 2.9

From this we obtain the equations of motion in scalar form in terms of radial and transverse components as

$$\Sigma F_r = ma_r = m(\ddot{r} - r\dot{\theta}^2)$$
$$\Sigma F_\theta = ma_\theta = m(r\ddot{\theta} + 2\dot{r}\dot{\theta})$$

(2.8)

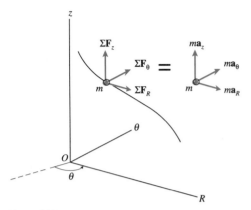

Figure 2.10

Spatial Motion: Cylindrical Coordinates

In the case of the motion of a particle along a three-dimensional space curve (Figure 2.10), the equation of motion $\Sigma\mathbf{F} = m\mathbf{a}$ can be expressed in terms of components in cylindrical coordinates as

$$\Sigma F_R = ma_R = m(\ddot{R} - R\dot{\theta}^2)$$
$$\Sigma F_\theta = ma_\theta = m(R\ddot{\theta} + 2\dot{R}\dot{\theta}) \qquad (2.9)$$
$$\Sigma F_z = ma_z = m\ddot{z}$$

EXAMPLE 2.7

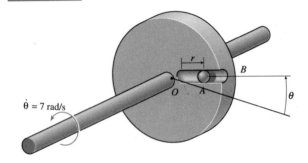

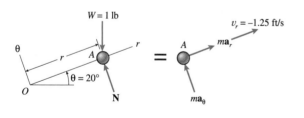

Ball A weighing 1 lb slides in a smooth groove inside a disk that rotates in the vertical plane with a constant angular velocity of 7 rad/s. At the instant when $\theta = 20°$, the ball is sliding toward the center O along OB with a velocity of 15 in./s. Determine the force exerted by the disk on the ball at this instant.

Solution   The free-body diagram of the ball A is shown. The force N that the disk exerts on the ball acts in the direction perpendicular to the groove OB as shown. The mass of the ball is

$$m = \frac{W}{g} = \frac{1}{32.2} = 0.031 \text{ lb} \cdot \text{s}^2/\text{ft} = 0.031 \text{ slug}$$

Applying the equation of motion in the transverse direction, we obtain

$$\stackrel{+}{\nearrow}\Sigma F_\theta = ma_\theta = m(r\ddot{\theta} + 2\dot{r}\dot{\theta})$$
$$N - 1\cos 20° = 0.031[0 + 2(-1.25)(7)]$$

from which we find the force exerted by the disk on the ball to be

$$N = 0.397 \text{ lb } 70° \triangle \;\blacktriangleleft$$

EXAMPLE 2.8

Pin A of 0.8-kg mass slides along the fixed vertical guide as the arm OB rotates about O. If $\dot{\theta} = 1$ rad/s and $\ddot{\theta} = -0.5$ rad/s^2 when $\theta = 30°$, determine the forces exerted on the pin by the vertical guide and arm OB, at this instant. Friction is negligible.

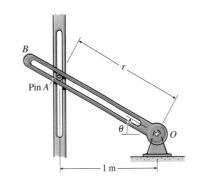

Solution   The free-body diagram of pin A is shown. The unknown forces F_1 and F_2 act in the directions perpendicular to the guide and to the arm, respectively, as shown.

The equations of motion in the radial and transverse directions can be written as

$(\nwarrow_+)\ \Sigma F_r = ma_r = m(\ddot{r} - r\dot{\theta}^2)$

$$F_1 \cos\theta - 7.85 \sin\theta = 0.8(\ddot{r} - r\dot{\theta}^2) \qquad \text{(a)}$$

$(\nearrow_+)\ \Sigma F_\theta = ma_\theta = m(r\ddot{\theta} + 2\dot{r}\dot{\theta})$

$$-F_1 \sin\theta + F_2 - 7.85 \cos\theta = 0.8(r\ddot{\theta} + 2\dot{r}\dot{\theta}) \qquad \text{(b)}$$

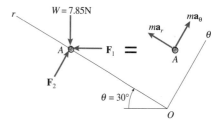

Relationship between r and θ coordinates.   The kinematic relationship between the coordinates r and θ can be expressed as

$$r \cos\theta = 1 \text{ m} \qquad r = \sec\theta$$

Differentiating successively with respect to time, we write

$$\dot{r} = \frac{dr}{d\theta}\dot{\theta} = (\tan\theta \sec\theta)\dot{\theta}$$

and

$$\ddot{r} = (\sec^3\theta + \tan^2\theta \sec\theta)\dot{\theta}^2 + (\tan\theta \sec\theta)\ddot{\theta}$$

Substituting the numerical values $\theta = 30°$, $\dot{\theta} = 1$ rad/s, and $\ddot{\theta} = -0.5$ rad/s^2 into the expressions for r, $\dot{r}$, and $\ddot{r}$, we obtain

$$r = 1.15 \text{ m} \qquad \dot{r} = 0.67 \text{ m/s} \qquad \ddot{r} = 1.59 \text{ m/s}^2$$

Forces.   Substituting the numerical values of θ, $\dot{\theta}$, $\ddot{\theta}$, r, $\dot{r}$, and $\ddot{r}$ into the equations of motion [Equations (a) and (b)], and solving for the unknown forces, we obtain

$$F_1 = 4.94 \text{ N} \ominus \ \blacktriangleleft$$
$$F_2 = 9.88 \text{ N} \ \triangle\ 60° \ \blacktriangleleft$$

EXAMPLE   2.9

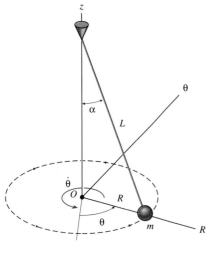

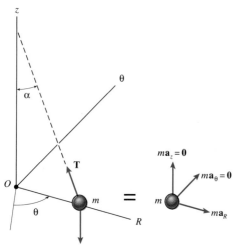

The conical pendulum of mass m rotates at a constant angular rate $\dot{\theta}$ in a horizontal circle about the vertical z axis as shown. Derive the expressions, in terms of $\dot{\theta}$, for (a) the tension in the cord, and (b) the angle α that the cord makes with the vertical.

Solution The free-body diagram of mass m shows two forces: the weight mg and the cord tension T acting on the particle. As the particle is moving at a constant angular rate $\dot{\theta}$ on a circular path, the transverse component of acceleration a_θ is zero. In addition, as the motion takes place at a constant elevation, the vertical component of acceleration a_z is also zero.

Applying the equations of motion in the radial direction, we obtain

$$\overset{\curvearrowright}{+}\;\Sigma F_R = ma_R = m(\ddot{R} - R\dot{\theta}^2)$$

$$-T \sin \alpha = m(0 - R\dot{\theta}^2)$$

Substituting $R = L \sin \alpha$ into the above equation, we obtain the expression for the tension in the cord:

$$T = mL\dot{\theta}^2 \;\blacktriangleleft$$

Next, we write the equation of equilibrium in the vertical direction as

$$\overset{\uparrow}{+}\;\Sigma F_z = 0 \qquad T \cos \alpha - mg = 0$$

Substituting the expression for T derived above, we obtain the expression for the angle α as

$$mL\dot{\theta}^2 \cos \alpha - mg = 0 \qquad \cos \alpha = \frac{g}{L\dot{\theta}^2} \;\blacktriangleleft$$

2.7 SUMMARY

In this chapter, we have covered the following:

1. Newton's second law of motion can be mathematically expressed as

$$\Sigma \mathbf{F} = m\mathbf{a} \tag{2.4}$$

in which $\Sigma\mathbf{F}$ is the sum of all the forces acting on a particle of mass m and $\mathbf{a}$ is the acceleration of the particle measured in an inertial reference frame. Equation (2.4) is called the equation of motion.

2. In applying Equation (2.4), it is essential that consistent kinetic units be used. The consistent units of force, mass, and acceleration, respectively, are lb, slug, and ft/s^2 in the U.S. Customary System; and N, kg, and m/s^2 in the SI units.

3. The equations of motion in scalar form are:
   a. *Rectangular coordinates*

$$\Sigma F_x = ma_x = m\ddot{x}$$
$$\Sigma F_y = ma_y = m\ddot{y}$$

   (2.5)

   b. *Tangential and normal coordinates*

$$\Sigma F_t = ma_t = m\dot{v} = m\ddot{s}$$
$$\Sigma F_n = ma_n = m\frac{v^2}{\rho} = m\frac{\dot{s}^2}{\rho}$$

   (2.7)

   c. *Polar coordinates*

$$\Sigma F_r = ma_r = m(\ddot{r} - r\dot{\theta}^2)$$
$$\Sigma F_\theta = ma_\theta = m(r\ddot{\theta} + 2\dot{r}\dot{\theta})$$

   (2.8)

4. Equations of motion in the scalar form are solved to determine the unknown force and/or acceleration components. If the velocity and the position of the particle are also desired, they are obtained by integrating the acceleration in accordance with the kinematic relationships of Chapter 1.

KEY TERMS

absolute motion *71*

centripetal force *80*

d'Alembert's principle *73*

dynamic equilibrium *73*

equation of motion *73*

inertia *71*

mass *71*

Newton's second law of motion *70*

Newtonian or inertial frames of reference *71*

PROBLEMS

SECTION 2.2

2.1 If an object weighs 25 lb on the earth, determine its weight on the planet Mars, where the acceleration due to gravity is 12.2 ft/s^2.

2.2 An astronaut weighs 580 N on the earth. Determine her weight on the planet Jupiter where the acceleration due to gravity is 25.5 m/s^2.

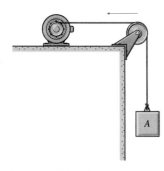

Figure P2.3 and P2.5

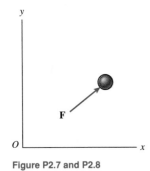

Figure P2.7 and P2.8

SECTION 2.4

2.3 An electric hoist is being used to raise crate A as shown. The crate weighs 2000 lb and is moving upward with a constant velocity of 5 ft/s. Determine the tension in the hoisting cable. Neglect the masses of the pulley and the cable, and assume that the pulley is frictionless.

2.4 Solve Problem 2.3 if the crate is moving upward with an acceleration of 12 ft/s².

2.5 The tension in the hoisting cable being used to lift a 300-kg crate is constant at 4500 N. If the crate was initially at rest, determine its velocity after it has moved through 3 m.

2.6 Solve Problem 2.5, if the tension in the cable is expressed by the equation $T = 6000t$ N, where t is in s.

2.7 A 15-lb particle initially at rest at position (0,0) is subjected to a force $\mathbf{F} = 10t\mathbf{i} + 20\mathbf{j}$ (lb), where t is in s. Determine the velocity and the position of the particle when $t = 5$ s.

2.8 A 4-kg particle is subjected to a force $\mathbf{F} = -30\mathbf{i} + 45\mathbf{j}$ (N). The initial position and the initial velocity of the particle are $\mathbf{r}_0 = 5\mathbf{i} - 7\mathbf{j}$ (m) and $\mathbf{v}_0 = 10\mathbf{i} + 15\mathbf{j}$ (m/s), respectively, when $t = 0$. Determine the position of the particle when its speed is 180 m/s.

2.9 A 7-kg particle initially at rest at position (0,0,0) is subjected to a force $\mathbf{F} = -20t\mathbf{i} + 90\mathbf{j} + 50t\mathbf{k}$ (N), where t is in s. Determine the velocity and the position of the particle when $t = 3$ s.

2.10 A 9-lb particle is subjected to a force $\mathbf{F} = 4\mathbf{i} + 12\mathbf{j} - 5\mathbf{k}$ (lb). The initial position and the initial velocity of the particle are $\mathbf{r}_0 = -1\mathbf{i} + 2\mathbf{j} + 1\mathbf{k}$ (ft) and $\mathbf{v}_0 = -3\mathbf{i} - 2\mathbf{j} + 2\mathbf{k}$ (ft/s), respectively, when $t = 0$. Determine the position of the particle when its speed is 45 ft/s.

2.11 A block given an initial velocity v_0 to the right on a horizontal surface stops after traveling 5 ft. If the coefficient of kinetic friction between the block and the surface is 0.2, determine the initial velocity v_0.

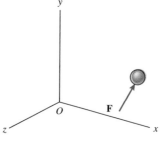

Figure P2.9 and P2.10

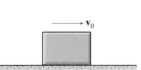

Figure P2.11

2.12 A truck weighing 5 kip is traveling with a constant velocity of 55 mph when brakes are applied causing a braking force of 2 kip to be exerted on the truck. If $\alpha = 0°$, determine the distance traveled by the truck before it stops.

2.13 Solve Problem 2.12 if $\alpha = 10°$.

2.14 A block is released from rest on an incline as shown in the figure. If the coefficient of kinetic friction between the block and the inclined surface is 0.25, determine the velocity of the block when $t = 4$ s, and the distance traveled during that interval.

2.15 A truck is traveling with a constant velocity of 85 km/h when brakes are applied, locking its wheels. If the truck stops after skidding 50 m, determine (a) the coefficient of kinetic friction between the wheels and the road surface, and (b) the time it takes for the truck to come to a stop. Use $\alpha = 0°$.

2.16 Solve Problem 2.15 if $\alpha = 10°$.

2.17 A block is given an initial velocity of 20 ft/s up an inclined surface. If the coefficient of kinetic friction between the block and the inclined surface is 0.3, determine (a) the time it takes for the block to stop, and (b) the distance traveled during that interval. Use $\alpha = 30°$.

2.18 Trailer B is being towed up a 10° incline by truck A with a constant velocity of 65 km/h, when the towing cable suddenly breaks. Determine the velocity of the trailer after 5 s. Neglect friction.

2.19 Block A weighing 700 lb is subjected to a constant towing force $F = 600$ lb as shown. The coefficient of kinetic friction between the block and the surface is 0.3. If the initial velocity v_0 of the block is 4 ft/s when $t = 0$, determine the distance traveled in 3 seconds, and the velocity at the end of that interval. Use $\alpha = 30°$ and $\beta = 0°$.

2.20 Solve Problem 2.19 if $\alpha = 15°$ and $\beta = 20°$.

2.21 Block A of 500-kg mass is subjected to a towing force $F = 3000t + 2000t^2$ N, where t is in s. If the initial velocity v_0 of the block is 6 m/s when $t = 0$, determine the distance traveled in 4 seconds and the velocity at the end of that interval. Use $\alpha = 45°$ and $\beta = 0°$. The coefficient of kinetic friction between the block and the surface is 0.2.

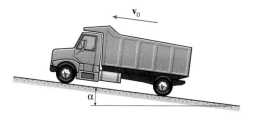

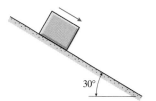

Figure P2.12 and P2.15

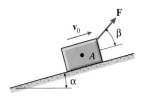

Figure P2.14

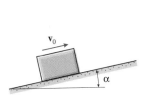

Figure P2.17

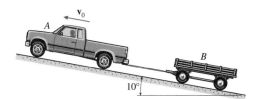

Figure P2.18

Figure P2.19 and P2.21

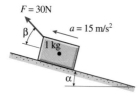

Figure P2.23

2.22 Solve Problem 2.21 if $\alpha = 20°$ and $\beta = 10°$.

2.23 A 1-kg block is subjected to a constant force of 30 N as shown. The coefficient of kinetic friction between the block and the surface is 0.2. Determine the values of the angle β for which the acceleration of the block will be 15 m/s^2 in the direction shown. Use $\alpha = 0°$.

2.24 Solve Problem 2.23 if $\alpha = 30°$.

2.25 A motorcycle weighing 1200 lb is coasting along a straight highway with a velocity of 25 mph. If the force due to aerodynamic drag resisting the motion can be approximated as $F = 0.1v$, where v is the velocity in ft/s, determine how far the motorcycle will travel before its velocity is reduced to 15 mph. Neglect friction between the motorcycle and the pavement.

2.26 For the motorcycle in Problem 2.25, determine the time required for the motorcycle to reduce its velocity to 20 mph, and the distance traveled during that interval.

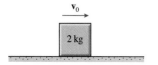

Figure P2.27

2.27 A 2-kg block is given an initial velocity v_0 of 15 m/s on a horizontal surface that is lubricated with oil. If the viscous friction force resisting the motion can be approximated as $F = 0.4v$, where v is the velocity in m/s, determine how far the block will travel before its velocity is reduced to 10 m/s.

2.28 For the block in Problem 2.27, determine the distance traveled by the block in 4 s, and its velocity at the end of that interval.

2.29 through 2.35 The system of blocks shown in the figure is released from rest. Determine (a) the acceleration of each block; (b) the tension in the cable(s); (c) the distance traveled by block B in 3 s; and (d) the velocity of block B at the end of that interval ($t = 3$ s). Neglect the masses of the pulleys and the cables, and assume that the pulleys are frictionless.

Figure P2.29

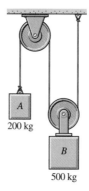

Figure P2.30

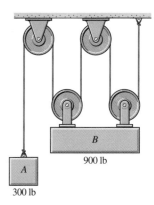

Figure P2.31

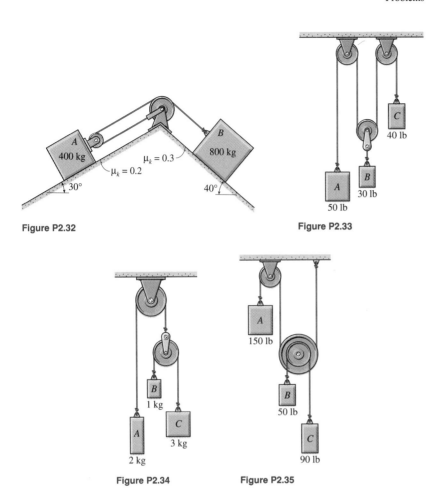

Figure P2.32

Figure P2.33

Figure P2.34

Figure P2.35

2.36 A three-cart trolley, initially at rest, starts moving down a 10° incline as shown. Neglecting friction between the wheels of the carts and the surface, determine (*a*) the acceleration of the carts, and (*b*) the tensions in the couplings connecting the carts.

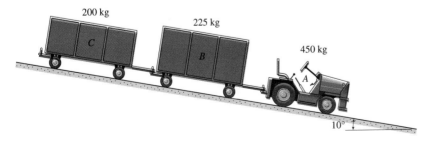

Figure P2.36

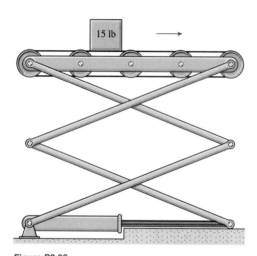

Figure P2.38

2.37 Solve Problem 2.36 if the friction forces resisting the motion of carts A, B, and C, respectively, are equal to 0.05, 0.1, and 0.2 times the normal force exerted on that cart by the ground.

2.38 The coefficient of static friction between the conveyor belt and the 15-lb box is 0.7. Determine the maximum acceleration in the horizontal direction with which the belt can be started from rest so that the box will not slip.

2.39 Solve Problem 2.38 if the conveyor belt is being raised upward with an acceleration of 2 ft/s² as it begins to accelerate horizontally.

2.40 A 6-kg block B rests on top of a 9-kg block A, which is subjected to a constant force of 80 N as shown in the figure. If the coefficient of kinetic friction at all surfaces of contact is 0.25, determine the accelerations of both blocks.

2.41 A system of two blocks A and B weighing 40 lbs and 20 lbs, respectively, is released from rest on a smooth incline as shown. Determine the smallest value of the coefficient of static friction for which block B will not slip relative to block A. The angle of inclination α is 25°.

2.42 A system of two blocks A and B is released from rest on an incline as shown. If the coefficient of kinetic friction at all surfaces of contact is 0.2, determine the accelerations of both blocks. The angle of inclination α is 35°.

2.43 A 20-kg block B is released from rest on a 60-kg block A, which rests on a horizontal surface as shown. If the coefficient of kinetic friction at all surfaces of contact is 0.1, determine the accelerations of both blocks. Use α = 35°.

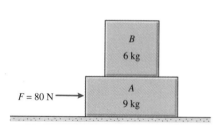

Figure P2.40

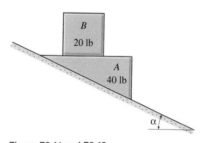

Figure P2.41 and P2.42

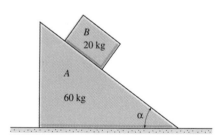

Figure P2.43

SECTION 2.5

2.44 A truck is traveling along a horizontal curve of 150-m radius with a constant speed of 80 km/h. Determine the smallest value of the coefficient of static friction, between the tires and the concrete pavement, necessary to prevent the truck from sliding.

2.45 A race car weighing 2700 lb is moving at a constant speed of 50 mph on an S-shaped horizontal track, composed of two semicircles of 800 ft and 600 ft radii, as shown in the figure. Determine the total horizontal force exerted on the car by the road at positions B, C, and D.

2.46 The car in Problem 2.45 starts from rest at A with a constant tangential acceleration of 2 ft/s². Determine the total horizontal force exerted on the car by the road at positions B, C, and D.

2.47 A 68-kg motorcyclist is driving on hilly terrain with a constant speed of 50 km/h. Determine the force exerted by his seat on the motorcycle at the top A and the bottom B of the hill shown in the figure.

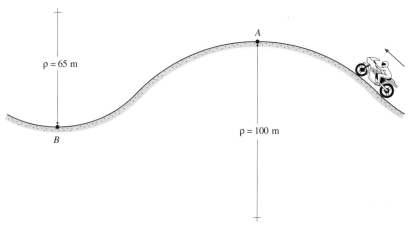

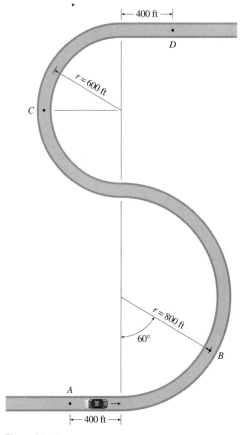

Figure P2.47

2.48 Determine the maximum constant speed at which the motorcycle in Problem 2.47 can travel over hill A without leaving the road.

2.49 Determine the force exerted on the motorcyclist in Problem 2.47 at position B if the motorcycle has a speed of 45 km/h increasing at a rate of 3 m/s².

2.50 A child of 18 kg mass is swinging on a swing. At the position shown, the tension in each of the two supporting cables is 100 N. Determine the velocity and the acceleration of the child at this instant.

Figure P2.45

2.51 The velocity of the 15-lb bob of a pendulum is 20 ft/s at the position shown in the figure. Determine the acceleration of the bob and the tension in the supporting cable at this instant.

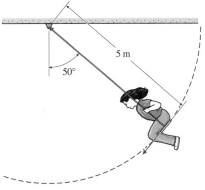

Figure P2.50

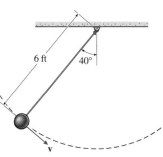

Figure P2.51

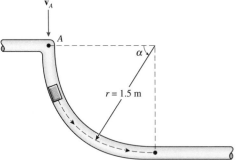

Figure P2.52

2.52 A 2-kg block is released from rest at point A and slides down a smooth circular chute of 1.5-m radius as shown in the figure. Determine the normal force exerted on the block by the chute when (*a*) $\alpha = 60°$ and (*b*) $\alpha = 90°$.

2.53 Solve Problem 2.52 if the block is given an initial downward velocity $v_A = 1$ m/s.

2.54 A block of mass m is released from rest at the top of a smooth semicircular cylinder of radius r as shown. Determine the velocity of the block when $\alpha = 30°$. Use $r = 2$ ft.

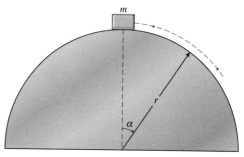

Figure P2.54

2.55 For Problem 2.54, determine the angle α at which the block loses contact with the circular path and becomes a freely falling projectile.

2.56 A skier passes the top, point A, of a smooth circular slope of 75-ft radius with an initial velocity $v_A = 25$ mph. Determine the velocity and the acceleration of the skier when $\alpha = 15°$.

2.57 For Problem 2.56, determine the angle α at which the skier leaves the circular path and becomes a freely falling projectile.

2.58 Derive the expression for the angle α at which the skier in Problem 2.56 loses contact with the surface, in terms of the initial velocity v_A and radius r of the circular path.

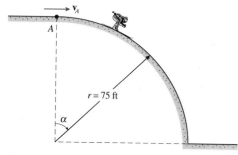

Figure P2.56

2.59 A 45-kg person is skating on a smooth curvilinear surface, the profile of which can be represented by the equation $y = x^2/12$. At the position $x = 0$, the speed of the skater is 8 m/s. Determine the force exerted by the surface on the skateboard at this instant.

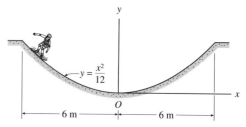

Figure P2.59

2.60 When the skater in Problem 2.59 is at position $x = -4$ m, his speed is 6 m/s. Determine (a) the acceleration of the skater at this instant, and (b) the force exerted by the surface on the skateboard at this instant.

2.61 On a highway curve of 800-ft radius, banked at an angle $\alpha = 10°$, determine the maximum safe speed at which a vehicle can travel so that there is no tendency to slide sideways.

2.62 Determine the banking angle α on a highway curve of 180-m radius, so that a vehicle traveling at a constant speed of 100 km/h will not tend to slide sideways.

2.63 Determine the maximum safe speed at which a vehicle can travel without sliding sideways on a highway curve of 600-ft radius, banked at an angle $\alpha = 10°$, if the coefficient of static friction between the tires and concrete pavement is 0.6.

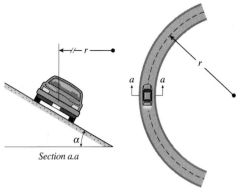

Section a.a

Figure P2.61, P2.62, and P2.63

SECTION 2.6

2.64 The position of a 3-kg particle in motion is described by the equations $r = -3t^3$ m, and $\theta = t^2 - 2t$ rad, where t is in s. Determine the radial and transverse components of the force exerted on the particle when $t = 1$ s.

2.65 The position of a 10-lb particle in motion is described by the equations $R = -2t + t^2$ in., $\theta = t^3/4$ rad, and $z = 2t^3 + 3t$ in., where t is in s. Determine the cylindrical components of the force exerted on the particle when $t = 3$ s.

2.66 The position of a 1-kg collar, which slides along a smooth rod, is given by the equation $r = 5 - 5t + 2t^3$ mm. If the rotation of the rod about a vertical axis passing through point O is described by the equation $\theta = 0.2t + 0.01t^2$, determine the radial and transverse components of the force acting on the collar when $t = 2$ s. In the given equations, t is in seconds.

2.67 The rod OA is rotating in the horizontal plane with a constant angular velocity $\dot{\theta} = 5$ rad/s, while the 2-lb collar C is moving along the rod at a constant rate $\dot{r} = 10$ in./s. If at this instant $r = 4$ in., determine the magnitude of the horizontal force exerted by the rod on the collar.

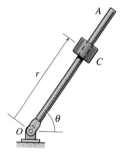

Figure P2.66, P2.67, and P2.68

2.68 The rod OA is rotating about a vertical axis through point O with a constant angular velocity $\dot{\theta} = 10$ rad/s, when the 2-kg collar C is released at $r_0 = 6$ mm with zero velocity relative to the rod. Determine the magnitude of the horizontal force exerted by the rod on the collar when $r = 12$ mm.

2.69 Pin A weighing 1 lb slides along the fixed horizontal guide as the arm OB rotates about O. If $\dot{\theta} = -2$ rad/s and $\ddot{\theta} = 0.3$ rad/s^2 when $\theta = 40°$, determine the forces exerted on the pin by the horizontal guide and arm OB at this instant. Neglect friction.

2.70 If the pin A in Problem 2.69 is moving to the left with a constant velocity of 0.5 ft/s, determine the forces exerted on the pin by the horizontal guide and arm OB when $\theta = 30°$.

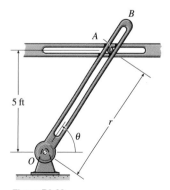

Figure P2.69

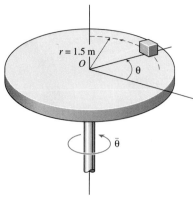

$r = 1.5$ m

O

θ

$\ddot{\theta}$

Figure P2.71

2.71 A 3-kg block is placed on a horizontal disk that is initially at rest. The disk is rotated about the vertical axis with a constant angular acceleration of $\ddot{\theta} = 1.2$ rad/s². If the coefficient of static friction between the block and the disk is 0.3, determine the time it takes for the block to start sliding on the disk.

2.72 Determine the maximum value of the constant angular acceleration $\ddot{\theta}$ with which the disk in Problem 2.71 can be rotated so that the block can attain a velocity of 1 m/s without sliding.

2.73 On an amusement park ride, determine the minimum constant angular velocity $\dot{\theta}$ with which the cylinder of 15-ft radius can be rotated so that a person does not slide down the vertical wall when the floor is lowered. The coefficient of static friction between the person and the metal wall is 0.25.

2.74 A 2-kg collar A moves along a circular guide of 1-m radius as the arm OB rotates about O. If $\dot{\theta} = 2$ rad/s and $\ddot{\theta} = -1$ rad/s² when $\theta = 10°$, determine the force exerted on the collar by the arm OB. Neglect friction.

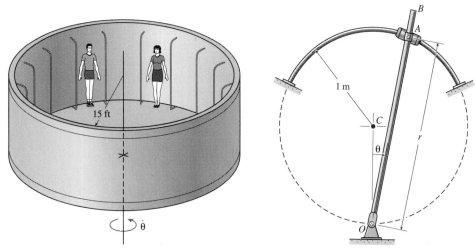

15 ft

$\dot{\theta}$

Figure P2.73

B

A

1 m

C

r

θ

O

Figure P2.74

2.75 During a ride at an amusement park, the motion of a 180-kg car A is described by the equations $z = 7 + 3 \sin(\pi t/15)$ m and $\theta = \pi t/60$ rad. Determine the cylindrical components of the force exerted by the track on the car when $\theta = 1.2$ rad.

2.76 The arm AC of a crankshaft mechanism rotates at a constant angular velocity $\dot{\alpha}$. Derive the expression for the horizontal force exerted on the cylinder B. Neglect friction.

2.77 Determine the horizontal force exerted on the 10-lb cylinder B of the crankshaft mechanism shown if arm AC is rotating at a constant angular velocity of 350 revolutions per minute. Let $L_1 = 1$ ft, $L_2 = 3$ ft, and $\alpha = 45°$. Neglect friction.

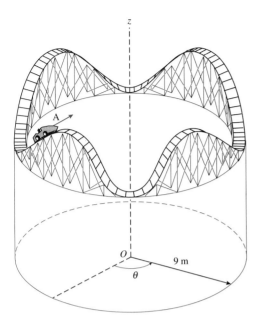

Figure P2.75

Figure P2.76, P2.77, and P2.78

2.78 Solve Problem 2.77 if $\alpha = 110°$.

2.79 Determine the minimum constant angular velocity $\dot{\theta}$ with which the cone shown in the figure can be rotated so that block A does not slide down the side. The coefficient of static friction between the block and the wall is μ_s.

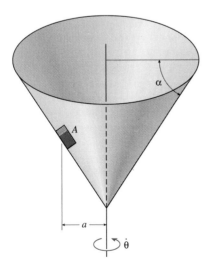

Figure P2.79

3

KINETICS OF PARTICLES: WORK AND ENERGY

3.1 INTRODUCTION

In Chapter 2, we analyzed the motion of a particle by using the fundamental equation of motion—Newton's second law—relating the external forces acting upon the particle to its mass and acceleration. To obtain the kinematic parameters of velocity and position of the particle at any given time, it was necessary to solve first for the acceleration and then apply established kinematic relationships between the acceleration, the velocity, and the position vectors. Since these relationships are differential in nature, the determination of the velocity and position of the particle requires the integration of the acceleration-velocity-displacement relationships.

However, when the primary focus of our attention is not the acceleration vector, it is possible to eliminate the need to solve a differential equation each time. Instead, we can integrate the equation of motion after replacing the acceleration vector by the appropriate kinematic expression given in terms of space or time derivatives. When the forces acting on the system can be expressed as functions of space coordinates, the equation of motion is integrated with respect to the displacement of the particle. The resulting equation represents the *principle of work and energy*. We will develop and study this principle in the present chapter. When the forces acting on the system are expressed as functions of time, the equation of motion is integrated with respect to time and yields the *impulse-momentum equation*, which will be the subject of Chapter 4.

3.2 WORK

The **work** done by a force on a body is simply defined as the force times the displacement of the body in the direction of the force. Consider a particle P moving along the path AB (Figure 3.1). At a given instant the particle occupies a position defined by the position vector $\mathbf{r}$, and is acted upon by a force $\mathbf{F}$. The expression for the infinitesimal work dU done by the force $\mathbf{F}$ on the particle P during its infinitesimal displacement was first introduced in the study of virtual work (see Chapter 10 of *Engineering Mechanics: Statics*). It is defined by the dot product

$$dU = \mathbf{F} \cdot d\mathbf{r}$$

where $d\mathbf{r}$ is the differential displacement vector.

The total work $\Sigma U_{A\to B}$ done by the force $\mathbf{F}$ on the particle P, as it moves between points A and B along the particle path AB, is defined by the line integral

$$U_{A\to B} = \int_{AB} dU = \int_{A}^{B} \mathbf{F} \cdot d\mathbf{r} \tag{3.1}$$

Recall that the dot product of two vectors is the product of their magnitudes multiplied by the cosine of the angle between them. The dot product can also be viewed as the component of one of the vectors in the direction of the other

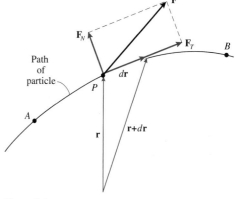

Figure 3.1

vector multiplied by the magnitude of the second vector. Therefore, the scalar quantity being integrated in Equation (3.1) can be considered as the component of the force in the direction of the displacement vector, $F \cos \theta$, multiplied by the length dr of the displacement vector. Or one can consider it to be the component of the displacement vector in the direction of the force, $dr \cos \theta$, multiplied by the magnitude F of the force vector.

$$U_{A \to B} = \int_A^B F \cos \theta \, dr$$

From this definition of work it follows that a force only produces work when it has a component in the direction of the displacement vector. In Figure 3.1 the incremental work done by $\mathbf{F}$, as the particle moves along the arbitrary path from position $\mathbf{r}$ to $\mathbf{r} + d\mathbf{r}$, is equal to the tangential component of the force multiplied by the incremental distance along the path covered by the particle. Note that the component of the force perpendicular to the path does not contribute to the work done. Furthermore, positive work is done when the angle between the force and displacement vectors is acute, and negative work is done when it is obtuse. The work is zero when the force is perpendicular to the displacement.

Work has units of force times distance. In the SI units, the unit of work is the *newton-meter* (N · m), also called a *joule* (J). In the U.S. Customary System of units, work is given in foot-pound (ft · lb).

Work Done by a Constant Force

The constant force $\mathbf{F}$ shown in Figure 3.2 acts on a particle P moving along an arbitrary path from point A to point B. Since the force has a constant magnitude and direction, we can remove it from inside the integral expression for work; thus, only the incremental displacement vector $d\mathbf{r}$ remains to be integrated. The integral of $d\mathbf{r}$ is the position vector at point B minus the position vector at point A, which we can see from Figure 3.2 to be the vector $\mathbf{AB}$. This can be written as

$$U_{A \to B} = \mathbf{F} \cdot \int_A^B d\mathbf{r} = \mathbf{F} \cdot (\mathbf{r}_B - \mathbf{r}_A) \tag{3.2}$$

where $\mathbf{F} = F_x \mathbf{i} + F_y \mathbf{j} + F_z \mathbf{k}$
        $\mathbf{r} = r_x \mathbf{i} + r_y \mathbf{j} + r_z \mathbf{k}$

From the definition of the dot product it follows that the work done by the constant force $\mathbf{F}$ can also be expressed as

$$U_{A \to B} = F_x(r_{x_B} - r_{x_A}) + F_y(r_{y_B} - r_{y_A}) + F_z(r_{z_B} - r_{z_A})$$

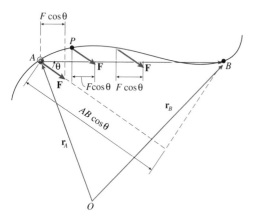

Figure 3.2

Note that any path between the two points would yield the same result or that the work done depends only on the initial and final positions.

Work Done by a Weight

When the force under consideration is the weight of a particle, we are dealing with a constant force (gravitational force) directed toward the center of the earth or in a "downward" direction. This force vector $\mathbf{F}$ can be represented by writing

$$\mathbf{F} = -W\mathbf{k}$$

where W is the weight of the particle and $\mathbf{k}$ the unit vector in the upward positive direction as indicated in Figure 3.3. After expressing the displacement vector $d\mathbf{r}$ in terms of its three Cartesian components as $(dx\mathbf{i} + dy\mathbf{j} + dz\mathbf{k})$, the work done during the motion of the particle from point A to point B along an arbitrary path becomes, in accordance with Equation (3.1),

$$U_{A \rightarrow B} = \int_A^B \mathbf{F} \cdot d\mathbf{r} = \int_A^B (-W\mathbf{k}) \cdot (dx\mathbf{i} + dy\mathbf{j} + dz\mathbf{k}) \qquad (3.3)$$

The only dot product that is nonzero in the equation above is the term $\mathbf{k} \cdot \mathbf{k}$. Therefore, the work done by a weight W can be expressed in the form

$$U_{A \rightarrow B} = \int_{z_A}^{z_B} -W \, dz = -W(z_B - z_A) = W(z_A - z_B) \qquad (3.4)$$

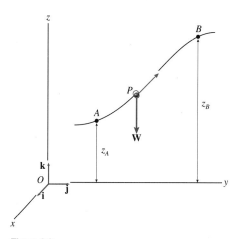

Figure 3.3

The work done by the weight of the particle is, thus, simply the weight times the negative change in elevation. When the initial elevation z_A is greater than the final elevation z_B—that is, when the particle moves down—the work is positive.

Work Done by a Spring

A spring is a device designed to provide a given deflection when subjected to a given load. The force required to stretch or compress it is dependent upon the spring material as well as on the details of its construction. The construction details for a coiled spring would include the diameter of the spring material, the diameter of the coil, and the length of the coil. To establish the relationship between the deflection of a spring and the magnitude of the applied load, the spring is subjected to a series of loads and the deflection is measured for each. The load is plotted versus the deflection; the resulting curve, similar to the one shown in Figure 3.4, is used to describe the action of the spring for any loading condition. For an elastic linear spring, the slope of the load-deflection curve is constant and is called the spring constant (or modulus) k. The spring constant

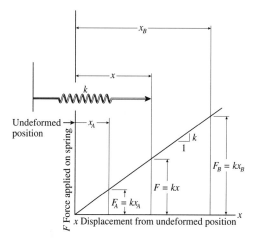

Figure 3.4

and the deflection x can be used to calculate the force F to which the spring is subjected. Alternately, the spring constant k and the force F can be used to determine the deflection x of the spring from its undeformed position. Elastic springs return to their original position when the force acting on them is removed. The applicable units for k are N/m (SI) and lb/ft (U.S.).

In this section, we will consider only elastic springs that have a linear relationship between the force in the spring and the deformation of the spring from its undeformed position. Furthermore, we will assume that the inertia (the mass) of the spring is negligible. In Figure 3.4 we consider the case in which the forces applied to the ends of the elastic spring are collinear and act along the axis of the spring. When the displacement of the end of the spring is entirely in the direction of the alignment of the spring, the dot product $\mathbf{F} \cdot d\mathbf{r}$ will be the scalar quantity $F\,dx$, since the cosine of the zero angle between the force and the displacement is one. The work required to stretch the spring and move its end point from a position defined by x_A to a position defined by x_B is given by

$$U_{A \to B} = \int_A^B \mathbf{F} \cdot d\mathbf{r} = \int_{x_A}^{x_B} F\,dx \tag{3.5}$$

After substituting for the magnitude of the force $\mathbf{F}$ the expression kx, the work done by the spring can be written as the opposite sign of the work done to deform it:

$$U_{A \to B(\text{spring})} = -\int_{x_A}^{x_B} F\,dx = -\int_{x_A}^{x_B} kx\,dx = -\frac{1}{2}k(x_B^2 - x_A^2) \tag{3.6}$$

Note that the expression for the work given above also represents the area under the force-deflection diagram of Figure 3.4.

Next, consider the case when the end of the spring moves in a more complicated pattern. We will show that the work required to stretch or compress the spring is the same expression developed above. The spring shown in Figure 3.5 stretches and also rotates about one of its end points. The displacement of the end of the spring from point A to point B can be accomplished by first stretching the spring—moving point A to point C—and then by rotating the spring about its end (point O) and thus bringing point C to point B. Stretching the spring from A to C accounts for the total work required for moving point A to point B. This is true because no work is done when the spring rotates without a change in length. We could also rotate the spring from point A to point D without any expenditure of work, and then stretch the spring along its axis from D to B by doing work in an amount equal to that given by Equation (3.6).

The spring could also be moved in a manner that would approximate the direct path from A to B by stretching the spring an incremental amount from point A to point E and then rotating the spring back to the path between A and

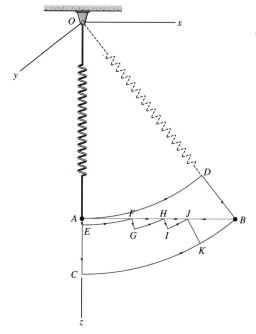

Figure 3.5

B along the arc from E to F. It is clear that all of the extensions of the spring along paths AE, FG, and HI would require work and all of the rotations along paths EF, GH, and IJ would require no work. Thus, the total work required to accomplish all of the extensions would be the same as the work required to make one large extension and one large rotation. Therefore, the work required to move the spring along the path from A to B is the same as that calculated from Equation (3.6), where x_A and x_B would represent the initial and final deflections of the spring, respectively. In short, the work done on or by the spring depends only on the initial and final deflected lengths of the spring.

When an undeformed and relaxed spring is compressed or stretched, the force exerted by the *spring* will always be in the direction opposite to the displacement, as the spring attempts to return to its undeformed position. Thus, the work done would be negative. However, if a spring that is deformed (compressed or stretched) is now being relaxed, the displacement and the force exerted by the spring will both be in the same direction (i.e., towards the undeformed position) and the work done by the spring will be positive. Note that the algebraic sign of the deflection has no effect on the work done by a spring.

The following examples will illustrate the methods of determining the work done by various force systems acting on a particle.

EXAMPLE   3.1

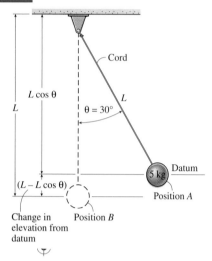

Cord

$L \cos \theta$

L

$\theta = 30°$

L

Datum

5 kg

Position A

$(L - L \cos \theta)$

Change in   Position B
elevation from
datum

T

θ

$W = mg$

A 5-kg particle connected to a 2-m cord is released from the position shown at A. Determine the work done by all of the forces acting on the particle as it moves from A to B.

Solution   The free-body diagram is shown. There are two forces acting on the particle as it moves from one position to another: its weight, and the tension in the cord. Consider the work of each of these forces separately.

Work done by the tension force.   The particle moves from point A to point B along an arc generated by the end point of the cord. The work done by the tension in the cord is given by

$$U_{A \to B(\text{tension})} = \int_A^B \mathbf{F} \cdot d\mathbf{r}$$

Since the tension in the cord is perpendicular to the direction of the motion of the particle, the dot product of the force and displacement vectors is zero. Another way of arriving at the same conclusion would be to consider a free-body diagram that was produced by cutting the cord right at the point of support. The tensile force in the cord does no work since the particle experiences no displacement along the cord.

Work done by the weight.   The work of the force due to the weight of the particle is equal to the product of the weight of the particle and the vertical distance it covers. We write this as

$$U_{A \to B(\text{weight})} = W(z_A - z_B) = W(L - L \cos \theta)$$
$$= mgL(1 - \cos \theta) = (5 \text{ kg})(9.81 \text{ m/s}^2)$$
$$\times (2 \text{ m})(1 - \cos 30°)$$
$$= 13.143 \ (\text{kg m/s}^2)(\text{m})$$

The total work done on the particle as it moves from A to B is the work done by the weight, or 13.1 N · m.

$$U_{A \to B(\text{weight})} = 13.1 \text{ N} \cdot \text{m} \ \blacktriangleleft$$

EXAMPLE 3.2

A 6-kg block moves in a smooth vertical slot as shown. A spring having an undeformed length of 0.5 m and a spring constant of 20 N/m is attached to the block. The block moves downward in the slot a distance of 0.75 m. Determine the work done by each and then all of the forces acting on the block as it moves from point A to point B.

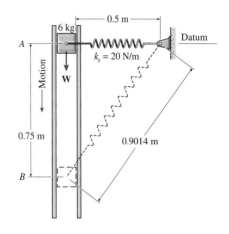

Solution A free-body diagram of the block shows the three forces that are acting on the block.

Work done by the normal force. The problem states that the slot is smooth. Therefore, frictional forces are absent and the only force present at the interface of the block and the slot is perpendicular to the surface. Since the motion of the block is vertical and thus perpendicular to the normal force, the work done by the normal force is zero.

$$U_{A \to B(\text{normal force})} = 0 \blacktriangleleft$$

Work done by the weight. The block moves downward a distance of 0.75 m. The work done by the weight of the particle is equal to its weight times the vertical distance that it moves. The work of the weight, then, is

$$U_{A \to B(\text{weight})} = Wz = mgz = (6 \text{ kg})(9.81 \text{ m/s}^2)(0.75 \text{ m})$$
$$U_{A \to B(\text{weight})} = 44.15 \text{ N} \cdot \text{m} \blacktriangleleft$$

Work done by the spring force. The work done by the spring is given by Equation (3.6). Since the spring described in this problem is initially at its undeformed position, the value of the initial displacement of the spring from this position (x_A) is zero. As the final length of the spring is $[(0.5)^2 + (0.75)^2]^{1/2} = 0.9014$ m, it has been stretched by 0.4014 m, which is the value for x_B. Therefore, the work done by the force of the spring is given by

$$U_{A \to B(\text{spring})} = -\frac{1}{2}k(x_B^2 - x_A^2)$$
$$= -\frac{1}{2}(20 \text{ N/m})[(0.4014)^2 - (0.0)^2]$$
$$U_{A \to B(\text{spring})} = -1.611 \text{ N} \cdot \text{m} \blacktriangleleft$$

The total work done by all of the forces acting on the block is

$$\Sigma U_{A \to B(\text{total})} = U_{A \to B(\text{weight})} + U_{A \to B(\text{spring})} + U_{A \to B(\text{normal force})}$$
$$\Sigma U_{A \to B(\text{total})} = 44.15 \text{ N} \cdot \text{m} - 1.611 \text{ N} \cdot \text{m} + 0.0 \text{ N} \cdot \text{m}$$
$$\Sigma U_{A \to B(\text{total})} = 42.5 \text{ N} \cdot \text{m} \blacktriangleleft$$

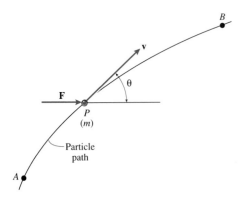

Figure 3.6

3.3 KINETIC ENERGY OF A PARTICLE

Consider a particle P of mass m moving at a given instant with the speed v along a curvilinear path AB as shown in Figure 3.6. The particle is acted upon by a force $\mathbf{F}$.

The **kinetic energy** of the particle is denoted by T and defined as

$$T = \frac{1}{2}m(\mathbf{v} \cdot \mathbf{v}) = \frac{1}{2}mv^2 \tag{3.7}$$

From this definition we note that kinetic energy is a scalar quantity that is always positive.

Kinetic energy has units of mass times the square of speed. In the SI system, the unit of kinetic energy is $\text{kg(m/s)}^2 = \text{joule (J)}$. And since, from Newton's equation of motion, we have $\text{kg(m/s}^2) = \text{N}$, the unit of kinetic energy is also expressed as

$$\text{joule} = \text{kg(m/s}^2)\text{m} = \text{N} \cdot \text{m}$$

which is the same as the unit of work. In the U.S. Customary system, kinetic energy is expressed in units of $\text{slug(ft/s}^2) = \text{lb} \cdot \text{ft}$.

3.4 EQUATION OF WORK AND KINETIC ENERGY

The equation of work and kinetic energy will now be developed by considering Newton's second law of motion, which can be written as

$$\Sigma\mathbf{F} = m\mathbf{a} = m\left(\frac{d\mathbf{v}}{dt}\right) \tag{3.8}$$

where $\Sigma\mathbf{F}$ is the *vector sum of all of the forces* acting on the particle and $\mathbf{a}$ the acceleration vector of the particle. The acceleration has also been expressed as the time derivative of the velocity vector $\mathbf{v}$.

The total work $\Sigma U_{A \to B}$ done by the resultant force $\Sigma\mathbf{F}$ acting on a particle of mass m as it moves between points A and B was developed in Section 3.2 and given in Equation (3.1) as

$$\Sigma U_{A \to B} = \int_A^B \Sigma\mathbf{F} \cdot d\mathbf{r}$$

Substituting into the above equation the expression for $\Sigma\mathbf{F}$ given in Equation (3.8), and introducing $d\mathbf{r} = \mathbf{v}\,dt$, yields

$$\Sigma U_{A \to B} = \int_{t_A}^{t_B} m\left(\frac{d\mathbf{v}}{dt} \cdot \mathbf{v}\right)dt \tag{3.9}$$

where t_A and t_B are the instants when the particle occupies points A and B, respectively. The dot product $(d\mathbf{v}/dt) \cdot (\mathbf{v})$ can be written as

$$\frac{d\mathbf{v}}{dt} \cdot \mathbf{v} = \frac{1}{2}\frac{d(\mathbf{v} \cdot \mathbf{v})}{dt} = \frac{1}{2}\frac{d(v^2)}{dt} \qquad (3.10)$$

Introducing the constant-mass assumption, Equation (3.9) can now be expressed in the form

$$\Sigma U_{A\rightarrow B} = \int_{t_A}^{t_B} \frac{1}{2}m\frac{d(v^2)}{dt}\,dt = \frac{1}{2}m\int_{t_A}^{t_B}\frac{d(v^2)}{dt}\,dt \qquad (3.11)$$

or as

$$\Sigma U_{A\rightarrow B} = \frac{1}{2}mv_B^2 - \frac{1}{2}mv_A^2$$

where v_A and v_B are the speed of the particle at t_A and t_B, respectively. Recalling from Equation (3.7) that the expression $\frac{1}{2}mv^2$ represents the kinetic energy T of a particle of mass m moving at a speed v, one can write the above equation as

$$\Sigma U_{A\rightarrow B} = T_B - T_A \qquad (3.12)$$

where $T_A = \frac{1}{2}mv_A^2$ and $T_B = \frac{1}{2}mv_B^2$. Equation (3.12) can also be expressed in the form

$$T_A + \Sigma U_{A\rightarrow B} = T_B \qquad (3.13)$$

Equation (3.12) states mathematically that the work done by all of the forces acting on a particle is equal to the change in the kinetic energy of the particle. The relationship is a scalar one and, unlike the equation describing the motion of the particle, involves no vector quantities. The left-hand side of Equation (3.12) represents a scalar quantity that can be positive, negative, or zero. Although kinetic energy is always positive or zero, the right-hand side of the equation represents a difference in the kinetic energy of the particle as it moves from one point to another and therefore can also be positive, negative, or zero. Since the work–kinetic energy relationship is a scalar equation, it can be used to solve for the speed (a scalar) but not for the velocity (a vector).

3.5 APPLICATIONS OF THE WORK–KINETIC ENERGY RELATIONSHIP

The method of solving problems using the work–kinetic energy equation should follow the step-by-step procedure outlined below. Following the outline, we will look at some examples that illustrate the type of problems to be solved using this method.

1. Draw a free-body diagram of the particle indicating all the forces acting on the particle as it moves from its initial to its final position. The forces must be either constant or expressed in terms of position vectors or space coordinates. Forces that are functions of variables other than position (e.g., time) cannot be integrated through Equation (3.1).

2. Determine the work done by each force during the movement of the particle from its initial to its final position. It is possible that not all of the forces will contribute continuously to the work done on the particle. However, the final work—a scalar quantity—is cumulative, and the partial contributions of individual forces will simply be added to determine the final work on the particle.

3. Determine the particle's kinetic energy at the initial and final locations.

4. Equate the sum of the work done by all of the forces acting on the particle as it moves from the initial to the final position, to the change in kinetic energy between the same two points.

It should be noted that the work–kinetic energy relationship provides only one scalar equation and therefore can be used to solve for only one unknown. In many problems it is necessary to generate an additional relationship by applying Newton's second law in a direction other than that tangent to the path.

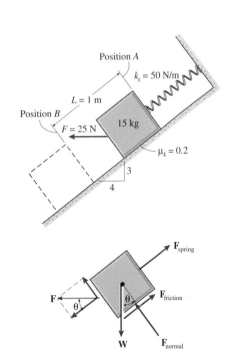

EXAMPLE 3.3

The 15-kg block moves on an inclined surface from the position shown to a position 1 m down the incline. The spring to which the block is attached is initially stretched by 0.25 m. The coefficient of kinetic friction between the block and the surface is 0.2. A constant horizontal force of 25 N is applied to the block as shown. If the block starts from rest at position A, determine the velocity of the block when it reaches position B, 1 m down the incline.

Solution   The free-body diagram shows that there are five forces that must be considered in the determination of the work: the spring force, the constant applied force of 25 N, the weight, the normal force between the block and the inclined surface, and the frictional force between the block and the inclined surface. From Equation (3.12) we write

$$\Sigma U_{A \rightarrow B(i)} = \frac{1}{2}m(v_B^2 - v_A^2)$$

where $i = 1, 2, 3, 4, 5$, each subscript corresponding to one of the five forces listed above. We will first determine the work of each force and obtain the total work by summing them

(*continued*)

EXAMPLE 3.3   (*concluded*)

up. Later we will equate the total work of all the forces to the change in the kinetic energy of the block.

Work done by the weight.   The work done by the weight is equal to the product of the weight and the vertical distance over which the block moves. Since the block moves down the incline a total of 1 m, its vertical motion is

$$L \sin \theta = L\left(\frac{3}{5}\right) = 0.600\,\text{m}$$

The work is positive since the force and the motion are in the same direction. For its value, now we can calculate $WL \sin \theta$:

$$U_{A \to B} = WL \sin \theta = mgL \sin \theta$$
$$= (15 \text{ kg})(9.81 \text{ m/s}^2)0.600 = 88.29 \text{ N} \cdot \text{m}$$

Work done by the normal force.   The normal force does no work since it is perpendicular to the motion of the block. However, we will need the magnitude of the normal force to determine the frictional force. We find the normal force by recognizing that there is no motion in the direction of the normal force and hence no acceleration; so the sum of the forces in the direction normal to the inclined surface is zero. Therefore, the normal force is equal to the component of the weight in the normal direction minus the component of the applied force in the same normal direction. Thus,

$$F_N = W \cos \theta - F \sin \theta = (mg)\cos \theta - F \sin \theta$$
$$= (15 \text{ kg})(9.81 \text{ m/s}^2)\left(\frac{4}{5}\right) - (25\text{N})\left(\frac{3}{5}\right) = 102.72 \text{ N}$$

Work done by the frictional force.   The frictional force is equal to the coefficient of kinetic friction times the normal force acting at the interface. Therefore, we can write

$$F_{Fr} = \mu(F_N) = (0.2)(102.72) = 20.54 \text{ N}$$

The work of the frictional force is equal to the force times the distance through which the block moves. The work will be negative since the frictional force always opposes the motion and thus is in the direction opposite to that of the motion.

$$U_{A \to B(\text{friction})} = -F_{Fr}L = -(20.54 \text{ N})(1 \text{ m}) = -20.54 \text{ N} \cdot \text{m}$$

Work done by the applied force.   The applied force has been broken into two components, one perpendicular to the inclined

surface ($F \sin \theta$), which does no work, and one parallel to the inclined surface ($F \cos \theta$), which does positive work given by ($F \cos \theta$)L. The total work done by the applied force, then, is

$$U_{A \to B(\text{applied force})} = (F \cos \theta)L = [(25 \text{ N})(0.8)(1 \text{ m})] = 20 \text{ N} \cdot \text{m}$$

Work done by the spring force.   The spring is initially stretched 0.25 m and its final stretch is 1.25 m. The work of the spring force is negative since it acts to resist the motion of the block. The work is given by

$$U_{A \to B(\text{spring})} = -\frac{1}{2}k(x_B^2 - x_A^2)$$

Substituting for k, x_A, and x_B the values of 50 N/m, 0.25 m, and 1.25 m respectively, we have

$$U_{A \to B(\text{spring})} = -\frac{1}{2}(50 \text{ N/m})[(1.25 \text{ m})^2 - (0.25 \text{ m})^2]$$
$$= -37.5 \text{ N} \cdot \text{m}$$

Total work.   The total work done is obtained by adding the scalar quantities (with the proper algebraic signs) of work done by each force during the movement of the block from position A to position B.

$$U_{A \to B(\text{total})} = (88.29 - 20.54 + 20 - 37.5)\text{N} \cdot \text{m} = 50.25 \text{ N} \cdot \text{m}$$

Equation of work-kinetic energy.   We now apply the equation of work–kinetic energy to determine the unknown velocity v_B at position B. Recall that the velocity v_A at the initial position is zero.

$$\Sigma U_{A \to B(\text{total})} = \frac{1}{2}m(v_B^2 - v_A^2)$$

$$50.25 \text{ N} \cdot \text{m} = \frac{1}{2}(15 \text{ kg})(v_B^2 - 0)$$

$$v_B = \left[(2)\left(\frac{50.25 \text{ N} \cdot \text{m}}{15 \text{ kg}}\right)\right]^{1/2}$$

$$v_B = 2.59 \text{ m/s} \blacktriangleleft$$

EXAMPLE 3.4

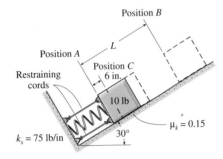

Position B

Position A

L

Position C

6 in.

Restraining
cords

10 lb

$\mu_k = 0.15$

$k_s = 75$ lb/in   30°

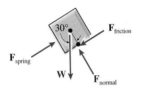

30° $\mathbf{F}_{\text{friction}}$

$\mathbf{F}_{\text{spring}}$

$\mathbf{W}$ $\mathbf{F}_{\text{normal}}$

A 10-lb block is resting on an inclined surface at an angle of 30 degrees, as shown. The block is in contact with a compressed spring that has a modulus of 75 lb/in. The spring has an initial compression of 6 inches that is released by cutting the restraining cords. If the coefficient of kinetic friction between the inclined surface and the block is 0.15, determine the distance that the block will rise. Also determine the speed of the block as it leaves the spring.

Solution   The free-body diagram of the block is shown. We will use the work–kinetic energy relationship given by $\Sigma U_{A \to B(\text{total})} = T_B - T_A$. The block begins at rest at point A and comes to rest at point B. Hence, the kinetic energy at each of these two points is zero and the change in kinetic energy is zero: $T_B - T_A = 0$. Since the right-hand side of the work–kinetic energy relationship is zero, the left-hand side must also be zero. Thus,

$$\Sigma U_{A \to B(\text{total})} = U_{A \to B(\text{spring})} + U_{A \to B(\text{friction})}$$
$$+ U_{A \to B(\text{weight})} + U_{A \to B(\text{normal})} = 0$$

where

$$U_{A \to B(\text{spring})} = \frac{1}{2}k(x_B^2 - x_A^2)$$

$$= \frac{1}{2}(75 \times 12 \text{ lb/ft})\left[(0)^2 - \left(\frac{6}{12}\right)^2\right] = 112.5 \text{ ft} \cdot \text{lb}$$

The sign of the work done by the spring force is positive because the motion and the force of the spring have the same sense. The spring will come to rest at its undeformed position C and will not contribute to the total work beyond that point. We also find that

$$U_{A \to B(\text{friction})} = -F_{Fr}L = -\mu F_N L = -(\mu W \cos \theta)L$$
$$= -(0.15)(10 \cos 30°)L = -1.299L(\text{ft} \cdot \text{lb})$$
$$U_{A \to B(\text{weight})} = -(W \sin \theta)L = -(10 \sin 30°)L = -5L(\text{ft} \cdot \text{lb})$$
$$U_{A \to B(\text{normal})} = 0$$

We now add all four contributions to the total work, and solve for L; thus,

$$\Sigma U_{A \to B(\text{total})} = 112.5 - 1.299L - 5L + 0 = 0$$

$$L = 17.86 \text{ ft} \blacktriangleleft$$

(continued)

EXAMPLE 3.4 *(concluded)*

Next we will determine the speed of the block as it leaves the spring. The block starts from rest at position A; thus $T_A = 0$. Position C is where the block leaves the spring: $T_C = \frac{1}{2}mv_C^2$. The total work done by the spring force, the weight, and the friction force is given by

$$\Sigma U_{A \to C(\text{total})} = U_{A \to C(\text{spring})} + U_{A \to C(\text{weight})}$$
$$+ U_{A \to C(\text{friction})} + U_{A \to C(\text{normal})}$$

$$= 112.5 \text{ ft} \cdot \text{lb} - (10 \sin 30° \text{ lb})\left(\frac{6}{12} \text{ ft}\right)$$

$$- (10 \cos 30° \text{ lb})(0.15)\left(\frac{6}{12} \text{ ft}\right) = 109.35 \text{ ft} \cdot \text{lb}$$

The application of the principle of work and kinetic energy would yield

$$\Sigma U_{A \to C(\text{total})} = T_C - T_A = \frac{1}{2}mv_C^2 - 0$$

and, after substituting for the left-hand side of the above equation $\Sigma U_{A \to C(\text{total})} = 109.35 \text{ ft} \cdot \text{lb}$, the equation is reduced to

$$\frac{1}{2}\left(\frac{W}{g}\right)v_C^2 = 109.35 \text{ ft} \cdot \text{lb}$$

where $W = 10$ lb and $g = 32.2 \text{ ft/s}^2$. Solving for v_C, we obtain

$$v_C = 26.5 \text{ ft/s} \blacktriangleleft$$

EXAMPLE 3.5

The system shown is originally kept at rest by a cord attached to block A. When the cord is suddenly cut, the entire system is set in motion. The masses of A and B are 50 and 250 kg, respectively. Assuming that the coefficient of kinetic friction between the blocks and the inclines is $\mu_k = 0.30$, determine the speed of the blocks after they have each moved 10 m along their corresponding surfaces. Neglect the friction of the pulley.

Solution The free-body diagram for the system is shown. The work–kinetic energy relationship when applied to the two-block system is

$$\Sigma U_{1 \to 2} = T_2 - T_1$$

where the subscripts 1 and 2 will now represent the initial and final positions of the system. Block A goes up and block B slides down during the motion of the system.

Kinetic energies. The blocks are initially at rest; hence, the initial velocity is $v_1 = 0$ and we have

$$T_1 = \frac{1}{2}m_A v_1^2 + \frac{1}{2}m_B v_1^2 = 0 \qquad \text{(a)}$$

$$T_2 = \frac{1}{2}(m_A + m_B)v_2^2 = 150v_2^2 \qquad \text{(b)}$$

(continued)

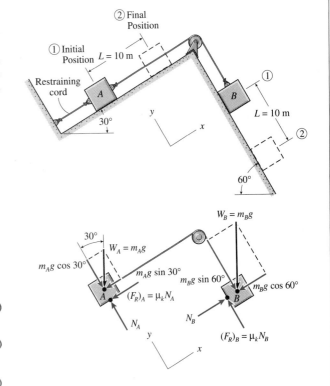

111

EXAMPLE 3.5 (*concluded*)

where $m_A = 50$ kg and $m_B = 250$ kg. We will determine v_2, the final speed of the blocks, using Equation (3.12).

Work. The total work done by all the forces acting on the blocks A and B is expressed as

$$\Sigma U_{1\to2(\text{total})} = U_{1\to2(\text{weight }A)} + U_{1\to2(\text{weight }B)}$$
$$+ U_{1\to2(\text{friction }A)} + U_{1\to2(\text{friction }B)} \quad (c)$$

The tension force developing within the cable connecting the two blocks A and B is an internal force and therefore will not contribute to the work on the system.

Work done by the weights. The work done by the weight W_A is equal to the product of the x component of the weight (i.e., $W_A \sin 30°$) and the distance L over which the block moves along the same x direction. Since the force is directed in the opposite sense to the displacement, the work is negative.

$$U_{1\to2(\text{weight }A)} = -(W_A \sin 30°)L = -(m_A g \sin 30°)L$$
$$= -(50 \text{ kg})(9.81 \text{ m/s}^2)\sin 30°(10 \text{ m})$$
$$= -2452.5 \text{ N} \cdot \text{m} \quad (d)$$

Similarly, the work done by the weight W_B is

$$U_{1\to2(\text{weight }B)} = (W_B \sin 60°)L = (m_B g \sin 60°)L$$
$$= (250 \text{ kg})(9.81 \text{ m/s}^2)\sin 60°(10 \text{ m})$$
$$= +21,239.3 \text{ N} \cdot \text{m} \quad (e)$$

Note that the force component ($W_B \sin 60°$) and the displacement are in the same direction and therefore the work is positive.

Work done by the friction forces. The friction forces always oppose the motion of the blocks and are therefore opposite in sense to their displacements and thus always negative.

$$U_{1\to2(\text{friction }A)} = -(F_R)_A L$$
$$U_{1\to2(\text{friction }B)} = -(F_R)_B L$$

Now let us evaluate the friction forces $(F_R)_A$ and $(F_R)_B$. The equilibrium equation in the y direction gives for block A

$\overset{\curvearrowright}{\text{⑤}}\Sigma F_y = 0$

$$N_A - W_A \cos 30° = 0$$
$$N_A = W_A \cos 30°$$

and introducing $(F_R)_A = \mu_k(m_A g)$, we obtain

$$(F_R)_A = \mu_k(m_A g)\cos 30°$$
$$= 0.30(50 \text{ kg})(9.81 \text{ m/s}^2)\cos 30° = 127.4 \text{ N} \quad (f)$$

Similarly, the equilibrium equation in the x direction gives for block B

$\overset{\curvearrowright}{\text{④}}\Sigma F_x = 0$

$$N_B - W_B \cos 60° = 0$$
$$N_B = W_B \cos 60°$$

and introducing $(F_R)_B = \mu_k(m_B g)$, we obtain

$$(F_R)_B = \mu_k(m_B g)\cos 60°$$
$$= 0.30(250 \text{ kg})(9.81 \text{ m/s}^2)\cos 60° = 367.9 \text{ N} \quad (g)$$

Thus, the work done by $(F_R)_A$ and $(F_R)_B$ is

$$U_{1\to2(\text{friction }A)} = -127.4 \text{ N}(10 \text{ m}) = -1274 \text{ N} \cdot \text{m}$$
$$U_{1\to2(\text{friction }B)} = -367.9 \text{ N}(10 \text{ m}) = -3679 \text{ N} \cdot \text{m}$$

The total work done by all the external forces acting upon the system becomes

$$\Sigma U_{1\to2(\text{total})} = -2452.5 + 21,239.3 - 1274 - 3679$$
$$= +13,833.8 \text{ N} \cdot \text{m}$$

Introducing the values calculated for T_1, T_2, and $\Sigma U_{1\to2(\text{total})}$ the work–kinetic energy relationship for the two-block system can now be expressed as

$$13,833.8 = 150v_2^2 - 0$$

and solving for the speed at the final position,

$$v_2 = 9.60 \text{ m/s} \blacktriangleleft$$

3.6 CONSERVATIVE FORCE FIELDS: POTENTIAL ENERGY

In Section 3.2, we encountered three different forces: the weight of a body, the force of a spring, and the force of constant magnitude. Recall that the work done by a weight was found [Equation (3.4)] to be dependent only on the difference in the vertical coordinates of the end points of the path and that the path itself was of no consequence. The work done by a spring was found [Equation (3.6)] to be dependent only on the final and initial deflections of the spring from its undeformed length and again the path that the end of the spring took during its motion was inconsequential. Finally, we saw in Equation (3.2) that the work done by a constant force acting on a particle was the dot product of the force vector and the displacement vector connecting the initial A to the final B position of the particle, regardless of which path was taken by the particle to go from A to B. In all three cases, the force was either constant or dependent *only* on the position of its point of application, that is, independent of the velocity and acceleration of the application point. When the work done by such a force vector is independent of the path and depends *only* on the initial and final positions of the particle upon which the force acts, then the force is called a **conservative force**.

Other forces, however, do not meet the above criteria. They are called *nonconservative forces*. For example, friction forces are nonconservative in nature. Indeed, the magnitude of the drag force exerted over an object moving through air is a function of the relative velocity of the body and therefore not solely dependent on the position of the point of application. Similarly, during the motion of a block sliding on a rough surface, the friction force developed along the interface between the block and the surface will always be present (nonzero) and always directed against the motion (negative), even if the block returns to its original position. It follows that the length of the path the block follows will determine the amount of work done by the friction force; the longer the path, the greater the magnitude of the work done. In short, the work done by the force will not be independent of the path.

When dealing with *conservative* force fields, it is often useful to introduce the concept of **potential energy**. The two most prominent conservative force fields are the force of gravity and the elastic force of a spring. The following analysis will consider the *gravitational* and the *elastic* potential energy of a particle.

Gravitational potential energy, V_g, of a particle with a *constant weight W* is defined as the work Wz done against the gravitational force field in moving the particle from a position of zero potential energy—along the datum plane—to its present location situated at a distance z above datum. The datum plane is an assumed plane of reference from which elevations or depths are measured.

The work done by the weight in opposition to such a move is (Figure 3.7)

$$U_{A \rightarrow B(\text{gravity})} = \int dU = -\int W\,dz = -W(z_B - z_A)$$

$$U_{A \rightarrow B(\text{gravity})} = -Wz \tag{3.14}$$

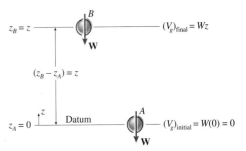

Figure 3.7

since $z_A = 0$ and $z_B = z$. The work done *against* the gravity field can now be expressed as

$$U_{A \to B(\text{against } g)} = +Wz$$

which also represents the gravitational potential energy V_g between points A (zero potential) and B; thus,

$$V_g = Wz \tag{3.15}$$

Introducing Equation (3.15) into Equation (3.14), one can relate the work $U_{A \to B}$ of the weight force acting on a particle moving from A to B to the variation of the particle's gravitational potential energy:

$$U_{A \to B} = V_A - V_B \tag{3.16}$$

From Equation (3.16) it follows that the potential energy will increase if the particle or body is elevated to a level higher than the datum plane. The **potential function** V_g introduced above can be viewed as the *potential* for the weight W to do work if the particle is allowed to move freely (under the gravitational force field) from its present position at z back to its initial position at some reference level or datum. In other words, the potential energy of a weight force is the negative of the work done by the weight of the particle during its motion from the zero potential level to its present elevation.

However, if the particle's motion does not take place in close proximity to the surface of the earth—where the weight of a body is usually assumed constant—then the gravitational force field is not a constant force field (Figure 3.8) and the weight W becomes

$$W = \frac{GMm}{r^2} = \frac{mgR^2}{r^2}$$

where G is the universal constant of gravitation and M and R are, respectively, the mass and mean radius of the earth. The mass of the particle is m and its radial position relative to the center of the earth is r. In SI units the constants are given as

$$G = 6.673(10)^{-11} \text{ m}^3/\text{kg} \cdot \text{s}^2$$

$$M = 5.976(10^{24}) \text{ kg}$$

$$R = 6378 \text{ km}$$

When working with U.S. Customary units, recall that $GM = gR^2$ and $R = 3960$ mi. In this case, the gravitational potential energy V_g of a particle is defined as the work done *against* the force field in order to move the particle from an initial and arbitrary radial position r at A to a reference point B where $r = r_B$ and where the potential energy is chosen to be zero.

The work done by the weight in opposition to such a move (Figure 3.8) is

$$U_{A \to B(\text{gravity})} = \int_A^B dU = -\int_r^{r_B} W \, dr = -mgR^2 \left(\frac{1}{r} - \frac{1}{r_B} \right)$$

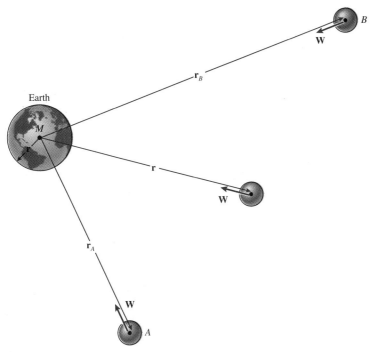

Figure 3.8

If point B is chosen at infinity where the gravitational force would be zero, then the work done *against* the gravity field can be reduced to

$$U_{A \to B(\text{against gravity})} = +\frac{mgR^2}{r} \qquad (3.17)$$

This also represents the variation in gravitational potential energy V_g between points A and B (where the potential is zero).

Introducing Equation (3.16) into Equation (3.17), the work $U_{A \to B}$ of the weight of a particle moving from A to B can now be related to the variation in gravitational potential energy $(V_g)_A - (V_g)_B$ by writing

$$V_g = -\frac{mgR^2}{r} \qquad (3.18)$$

since at B the potential energy is zero.

The **_elastic potential energy_** V_e of a particle attached to the end of a linear spring of modulus k is defined as the work done *against* the spring during the displacement of its movable end from its undeformed reference position ($x_A = 0$) to its present position ($x_B = x$). The work done by the spring in opposition to such a move is negative and can be expressed as

$$U_{A \to B(\text{spring})} = -\int kx\,dx = -\left[\frac{kx^2}{2} - 0\right] = -\frac{kx^2}{2}$$

and the work done *against* the spring will thus be of opposite sign (positive),

$$U_{A \to B(\text{against spring})} = +\frac{kx^2}{2}$$

This also represents the variation in elastic potential V_e of the spring's end between its undeformed and stretched (or compressed) positions; thus,

$$V_e = \frac{kx^2}{2} \tag{3.19}$$

Since $U_{A \to B(\text{spring})} = -\int_A^B kx\, dx = \frac{kx_A^2}{2} - \frac{kx_B^2}{2}$, upon introducing Equation (3.19) we can write once again

$$U_{A \to B(\text{spring})} = V_A - V_B \tag{3.16}$$

*Conservative Force Field: Potential Function

As we saw, when the work done by a force in moving a particle from A to B is *independent* of the path followed, the force is defined as *conservative.* The function V describing the potential energy of a particle under a conservative force field is called the *potential function* of the force under consideration and the work done is written as

$$U_{A-B} = V(x,y,z)_A - V(x,y,z)_B$$

For an infinitesimal displacement from A to B, the above expression yields

$$dU = V(x,y,z)_A - V(x + dx, y + dy, z + dz)_B$$

or

$$dU = -dV(x,y,z)$$

We conclude that the infinitesimal work of a conservative force is an exact differential that can be expressed in the form

$$dU = -\left(\frac{\partial V}{\partial x} dx + \frac{\partial V}{\partial y} dy + \frac{\partial V}{\partial z} dz \right)$$

or

$$dU = -(\nabla V \cdot \mathbf{r})$$

And since $dU = \mathbf{F} \cdot d\mathbf{r}$, it follows that a conservative force $\mathbf{F}$ can be derived from a scalar function V as

$$\mathbf{F} = -\nabla V = -\operatorname{grad} V$$

We can also express this as

$$F_x\mathbf{i} + F_y\mathbf{j} + F_z\mathbf{k} = -\left(\frac{\partial V}{\partial x}\mathbf{i} + \frac{\partial V}{\partial y}\mathbf{j} + \frac{\partial V}{\partial z}\mathbf{k}\right)$$

or

$$F_x = -\frac{\partial V}{\partial x} \qquad F_y = -\frac{\partial V}{\partial y} \qquad F_z = -\frac{\partial V}{\partial z} \qquad (3.20)$$

Given a force field **F**, it would be desirable to know if it is a conservative field. We recall from vector calculus that if a vector is the gradient of a scalar function, then its curl is zero and we write

$$\nabla \times \mathbf{F} = \text{curl}(-\text{grad } V) = 0$$

In order for the curl vector ($\nabla \times \mathbf{F}$) to be zero, all three of its components must be zero. Hence, by equating to zero the three Cartesian components of the vector ($\nabla \times \mathbf{F}$) we obtain the necessary and sufficient conditions for a force to be conservative:

$$\frac{\partial F_y}{\partial z} = \frac{\partial F_z}{\partial y} \qquad \frac{\partial F_z}{\partial x} = \frac{\partial F_x}{\partial z} \qquad \frac{\partial F_x}{\partial y} = \frac{\partial F_y}{\partial x} \qquad (3.21)$$

EXAMPLE 3.6

Show that the force $\mathbf{F} = xy\mathbf{i} + (x^2/2)\mathbf{j} + 4\mathbf{k}$ is conservative and determine the potential function of the force field.

Solution Since $F_x\mathbf{i} + F_y\mathbf{j} + F_z\mathbf{k} = (xy)\mathbf{i} + (x^2/2)\mathbf{j} + (4)\mathbf{k}$ we find that the Cartesian components of the force vector are given by

$$F_x = xy \qquad F_y = \frac{x^2}{2} \qquad F_z = 4$$

We can now insert the above expressions into Equation (3.21) to determine whether the force field meets the necessary and sufficient conditions for it to be conservative:

$$\frac{\partial F_x}{\partial y} = \frac{\partial F_y}{\partial x} = x \qquad \frac{\partial F_z}{\partial x} = \frac{\partial F_x}{\partial z} = 0 \qquad \frac{\partial F_y}{\partial z} = \frac{\partial F_z}{\partial y} = 0$$

Therefore, the force field is conservative. Now, to determine the potential function V of the force field, from Equation (3.20) we write

$$\frac{\partial V}{\partial x} = -xy = -F_x \qquad \frac{\partial V}{\partial y} = -\frac{x^2}{2} = -F_y$$

$$\frac{\partial V}{\partial z} = -4 = -F_z$$

The above equations, upon integration, yield

$$V = -\frac{x^2 y}{2} - 4z + C \quad \blacktriangleleft$$

3.7 THE EQUATION OF WORK AND POTENTIAL ENERGY: CONSERVATION OF MECHANICAL ENERGY

For conservative force systems, the result established in Equation (3.16), $\Sigma U_{A \to B} = V_A - V_B$, can now be viewed as a statement of the relationship between work and the change in the potential energy of a particle. On the other hand, Equation (3.12) also established that $\Sigma U_{A \to B} = T_B - T_A$. By equating the right-hand sides of these two equations, we obtain

$$V_A - V_B = T_B - T_A$$

and, after rearranging terms,

$$T_A + V_A = T_B + V_B \tag{3.22}$$

The sum $(T + V)$ of the kinetic and potential energy of a particle is called its *total mechanical energy*. Thus, Equation (3.22) expresses the principle of the **conservation of mechanical energy**. This states that the sum of kinetic and potential energy of a particle, subjected to conservative forces *only*, does not change as the particle moves from point A to another point B, although energy is being transformed continuously from one form into the other during the motion of the particle. Thus we write

$$\text{(Mechanical energy)}_A = \text{(Mechanical energy)}_B$$

It must be emphasized that, in general, the total energy of a particle is not always limited to the sum of its kinetic and potential energies. In some systems it will include thermal, electrical, and chemical energies as well. Indeed, when friction forces are considered, the transformation of kinetic energy into heat is part of the energy balance. Since it is difficult to determine the amount of heat dissipated during the motion, we will limit the application of the principle of conservation of mechanical energy to conservative force fields, thus excluding those involving friction forces.

Recall that potential energy represents the potential of a force to do work as the particle upon which it acts moves from its present position to another one. It is useful to realize that any reference point (or datum line) can be used to evaluate the change in the potential energy of a particle, and that different reference points can be chosen for different forces acting on the particle.

We will now apply the principle of the conservation of mechanical energy to several example problems.

EXAMPLE 3.7

A 6-kg mass is released from rest 1 m above the end of an unstressed spring as shown. The spring has a modulus of 100 N/m.
Determine the maximum deflection of the spring and compare it
to the deflection that would occur if the mass were lowered, without being allowed to fall, onto the spring (static deflection).

Solution The forces acting on the body mass during its
motion from point A to point B are shown. Since both of these
forces—weight force and spring force—have been shown to be
conservative, we will use the principle of conservation of
mechanical energy, $T_A + V_A = T_B + V_B$.

Kinetic energies. The weight starts from rest at position A
($v_A = 0$) and comes to rest at position B ($v_B = 0$) when
the spring reaches its maximum compression. Therefore, the
kinetic energies at A and B are zero, or $T_A = T_B = 0$.
Substituting this equality into the conservation of mechanical
energy relationship yields $V_A = V_B$.

Potential energies. In evaluating the potential energies V_A and
V_B, we choose as datum for the weight its final position, and for
the spring the undeformed position of its free end. The
potential energies V_A and V_B can be expressed as

$$V_{A(total)} = V_{A(weight)} + V_{A(spring)} = W(h + d) + 0$$

$$V_{B(total)} = V_{B(weight)} + V_{B(spring)} = W(0) + \frac{1}{2}kd^2$$

The total potential energies can now be equated as

$$W(h + d) = \frac{1}{2}kd^2$$

where $W = mg = (6 \text{ kg})(9.81 \text{ m/s}^2) = 58.86 \text{ kg m/s}^2$
$h = 1 \text{ m}$
$k = 100 \text{ N/m}$

and the above equation is reduced to the form

$$50d^2 - 58.86d - 58.86 = 0$$

The following values of d satisfy the quadratic equation above:

$$d = 1.82 \text{ m}; d = -0.65 \text{ m}$$

The positive quantity is the value that applies here. The size of
the compression is rather large and is due to the small value
of k, which indicates a very soft spring. This compression
would only be possible if the spring were long enough to allow

(continued)

EXAMPLE 3.7   *(concluded)*

a deflection of this magnitude before it became fully compressed, and the spring did not buckle.

   If the mass is now slowly lowered on the spring, the weight must be equal to the force in the spring. Thus, we can solve for *d* by writing

$$W = mg = kd$$

$$= (6 \text{ kg})(9.81 \text{ m/s}^2) = (100 \text{ N/m})(d)$$

$$d = 0.59 \text{ m} \blacktriangleleft$$

Note: We can see that the impact loading that occurs when the mass is dropped on the spring results in a much higher spring deflection than when the impact is eliminated by gradually lowering the mass on the spring. One can show that when a mass is brought in contact with a spring and then suddenly released, the compression would be twice as large as that observed when the mass is lowered gradually onto the spring.

EXAMPLE 3.8

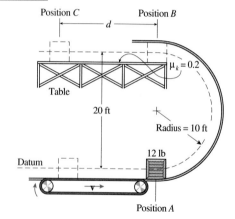

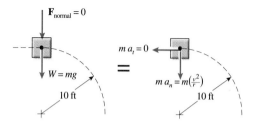

A 12-lb block moves from the conveyor belt to the table by traveling around a smooth, semicircular track of 10-ft radius, as shown. Determine the speed required on the conveyor to ensure that the block stays on the semicircular track and makes it to the table. Determine also the distance that the block moves along the length of the table. The coefficient of kinetic friction between the block and the table is 0.2.

Solution   The figure shows the final position *B* of the block before landing on the table. A free-body diagram is also given. As the forces acting on the body are conservative, we can use the equation of conservation of mechanical energy. The potential energy of the normal reaction force does not change since there is no displacement in the direction of this force. With the datum line for the weight taken as shown, the potential energy of the weight is zero at *A* and at *B* is the weight times the vertical distance from *A* to *B*.

   As the block rises from *A* to *B* its potential energy increases at the expense of its kinetic energy. The block will stay on the track as long as there is a normal force between the track and the block. When the velocity of the block becomes small enough to reduce the normal force to zero, the block leaves the track and becomes a free falling object. Therefore, when the block is in position *B*, the normal force can be zero allowing the block to fall onto the table.

   We will use Newton's second law of motion to determine

(continued)

EXAMPLE 3.8 (*concluded*)

the minimum speed that the block can have at position B. As long as the block is on the track, it is moving in a circular path and has normal and tangential components of acceleration. The external forces acting on the block are equated to the mass times the acceleration of the center of mass. At B, the weight becomes the only external force acting in the normal direction and it is equal to the mass times the normal component of the acceleration. We obtain

$$W = ma_n \qquad W = \frac{W}{g}\frac{v^2}{r}$$

After simplifying we obtain

$$v^2 = gr$$

and the speed at the top of the track must be

$$v = [(32.2 \text{ ft/s}^2)(10 \text{ ft})]^{1/2} = 17.94 \text{ ft/s}$$

We can now use the equation of conservation of mechanical energy, $T_A + V_A = T_B + V_B$, where

$$V_A = 0 \quad V_B = (12 \text{ lb})(20 \text{ ft})$$

$$T_B = \frac{1}{2}\left(\frac{W}{g}\right)(v_B^2) = \frac{1}{2}\left(\frac{12}{32.2}\right)(17.94)^2$$

$$T_A = \frac{1}{2}\left(\frac{W}{g}\right)(v_A^2) = \frac{1}{2}\left(\frac{12}{32.2}\right)(v_A^2)$$

Substituting these into the above equation gives

$$\frac{1}{2}\left(\frac{12}{32.2}\right)(v_A^2) + 0 = \frac{1}{2}\left(\frac{12}{32.2}\right)(17.94)^2 + (12)(20)$$

and solving for v_A, the speed of the conveyor belt, we have

$$v_A = 40.1 \text{ ft/s} \ \blacktriangleleft$$

In determining the distance the block will move along the length of the table, we see that friction is present and energy is not conserved. Therefore, we will use the equation of work and kinetic energy rather than the conservation of mechanical energy relationship. Thus we write

$$\Sigma U_{B\to C} = T_C - T_B$$

where $\quad U_{B\to C} = -(12)(0.2)(d) = -2.4d \text{ lb} \cdot \text{ft}$

$\qquad\qquad T_C \ \ = 0$

$\qquad\qquad T_B \ \ = \frac{1}{2}\left(\frac{12}{32.2}\right)(17.94)^2 \text{ lb} \cdot \text{ft}$

Solving for d the work–kinetic energy equation yields

$$d = 25.0 \text{ ft} \ \blacktriangleleft$$

EXAMPLE 3.9

A ball weighing W is swinging at the end of a rod (length $= R$) of negligible mass. The ball is initially at rest when $\theta = 0$. Determine the position θ at which the rod exerts no reaction on the ball, if the ball is started with a slight displacement.

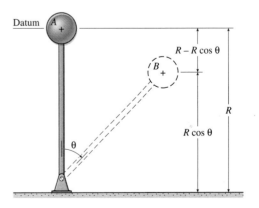

(*continued*)

EXAMPLE 3.9   *(continued)*

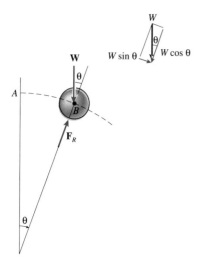

Solution

Solution by the work–kinetic energy equation.   The two forces acting on the ball are shown on the free-body diagram. They are the weight **W** of the ball, and the reaction force $\mathbf{F}_R$ exerted by the rod. The reaction of the rod on the ball is radial because the bar has no mass. Since the ball follows the circular arc AB, the work done by the reaction force $\mathbf{F}_R$ (which, at all times, remains normal to the path) will be zero. The work done by the weight can be evaluated by integrating along the arc AC the product of the tangential component of the force (that is, $W \sin \theta$) with the infinitesimal displacement ds ($= R\, d\theta$).

$$\Sigma U_{A \to B} = \int_{AB} W \sin \theta\, ds = \int_{\theta = 0}^{\theta} (W \sin \theta) R\, d\theta$$

$$= WR \int_0^\theta \sin \theta\, d\theta$$

$$\Sigma U_{A \to B} = WR(1 - \cos \theta) \tag{a}$$

This result could also have been obtained by expressing the work $\Sigma U_{A \to B}$ as the product of the force W with the vertical component of the displacement, that is, with $R(1 - \cos \theta)$.

Kinetic energies.   The kinetic energy of the ball at A ($v_A = 0$) and B are

$$T_A = \frac{1}{2}\left(\frac{W}{g}\right)v_A^2 = 0 \qquad T_B = \frac{1}{2}\left(\frac{W}{g}\right)v_B^2$$

Substituting the expressions for $U_{A \to B}$, T_A, and T_B, the equation of work and kinetic energy $\Sigma U_{A \to B} = T_A - T_B$ will yield

$$WR(1 - \cos \theta) = \frac{1}{2}\left(\frac{W}{g}\right)v_B^2$$

$$v_B = [2gR(1 - \cos \theta)]^{1/2} \tag{b}$$

The position θ of the rod can now be obtained from the n component of the equation of motion

$$F_n = \left(\frac{W}{g}\right)a_n \tag{c}$$

where $F_n = W \cos \theta$ and $a_n = (v_B)^2/R$. Introducing Equation (b) into Equation (c) yields

$$W \cos \theta = 2W(1 - \cos \theta)$$

(continued)

EXAMPLE   3.9   (*concluded*)

and reducing this, we find the desired angle as

$$3 \cos \theta = 2$$
$$\theta = 48.2° \blacktriangleleft$$

Alternate Solution Since the problem does not involve nonconservative forces such as the friction drag exerted by the air on the ball, the final velocity of the ball (v_B) can also be determined by applying the equation of conservation of mechanical energy [Equation (3.22)] to the ball between A and B as

$$T_A + V_A = T_B + V_B$$

where $T_A = \dfrac{1}{2}\left(\dfrac{W}{g}\right)(0)^2 = 0$

$V_A = W(0) = 0$

$T_B = \dfrac{1}{2}\left(\dfrac{W}{g}\right)v_B^2$

$V_B = -W(R - R \cos \theta)$

After substituting for the kinetic and potential energy terms, Equation (3.22) yields

$$\frac{1}{2}\left(\frac{W}{g}\right)v_B^2 - WR(1 - \cos \theta) = 0$$

and solving for the final velocity

$$v_B = [2gR(1 - \cos \theta)]^{1/2}$$

which is the expression obtained previously.

3.8 POWER AND EFFICIENCY

Power

Power is defined as the time rate of doing work. It is mathematically expressed in the form

$$P = \frac{dU}{dt}$$

where P is power, and dU the infinitesimal work done by a force **F** during the infinitesimal time interval dt. Since in Section 3.2 we defined the infinitesimal work as

$$dU = \mathbf{F} \cdot d\mathbf{r}$$

and recalling that $\mathbf{v} = d\mathbf{r}/dt$, then

$$\text{Power} = \mathbf{F} \cdot \left(\frac{d\mathbf{r}}{dt}\right) = \mathbf{F} \cdot \mathbf{v}$$

$$P = \mathbf{F} \cdot \mathbf{v} \qquad\qquad (3.23)$$

The unit of power is derived from its definition given above as work (N · m) or energy (J) per unit of time (s). Thus, in SI units, the basic unit of power (*watt*) is equivalent to

$$1 \text{ W} = 1 \frac{\text{N} \cdot \text{m}}{\text{s}} = 1 \frac{\text{J}}{\text{s}}$$

In U.S. Customary units, the derived unit of power is ft · lb/s. However, the most commonly used unit of power is the *horsepower* (hp), which is equivalent to 550 ft · lb/s. For conversion between the two systems of units we have

$$1 \text{ hp} = 746 \text{ W}$$

Note that power, like work, is a scalar quantity.

EFFICIENCY

In discussing the concept of power we must distinguish between total work and useful work. In any mechanical system, part of the effort (energy) expended to carry out a certain task will always be lost during the process. Friction losses during the movement of any object, whether it is solid against solid or solid against fluid, are to be expected. Furthermore, there are hysteresis losses in materials and resistance losses in electrical conductors. **Efficiency** is defined as the ratio of the useful work (**output**) to the total work (**input**), and is a bulk representation of all these losses. Thus, we write

$$\text{Efficiency} = \eta = \frac{\text{useful work}}{\text{total work}} = \frac{\text{output work}}{\text{input work}} \qquad (3.24)$$

Since power is the work being done per unit of time, efficiency can also be expressed in terms of output and input power.

$$\text{Efficiency} = \eta = \frac{\text{useful power}}{\text{total power}} = \frac{\text{output power}}{\text{input power}} \qquad (3.25)$$

For all real mechanical systems, output is always less than input and thus the efficiency of any system is always less than one. If a system consists of several machines placed in series, the efficiency of the overall system can be determined by taking the product of the efficiencies of all the various components of the system.

EXAMPLE   3.10

A 60-kg block is being pulled up a slope by an electric motor as shown. Determine the power required to move the block at a constant speed of 3 m/s. The coefficient of friction between the block and the inclined surface is 0.2.

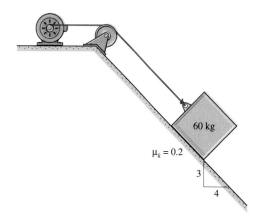

Solution The free-body diagram shows the forces acting on the block. In the absence of any acceleration in the direction of motion, Newton's second law is reduced to an equilibrium statement and we can write in the direction of motion

$$F_T = F_{\text{friction}} + W \sin \theta$$

where $F_{\text{friction}} = \mu F_{\text{normal}}$; and in the direction normal to the plane of the incline we have

$$F_{\text{normal}} = W \cos \theta$$

Solving for the tensile force in the cord pulling the block, we get

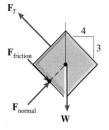

$$F_T = (0.2)[(60 \text{ kg})(9.81 \text{ m/s}^2)]\left(\frac{4}{5}\right)$$

$$+ [(60 \text{ kg})(9.81 \text{ m/s}^2)]\left(\frac{3}{5}\right)$$

$$F_T = 94.18 + 353.16 = 447.3 \text{ kg m/s} = 447.3 \text{ N}$$

Now we can calculate the power supplied by the motor since it is the product of the driving force F_T and the speed v of the block. Since the force $\mathbf{F}_T$ and the velocity vector $\mathbf{v}$ are collinear, the dot product is reduced to a simple algebraic operation.

$$P = \mathbf{F}_T \cdot \mathbf{v} = F_T v = (447.3 \text{ N})(3 \text{ m/s}) = 1341.9 \text{ N} \cdot \text{m/s}$$

$$P = 1342 \text{ watts} = 1.34 \text{ kW} \blacktriangleleft$$

EXAMPLE 3.11

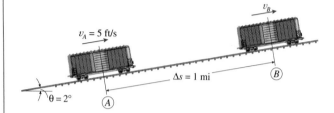

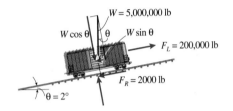

A locomotive exerts a constant force $F_L = 200,000$ lb on a set of series-connected railroad cars weighing all together $W = 5,000,000$ lb and having a total axle friction and rolling resistance of $F_R = 2000$ lb. The train travels up a ramp of $\theta = 2°$ with an initial speed $v_A = 5$ ft/s from point A to point B as shown. The distance from A to B is one mile. Determine the power delivered by the locomotive when it has reached point B.

Solution   The power delivered by the locomotive at B is given by Equation (3.23) as

$$P = \mathbf{F}_L \cdot \mathbf{v}_B = F_L v_B$$

where $F_L = 200,000$ lb. The problem is thus reduced to the determination of the train's speed at B. To achieve that we will appeal to the equation of work and kinetic energy,

$$\Sigma U_{A \to B} = T_B - T_A$$

where

$$T_A = \left(\frac{1}{2}\right)\left(\frac{W}{g}\right)v_A^2 = \left(\frac{1}{2}\right)\left(\frac{5,000,000}{32.2}\right)(5)^2$$
$$= 1.94 \times 10^6 \ (\text{lb} \cdot \text{ft})$$

$$T_B = \left(\frac{1}{2}\right)\left(\frac{W}{g}\right)v_B^2 = \left(\frac{1}{2}\right)\left(\frac{5,000,000}{32.2}\right)(v_B)^2$$
$$= (7.76 \times 10^4)(v_B)^2 \ (\text{lb} \cdot \text{ft})$$

$$\Sigma U_{A \to B} = F_L(\Delta s) - F_R(\Delta s) - (W \sin \theta)(\Delta s)$$

Substituting the known values (using $\Delta s = 5,280$ ft), we have

$$\Sigma U_{A \to B} = (F_L - F_R - W \sin \theta)\Delta s = 1.24 \times 10^8 \ \text{lb} \cdot \text{ft}$$

Substituting for T_A, T_B, and U_{A-B}, Equation (3.13) yields

$$v_B = 40.3 \ \text{ft/s}$$

Thus, the power delivered at B by the locomotive is

$$P = F_L v_B = (200,000)(40.3) = 8.06 \times 10^6 \ \text{lb} \cdot \text{ft/s}$$

or

$$P = \frac{8.06 \times 10^6}{550} = 14,655 \ \text{hp} \blacktriangleleft$$

EXAMPLE   3.12

The 50-kg crate shown rests on a rough horizontal surface for which the coefficient of kinetic friction is $\mu_k = 0.30$. An electrically powered winch is utilized to accelerate the crate at a constant rate until it attains a speed of $v = 5$ m/s within a distance of $s = 20$ m. If the motor and winch have an efficiency of $\eta = 0.70$, determine the power that must be supplied to the motor when $s = 20$ m.

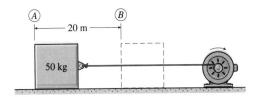

Solution   The power that must be supplied (input power) to the motor is equal to the output power of the motor divided by its mechanical efficiency; thus,

$$P_{\text{input}} = \frac{P_{\text{output}}}{\eta} = \frac{F_T v}{\eta} \qquad \text{(a)}$$

where F_T is the cable force produced by the winch and v is the speed of the crate at the given instant. Thus the problem is reduced to determining the cable force F_T.

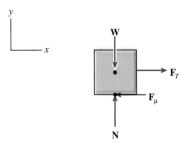

Cable force F_T.   From the free-body diagram shown, we write the x and y components of the equation of motion:

$(\stackrel{y}{+}\uparrow) \, \Sigma F_y = 0$

$$N - mg = 0 \qquad N = mg \qquad F_\mu = \mu_k mg \qquad \text{(b)}$$

$(\stackrel{+}{\to}) \, \Sigma F_x = ma$

$$F_T - F_\mu = ma_c \qquad F_T = F_\mu + ma_c$$

and substituting for F_μ from Equation (b) above, we obtain

$$F_T = \mu_k mg + ma_c \qquad \text{(c)}$$

where a_c is the constant acceleration to be determined from kinematic considerations established in Chapter 1 for uniformly accelerated motion. Hence, we write

$$v^2 = v_0^2 + 2a_c(s - s_0)$$

where $v_0 = 0$ when $s = 0$ and $v = 5$ m/s when $s = 20$ m. Solving for the constant acceleration a_c,

$$a_c = \frac{v^2 - v_0^2}{2(s - s_0)}$$

$$a_c = \frac{5^2 - 0}{2(20 - 0)} = \frac{25}{40} = 0.625 \text{ m/s}^2$$

Substituting for $a_c = 0.625$ m/s^2 in Equation (c) yields

$$F_T = 0.30(50)(9.81) + 50(0.625) = 178.4 \text{ N}$$

Power input.   Now, the power input to the motor can be obtained as

$$P_{\text{input}} = \frac{(178.4 \text{ N})(5 \text{ m/s})}{0.70} = 1274 \text{ W}$$

$$P_{\text{input}} = \frac{1274}{746} = 1.7 \text{ hp} \quad \blacktriangleleft$$

Alternate Solution   The evaluation of the cable force F_T does not necessarily require the determination of the acceleration a_c. Indeed, the work–kinetic energy relationship is ideally suited for such cases. The relationship is expressed as

$$\Sigma U_{A \to B} = T_B - T_A$$

where $T_A = 0$

$$T_B = \left(\frac{1}{2}\right)\left(\frac{W}{g}\right)v_B^2 = \left(\frac{1}{2}\right)(50)(5)^2 = 625 \text{ N} \cdot \text{m}$$

$$U_{A \to B} = F_T(s) - F_\mu(s) = 20F_T - 20[0.3(50)(9.81)]$$

$$= 20F_T - 2943$$

Substituting the numerical values above into the work–kinetic energy equation and solving for F_T yields the same answer as before:

$$F_T = \frac{2943 + 625}{20} \qquad F_T = 178.4 \text{ N} \quad \blacktriangleleft$$

3.9 SUMMARY

In this chapter, we have learned the following:

1.   The work done by a force F in moving a particle from its initial position A to its final position B is the line integral

$$U_{A \to B} = \int_A^B \mathbf{F} \cdot d\mathbf{r} \tag{3.1}$$

a.   The work done by a constant force $\mathbf{F}$ is

$$U_{A \to B} = \mathbf{F} \cdot (\mathbf{r}_B - \mathbf{r}_A) \tag{3.2}$$

where $\mathbf{r}_A$ and $\mathbf{r}_B$ are the initial and final position vectors of the particle P.

b.   The work done by a particle's own weight W is

$$U_{A \to B} = W(z_A - z_B) \tag{3.4}$$

where z_A and z_B are the initial and final elevations of the weight measured from a datum.

c.   The work done by a spring having a spring constant k is

$$U_{A \to B} = -\frac{1}{2}k(x_B^2 - x_A^2) \tag{3.6}$$

where x_A and x_B are the initial and final displacements of the spring's end measured from its undeformed position.

2.   The kinetic energy of a particle of mass m moving at speed v is

$$T = \frac{1}{2}mv^2 \tag{3.7}$$

3.   The equation of work and kinetic energy is

$$\Sigma U_{A \to B} = T_B - T_A \tag{3.13}$$

where $\Sigma U_{A \to B}$ is the work of all external forces moving a particle from A to B, T_A is the initial kinetic energy of the particle at A, and T_B is the final kinetic energy of the particle at B.

4.   The work done by a conservative force acting on a particle is given as

$$U_{A \to B} = V_A - V_B \tag{3.16}$$

where V_A and V_B are the initial and the final potential energy of the particle.

5.   A conservative force field $\mathbf{F}$ can be defined by identifying a scalar function V called *potential function*.

$$\mathbf{F} = -\operatorname{grad} V = -\nabla V$$

$$\mathbf{F} = -\left(\frac{\partial V}{\partial x}\mathbf{i} + \frac{\partial V}{\partial y}\mathbf{j} + \frac{\partial V}{\partial z}\mathbf{k}\right) \tag{3.20}$$

A force field is *conservative* if it satisfies the condition expressed in

$$\nabla \times \mathbf{F} = 0 \tag{3.21}$$

6. The equation of conservation of mechanical (kinetic plus potential) energy of a particle in conservative force fields is

$$T_A + V_A = T_B + V_B \tag{3.22}$$

7. Power is the time rate of doing work and is expressed as

$$P = \frac{dU}{dt} = \mathbf{F} \cdot \mathbf{v} \tag{3.23}$$

and efficiency as

$$\eta = \frac{\text{output}}{\text{input}} = \frac{\text{useful work}}{\text{input work}} \tag{3.24}$$

$$\eta = \frac{\text{useful power}}{\text{input power}} \tag{3.25}$$

KEY TERMS

conservative force *113*

conservation of mechanical
energy *118*

efficiency *124*

kinetic energy *106*

potential energy *113*

elastic *115*

gravitational *113*

potential function *114*

power *123*

input *124*

output *124*

work *99*

PROBLEMS

SECTION 3.2

3.1 A force F given by its Cartesian components $F_x = 3t$ and $F_y = t^2$, where F is in lb and t is the time parameter in s, acts upon a particle during the period from $t = 2$ s to $t = 10$ s. Determine the work done by the force on the particle as it moves along a path given by the parametric equations $x = 2t^2$ and $y = t$, where x and y are in feet.

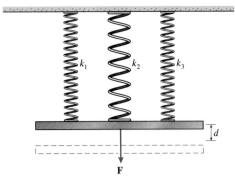

Figure P3.2

3.2 Three springs (in their unstretched positions) are arranged between two parallel plates as shown. Determine the work done by the force F as the lower plate is stretched through a distance d. For a system of springs in parallel, calculate an equivalent spring constant in terms of the individual spring constants. The lower plate is not allowed to rotate.

3.3 The figure shows a block weighing W moving a distance L along a horizontal plane. It is pulled by a force F acting at the end of a cord passing over a pulley. The coefficient of kinetic friction between the block W and the horizontal surface is 0.2. Express the works done by the force F, the weight W, and the friction force F_μ in terms of the displacement L, the friction coefficient μ_k, and the initial and final angles θ_A and θ_B of the cord.

3.4 A constant 170-lb force is applied to a cord that passes over a massless and frictionless pulley and is connected to a 100-lb block as shown. The block is on a 20° inclined surface with a coefficient of friction between the block and the surface of 0.15. Determine the work on the block as it moves up the plane 1 ft.

3.5 A 70-kg crate slides down the inclined surface shown. Determine the work done on the crate as it moves from the position shown to a position 750 mm down the inclined surface. The spring constant is 30 kN/m and the coefficient of friction between the crate and the surface is 0.22.

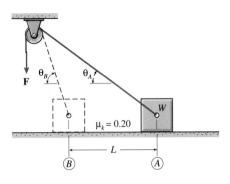

Figure P3.3

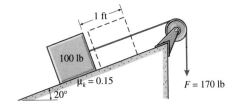

Figure P3.4

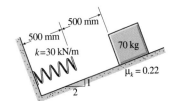

Figure P3.5

3.6 A 4-kg mass moves from a point A to a point B on the smooth quarter circular guide rod shown. A spring with an unstretched length of 200 mm and a spring constant of 10 kN/m is attached to the mass. Determine the total work done on the mass.

3.7 A 30-lb block rests on a horizontal surface as shown. A 50-lb force is applied to the block at 30° to the horizontal. The block moves 1 ft on a rough surface with a coefficient of friction of 0.18 and 2 ft on a smooth surface. Determine the work done on the block as it moves from point A to point B.

3.8 A 75-lb block shown moves down 2 ft from its initial position. All of the springs have constants of 10 lb/in. The undeformed lengths of springs A and B are 1.75 ft and that of spring C is 1 ft. Determine the work done on the block as it moves down 2 ft.

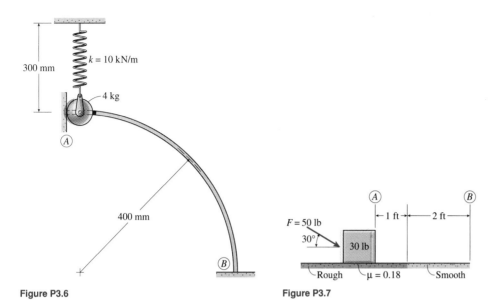

Figure P3.6

Figure P3.7

3.9 The 20-kg box shown is raised 0.75 m by a constant 25-N force applied at the end of the cord. If the pulleys are considered massless, determine the work done on the crate.

3.10 A 5-kg block is raised in a smooth vertical slot by a constant 100-N force applied at the end of the cord as shown. Determine the work done on the block as it moves 3 m up the slot.

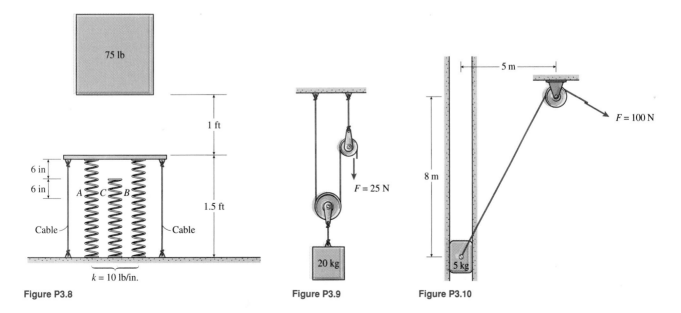

Figure P3.8

Figure P3.9

Figure P3.10

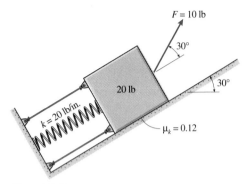

Figure P3.11

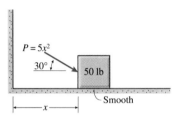

Smooth

Figure P3.12 and P3.13

3.11 A 20-lb block is resting on a surface that is inclined 30° to the horizontal as shown. The spring has been compressed 8 in. by the cables. The coefficient of friction between the block and the surface is 0.12. A constant force of 10 lb is applied to the block as shown. Determine the work done on the block as the cables are released and the spring moves to its equilibrium position.

3.12 The magnitude of the force P shown is given by the equation $P = 5x^2$, where x is in ft and P in lb. Determine the work done by all of the forces acting on the 50-lb box as it moves from $x = 1$ ft to $x = 4$ ft from the wall. The horizontal surface is smooth.

3.13 Repeat Problem 3.12 assuming that the coefficient of friction between the horizontal surface and the box is 0.1.

3.14 As the 50-kg package descends the incline shown, it is caught by a bumper-spring at point A. The spring constant is 100 N/m. The spring is initially held under a 50-N compression by two tensioned cables. The coefficient of kinetic friction between package and incline is 0.20. Determine the work done by (a) the spring force; (b) the friction force; and (c) the weight of the package during a movement of the block from point A to point B at 0.10 m from point A.

3.15 The force $\mathbf{F}$ shown acts in the given direction on the sliding 100-lb block B. The magnitude of the force $\mathbf{F}$ varies with the position x of the block, where x is in ft and F in lb. The coefficients of static and kinetic friction between the block and the horizontal surface are 0.5 and 0.3, respectively. Determine the work done by all the forces acting on the block as it slides from $x = 2$ ft to $x = 5$ ft.

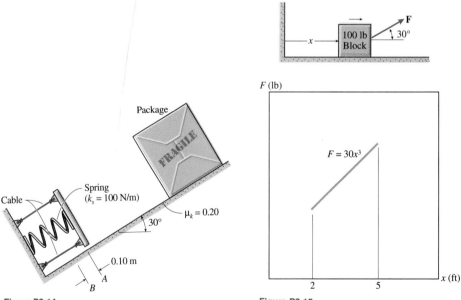

Figure P3.14   **Figure P3.15**

3.16 The 10-kg block is subjected to a force having the constant direction shown and a magnitude $F = 250(1 + x)$ N, where x is measured in meters. If the coefficient of kinetic friction between the block and the horizontal surface is $\mu_k = 0.20$, determine the work done by all the forces acting on the block during a movement of the block from A to B.

3.17 A spring is used to stop a 100-lb block sliding downward along a 15° incline as shown. The spring ($k_s = 50$ lb/ft) is initially compressed 2 ft. If the block comes to rest at B after causing the spring to have an additional compression of 1 ft, determine the work done by all the forces acting on the block during its movement from A ($x = 0$) to B ($x = 5$ ft). The coefficient of kinetic friction between the block and the incline is $\mu_k = 0.25$.

3.18 Repeat Problem 3.17 when the spring is initially stretched 2 ft by a stopper as shown. The stopper is removed at the instant when the block comes into contact with the spring.

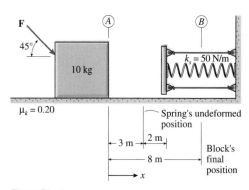

Figure P3.16

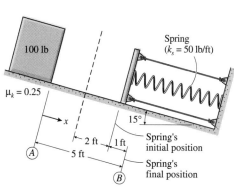

Figure P3.17

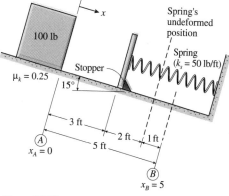

Figure P3.18

SECTIONS 3.3, 3.4, AND 3.5

3.19 A 40-kg block is moved from rest by a 500-N force as shown. If the coefficient of friction is 0.15 between the block and the horizontal surface, determine the velocity of the block after it has moved 3 m to the right.

3.20 A 4-lb mass is connected to a massless rod as shown. The spring has an equilibrium length of 3 in. and a spring constant of 10 lb/in. The mass is released from rest in the position shown. Determine the velocity of the mass when it reaches its lowest position.

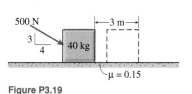

Figure P3.19

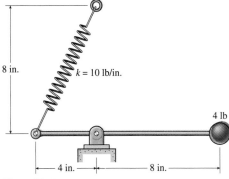

Figure P3.20

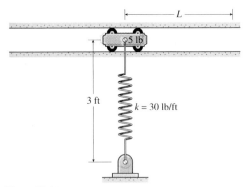

Figure P3.21

3.21 A 5-lb block moves in a smooth horizontal slot as shown. The spring has an undeformed length of 3 ft and a spring constant of 30 lb/ft. At the position shown the block has a speed of 25 ft/s. Determine the distance L that it will travel before its speed is reduced to 10 ft/s.

3.22 A 100-kg carton leaves a conveyor with a speed of 5 m/s and slides down a chute inclined at 10° as shown. If the coefficient of friction between the carton and the chute is 0.1, determine the maximum deflection of the spring pad. The spring constant of the bumper is 30 kN/m.

3.23 A 2-kg particle is attached to an inextensible cord as shown. If the particle is released from rest in the position shown, determine the tension in the cord when the particle reaches its lowest position.

3.24 Referring to Problem 3.23, determine the initial angle of the cord that would produce a maximum tension in the cord equal to twice the weight.

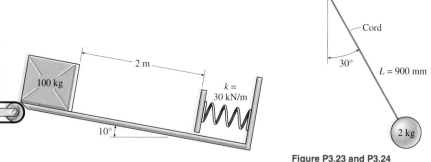

Figure P3.23 and P3.24

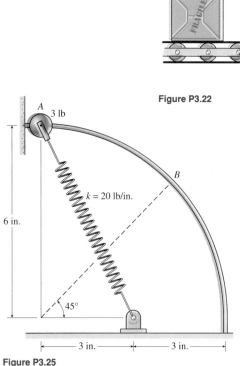

Figure P3.22

Figure P3.25

3.25 A 3-lb particle is released from rest at point A on the circular guide rod shown. If the rod is smooth, determine the speed of the particle when it reaches point B. The undeformed length of the spring is 4 in. and the spring constant is 20 lb/in.

3.26 A particle starts from rest at the highest point of the cylindrical surface shown. Determine the angle at which the particle leaves the surface.

3.27 Determine where the particle in Problem 3.26 lands on the horizontal surface. The particle weighs 2 lb and the radius of the cylindrical surface is 8 ft.

3.28 If the particle in Problem 3.26 is given an initial velocity of 10 ft/s, determine the angle at which the particle leaves the cylindrical surface.

3.29 A constant 35-N force is applied to the end of the cord shown. Determine the distance H that the 5-kg block will rise from rest before it has a velocity of 2 m/s.

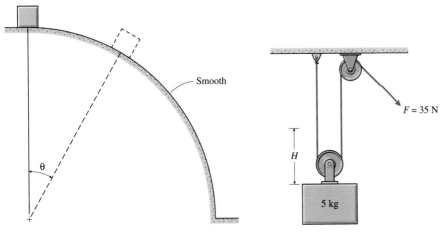

Figure P3.26, P3.27, and P3.28

Figure P3.29

3.30 A 4-lb ball is fired from a toy cannon as shown. The firing mechanism is a compressed spring with a modulus of 30 lb/in. Determine the range of the cannon if the spring is compressed 6 in. and the cannon bore is smooth. The cannon is inclined 30° to the horizontal.

3.31 A coal car weighing 60 tons starts from rest in the position shown and moves down a 2° incline. The rolling resistance of the wheels is 0.01 times the normal component of weight. Determine the spring constant required for the bumper pad to stop the car after a displacement of 15 in.

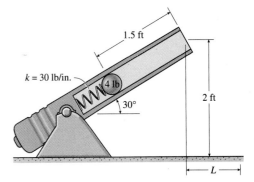

Figure P3.30

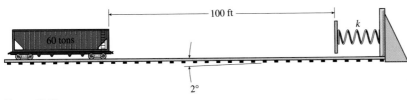

Figure P3.31

3.32 A bobsled with riders weighs 1500 lb and passes point A with a speed of 60 ft/s. If the coefficient of friction is 0.03 and the slope of the incline is 1:20, determine the speed of the sled as it passes a point B located 80 ft down the incline.

3.33 An automobile that weighs 3750 lb is traveling at 60 mph when suddenly the brakes are applied, locking all of the wheels. If the weight is distributed 40% in the rear and 60% in the front and the coefficient of friction between the tires and the ground is 0.45, determine the stopping distance.

3.34 As a 50-lb block descends the incline shown, it is caught at point A (x_A = 5 ft) by a spring having a spring coefficient k_s = 50 lb/ft. The spring is initially held under a 50-lb compression by two tensioned cables. The coeffiient of kinetic friction between the block and the incline is 0.30. The block comes to rest after 2 ft additional compression of the spring. Determine the speed of the block at $x = 0$.

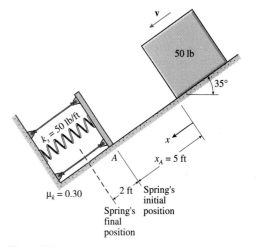

Figure P3.34

3.35 If the block shown in Problem 3.15 has a speed of 20 ft/s when $x = 2$ ft, determine its speed when $x = 5$ ft.

3.36 How far would the block given in Problem 3.15 slide during a period when its speed increases from $v_1 = 20$ ft/s at $x = 2$ ft to $v_2 = 40$ ft/s at $x = 5$ ft?

3.37 Determine the speed at A $(x = 0)$ of the block given in Problem 3.17.

3.38 A spring is used to stop a 500-kg block sliding down along a 25° incline as shown. The spring ($k_s = 400$ N/m) is initially compressed 1 m. If the speed of the block is 5 m/s when it is 15 m from the spring, and the additional deformation of the spring in bringing the package to rest is 3 m, determine the kinetic friction coefficient between the block and the incline.

3.39 A 10,000-lb airplane is stopped by an arresting cable when landing at 80 mph on the deck of an aircraft carrier. Using the arresting force-cable deflection diagram shown, determine the distance required for the plane to come to rest.

3.40 A 10,000-lb airplane is launched from a catapult. The spring of the catapult ($k_s = 150$ lb/in.) is initially compressed 10 ft and then released. During the launching the airplane engine exerts a constant horizontal force $F = 2000$ lb. Assuming friction to be negligible, determine the takeoff speed of the airplane at the instant when the spring reaches its undeformed position.

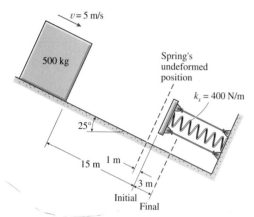

Figure P3.38

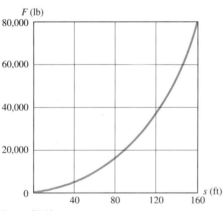

Figure P3.39

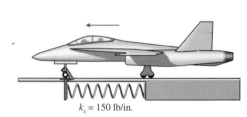

Figure P3.40

3.41 Two 5-kg spheres pivot in the vertical plane about pins O_1 and O_2 as shown. The rods supporting the spheres have negligible masses and are linked to each other by a spring ($k = 200$ N/m, undeformed length $= 0.20$ m). If the spheres are released from rest when $\theta = 45°$, determine the speed of each sphere when $\theta = 90°$.

3.42 The manufacturer of a 4000-lb car will equip it with a spring bumper capable of bringing the car to rest from a speed of 5 mph. The compression allowed for the pair of springs supporting the bumper will be limited to 4 in. Assuming that the springs are not initially compressed and that all the energy is absorbed by the springs, find the required spring constant k for each of the springs.

side view

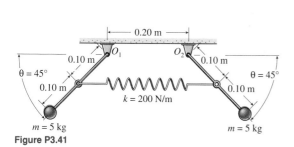

Figure P3.41

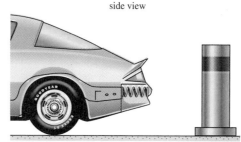

Figure P3.42

3.43 The arresting mechanism of an aircraft carrier applies a constant tension T to the cable during braking as shown. Determine the tension T of the cable required to stop a 12,000-lb aircraft landing at a speed of 150 ft/s within a horizontal distance of 550 ft.

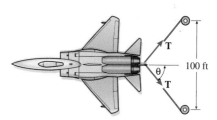

Figure P3.43

3.44 A wrecking ball with a mass m is suspended from the boom of a crane as shown. If the crane is moving at a constant speed v before it is suddenly brought to rest, determine the maximum angle θ through which the cable will swing.

3.45 A 4000-lb car is equipped with a suspension system consisting of four springs, each having an undeformed length of 10 in. Assuming that the car mass is positioned 2 in. above the end of the springs as shown, determine the required spring constant k in order for the springs to support the weight of the car at rest with a compression of 5 in. in each spring.

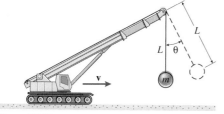

Figure P3.44

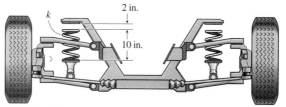

Figure P3.45

3.46 A navy pier will be equipped with shock-absorbing fenders designed to bring to rest a 75-ton ship moving at 1.2 mph. Two types of fenders have been tested under various loading and their deflections recorded. The load-deflection curve for each type is shown in the graph. Determine the maximum deflection to be expected of each fender when it is impacted by the ship.

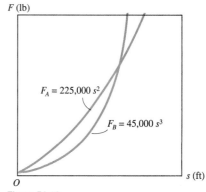

Figure P3.46

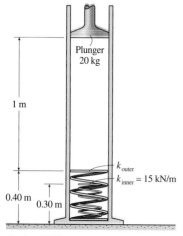

Figure P3.47

3.47 A nested spring assembly is designed as part of a shock absorber to be used to arrest the downward motion of a 20-kg plunger. The spring constant of the inner spring is 15 kN/m. The undeformed lengths of the outer and inner springs are 0.40 and 0.30 m, respectively. If the plunger is released from a height of 1 m above the outer spring and if the maximum allowable deflection of the outer spring is 0.20 m, determine the required spring constant of the outer spring.

3.48 A 50-lb collar is at rest when supported on a smooth horizontal rod by two springs attached to the collar. At the position shown, the springs are undeformed. Suddenly a 75-lb force is applied in the direction indicated. Determine the speed of the collar when the springs are both deformed by 5 in.

3.49 Solve Problem 3.48 when the rod is in the vertical position and the lower spring (k_1 = 3 lb/ft) is initially compressed 5 in. The upper spring (k_2 = 2 lb/ft) is initially undeformed.

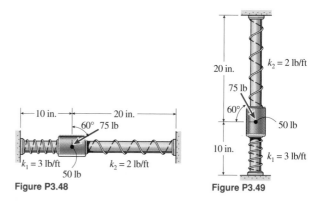

Figure P3.48   **Figure P3.49**

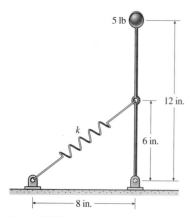

Figure P3.50

SECTIONS 3.6 AND 3.7

3.50 A 5-lb particle is connected to a 12-in. massless bar that is pivoted at one end as shown. The undeformed length of the spring is 8 in. In the position shown, the particle has a speed to the right of 2 ft/s. Determine the spring constant if the particle has a speed of 6 ft/s when it reaches the horizontal position.

3.51 A weight W is displaced a distance L upward from its initial position and then released from rest. Determine the speed of the weight when it returns to its initial position in terms of the spring constant k, the displacement L, and the weight W.

3.52 A 200-g toy car is propelled around a vertical loop by a compressed spring with a spring constant of 120 N/m. Determine the minimum initial compression in the spring for the car to make the complete trip around the loop. Determine the force of the loop on the car when it is in position P.

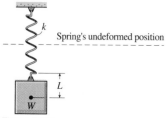

Figure P3.51

3.53 A 30-lb weight moves on a smooth vertical guide rod. The weight is released from rest in the position shown. Determine the speed of the weight when it moves down 5 ft. Each spring has an undeformed length of 1.5 ft and a spring constant of 75 lb/ft.

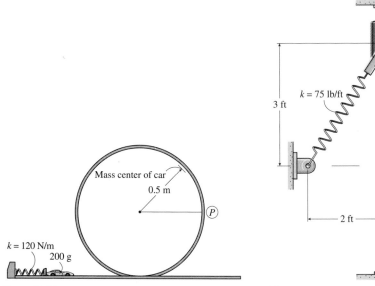

Figure P3.53

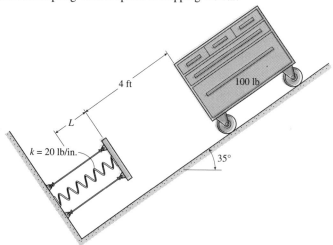

Figure P3.52

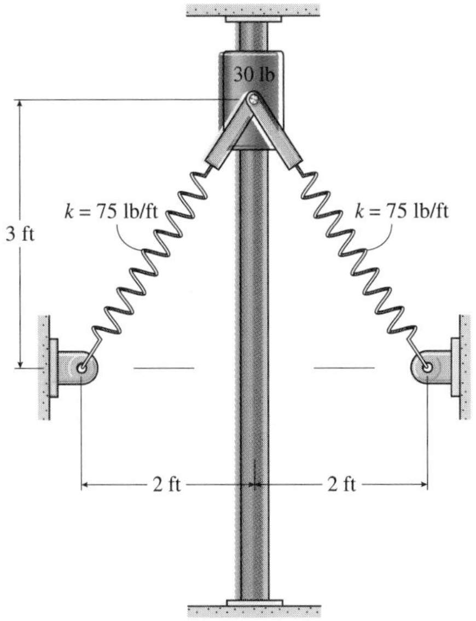

3.54 A 2-kg mass is connected by a massless rod to a support that moves in a horizontal slot as shown. The system is moving to the right with a speed of 3 m/s when the support is suddenly stopped. Determine the angle through which the weight and massless rod will rotate.

3.55 Determine the initial speed of the system shown that will cause the weight and massless rod to rotate 30° when the support is suddenly brought to rest.

3.56 A 100-lb car rolls down a 35° incline as shown. A spring-loaded stop is located at the bottom of the incline 4 ft away. The spring constant is 20 lb/in. and the spring is initially compressed to 50 lb. Determine the maximum additional distance that the spring will compress in stopping the car.

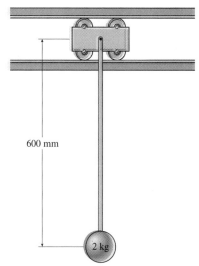

Figure P3.54 and P3.55

Figure P3.56

3.57   A 12-kg particle is released from rest on the smooth, circular guide rod at the position shown. The spring has an undeformed length of 800 mm and a modulus of 40 N/m. Determine the speed of the particle when it is at point P.

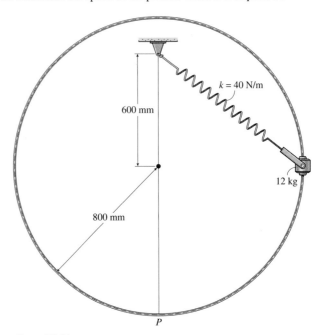

Figure P3.57

3.58   The weight W shown is dropped from a distance L onto a spring with modulus of k. The spring is initially unstressed. Determine the distance L from which the weight must be dropped to produce a maximum compressive force in the spring that is 10 times the weight of the block. Express L in terms of W and k.

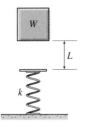

Figure P3.58

3.59   A carton of weight W leaves a conveyor belt with a speed v and passes over a smooth circular arc transition and onto a smooth surface inclined at 45° as shown. Determine the speed v of the conveyor required to move the carton up the incline a distance H. The speed v will be expressed in terms of H, R, and g.

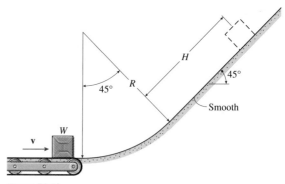

Figure P3.59

3.60 Two cylinders A and B move in opposite directions as shown starting from rest. Assuming the masses of the cord and pulleys to be negligible, and using the conservation of energy equation, determine the speed of the cylinders after cylinder B has moved downward 10 ft. The cylinders A and B weigh 10 lb and 15 lb respectively.

3.61 A 5-kg cylinder A and a 12-kg cylinder B start from rest and move in opposite directions as shown. Using the conservation of energy equation, determine their speeds at the instant when cylinder B has moved downward 5 m. Assume the mass of the cord and pulleys to be negligible.

3.62 A 5-kg block is moving down a smooth incline. If its speed $v_A = 10$ m/s when at point A, determine the speed of the block after it has moved 4 m down the incline.

3.63 A 40-lb block is moving up a smooth incline. If its speed at point B must be equal to 10 ft/s, determine the speed required at point A.

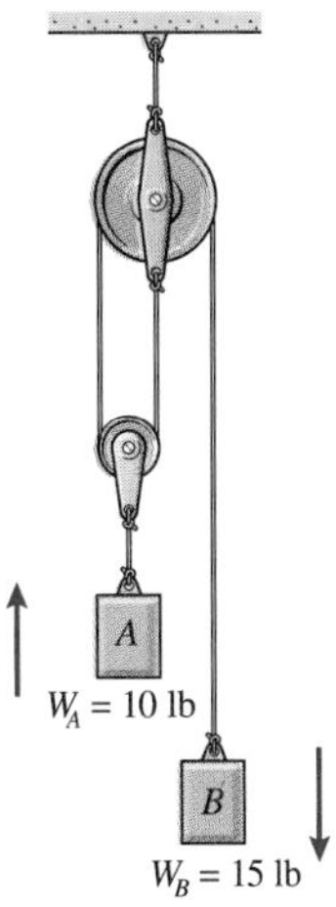

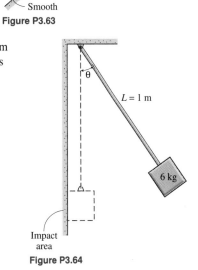

Figure P3.60

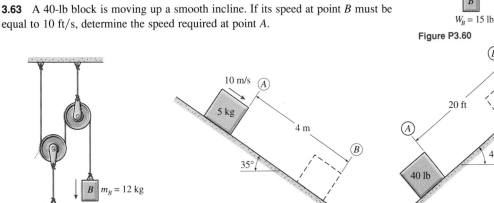

Figure P3.61

Figure P3.62

Figure P3.63

3.64 The impact tester shown consists of a 6-kg block attached at the end of a 1-m long rigid rod of negligible mass. If the speed of the block at the point of impact is required to be 2 m/s, determine the release angle θ.

3.65 The 20-lb ball is fixed to a 5-ft-long rod of negligible mass as shown and is released from rest when $\theta = 0°$. Determine the angle θ at which the compressive force along the rod is zero.

Figure P3.64

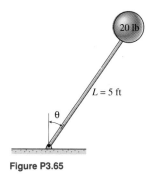

Figure P3.65

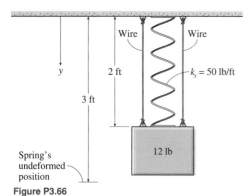

Figure P3.66

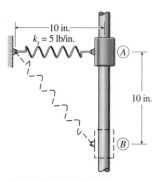

Figure P3.67

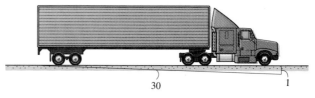

Figure P3.68 and P3.69

3.66 Determine the maximum deformation of the spring ($k_s = 50$ lb/ft) if the 12-lb block shown is released from rest when the spring is initially compressed to a length of 2 ft. The spring has an undeformed length of 3 ft.

3.67 A 30-kg block is attached to two identical springs ($k_s = 50$ N/m) which are undeformed when $\theta = 0°$. If the block is released from rest when $\theta = 0°$, determine its speed when $\theta = 45°$.

3.68 A 30-lb collar slides without friction along a vertical rod after being released from rest in the initial position (A) shown. A spring ($k_s = 5$ lb/in.) is attached to the collar and is unstretched in the position A. Determine the speed of the collar after it has moved down 10 in. to position B.

3.69 Solve Problem 3.68, if the spring has an undeformed length of 12 in.

3.70 The force $\mathbf{F} = x\mathbf{i} + y\mathbf{j} + z\mathbf{k}$ acts on a particle. Determine if the force is conservative and, if it is, find its potential function.

3.71 The force $\mathbf{F} = 3x^2\mathbf{i} + 4y^3\mathbf{j}$ acts on a particle. Determine if the force is conservative and, if it is, find its potential function.

3.72 The force $\mathbf{F} = 2x^2y\mathbf{i} + 2xy^2\mathbf{j}$ acts on a particle and moves in the xy plane. Determine whether the force is conservative and, if so, find its potential function.

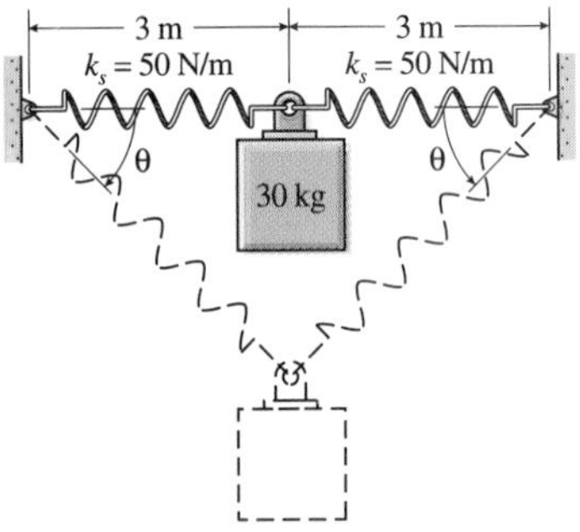

SECTION 3.8

3.73 The 20-ton trailer truck shown is traveling at 40 mph up a 1:30 incline. The rolling resistance is 0.07 times the weight on the tires. The wind resistance is given in lb by $0.3v^2$, where v is in ft/s. If the efficiency of the power transmission system is 75 percent, determine the horsepower that the engine must supply.

3.74 The 20-ton trailer truck of Problem 3.73 is equipped with a 600-hp engine and a power transmission system with an efficiency of 75 percent. The rolling resistance and the wind resistance are the same as those given in Problem 3.73. Determine the slope of the incline that this truck can climb at 55 mph.

Figure P3.73 and P3.74

3.75 The electric hoist shown raises a 1000-kg crate at a constant speed of 3 m/s. If the hoist efficiency is 90 percent, determine the power that the hoist must produce.

3.76 At a given instant the electric hoist raises a 1000-kg crate at a speed of 3 m/s and accelerates it upward at 2 m/s². If the hoist efficiency is 90 percent, determine the power that the hoist must supply at this instant.

3.77 A man weighing 780 N runs up the stairway shown in 6 s. Determine the average power that the man must deliver.

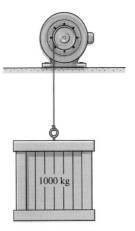

Figure P3.75 and P3.76

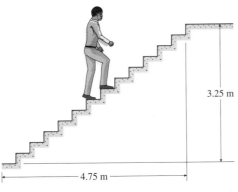

Figure P3.77

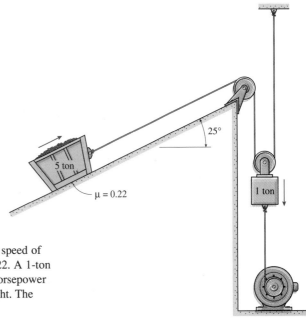

3.78 A 5-ton coal skip slides on a surface inclined at 25° at a constant speed of 8 ft/s. The coefficient of friction between the skip and the surface is 0.22. A 1-ton counterweight is attached to the hoist motor as shown. Determine the horsepower that the hoist motor must provide to move the skip and the counterweight. The masses of the pulleys are negligible.

Figure P3.78

3.79 A 2500-lb automobile engine starting from rest develops 90 hp in accelerating to 60 ft/s in 12 s. Determine the mechanical efficiency of the engine.

3.80 A 4000-lb car accelerates on a level test ground from a speed of 25 mph to 55 mph in 200 ft under the action of a tractive force F as shown. Determine the maximum power delivered by the engine during the period. (Engine efficiency = 70 percent.)

Figure P3.80

4

KINETICS OF PARTICLES: IMPULSE AND MOMENTUM

OUTLINE

4.1 INTRODUCTION

In Chapter 3 we saw that, when the primary focus is not the acceleration vector and when the forces acting on the system are expressed as a function of space coordinates, it is possible to integrate the equation of motion—after substituting for the acceleration vector the appropriate kinematic form in terms of space derivative—and thus eliminate the need to solve a differential equation each time. The resulting scalar equation represented the principle of work and kinetic energy. However, when the forces acting on the system are expressed as a function of time, the equation of motion can be integrated with respect to time, after substituting for the acceleration vector its appropriate kinematic form in terms of time derivative of space coordinates. The resulting vector relationship represents the principle of linear impulse and momentum. Furthermore, by considering the moments of the forces and momenta, a similar relationship representing the principle of angular impulse and momentum can also be developed.

Impulse and momentum principles have significant applications in problems relating to impulsive motion, impact or collision, and a vast array of attractive or repulsive forces called central forces, which play an important role in celestial and orbital mechanics as well as in quantum mechanics and theoretical physics.

4.2 LINEAR MOMENTUM AND IMPULSE

Linear Momentum

Considering the motion of a particle of mass m subjected to a force $\mathbf{F}$, we can write Newton's second law of motion as

$$\mathbf{F} = m\mathbf{a} = m\frac{d\mathbf{v}}{dt} \tag{4.1}$$

Assuming that the mass of a particle is constant, Equation (4.1) can be arranged to read

$$\mathbf{F} = \frac{d}{dt}(m\mathbf{v}) = \frac{d}{dt}(\mathbf{G}) = \dot{\mathbf{G}} \tag{4.2}$$

The vector $m\mathbf{v}$ is called the ***linear momentum*** of the particle. It is usually denoted by $\mathbf{G}$. If, however, the particle is subjected simultaneously to several forces having a resultant $\Sigma\mathbf{F}$, one can write

$$\Sigma\mathbf{F} = \frac{d}{dt}(m\mathbf{v}) \tag{4.3}$$

This equation states that *the resultant force acting on a particle is equal to the time rate of change of the linear momentum of the particle.* The units of linear momentum are N · s or kg · m/s in SI units and lb · s or slug ft/s in U.S. Customary units.

Linear Impulse

Multiplying both sides of Equation (4.3) by dt and integrating between the time limits $t_1(v = v_1)$ and $t_2(v = v_2)$ yields

$$\sum \int_{t_1}^{t_2} \mathbf{F}\, dt = \int_{v_1}^{v_2} d(m\mathbf{v}) = m\mathbf{v}_2 - m\mathbf{v}_1 = \mathbf{G}_2 - \mathbf{G}_1 \tag{4.4}$$

and, after rearranging terms,

$$m\mathbf{v}_1 + \sum \int_{t_1}^{t_2} \mathbf{F}\, dt = m\mathbf{v}_2 \tag{4.5}$$

The integral $\displaystyle\sum \int_{t_1}^{t_2} \mathbf{F}\, dt$ is called the resultant of all the **linear impulses** acting on the particle. Equation (4.5) states that *when a particle is acted upon by external forces acting during a given time interval* $(t_2 - t_1)$, *the final linear momentum* $m\mathbf{v}_2$ *of the particle is equal to the sum of its initial linear momentum* $m\mathbf{v}_1$ *and the linear impulses of the external forces.* The units of linear impulse are N · s or kg · m/s in SI units and lb · s or slug ft/s in U.S. Customary units, the same units as for linear momentum.

Figure 4.1 shows a graphical representation, called an *impulse diagram*, of the linear impulse–momentum equation. The vector summation on the left-hand side yields a resultant vector equal to the final linear momentum $m\mathbf{v}_2$.

Equation (4.5) is a vector relationship. When expressed in scalar form it is usually represented by three scalar equations. In the Cartesian coordinate system these are given in the form

$$\left.\begin{array}{l} m(v_1)_x + \displaystyle\sum \int_{t_1}^{t_2} F_x\, dt = m(v_2)_x \\[2ex] m(v_1)_y + \displaystyle\sum \int_{t_1}^{t_2} F_y\, dt = m(v_2)_y \\[2ex] m(v_1)_z + \displaystyle\sum \int_{t_1}^{t_2} F_z\, dt = m(v_2)_z \end{array}\right\} \tag{4.6}$$

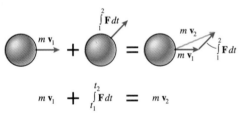

Figure 4.1

EXAMPLE 4.1

A 130-lb package is initially at rest on the floor of a plant. Suddenly a force $P = 250$ lb is applied to the package as shown.

Determine the package's speed 3 s after the force has been applied. The coefficient of kinetic friction between the package and the floor is 0.35.

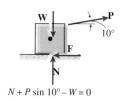

$N + P \sin 10° - W = 0$

Solution Considering the package to represent a particle of mass $m = W/g = (130/32.2)$ slug, we apply Equation (4.5) along the y axis and write

$$(\uparrow +) \; m(v_1)_y + \sum \int_{t_1}^{t_2} F_y \, dt = m(v_2)_y$$

Since $(v_1)_y = (v_2)_y = 0$,

$$0 + (P \sin 10° + N - W)(t_2 - t_1) = 0$$

$$(250 \sin 10° + N - 130)(3) = 0$$

$$N = 86.6 \text{ lb}$$

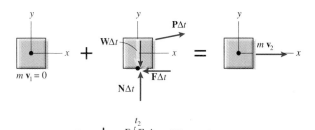

$$m\,\mathbf{v}_1 \;+\; \Sigma \int_{t_1}^{t_2} \mathbf{F}_i \, dt \;=\; m\,\mathbf{v}_2$$

Writing Equation (4.5) along the x axis with $(v_1)_x = 0$ and $(v_2)_x = v_2$, we have

$$(\xrightarrow{\pm}) \; 0 + (P_x - F_\mu)(\Delta t) = \left(\frac{W}{g}\right) v_2$$

and since $F_\mu = \mu_k N = (0.35)(86.6)$, $P_x = 250 \cos 10°$, and $\Delta t = 3$ s,

$$[250 \cos 10° - 0.35(86.6)]3 = \left(\frac{130}{32.2}\right) v_2$$

$$v_2 = 160 \text{ ft/s} \;\blacktriangleleft$$

Note that we could have alternately solved for N by using Newton's second law in the y-direction, with the acceleration in the y-direction being zero.

EXAMPLE 4.2

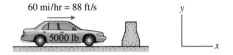

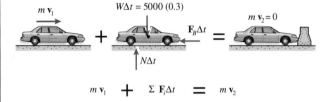

$$m\,\mathbf{v}_1 \quad + \quad \Sigma\,\mathbf{F}_i\Delta t \quad = \quad m\,\mathbf{v}_2$$

Determine the magnitude of the average force acting on a highway bumper, called a ''Jersey Barrier,'' when a 5000-lb car traveling at 60 mph crashes against it. The time interval during which the car is brought to rest is 0.3 s.

Solution The equation of linear impulse and momentum is written in the x direction, the car being the free body; thus,

$$mv_1 + (-F_B)_{\text{avg}}\,\Delta t = mv_2 = 0$$

$(F_B)_{\text{avg}}$ is the average force exerted by the bumper on the car and is given as

$$(F_B)_{\text{avg}} = \frac{1}{\Delta t}\int F(t)\,dt$$

After substituting for the initial velocity $v_1 = 60$ mph $= 88$ ft/s, and for the impulse period $\Delta t = 0.3$ s, we write

$$\left(\frac{5000}{32.2}\right)(88) - (F_B)_{\text{avg}}(0.3) = 0$$

$$(F_B)_{\text{avg}} = 45{,}500 \text{ lb (to the left)}$$

The force acting on the bumper is equal and opposite; hence,

$$(F_B)_{\text{avg}} = 45{,}500 \text{ lb (to the right)} \quad \blacktriangleleft$$

EXAMPLE 4.3

The initial velocity of a 15-lb block is given as $\mathbf{v}_1 = 15\mathbf{i} + 15\mathbf{j}$ (ft/s). A force defined by $\mathbf{F} = 250\mathbf{i} - 250t\mathbf{j}$ (lb) acts on the particle from time $t = 0$ to time $t = 0.3$ s for a total duration of 0.3 s. Determine the particle's velocity at $t = 1$ s. Neglect friction.

Solution The linear impulse–momentum equation when applied to the block between $t = 0$ and $t = 0.3$ s yields

$$m\mathbf{v}_1 + \int_{t=0}^{t=0.3} \mathbf{F}\,dt = m\mathbf{v}_2$$

and, upon substitution,

$$\left(\frac{15}{32.2}\right)(15\mathbf{i} + 15\mathbf{j}) + \int_0^{0.3}(250\mathbf{i} - 250t\mathbf{j})\,dt = \left(\frac{15}{32.2}\right)\mathbf{v}_2$$

Solving for $\mathbf{v}_2$,

$$\mathbf{v}_2 = 176\mathbf{i} - 9.15\,\mathbf{j}\,(\text{ft/s}) \quad \blacktriangleleft$$

The particle will maintain its final velocity (at $t = 0.3$) at all times $t > 0.3$ s.

EXAMPLE 4.4

A force F acting on a 25-lb block varies as shown. If the block is initially at rest, determine (*a*) the maximum speed of the block, and (*b*) the time when the block will change direction and move to the left. The coefficient of kinetic friction between the block and the horizontal surface is 0.20.

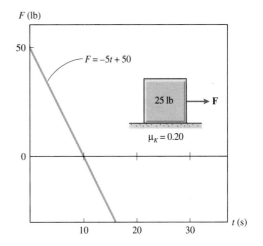

Solution

Part a. The equation of motion in the y direction yields immediately $N = W = 25$ lb and the friction force developed along the contact surface becomes

$$\mu_k N = \mu_k W = (0.20)(25) = 5 \text{ lb}$$

as long as the body remains in motion. The speed of the block will continue increasing as long as the force F is larger than the frictional resistance $\mu_k N$, which is constant and equal to 5 lb. Therefore, the maximum speed will occur when $F = 5$ lb. From the figure shown we conclude that the maximum speed will occur at $t_1 = 9$ s, and its magnitude can now be obtained through the x component of the linear impulse–momentum relationship

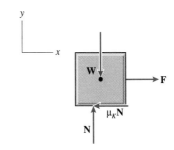

$$mv_0 + \left[\int_0^{t_1} F\, dt - \int_0^{t_1} \mu_k N\, dt \right] = mv_1 \qquad (a)$$

where v_0, the initial speed, is zero and v_1 is the maximum speed at time $t_1 = 9$ s.

Initial linear momentum:

$$mv_0 = \left(\frac{25}{32.2} \right)(0) = 0$$

Final linear momentum:

$$mv_1 = \left(\frac{25}{32.2} \right)v_1$$

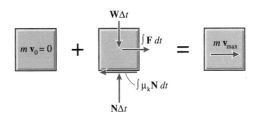

Linear impulse due to F:

$$\int_0^{t_1 = 9} F\, dt = \int_0^{t_1 = 9} (-5t + 50)\, dt = 247.5 \text{ lb} \cdot \text{s}$$

Linear impulse due to $(-\mu_k N)$:

$$-\mu_k W \int_0^{t_1 = 9} dt = -(0.2)(25)(9) = -45 \text{ lb} \cdot \text{s}$$

Substituting the above values into Equation (a) yields

$$0 + (247.5 - 45) = \left(\frac{25}{32.2} \right)v_1$$

(*continued*)

EXAMPLE 4.4   *(concluded)*

and solving for v_1 we obtain the maximum speed of the block as

$$v_1 = \left[\frac{202.5}{\left(\dfrac{25}{32.2} \right)} \right]$$

$$v_1 = 260.8 \text{ ft/s} \blacktriangleleft$$

Part b. At the instant when the block changes direction, its speed will become zero. Therefore, the final linear momentum of the block will also be zero and the x component of the linear

impulse–momentum equation can be written as

$$(mv_0 = 0) + \int_0^{t_2} F\,dt - \int_0^{t_2} \mu_k N\,dt = (mv_2 = 0)$$

$$\left[-\frac{5}{2}t_2^2 + 50t_2 \right] - [5t_2] = 0$$

Upon dividing by t_2, we have

$$2.5t_2 = 45 \qquad\qquad t_2 = 18 \text{ s} \blacktriangleleft$$

The block will reverse direction after 18 seconds.

4.3 CONSERVATION OF LINEAR MOMENTUM

When the resultant of all the linear impulses acting on a particle of constant mass is zero, Equation (4.5) is reduced to

$$m\mathbf{v}_1 = m\mathbf{v}_2$$

It follows that the magnitude and direction of the linear momentum $m\mathbf{v}$ of the particle will not change with time. For a particle of constant mass, the above result represents the **conservation of linear momentum**. It states that when the resultant of all the linear impulses acting on a particle of constant mass is zero, the velocity of the particle will remain constant for the duration and the particle will not accelerate (Newton's first law of motion).

4.4 IMPULSIVE MOTION

The linear impulse–momentum relationship can be applied to a special case that occurs when a very large force acts on a particle during a very short period of time $\Delta t = t_2 - t_1$. The very large magnitude of this force—called an **impulsive force**—would justify neglecting all other forces; and, assuming that it remains constant during the time interval Δt, the integral term is reduced to

$$\int_{t_1}^{t_2} \mathbf{F}\,dt = \mathbf{F}\int_{t_1}^{t_2} dt = \mathbf{F}(t_2 - t_1) = \mathbf{F}\,\Delta t$$

Equation (4.5) can then be written as

$$m\mathbf{v}_1 + \mathbf{F}\,\Delta t = m\mathbf{v}_2 \tag{4.7}$$

The above analysis of the impulsive motion can be used to solve problems involving multiple particles. By writing a separate impulse–momentum equation for each particle and summing them up vectorially, we obtain

$$\Sigma(m\mathbf{v}_i)_1 + \Sigma \int_{t_1}^{t_2} \mathbf{F}\, dt = \Sigma(m\mathbf{v}_i)_2 \qquad (4.8)$$

Considering the fact that the force exerted by one particle on another is equal but opposite to the reaction exerted by the impacted particle (action-reaction principle, Newton's third law), the sum of the impulses of such internal forces is zero. The only impulsive forces contributing to the second term of Equation (4.8) are the external forces.

The collision between two particles moving freely is a special case in which no external impulsive forces are involved and, hence, the impulse term is zero. Equation (4.8) is thus reduced to

$$\Sigma(m\mathbf{v}_i)_1 = \Sigma(m\mathbf{v}_i)_2 \qquad (4.9)$$

This states that the total momentum of the system of particles is conserved; that is, the sum of their precollision momenta is equal to the sum of their postcollision momenta.

EXAMPLE 4.5

A pitcher throws a fast ball that is moving at a speed of 90 mph. The batter hits the ball in the direction shown. The ball leaves the bat at a speed of 175 mph. If the bat and the ball are in contact for 0.020 s, determine the average impulsive force exerted on the ball by the batter during the impact. The ball weighs 0.25 lb.

Solution The linear impulse–momentum equation written in the x direction becomes

$$\overset{+}{(\to)}\ (mv_1)_x + (F_B)_x \Delta t = (mv_2)_x$$

$$\left(\frac{0.25}{32.2}\right)(90)\left(\frac{88\ \text{ft/s}}{60\ \text{mph}}\right) - (F_B)_x(0.020)$$

$$= \left(\frac{0.25}{32.2}\right)(-175)\left(\frac{88}{60}\right)(\cos 35°)$$

$$(F_B)_x = 133\ \text{lb}$$

Expressing the linear impulse–momentum equation in the y direction, we obtain

$$\overset{+}{(\uparrow)}\ (mv_1)_y + (F_B)_y \Delta t = (mv_2)_y$$

$$\left(\frac{0.25}{32.2}\right)(0) + (F_B)_y(0.02) = \left(\frac{0.25}{32.2}\right)(175)\left(\frac{88}{60}\right)(\sin 35°)$$

$$(F_B)_y = 57.2\ \text{lb}$$

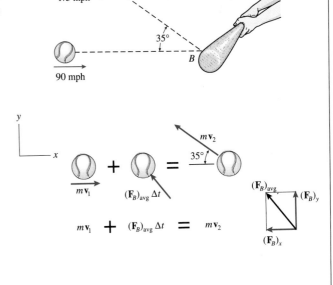

(*continued*)

EXAMPLE 4.5 *(concluded)*

The resultant impulsive force exerted on the ball is

$$\mathbf{F}_B = 133\mathbf{i} + 57.2\mathbf{j} \text{ (lb)} \blacktriangleleft$$

having a magnitude and a direction (given by angle α) of

$$F_B = (133^2 + 57.2^2)^{1/2} \qquad F_B = 145 \text{ lb} \blacktriangleleft$$

$$\alpha = \tan^{-1}\left(\frac{57.2}{133}\right) \qquad \alpha = 23.3° \blacktriangleleft$$

It is important to note that in the solution of the problem we have ignored the weight of the ball. The gravitational force, which is a nonimpulsive force, is significantly smaller than the

impulsive force of the bat. Inclusion of the weight of the ball (0.25 lb) during impact would alter the y equation in the following manner.

$$[(F_B)_y - W](0.02) = \left(\frac{0.25}{32.2}\right)\left(\frac{88}{60}\right)(175 \sin 35°)$$

$$(F_B)_y = \left(\frac{0.25}{32.2}\right)\left(\frac{88}{60}\right)\left(\frac{175 \sin 35°}{0.02}\right) + W$$

$$(F_B)_y = 57.2 + 0.25 = 57.2(1 + 0.004) = 57.4 \text{ lb}$$

Thus the error introduced by ignoring the nonimpulsive force (weight) is less than 0.5 percent.

EXAMPLE 4.6

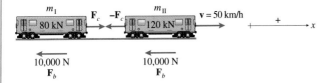

Car I and Car II
$(m_1 + m_{II})$

$(m_1 + m_{II})\mathbf{v}_1 \quad - \quad 2\,\mathbf{F}_B\Delta t \quad = \quad (m_1 + m_{II})\mathbf{v}_2 = 0$

A subway train made of two cars is shown. It travels at a speed of 50 km/h. When the brakes are applied, a braking force of 10,000 N is applied to each car. Determine (*a*) the time required for the train to stop after the brakes are applied, and (*b*) the brake force in the coupling between the cars.

Solution

Part a. Considering the entire train as a single element, the total brake force acting on the train is 20,000 N and the linear impulse–momentum relationship, Equation (4.8), is expressed as

$$\Sigma(m\mathbf{v}_1) + \Sigma(\mathbf{F}\,\Delta t) = \Sigma(m\mathbf{v}_2)$$

When written along the x axis, this equation becomes

$$\overset{+}{\oplus}\left(\frac{200,000}{9.81}\right)\left(\frac{50,000}{3,600}\right) - (20,000)(\Delta t) = \left(\frac{200,000}{9.81}\right)(0)$$

$$\Delta t = 14.158 \text{ s} \blacktriangleleft$$

It will take 14.158 seconds for the train to come to a full stop.

(continued)

EXAMPLE 4.6   (*concluded*)

Part b. Next, we apply the linear impulse–momentum equation to either one of the cars. For the second car, we write

$$m_{II}\mathbf{v}_1 + \mathbf{F}\,\Delta t = m_{II}\mathbf{v}_2 \qquad (a)$$

which upon substitution yields, in the *x* direction,

$$\oplus \left(\frac{120{,}000}{9.81}\right)\left(\frac{50{,}000}{3{,}600}\right) - (10{,}000 + F_c)(14.158) = 0$$

$$10{,}000 + F_c = 12{,}000$$

$$F_c = +2000 \text{ N (Tension)} \; \ominus \; \blacktriangleleft$$

If we applied Equation (4.8) to the first car ($m_I = 80{,}000/9.81$) we would obtain

$$m_I\mathbf{v}_1 + \mathbf{F}\,\Delta t = m_I\mathbf{v}_2 \qquad (b)$$

which upon substitution yields, in the *x* direction,

$$\oplus \left(\frac{80{,}000}{9.81}\right)\left(\frac{50{,}000}{3{,}600}\right) - (10{,}000 - F_c)(14{,}158) = 0$$

$$10{,}000 - F_c = 8000$$

$$F_c = +2000 \text{ N (Tension)} \; \oplus$$

which is the same answer as obtained using Equation (a), except that the internal force of the coupling (F_c) is now in the opposite direction.

As indicated by the arrow signs, the coupling force F_c is a tensile force.

Car I

$$m_I\mathbf{v}_1 \quad - \quad (\mathbf{F}_b - \mathbf{F}_c)\Delta t \quad = \quad m_I\mathbf{v}_2 = 0$$

or
Car II

$$m_{II}\mathbf{v}_1 \quad - \quad (\mathbf{F}_b + \mathbf{F}_c)\Delta t \quad = \quad m_{II}\mathbf{v}_2 = 0$$

EXAMPLE 4.7

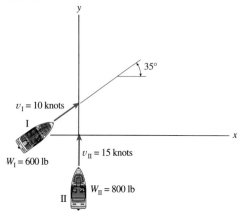

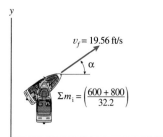

A 600-lb boat is traveling at a speed of 10 knots when it collides with an 800-lb boat moving at 15 knots. The boats move in the directions indicated. Upon impact the two boats remain interlocked and move as a single unit. Determine the velocity of the combined mass and its direction right after impact. (Ignore the fluid friction over the hull.)

Solution   The only forces external to the system formed by the two boats are their vertical weights. Therefore, there are no horizontal external forces and the linear momentum is conserved in the horizontal plane along both the x and y directions. Using Equation (4.9), we write

$$(m_\mathrm{I}\mathbf{v}_\mathrm{I} + m_\mathrm{II}\mathbf{v}_\mathrm{II})_\mathrm{initial} = (m_\mathrm{I} + m_\mathrm{II})(\mathbf{v})_\mathrm{final}$$

This equation can be projected along the x and the y directions to yield

$$\left(\frac{600}{32.2}\right)(10 \times 1.69)(\cos 35°) + \left(\frac{800}{32.2}\right)(0) = \left(\frac{1400}{32.2}\right)(v_f)_x$$

$$(v_f)_x = 5.93 \text{ ft/s}$$

$$\left(\frac{600}{32.2}\right)(10 \times 1.69)(\sin 35°) + \left(\frac{800}{32.2}\right)(15 \times 1.69)$$

$$= \left(\frac{1400}{32.2}\right)(v_f)_y$$

$$(v_f)_y = 18.6 \text{ ft/s}$$

The velocity of the combined mass is given by

$$\mathbf{v} = 5.93\mathbf{i} + 18.6\mathbf{j} \text{ (ft/s)} \blacktriangleleft$$

and the speed can be calculated from this as

$$v = (5.93^2 + 18.6^2)^{1/2} = 19.52 \text{ ft/s}$$

or considering that 1 knot = 1.69 ft/s

$$v = \frac{19.52}{1.69} = 11.6 \text{ knots}$$

The inclination of the velocity vector is given by the angle α which is evaluated from

$$\alpha = \tan^{-1}\left(\frac{18.6}{5.93}\right) \qquad \alpha = 72.32° \blacktriangleleft$$

4.5 IMPACT

The collision between two deformable bodies is another special case to which the principle of linear impulse and momentum can be applied. Although rigid bodies will remain the main focus of our attention throughout this text, the problem of two deformable bodies exerting upon each other a relatively large contact force for a very short duration is of considerable interest and is called *impact*.

The relative motions of two particles impacting upon each other are described with reference to their line of impact—the line normal to the plane of contact between the two bodies—as either *central impact*, or *eccentric impact*. Central impact occurs when the mass centers of the two bodies are along the line of impact, as in Figure 4.2a. All other cases are defined as eccentric impact (Figure 4.2b) and are beyond the scope of the present text. Central impact, which we will discuss in more detail below, can be described either as *direct central impact*, or *oblique central impact*. Direct central impact (Figure 4.2c) occurs when the velocities of the two particles are collinear with the line of impact. Oblique central impact (Figure 4.2d) is defined as the impact of two particles of which either or both have velocities that are not collinear with the line of impact.

Direct Central Impact

When two deformable bodies, each assumed to be particle size, collide during a collinear impact, each is acted upon by a very large force for a very short duration. (The reason for considering the bodies as particles is to limit the discussion to cases involving purely linear impulse and momentum.)

Consider two spheres moving along a straight line called the line of impact as shown in Figure 4.3. Figure 4.3a represents the situation prior to the col-

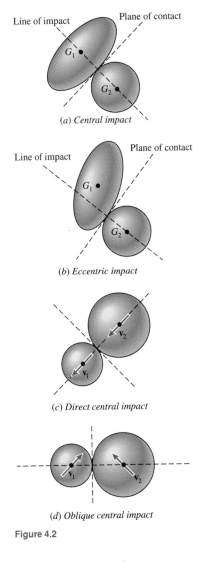

(a) Central impact

(b) Eccentric impact

(c) Direct central impact

(d) Oblique central impact

Figure 4.2

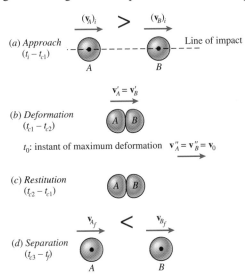

(a) Approach
$(t_i - t_{c1})$

(b) Deformation
$(t_{c1} - t_{c2})$

t_0: instant of maximum deformation $\mathbf{v}''_A = \mathbf{v}''_B = \mathbf{v}_0$

(c) Restitution
$(t_{c2} - t_{c1})$

(d) Separation
$(t_{c3} - t_f)$

Figure 4.3

lision of the bodies. The bodies may be moving in the same direction or in opposite directions. Together, Figures 4.3b and 4.3c represent the period during which the two bodies are in contact and deforming continually while maintaining a common speed. The deformation first increases (Figure 4.3b) and later decreases (Figure 4.3c). These periods of increasing and decreasing deformations are called deformation and restitution periods, respectively. Finally the two bodies move apart and the dynamic condition called impact comes to an end (Figure 4.3d). Each body now has acquired a new velocity and momentum, the direction and magnitude of which are determined by the initial momenta of the spheres and the energy they have lost during impact.

Applying the principle of conservation of linear momentum along the line of impact yields

$$(m_A v_A)_i + (m_B v_B)_i = (m_A v_A)_f + (m_B v_B)_f \tag{4.10}$$

In writing this equation we have assumed the following:

1. All external forces acting on the two-body system during impact are negligible compared to the internal impact force.
2. The duration of impact is short enough to justify ignoring the displacement of the two bodies while they are in contact with each other.

Let us now write, for each body, the linear impulse–momentum equations for the deformation and restitution periods. Thus, for body A, we obtain for the components along the line of impact

Deformation period $\quad m_A(v_A)_i - \int_0^{t_0} F_d \, dt = m_A(v_0) \tag{4.11a}$

Restitution period $\quad m_A(v_0) - \int_{t_0}^{t} F_r \, dt = m_A(v_A)_f \tag{4.11b}$

where F_d and F_r are the impulsive forces exerted on the body A during the deformation and restitution periods, respectively. Note that they are in opposition to the movement of the particle.

Dividing Equation (4.11a) into Equation (4.11b), we obtain the *coefficient of restitution e* in the form

$$e = \frac{\displaystyle\int_{t_0}^{t} F_r \, dt}{\displaystyle\int_0^{t_0} F_d \, dt} = \frac{m_A[v_0 - (v_A)_f]}{m_A[(v_A)_i - v_0]} = \frac{v_0 - (v_A)_f}{(v_A)_i - v_0} \tag{4.12}$$

For body B, the corresponding linear impulse–momentum equations, written along the same line of impact, become

Deformation period $\quad m_B(v_B)_i + \int_0^{t_0} F_d \, dt = m_B(v_0) \tag{4.13a}$

Restitution period $\qquad m_B(v_0) + \displaystyle\int_{t_0}^{t} F_r \, dt = m_B(v_B)_f \qquad$ (4.13b)

Note that the impulsive forces F_d and F_r acting on the body B during the deformation and restitution periods, respectively, are in the same direction with the motion of the particle. The ratio e for body B is written as

$$ e = \frac{\displaystyle\int_{t_0}^{t} F_r \, dt}{\displaystyle\int_{0}^{t_0} F_d \, dt} = \frac{m_B[v_0 - (v_B)_f]}{m_B[(v_B)_i - v_0]} = \frac{v_0 - (v_B)_f}{(v_B)_i - v_0} \qquad (4.14) $$

Eliminating v_0 between Equations (4.12) and (4.14) yields for the coefficient of restitution an expression in terms of the velocities of approach (indicated by the subscript i) and the velocities of separation (indicated by the subscript f),

$$ e = \frac{(v_B)_f - (v_A)_f}{(v_A)_i - (v_B)_i} \qquad (4.15) $$

where both velocity differences are in the line-of-impact direction.

Equation (4.15) has been derived for the case represented in Figure 4.3. Should particles A and B approach toward each other or move to the left, the signs of the numerator and of the denominator would be affected. A general form of the expression for the coefficient of restitution is given as

$$ e = \left| \frac{\text{relative velocity of separation}}{\text{relative velocity of approach}} \right| \qquad (4.16) $$

The value of the coefficient of restitution e is between $e = 1$ and $e = 0$. All real impact cases are represented by a value of e between these two extremes. The ideal impact case represented by $e = 1$ is referred to as *perfectly elastic impact*. The two bodies will separate from each other with the same relative velocity at which they were approaching each other. The restitution or recovery from deformation is complete and there is no energy loss in the process. The other ideal impact case represented by $e = 0$ is called *perfectly plastic (inelastic) impact*. In the absence of any restoring force (i.e., $F_r = 0$) the two bodies will remain permanently deformed and unable to separate from each other. Energy loss is at a maximum, although the total momentum of the system is conserved. Energy losses accompanying impact are due to the generation and eventual loss of heat during the deformation of the material. They are also caused by the generation and dissipation of stress and sound waves through the bodies. Thus the coefficient of restitution depends not only on the relative impact velocity but also on the contacting materials.

Oblique Central Impact

In analyzing this case we shall assume the surface of the colliding bodies to be smooth enough so that we may ignore all friction forces developing between the two bodies.

Applying the linear impulse–momentum relationship to each body between initial (pre-impact) and final (postimpact) positions, as shown in Figure 4.4, and written along the plane of contact (y axis) yields, for body A,

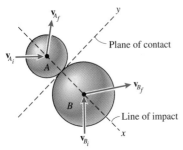

Plane of contact

Line of impact

Figure 4.4

$$[m_A(v_A)_i]_y + \underbrace{\int_{t_i}^{t_f} F_y \, dt}_{= \, 0} = [m_A(v_A)_f]_y \tag{4.17}$$

and for body B,

$$[m_B(v_B)_i]_y + \underbrace{\int_{t_i}^{t_f} F_y \, dt}_{= \, 0} = [m_B(v_B)_f]_y \tag{4.18}$$

Since the only impulsive forces acting along the plane of contact are the friction forces, the assumption of smooth contact surfaces allows us to reduce the equations to

$$[(v_A)_i]_y = [(v_A)_f]_y \tag{4.19}$$

$$[(v_B)_i]_y = [(v_B)_f]_y \tag{4.20}$$

Hence, the y component of the velocity vector of each body remains unchanged.

Along the line of impact (x axis) the impulsive forces occurring between the two bodies are equal and opposite, their net effect is zero, and the conservation of linear momentum relationship [Equation (4.9)] when applied to the two-body system will give

$$\underbrace{[m_A(v_A)_i]_x + [m_B(v_B)_i]_x}_{\substack{\text{Total initial momentum} \\ \text{(before impact)}}} = \underbrace{[m_A(v_A)_f]_x + [m_B(v_B)_f]_x}_{\substack{\text{Total final momentum} \\ \text{(after impact)}}} \tag{4.21}$$

The fourth and final relationship necessary for determining the four unknowns $[(v_A)_f]_x$, $[(v_A)_f]_y$, $[(v_B)_f]_x$, and $[(v_B)_f]_y$ is the relationship between the relative velocity of approach $[(v_A)_i - (v_B)_i]_x$ and the relative velocity of separation $[(v_B)_f - (v_A)_f]_x$, indicated by the coefficient of restitution e. Since the motion along the plane of contact does not contribute to the deformation and recovery (restitution) periods, it is the velocity components along the line of impact that are again considered, and we write

$$[(v_B)_f - (v_A)_f]_x = e[(v_A)_i - (v_B)_i]_x \tag{4.22}$$

Equations (4.21) and (4.22) can now be solved simultaneously for $[(v_A)_f]_x$ and $[(v_B)_f]_x$.

Displacement before and after Impact

The linear impulse–momentum relationship is a powerful tool in the solution of problems involving impulsive forces. Recall that it is the integral form of the equation of motion, with the integration carried out over time and between the instant prior to impact and the instant immediately following it. In certain problems, it might be necessary to determine the kinematic conditions prevailing before or after the impact. For example, the impact velocity of a body A may not be given explicitly, but instead the body's motion prior to impact may have been defined. Or the problem may focus on the kinematic conditions describing the motion of a body B after it has been impacted by body A. In such cases, the use of the equation of motion ($\mathbf{F} = m\mathbf{a}$) or the work-energy methods applied to a single body will prove effective. However, the work-energy relationship, which is an integrated form of the equation of motion, cannot be applied between a pre-impact and a postimpact position, as the impact phenomena are almost always accompanied by energy losses.

EXAMPLE   4.8

Two smooth spheres of equal mass collide as shown. The velocity vectors of the mass centers of the spheres, prior to impact, are given as $\mathbf{v}_A = 40\mathbf{i} + 20\mathbf{j}$ (ft/s), and $\mathbf{v}_B = -20\mathbf{i} - 40\mathbf{j}$ (ft/s). Assuming the coefficient of restitution to equal 0.75, determine the postimpact velocities of the spheres.

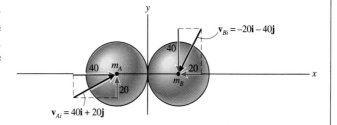

Solution   Writing Equations (4.19) and (4.20) for two spheres A and B of identical masses m, we have

For sphere A: $[(v_A)_f]_y = [(v_A)_i]_y = 20$ ft/s   (a)

For sphere B: $[(v_B)_f]_y = [(v_B)_i]_y = -40$ ft/s   (b)

Next, considering the system consisting of the two spheres, the conservation of linear momentum equation [Equation (4.21)] gives

$$m(40) + m(-20) = m[(v_A)_f]_x + m[(v_B)_f]_x$$

After simplification this becomes

$$[(v_A)_f]_x + [(v_B)_f]_x = 20$$ (c)

Finally, Equation (4.22) can be written as

$$[(v_B)_f]_x - [(v_A)_f]_x = 0.75[40 - (-20)]$$
$$[(v_B)_f]_x - [(v_A)_f]_x = 45$$ (d)

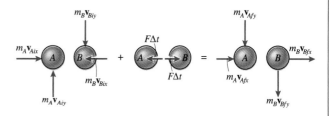

(continued)

EXAMPLE 4.8 *(concluded)*

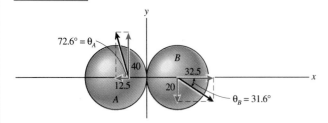

Solving Equations (c) and (d) simultaneously, we obtain

$$[(v_B)_f]_x = \frac{65}{2} = 32.5 \text{ ft/s}$$

$$[(v_A)_f]_x = \frac{-25}{2} = -12.5 \text{ ft/s}$$

The final, or postimpact, velocities can now be expressed in vector form as

$$(\mathbf{v}_A)_f = -12.5\mathbf{i} + 20\mathbf{j} \text{ (ft/s)} \blacktriangleleft$$
$$(\mathbf{v}_B)_f = 32.5\mathbf{i} - 40\mathbf{j} \text{ (ft/s)} \blacktriangleleft$$

The magnitude and the direction of the velocities can also be given as

$$(\mathbf{v}_A)_f = 23.58 \text{ ft/s}, \ \theta_A = 58°$$
$$(\mathbf{v}_B)_f = 51.54 \text{ ft/s}, \ \theta_B = 50.9°$$

EXAMPLE 4.9

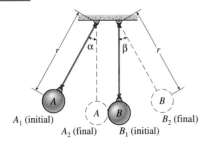

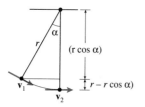

Two spheres of equal mass occupy the initial positions shown. Sphere A is released from rest. Determine the angle β through which the sphere B is expected to swing. The coefficient of restitution between the spheres is e.

Solution

Pre-impact conditions. We need to determine the velocity of sphere A right before impact. For this, we will apply the work–kinetic energy relationship to sphere A.

For the velocity of A at position 1, $(v_A)_1 = 0$; for the kinetic energy of A at 1, $(T_A)_1 = 0$.

For the velocity of A at position 2, $(v_A)_2 = (v_A)_i$; for the kinetic energy of A at 2, $(T_A)_2 = \frac{1}{2}m(v_A^2)_i$. The work done by A from 1 to 2 is

$$(U_A)_{1\rightarrow2} = mg[r(1 - \cos \alpha)]$$

Hence we write the equation $T_1 + U_{1\rightarrow2} = T_2$ by substituting the various terms,

$$0 + mg[r(1 - \cos \alpha)] = \frac{1}{2}m(v_A^2)_i$$

(continued)

EXAMPLE 4.9   (*concluded*)

and solving for $(v_A)_i$, we write

$$(v_A)_i = [2gr(1 - \cos \alpha)]^{1/2} \tag{a}$$

Impact. To analyze the impact between A and B, we will apply the principle of conservation of linear momentum, Equation (4.10), and the expression for the coefficient of restitution, Equation (4.16). First we state the initial or pre-impact and final or postimpact conditions on the velocities of the spheres.

For sphere A, from Equation (a), $(v_A)_i = [2gr(1 - \cos \alpha)]^{1/2}$; $(v_A)_f$ is to be determined and will be assumed to be to the right. For sphere B, $(v_B)_i = 0$, and $(v_B)_f$ is to be determined.

From Equation (4.10)

$$m(v_A)_i + 0 = m(v_A)_f + m(v_B)_f \tag{b}$$

From Equation (4.16)

$$(v_B)_f - (v_A)_f = e[(v_A)_i - 0] \tag{c}$$

Eliminating $(v_A)_f$ between Equations (b) and (c) and solving for $(v_B)_f$ yields

$$2(v_B)_f = (v_A)_i + e(v_A)_i$$

$$(v_B)_f = \frac{1 + e}{2}(v_A)_i \tag{d}$$

Postimpact conditions. Once we know the postimpact velocity of sphere B, that is, $(v_B)_f$, we can analyze the motion of B,

again using the work–kinetic energy principle.

For the velocity of B at 1, $(v_B)_1 = (v_B)_f$; for the kinetic energy of B at 1, $(T_B)_1 = \frac{1}{2}m(v_B)_f^2$.

For the velocity of B at 2, $(v_B)_2 = 0$; for the kinetic energy of B at 2, $(T_B)_2 = 0$.

For the work done by B from 1 to 2, $(U_B)_{1\to2} = -mg[r(1 - \cos \beta)]$. Note that the work term $(U_B)_{1\to2}$ carries a minus sign because the vertical displacement is upward and the gravity force (weight) is downward. Hence we write the relationship $T_1 + (U_B)_{1\to2} = T_2$ in the form

$$\frac{1}{2}m(v_B)_f^2 - mg[r(1 - \cos \beta)] = 0$$

Solving for $(v_B)_f$ yields

$$(v_B)_f = [2gr(1 - \cos \beta)]^{1/2} \tag{e}$$

Eliminating $(v_A)_i$ and $(v_B)_f$ from Equations (a), (d), and (e) we have

$$\frac{1 + e}{2}[2gr(1 - \cos \alpha)]^{1/2} = [2gr(1 - \cos \beta)]^{1/2}$$

and from this we solve for the angle β:

$$\beta = \cos^{-1}\left[1 - \left(\frac{1 + e}{2}\right)^2(1 - \cos \alpha)\right] \blacktriangleleft$$

4.6 ANGULAR MOMENTUM AND IMPULSE

Angular Momentum

Consider a particle P of mass m moving with a velocity $\mathbf{v}$ in a fixed xyz coordinate system as shown in Figure 4.5. The **angular momentum $\mathbf{H}_O$** of the particle about the origin O is defined as the moment of the particle's linear momentum $m\mathbf{v}$, and is indicated by

$$\mathbf{H}_O = \mathbf{r} \times m\mathbf{v} \tag{4.23}$$

The angular-momentum vector $\mathbf{H}_O$ is, therefore, perpendicular to the instantaneous plane of motion defined by $\mathbf{r}$ and $\mathbf{v}$. Equation (4.23) is a vector relationship; it can be evaluated after being reduced to its three scalar components.

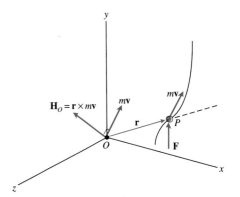

Figure 4.5

In the Cartesian coordinate system, we write

$$(H_O)_x\mathbf{i} + (H_O)_y\mathbf{j} + (H_O)_z\mathbf{k} = \begin{vmatrix} \mathbf{i} & \mathbf{j} & \mathbf{k} \\ x & y & z \\ mv_x & mv_y & mv_z \end{vmatrix}$$

and after expanding the determinant, we obtain

$$(H_O)_x = m(yv_z - zv_y)$$
$$(H_O)_y = m(zv_x - xv_z) \qquad (4.24)$$
$$(H_O)_z = m(xv_y - yv_x)$$

Next, we will consider the relationship between the forces acting on the particle and the particle's angular momentum. The equation of motion for a particle P of constant mass m is

$$\Sigma\mathbf{F} = m\mathbf{a} = \frac{d}{dt}(m\mathbf{v})$$

where $\Sigma\mathbf{F}$ is the net resultant of all the external forces acting on the particle.

If, now, we develop the vector product multiplication of each side of the above equation by the position vector $\mathbf{r}$, we have

$$\Sigma\mathbf{M}_O = \mathbf{r} \times \Sigma\mathbf{F} = \mathbf{r} \times m\mathbf{a} = \mathbf{r} \times \frac{d}{dt}(m\mathbf{v}) \qquad (4.25)$$

From vector calculus, we write

$$\mathbf{r} \times \frac{d}{dt}(m\mathbf{v}) = \frac{d}{dt}(\mathbf{r} \times m\mathbf{v}) - \dot{\mathbf{r}} \times m\mathbf{v} \qquad (4.26)$$

However, since $\dot{\mathbf{r}} = \mathbf{v}$, the second term on the right-hand side is zero ($\mathbf{v} \times m\mathbf{v} = 0$) and Equation (4.25) can now be written as

$$\Sigma\mathbf{M}_O = \mathbf{r} \times m\mathbf{a} = \frac{d}{dt}(\mathbf{r} \times m\mathbf{v})$$

and we conclude

$$\Sigma\mathbf{M}_O = \dot{\mathbf{H}}_O \qquad (4.27)$$

Equation (4.27) states that the *moment—about a fixed origin O—of all the external forces acting on a particle is equal to the time rate of change of the angular momentum of the particle.*

Expressed in scalar form, Equation (4.27) can be written as

$$\Sigma(M_O)_x\mathbf{i} + \Sigma(M_O)_y\mathbf{j} + \Sigma(M_O)_z\mathbf{k} = (\dot{H}_O)_x\mathbf{i} + (\dot{H}_O)_y\mathbf{j} + (\dot{H}_O)_z\mathbf{k} \qquad (4.28)$$

or in determinant form

$$\begin{vmatrix} \mathbf{i} & \mathbf{j} & \mathbf{k} \\ x & y & z \\ \Sigma F_x & \Sigma F_y & \Sigma F_z \end{vmatrix} = \frac{d}{dt} \begin{vmatrix} \mathbf{i} & \mathbf{j} & \mathbf{k} \\ x & y & z \\ mv_x & mv_y & mv_z \end{vmatrix} \qquad (4.29)$$

The final three scalar equations, in the Cartesian coordinate system, become

$$\Sigma(M_O)_x = yF_z - zF_y = \frac{d}{dt}[m(yv_z - zv_y)] = (\dot{H}_O)_x$$

$$\Sigma(M_O)_y = zF_x - xF_z = \frac{d}{dt}[m(zv_x - xv_z)] = (\dot{H}_O)_y \qquad (4.30)$$

$$\Sigma(M_O)_z = xF_y - yF_x = \frac{d}{dt}[m(xv_y - yv_x)] = (\dot{H}_O)_x$$

When considering plane curvilinear motion of a particle (Figure 4.6), the angular-momentum vector $\mathbf{H}_O = \mathbf{r} \times m\mathbf{v}$ will always be perpendicular to the xy plane of the motion and its direction determined by the right-hand rule. The magnitude of the angular momentum can be written as

$$H_O = rmv \sin \phi = rm(v \sin \phi) = rmv_\theta \qquad (4.31)$$

and, since $v_\theta = r\dot{\theta}$,

$$H_O = mr^2\dot{\theta} \qquad (4.32)$$

The units of angular momentum are $N \cdot m \cdot s$ or $kg \cdot m^2/s$ in SI units, and $lb \cdot ft \cdot s$ or $slug \cdot ft^2/s$ when using U.S. Customary units.

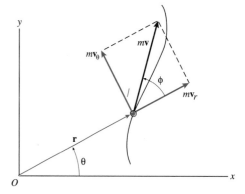

Figure 4.6

Angular Impulse

Integrating Equation (4.27) between time limits t_1 and t_2, we obtain

$$\Sigma \int_{t_1}^{t_2} \mathbf{M}_O \, dt = (\mathbf{H}_O)_2 - (\mathbf{H}_O)_1 \qquad (4.33)$$

The left-hand side of Equation (4.33) represents the *angular impulse* about O of the resultant external force acting on the particle. Equation (4.33) states that the angular impulse about O of all external forces acting on a particle is equal to the change of angular momentum of the particle during the period of time under consideration. Rearranging the terms, we write Equation (4.33) as

$$(\mathbf{H}_O)_1 + \Sigma \int_{t_1}^{t_2} \mathbf{M}_O \, dt = (\mathbf{H}_O)_2 \qquad (4.34)$$

The units of angular impulse, like those of angular momentum, are $N \cdot m \cdot s$ or $kg \cdot m^2/s$ in SI units, and $lb \cdot ft \cdot s$ or $slug \cdot ft^2/s$ in U.S. Customary units.

4.7 CONSERVATION OF ANGULAR MOMENTUM

If and when the angular impulse $\Sigma M_O \, dt$, about a fixed point O, of all the external forces acting on a particle is zero, Equation (4.33) yields

$$(\mathbf{H}_O)_1 + \underbrace{\Sigma \int_{t_1}^{t_2} \mathbf{M}_O \, dt}_{= \, 0} = (\mathbf{H}_O)_2 \tag{4.35}$$

The above expression will also be obtained, if and when the resultant moment ΣM_O, about a fixed point O, of all the external forces acting on a particle is zero such as the case when all forces are directed toward O. This represents a special case of the above condition. Thus, we have

$$\Sigma \mathbf{M}_O = \dot{\mathbf{H}}_O = 0$$

which represents a constant angular momentum $\mathbf{H}_O$ or

$$(\mathbf{H}_O)_1 = (\mathbf{H}_O)_2 = \text{constant} \tag{4.36}$$

Equation (4.36) illustrates *the conservation of angular momentum* with reference to a fixed point O.

EXAMPLE 4.10

A 2-kg particle is defined by its position vector $\mathbf{r} = 7t^2\mathbf{i} + 3t^3\mathbf{j}\,(m)$, where t is in seconds. Determine the expression for the angular momentum $\mathbf{H}_O$ of the particle about the origin O. Also, find the expression for the force $\mathbf{F}$ under the action of which the particle is moving. Finally, calculate $\mathbf{H}_O$ and $\mathbf{F}$ at time $t = 5$ s.

Solution The velocity of the particle is given from

$$\mathbf{v} = \frac{d\mathbf{r}}{dt} = \frac{d}{dt}(7t^2\mathbf{i} + 3t^3\mathbf{j})$$

$$\mathbf{v} = 14t\mathbf{i} + 9t^2\mathbf{j}\,(m/s)$$

Thus, the angular momentum $\mathbf{H}_O$ becomes

$$\mathbf{H}_O = \mathbf{r} \times m\mathbf{v} = (7t^2\mathbf{i} + 3t^3\mathbf{j}) \times 2(14t\mathbf{i} + 9t^2\mathbf{j})$$

$$\mathbf{H}_O = 126t^4(\mathbf{i} \times \mathbf{j}) + 84t^4(\mathbf{j} \times \mathbf{i}) = (126 - 84)t^4\mathbf{k}$$

$$\mathbf{H}_O = 42t^4\mathbf{k}\,(kg\,m^2/s) \blacktriangleleft$$

From the equation of motion, $\mathbf{F} = m\dfrac{d\mathbf{v}}{dt}$, we write

$$\mathbf{F} = m\frac{d}{dt}(14t\mathbf{i} + 9t^2\mathbf{j}) = 2(14\mathbf{i} + 18t\mathbf{j})$$

$$\mathbf{F} = 28\mathbf{i} + 36t\mathbf{j}\,(N) \blacktriangleleft$$

Finally, we have, at $t = 5$ s,

$$\mathbf{H}_O(t = 5) = 42(5)^4\mathbf{k} = 26{,}250\mathbf{k}\,(kg \cdot m^2/s) \blacktriangleleft$$

and

$$\mathbf{F}(t = 5) = 28\mathbf{i} + 180\mathbf{j}\,(N) \blacktriangleleft$$

EXAMPLE   4.11

The motion of a small spherical mass m attached by a string to a fixed point O and rotating in a horizontal circle about a vertical axis describes a cone of constant half-angle θ as shown. Show that the tangential speed of the particle must be constant. Also, find an expression for the tangential speed ($\dot{\phi}$) in terms of the string length R and the angle θ.

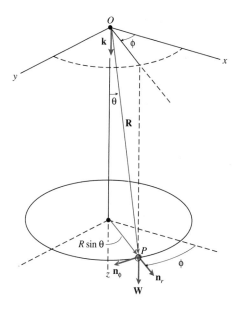

Solution We first develop an expression for the position vector $\mathbf{OP} = \mathbf{r}$ of the particle. In cylindrical coordinates (r, ϕ, and z) we have

$$\mathbf{r} = R(\sin\theta)\mathbf{n}_r + R(\cos\theta)\mathbf{k} \qquad (a)$$

where R is the string length and θ the half-angle of the cone of revolution. We can now obtain the velocity vector $\mathbf{v}$ from $\mathbf{v} = \dot{\mathbf{r}}$ as

$$\mathbf{v} = \dot{\mathbf{r}} = (R\sin\theta)\dot{\mathbf{n}}_r + (R\cos\theta)\dot{\mathbf{k}} \qquad (b)$$

However, from particle kinematics we have

$$\dot{\mathbf{n}}_r = \dot{\phi}\mathbf{n}_\phi \qquad (c)$$

and since the unit vector $\mathbf{k}$ and the cone half-angle θ are constant, we also have

$$\dot{\mathbf{k}} = 0 \qquad \theta = \text{constant} \quad (\dot{\theta} = 0)$$

Thus, we write

$$\mathbf{v} = R\dot{\phi}\sin\theta\,\mathbf{n}_\phi \qquad (d)$$

The equation relating the moment of the external forces ($\Sigma\mathbf{M}_O$) to the moment of the linear momentum (i.e., to the angular momentum, $\mathbf{H}_O$) will now be introduced and the terms evaluated.

$$\mathbf{M}_O = \mathbf{r} \times W\mathbf{k} = (R\sin\theta\,\mathbf{n}_r + R\cos\theta\,\mathbf{k}) \times (mg\mathbf{k})$$

since $\mathbf{n}_r \times \mathbf{k} = -\mathbf{n}_\phi$ and $\mathbf{k} \times \mathbf{k} = 0$

$$\mathbf{M}_O = (-mgR\sin\theta)\mathbf{n}_\phi \qquad (e)$$

To find the rate of change of angular momentum, $\dot{\mathbf{H}}_O$, we begin by writing

$$\mathbf{H}_O = \mathbf{r} \times m\mathbf{v} = (R\sin\theta\,\mathbf{n}_r + R\cos\theta\,\mathbf{k})$$
$$\times [m(R\dot{\phi}\sin\theta)]\mathbf{n}_\phi$$
$$\mathbf{H}_O = -mR^2\dot{\phi}\sin\theta\cos\theta\,\mathbf{n}_r + mR^2\dot{\phi}\sin^2\theta\,\mathbf{k} \qquad (f)$$

since $(\mathbf{n}_r \times \mathbf{n}_\phi) = \mathbf{k}$ and $(\mathbf{k} \times \mathbf{n}_\phi) = -\mathbf{n}_r$. Time differentiating $\mathbf{H}_O$, we obtain

$$\dot{\mathbf{H}}_O = -mR^2\ddot{\phi}\sin\theta\cos\theta\,\mathbf{n}_r - mR^2\dot{\phi}^2\sin\theta\cos\theta\,\mathbf{n}_\phi$$
$$+ mR^2\ddot{\phi}\sin^2\theta\,\mathbf{k} \qquad (g)$$

Now, equating Equations (e) and (g), we obtain three scalar equations in the three coordinate directions defined by the unit vectors $\mathbf{n}_r$, $\mathbf{n}_\phi$, $\mathbf{k}$. Along $\mathbf{n}_r$,

$$mR^2\ddot{\phi}\sin\theta\cos\theta = 0$$

thus,

$$\ddot{\phi} = 0 \qquad \dot{\phi} = \text{constant}$$

and we have for the tangential speed a constant magnitude.

Along $\mathbf{n}_\phi$, after substituting for $\dot{\phi} = \omega$,

$$mR^2\omega^2\sin\theta\cos\theta = mgR\sin\theta$$

and solving for the angular speed ω of the radial line, we obtain

$$\omega = \left[\frac{g}{R\cos\theta}\right]^{1/2} \quad \blacktriangleleft$$

A pendulum with a motion as described above is called a *conical pendulum*.

EXAMPLE 4.12

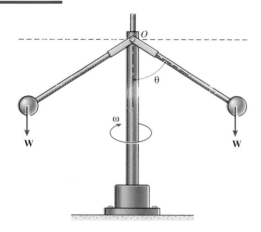

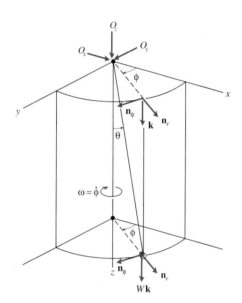

The mechanical governor shown consists of two spheres of identical masses m mounted on two rigid rods of negligible mass and of length L, rotating freely about the vertical shaft. An internal mechanism adjusts the angular position θ of the rods to secure the desired angular velocity of the shaft. If the angular velocity of the spheres is given as ω_{90} when the rods are horizontal ($\theta_O = 90°$), determine its magnitude for $\theta_1 = 45°$.

Solution   Since all external forces are either passing through O or are parallel to the axis of rotation (z axis), the moment of all the forces about the z axis is zero; thus,

$$(\Sigma M_O)_z = 0 = (\dot{H}_O)_z \tag{a}$$

We conclude that the angular momentum is conserved in the z direction, and

$$(H_O)_{\theta = 90°} = (H_O)_{\theta = 45°} = \text{constant} \tag{b}$$

$$(H_O)_{\theta = 90°} = 2Lmv_\phi = 2Lm(L\omega_{90})$$

$$(H_O)_{\theta = 90°} = 2mL^2\omega_{90} \tag{c}$$

Similarly, we have

$$(H_O)_{\theta_1 = 45°} = (L \sin \theta_1)2mv_\phi$$

$$= (L \sin \theta_1)2m[(L \sin \theta_1)\omega_{\theta_1}]$$

$$(H_O)_{\theta_1 = 45°} = 2mL^2 \sin^2 \theta_1 \omega_{\theta_1} \tag{d}$$

Now, equating (c) and (d) and simplifying, we obtain a general expression for the angular velocity at any position θ_1 if the angular velocity at $\theta = 90°$ is given:

$$\omega_{\theta_1} = \frac{\omega_{90}}{\sin^2 \theta_1} \tag{e}$$

From Equation (e) we conclude that for an angular position of the rods defined by $\theta_1 = 45°$, the angular velocity of the shaft is twice that for $\theta = 90°$, or

$$\omega_{45} = \frac{\omega_{90}}{\sin^2 45°} \qquad \omega_{45} = 2\omega_{90} \blacktriangleleft$$

*4.8 CENTRAL FORCE FIELD

A particle P is said to move under the action of a central force when the line of action of the force vector always passes through a fixed point O, called the force center. By selecting this particular fixed point as the origin of an absolute (fixed) frame of reference, the line of action of the central force passes through the origin of the coordinate system and we have

$$\Sigma \mathbf{M}_O = 0 = \dot{\mathbf{H}}_O \qquad \mathbf{H}_O = \text{constant} \qquad (4.37)$$

We conclude that if the vector $\mathbf{H}_O = (\mathbf{r} \times m\mathbf{v})$ is constant, then the vectors $\mathbf{r}$ and $m\mathbf{v}$ are in a fixed plane normal to $\mathbf{H}_O$, and the motion and trajectory of the particle, under a central force field, will always be planar. The plane within which the motion will take place will be normal to the constant vector $\mathbf{H}_O$. Therefore, it is convenient to refer the position of the particle to a system of polar coordinates in the plane of the trajectory. Recalling Equation (4.31b) we have

$$H_O = mr^2\dot{\theta} = \text{constant}$$

Division by m of the above equation yields an expression for the angular momentum per unit mass as

$$\frac{H_O}{m} = r^2\dot{\theta} = h_O \qquad (4.38)$$

where h_O is a constant.

Next, we consider the equation governing the motion of the particle by writing in polar coordinates

$$F(r,\theta) = -ma_r = -m(\ddot{r} - r\dot{\theta}^2)$$

where $F(r, \theta)$ is an attractive central force acting on the particle P of mass m. Combining the above expression with Equation (4.38) and eliminating $\dot{\theta}$ yields

$$\ddot{r} - \frac{h_O^2}{r^3} + \frac{F}{m} = 0 \qquad (4.39)$$

Equation (4.39) describes the radial position of the particle as a function of time t. In order to determine the path of the particle, the radial coordinate r must be expressed in terms of the angular coordinate θ as $r = f(\theta)$ by eliminating t. Applying the chain rule of calculus we can write

$$\ddot{r} = \frac{d}{dt}(\dot{r}) = \frac{d}{dt}\left(\frac{dr}{d\theta}\dot{\theta}\right) = \frac{d}{d\theta}\left(\frac{dr}{d\theta}\dot{\theta}\right)\dot{\theta}$$

Recalling Equation (4.38), we substitute $\dot{\theta} = h_O/r^2$ into the above expression for r and obtain

$$\ddot{r} = \frac{d}{d\theta}\left(\frac{dr}{d\theta}\frac{h_O}{r^2}\right)\frac{h_O}{r^2}$$

This expression for $\ddot{r}$, when introduced into the equation of motion given by Equation (4.39), yields

$$\frac{h_O^2}{r^2}\frac{d}{d\theta}\left(\frac{1}{r^2}\frac{dr}{d\theta}\right) - \frac{h_O^2}{r^3} + \frac{F}{m} = 0 \tag{4.40}$$

which after division by h_O^2/r^2 and rearranging terms becomes

$$\frac{d^2}{d\theta^2}\left(\frac{1}{r}\right) + \frac{1}{r} - \frac{\left(\dfrac{F}{m}\right)}{h_O^2}r^2 = 0 \tag{4.41}$$

When the central force $F(r, \theta)$ is known and depends only on the position of the particle P, the trajectory can be calculated by means of Equation (4.41). Conversely, given a trajectory and the force center, the same equation determines the central force that will make the particle describe the specified trajectory.

Among all the central force fields defined by $F = F(r, \theta)$, of particular interest are those that depend only on the radial coordinate r, that is, $F = F(r)$. In the discussion that follows we shall consider exclusively the central force fields $F = F(r)$. Among these there is a category of force fields that plays a significant role in theoretical physics and in celestial mechanics. This category is composed of central forces that are attractive rather than repulsive, and inversely proportional to some power s of the distance r, and are represented in the form $F(r) = C/r^s$.

The case of a central force varying as r^{-5} or r^{-3}, though important in certain fields of theoretical physics, will not be discussed here. Instead we will focus our attention on the case of the central force varying as r^{-2}, that is, the inverse-square law.

Newton's Law of Universal Gravitation

The inverse-square law corresponds to the law of universal gravitation discovered by Newton during his study of planetary motion. Since the gravitational attraction exerted by the sun on a planet is always directed toward the mass center of the sun, it follows that planetary motion is governed by a central force field. Similarly, when a satellite or space vehicle orbits the earth, neglecting the gravitational pull of the sun or the moon, the only force the satellite is subject to would be the gravity field of the earth, and thus its angular momentum would be conserved since it moves in a central force field.

The mathematical formulation proposed by Newton for the mutual force F of gravitational attraction between two masses M and m separated by a distance r is given in the form

$$F = G\frac{Mm}{r^2} \tag{4.42}$$

where G is a universal constant, called the *constant of gravitation*. The value of G, determined experimentally, is

$G = 6.673 \times 10^{-11}\,\text{m}^3/\text{kg}\cdot\text{s}^2$ (SI units)

$G = 3.442 \times 10^{-8}\,\text{ft}^4/\text{lb}\cdot\text{s}^4$ (U.S. Customary units)

Equation (4.42) can be used to determine the gravitational acceleration g, by observing that the weight of an object of mass m represents the mutual attractive force between the object and the mass of the earth, or

$$W = G\frac{Mm}{R^2} = mg, \qquad g = \frac{Gm}{R^2} \tag{4.43}$$

where R is the radius of the earth, given as 3960 miles. Since the earth is not perfectly spherical, R is not constant over the surface of the earth and, therefore, g will vary with location. Another approximation that leads to a variation in g is the fact that the mass of the earth is not uniformly distributed and, as a result, the center of mass of the earth is not located at the center of the sphere that is assumed to represent the earth. Finally, we must remember that the formulation of the principle of angular impulse and momentum and its application to the central force field was based upon our use of a fixed frame of reference. In the case of the law of gravitational attraction the frame of reference has been attached to the earth, which is not fixed in space. To be exact, the formulation should include the effect of the earth's rotation, by writing the equations of motion for a rotating frame of reference. However, for most engineering problems, these three assumptions will not cause significant errors in the calculations that lead to the determination of the acceleration of gravity g, which will be given as

$g = 9.81\ \text{m/s}^2$ (SI units)

$g = 32.2\ \text{ft/s}^2$ (U.S. Customary units)

*Kepler's Laws of Planetary Motion

Newton's development of the law of universal gravitation was preceded by three empirical laws proposed by Kepler (German astronomer Johannes Kepler, 1571–1630). These were:

1.   Each planet moves along an ellipse with the sun's center at one focus.

2. The radial vector drawn from the sun to a planet sweeps equal areas in equal times.

3. The ratio of the cube of the major axis of the ellipse to the square of the revolution period is the same for all the planets.

We will now develop the above laws and establish the equation of the orbital trajectory for an object moving under a central force field. Earlier we obtained

$$\frac{H_O}{m} = r^2\dot{\theta} = h_O = \text{constant} \tag{4.38}$$

In order to interpret the significance of Equation (4.38) we shall introduce the concept of *areal velocity*. When a particle P moves along a plane curvilinear path, it sweeps an infinitesimal area dA (Figure 4.7), which can be expressed as

$$dA = \frac{1}{2}r^2\,d\theta$$

The ratio $\dfrac{dA}{dt}$ is defined as the areal velocity of the particle, and written as

$$\dot{A} = \frac{1}{2}r^2\dot{\theta}$$

Since by Equation (4.38) we know that the right-hand side of the above expression is constant, we conclude that

$$\dot{A} = \text{constant} \tag{4.44}$$

Equation (4.44) states that *the areal velocity of a particle moving under a central force field is constant* (Kepler's first law).

Next, we will establish the mathematical expression for the path described by a planet during its movement around the sun. In Figure 4.8 we consider the plane curvilinear motion of a planet of mass m around the sun (mass M). Restating Equation (4.42), Newton's law of universal gravitation, and Equation (4.41), we write

$$\frac{F}{m} = \frac{GM}{r^2}$$

and

$$\frac{d^2}{d\theta^2}\left(\frac{1}{r}\right) + \frac{1}{r} = \frac{F}{mh_O^2}r^2$$

Substituting Equation (4.42) into Equation (4.41) yields

$$\frac{d^2}{d\theta^2}\left(\frac{1}{r}\right) + \frac{1}{r} = \frac{GM}{h_O^2}$$

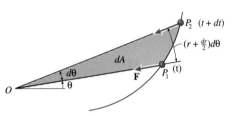

$$dA = \tfrac{1}{2}(r + \tfrac{dr}{2})^2\,d\theta$$
$$\lim_{dt\to 0} dA = \tfrac{1}{2}r^2\,d\theta$$

Figure 4.7

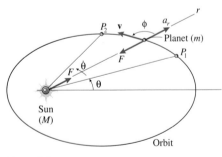

Figure 4.8

With the introduction of a transformation of variable ($u = 1/r$) the above expression is reduced to

$$\frac{d^2u}{d\theta^2} + u = \frac{GM}{h_O^2} \tag{4.45}$$

Equation (4.45) is a second-order nonhomogeneous ordinary differential equation. The general solution can be expressed as the sum of the complementary and particular solutions. The complementary solution is the solution of the homogeneous equation (that is, when the right-hand side of the equation is zero). It is given as

$$u_c = K \cos(\theta - \theta_O)$$

where K and θ_O, the phase angle, are the two constants of integration. By a judicious selection of the polar axis one can eliminate the phase angle θ_O. This will occur if the polar axis is such that the radial distance r is a minimum when the angular coordinate θ is zero (Figure 4.9). Then, the complementary solution becomes

$$u_c = K \cos \theta$$

As for the particular solution, it is given as

$$u_p = \frac{GM}{h_O^2}$$

The general solution $u = u_c + u_p$ can now be expressed in the form

$$u = K \cos \theta + \frac{GM}{h_O^2}$$

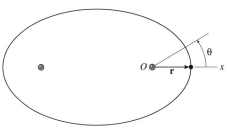

Figure 4.9

Recalling the transformation of variable $u = 1/r$, we write the radial coordinate r as a function of the angular coordinate θ as

$$\frac{1}{r} = K \cos \theta + \frac{GM}{h_O^2} \tag{4.46}$$

Equation (4.46) describes, in polar coordinates, what is known as a **conic section**. A conic section is generated by a point that moves in such a way that the ratio e of its distance from a *focal point* to a line called *directrix* is always constant. The general form of the expression for the conic section is

$$\frac{1}{r} = \frac{1}{p} \cos \theta + \frac{1}{ep} \tag{4.47}$$

where p is the distance from the focal point (focus) to the line called directrix (Figure 4.10), and e is the **eccentricity** of the conic section, expressed as the

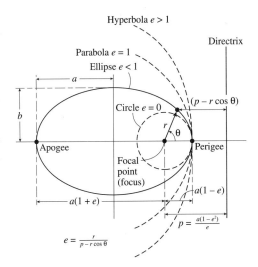

Figure 4.10

ratio

$$e = \frac{K}{GM} \Big/ h_O^2$$

Thus, the planetary motion describes a conic section with

$$p = \frac{1}{K} \quad \text{and} \quad e = \frac{h_O^2 K}{GM} \quad \text{or} \quad ep = \frac{h_O^2}{GM} = \text{constant} \qquad (4.48)$$

Rearranging the constants K and GM/h_O^2, Equation (4.46) is rewritten in the form

$$\frac{1}{r} = \frac{1}{ep}(1 + e\cos\theta) \qquad (4.49)$$

or

$$r = \frac{h_O^2/GM}{1 + e\cos\theta} \qquad (4.50)$$

The above expression for the trajectory will be investigated for the following values of the eccentricity: $e = 0$, $e < 1$, $e = 1$, and $e > 1$.

Case I: Circle ($e = 0$)   When the eccentricity of the trajectory is zero, from Equation (4.50) we have

$$r = \frac{h_O^2}{GM} = \text{constant}$$

and the particle is in circular orbit.

Case II: Ellipse ($e < 1$)   From Equation (4.49) we can see that the minimum (perigee) and maximum (apogee) values of the radial coordinate occur when $\theta = 0$ and $\theta = \pi$ respectively.

For $\theta = 0$:
$$r_{\min} = \frac{h_O^2/GM}{1 + e} = \frac{ep}{1 + e}$$

For $\theta = \pi$:
$$r_{\max} = \frac{h_O^2/GM}{1 - e} = \frac{ep}{1 - e}$$

The major axis of the ellipse can be evaluated by adding $r_{\min}$ and $r_{\max}$ to obtain $2a$. We obtain

$$2a = r_{\min} + r_{\max} = \frac{2ep}{1 - e^2} \qquad a = \frac{ep}{1 - e^2}$$

The distance p from the focus to the directrix is now given as

$$p = \frac{a(1 - e^2)}{e} \tag{4.51}$$

Substituting Equation (4.51) into Equation (4.49) yields

$$\frac{1}{r} = \frac{1 + e \cos \theta}{a(1 - e^2)}$$

and the maximum and minimum values of the radial coordinate become

$$\left. \begin{array}{l} r_{max} = \dfrac{a(1 - e^2)}{1 - e} = a(1 + e) \\[3mm] r_{min} = \dfrac{a(1 - e^2)}{1 + e} = a(1 - e) \end{array} \right\} \tag{4.52}$$

which are referred to, respectively, as the apogee and the perigee.

Case III: Parabola (e = 1)   Equations (4.48) and (4.49), when expressed for the case $e = 1$, become

$$\frac{1}{r} = \frac{1}{p}(1 + \cos \theta)$$

and

$$p = \frac{h_O^2}{GM}$$

For values of θ approaching π the position vector becomes infinitely large and the trajectory is a parabola.

Case IV: Hyperbola (e > 1)   From Equation (4.50) we can observe that the radial coordinate becomes infinitely large for values of the polar angle satisfying the condition

$$1 + e \cos \theta = 0 \qquad \cos \theta_1 = -\frac{1}{e}$$

The trajectory will therefore be determined for values of the polar angle between $-\theta_1$ and $+\theta_1$. It is the only range of polar angles for which a physically possible motion exists.

Escape Velocity

An important feature of gravitational central force fields is the velocity required to enable a satellite orbiting around another body to overcome the gravitational

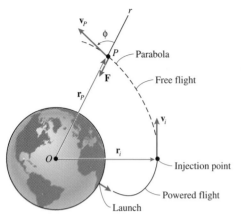

Figure 4.11

pull of the attracting body and "escape" into space, that is, the **escape velocity**. Initially, the satellite is carried aloft by a booster rocket and the trajectory of the flight is governed by it. At the end of what is commonly referred to as the *powered flight* stage of the motion, the satellite separates from its booster rocket (injection point) and begins its *free flight*. It is the velocity at the beginning of the free flight that we will now consider (Figure 4.11).

If $\mathbf{r}_i$ and $\mathbf{v}_i$ are the radial position and velocity vectors, respectively, at the injection point along the trajectory, we can express the kinematic conditions prevailing under Kepler's Laws by using Equation (4.38) as

$$\frac{H_O}{m} = r_i^2 \dot{\theta}_i = h_O$$

Furthermore, from Equation (4.46), after differentiation we obtain

$$-\frac{\dot{r}_i}{r_i^2} = -K\dot{\theta}_i \sin \theta_i$$

and since, in polar coordinates $(v_i)_r = \dot{r}$, we write, after substituting for $r_i^2\dot{\theta}_i = h_O$,

$$(v_i)_r = v_i \cos \phi_i = h_O K \sin \theta_i \tag{4.53}$$

Next, we consider the transverse component of the velocity. Since, in polar coordinates $(v_i)_\theta = r_i\dot{\theta}_i$, we write, after substituting again for $r_i^2\dot{\theta}_i = h_O$,

$$(v_i)_\theta = v_i \sin \phi_i = \frac{h_O}{r_i} \tag{4.54}$$

and

$$h_O = r_i v_i \sin \phi_i \tag{4.55}$$

With the help of Equation (4.50) the Equation (4.54) becomes

$$(v_i)_\theta = v_i \sin \phi_i = \frac{GM(1 + e \cos \theta_i)}{r_i v_i \sin \phi_i} \tag{4.56}$$

and similarly Equation (4.53) can be written as

$$(v_i)_r = v_i \cos \phi_i = \frac{GM e \sin \theta_i}{r_i v_i \sin \phi_i} \tag{4.57}$$

Equations (4.56) and (4.57) can now be rearranged to give

$$e^2 \cos^2 \theta_i = \left(\frac{r_i v_i^2 \sin^2 \phi_i}{GM} - 1\right)^2$$

and

$$e^2 \sin^2 \theta_i = \left(\frac{r_i v_i^2 \sin^2 \phi_i \cos \phi_i}{GM}\right)^2$$

and after adding the two equations we have

$$\underbrace{e^2(\cos^2\theta_i + \sin^2\theta_i)}_{=\,1} = \left(\frac{r_i v_i^2}{GM}\right)^2 \underbrace{(\sin^2\phi_i + \cos^2\phi_i)}_{=\,1}$$

$$\times \sin^2\phi_i - 2\left(\frac{r_i v_i^2}{GM}\right)\sin^2\phi_i + \sin^2\phi_i + \cos^2\phi_i$$

After collecting terms, this yields

$$e^2 = \left(\frac{r_i v_i^2}{GM} - 1\right)^2 \sin^2\phi_i + \cos^2\phi_i \qquad (4.58)$$

Equation (4.58) can now be used to determine the velocity v_p at any point P along the trajectory by simply replacing v_i with v_p. The minimum value of the escape velocity corresponds to a parabolic trajectory, that is, the trajectory when $e = 1$. Then the above equation becomes

$$\left(\frac{r_i v_e^2}{GM} - 1\right)^2 \sin^2\phi_i + \cos^2\phi_i = 1$$

or, after introducing $\sin^2\phi_i = 1 - \cos^2\phi_i$ and canceling $\sin^2\phi_i$ from both sides of the equation, we obtain

$$\frac{r_i v_e^2}{GM} = 2$$

where v_e is the escape velocity. Solving the above relationship for the escape velocity yields

$$v_e = \left[\frac{2GM}{r_i}\right]^{1/2} \qquad (4.59)$$

An important conclusion to be drawn from Equation (4.59) is that the escape velocity is independent of the inclination angle ϕ of the injection velocity.

Periodic Time

The time required by an orbiting body to describe its orbit, called the *periodic time*, T, can be obtained from the definition of the areal velocity as it applies to an ellipse,

$$\frac{dA}{dt} = \frac{\text{area of ellipse}}{\text{periodic time}} = \frac{\pi ab}{T}$$

From Equations (4.38) and (4.44) we have

$$\frac{dA}{dt} = \frac{1}{2}r^2\dot{\theta} = \frac{h_O}{2}$$

Equating the two expressions for $\dot{A}$, we get

$$\frac{\pi ab}{T} = \frac{h_O}{2} \qquad \boxed{T = \frac{2\pi ab}{h_O}} \qquad (4.60)$$

Next, introducing Equations (4.48) and (4.51), we can develop Kepler's third planetary law by writing

$$T^2 = \frac{4\pi^2}{GM} \frac{ab^2}{(1 - e^2)}$$

$$\boxed{T^2 = \frac{4\pi^2}{GM}a^3} \qquad \text{(Kepler's third law)} \qquad (4.61)$$

Equation 4.61 states that the ratio a^3/T^2 of the cube of the major axis a of the ellipse to the square of the period T is the same for all the planets and equal to $4\pi^2/GM$.

EXAMPLE 4.13

A satellite will be placed in a circular orbit 750 miles high above the earth. What should the injection velocity of the free flight be? What is the periodic time of the orbit?

Solution   For a circular orbit, the injection velocity will always be parallel to the earth's surface; hence, $\phi_i = 90°$ and Equation (4.58) becomes

$$e = \left(\frac{r_i v_i^2}{GM} - 1\right) = 0$$

since the eccentricity is zero. Thus we write

$$r_i v_i^2 = GM$$

and the injection velocity for a circular orbit becomes

$$v_i = \left[\frac{GM}{r_i}\right]^{1/2} \quad \blacktriangleleft$$

   Assuming that the earth's radius is 3960 miles, we have from Equation (4.43)

$$GM = gR^2$$
$$GM = (32.2)(3960 \times 5280)^2 = 1.408 \times 10^{16} \text{ ft}^3/\text{s}^2$$

The radial distance from the center of the earth to the satellite is

$$r_i = (3960 + 750)5280 = 2.487 \times 10^7 \text{ ft}$$

The required injection velocity is

$$v_i = \left[\frac{1.408 \times 10^{16}}{2.487 \times 10^7}\right]^{1/2} = 23,800 \text{ ft/s} = 16,200 \text{ mph}$$

The periodic time can be secured from Equation (4.61) by letting $a = r_i$; thus,

$$T^2 = \frac{4\pi^2}{GM}a^3 = \frac{4\pi^2(2.487 \times 10^7)^3}{1.408 \times 10^{16}} = 4.31 \times 10^7$$

$$T = 6567 \text{ s} = 1.82 \text{ h} \quad \blacktriangleleft$$

It must be noted that the injection velocity for a circular orbit ($e = 0$) is $1/\sqrt{2}$ times the escape velocity necessary for a parabolic trajectory ($e = 1$).

EXAMPLE 4.14

A space probe will be sent on a mission around a planet. The free flight is planned to take place from a point P located at an altitude of 400 miles as shown. Determine (a) the smallest value of the injection velocity necessary for achieving escape from earth's orbit, and (b) the trajectory of the probe in terms of its radial distance from the center of the earth.

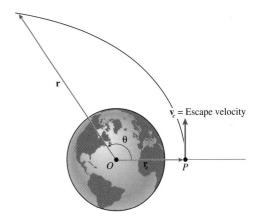

Solution

Part a. The smallest value of the escape velocity is for the parabolic trajectory ($e = 1$). The injection point will be at $r_i = 3960 + 400 = 4360$ mi from the center of the earth. From Example 4.13, $GM = gR^2 = 1.408 \times 10^{16}$ ft^3/s^2. From Equation (4.59),

$$v_e = \left[\frac{2GM}{r_i}\right]^{1/2} = \left[\frac{2 \times 1.408 \times 10^{16}}{4360 \times 5280}\right]^{1/2} = 34{,}875 \text{ ft/s}$$

$$v_e = 23{,}779 \text{ mph} \blacktriangleleft$$

Part b. For $e = 1$, Equation (4.49) becomes

$$\frac{1}{r} = \frac{GM}{h_O^2}(1 + \cos\theta)$$

At the injection point P ($r = r_i$, $\theta = 0$) this gives

$$\frac{1}{r_i} = \frac{GM}{h_O^2}(1 + 1)$$

$$\frac{GM}{h_O^2} = \frac{1}{2r_i}$$

Substituting this equation into Equation (4.50), the equation of the trajectory of the probe becomes

$$\frac{1}{r} = \frac{1}{2r_i}(1 + \cos\theta) \qquad \cos\theta = \frac{2r_i}{r} - 1 \blacktriangleleft$$

4.9 SUMMARY

In this chapter we have learned the following:

1. The equation describing the motion of a particle of mass m can be expressed as

$$\Sigma \mathbf{F} = \frac{d}{dt}(m\mathbf{v}) \qquad (4.3)$$

where $m\mathbf{v}$ is the linear momentum of the particle and $\Sigma\mathbf{F}$ the resultant of all the external forces acting on it.

2.   The integral form of the equation of motion can be expressed in the form

$$m\mathbf{v}_1 + \Sigma \int_{t_1}^{t_2} \mathbf{F}\,dt = m\mathbf{v}_2 \tag{4.5}$$

where $\Sigma \int \mathbf{F}\,dt$ is the total linear impulse.

3.   If the net force or the linear impulse acting on a particle is zero, we have

$$m\mathbf{v}_1 = m\mathbf{v}_2 = \text{constant}$$

which represents the conservation of linear momentum.

4.   For a direct central impact of two deformable bodies the coefficient of restitution e is given as

$$e = \left| \frac{\text{relative velocity of separation}}{\text{relative velocity of approach}} \right| \tag{4.16}$$

5.   The moment, about a fixed point O, of the linear momentum mv of a particle is the angular momentum $\mathbf{H}_O$ and is given by

$$\mathbf{H}_O = \mathbf{r} \times m\mathbf{v} \tag{4.23}$$

The equation of motion can be written in the form

$$\mathbf{r} \times \Sigma\mathbf{F} = \frac{d}{dt}(\mathbf{r} \times m\mathbf{v}) = \dot{\mathbf{H}}_O$$

$$\Sigma\mathbf{M}_O = \dot{\mathbf{H}} \tag{4.27}$$

where $\dot{\mathbf{H}}_O$ is the time rate of change of angular momentum.

6.   When integrated with respect to time, the angular impulse-momentum equation becomes

$$(\mathbf{H}_O)_1 + \Sigma \int_{t_1}^{t_2} \mathbf{M}_O\,dt = (\mathbf{H}_O)_2 \tag{4.33}$$

where $\Sigma \int_{t_1}^{t_2} \mathbf{M}_O\,dt$ is the angular impulse, about O, of all the external forces acting on the particle.

7.   When the moment $\Sigma\mathbf{M}_O$ or the angular impulse $\Sigma\int \mathbf{M}_O\,dt$ about a fixed point is zero, we have

$$(\mathbf{H}_O)_1 = (\mathbf{H}_O)_2 = \text{constant} \tag{4.36}$$

which is the conservation of angular momentum.

8.   Newton's law of gravitation is written as

$$F = G\frac{Mm}{r^2} \tag{4.42}$$

where F is the gravitational attraction force between two masses M and m separated by a distance r, and G is the universal constant of gravitation given as $G = 6.673 \times 10^{-11} \text{ m}^3/\text{kg} \cdot \text{s}^2 = 3.442 \times 10^{-8} \text{ ft}^4/\text{lb} \cdot \text{s}^4$.

9. Kepler's laws of planetary motion are as follows:
   a. The areal velocity of a particle moving under a central force field is constant.
   b. The planetary motion describes a conic section.
   c. The square of the periodic time of the elliptical orbit is in a constant ratio to the cube of its semimajor axis.

KEY TERMS

angular impulse *163*

angular momentum *161*

areal velocity *170*

coefficient of restitution *156*

conic section *171*

conservation of linear
  momentum *150*

eccentricity *171*

escape velocity *174*

impact *155*

impulsive force *150*

linear impulse *146*

linear momentum *145*

PROBLEMS

SECTION 4.2

4.1 An automobile weighing 3000 lb is moving at a speed of 55 mph. Determine (*a*) its linear momentum; (*b*) the constant retarding force required to stop the car in 3 s; and (*c*) the distance the car will travel before coming to rest.

4.2 When a 60-g tennis ball moving horizontally at a speed of 8 m/s is struck by a racket, it leaves in the opposite direction with a speed of 12 m/s. Determine the impulse applied to the ball by the racket.

4.3 A tugboat is towing a tanker that has a total mass of 2×10^9 kg. The tanker is initially at rest. If it takes 5 min to bring the tanker to a speed of 2 knots from rest, determine the constant tensile force developed in the tow cable of the tugboat. The cable is inclined at 30° to the horizontal and the water friction on the hull is negligible.

4.4 A 5-kg particle has its velocity changed from $\mathbf{v}_1 = 3\mathbf{i} + 2\mathbf{j} - \mathbf{k}$ (m/s) to $\mathbf{v}_2 = \mathbf{i} - 2\mathbf{j} + 3\mathbf{k}$ (m/s) in 3 s. Determine the constant resultant force necessary to cause this change.

Figure P4.3

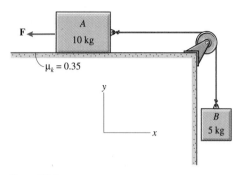

Figure P4.5

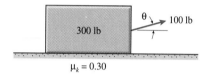

Figure P4.7

4.5 Blocks A and B have masses of 10 kg and 5 kg respectively, and are at rest. Assuming the pulley shown to be frictionless, determine the value of the constant force F to give block A a velocity of 5 m/s in 4 s. The coefficient of friction between block A and the horizontal surface is 0.35.

4.6 The rectilinear motion of a 5-lb particle is described by the displacement-time relationship given by $s = 2t(1 - 2t)$ where s is in ft and t in s. Determine the linear momentum of the particle at $t = 1$ s and at $t = 3$ s.

4.7 A 100-lb force is being exerted upon a 300-lb block for a duration of 10 s. Determine (*a*) the angle of inclination θ necessary for the 100-lb force in order to achieve the maximum resultant linear impulse and (*b*) the maximum linear impulse vector. The coefficient of kinetic friction is 0.30.

4.8 A crane is lifting a 2000-kg crate that is initially at rest on the floor. After 2 s, the crate reaches an upward velocity of 3 m/s. Determine the average overturning moment at the base A of the crane.

4.9 A 2-kg block moves on a smooth horizontal plane under the action of a force F varying as shown. Determine the maximum velocity of the block, which is initially at rest.

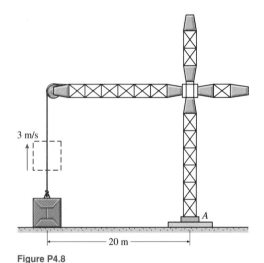

Figure P4.8

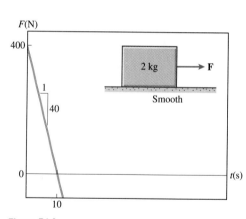

Figure P4.9

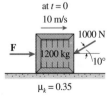

Figure P4.10

4.10 A 1200-kg package is being moved on the floor of a plant at a speed of 10 m/s under the action of a horizontal force F. Suddenly an additional force of 1000 N is applied to the package to retard its motion. Determine the time required to bring the package's speed down to 5 m/s. The coefficient of kinetic friction between the package and the floor is 0.35.

4.11 A 25-lb particle ($\mathbf{W} = -25\mathbf{k}$) is acted upon by a force given in pounds as $\mathbf{F} = 3t^2\mathbf{i} + (4t - 1)\mathbf{j} + 2t^3\mathbf{k}$ (lb). If the initial velocity of the particle is $\mathbf{v} = 25\mathbf{i} + 75\mathbf{j} + 50\mathbf{k}$ (ft/s), determine the expression for the velocity vector at any other time t.

4.12 A 2000-kg car is moving down an incline ($\theta = 20°$) at a speed of 108 km/h when the brakes are applied and the car begins to skid. Determine the coefficient of kinetic friction between the tires and the pavement if the car is brought to rest within 12 s.

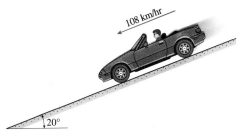

Figure P4.12

4.13 A 5-kg particle is acted upon by a force given as $\mathbf{F} = -50t^2\mathbf{i} - t\mathbf{j} - t^3\mathbf{k}$ (N) where t is in seconds. The initial velocity of the particle is $\mathbf{v}_O = 5\mathbf{i} + 5\mathbf{j} + 25\mathbf{k}$ (m/s). Determine the instant when the y component of the velocity vector becomes zero.

4.14 A 20-lb block is acted upon, for a duration of 4 s, by a force F which decreases as shown. The block is initially at rest. Determine the velocity of the block at time $t = 2$ s. The coefficients of static and kinetic friction are 0.35 and 0.30, respectively.

4.15 The 20-lb block shown is acted upon by a force F which increases linearly from zero to 10 lb within 4 s. The block is initially at rest. Determine (a) the time when the block will start moving, and (b) the time when it will reach a velocity of 10 ft/s. The coefficients of static and kinetic friction are equal to 0.35 and 0.30, respectively.

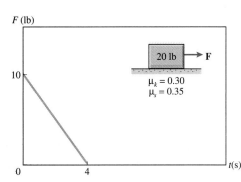

Figure P4.14

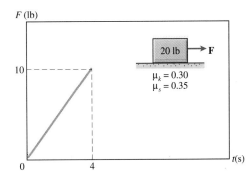

Figure P4.15

4.16 A 5-kg particle has an initial velocity of $\mathbf{v}_O = 50\mathbf{i}$ m/s when two forces $\mathbf{F} = -2t^2\mathbf{i}$ (N) and $\mathbf{P} = 4t^2\mathbf{j}$ (N) act on the particle. Determine the magnitude and direction of the velocity of the particle at time $t = 2$ s.

SECTIONS 4.3 AND 4.4

4.17 A 300-g ball moving to the right with a speed of 2 m/s collides with a 500-g ball moving to the left. If, after collision, the two balls come to rest and remain in contact with each other, determine the initial velocity of the 500-g ball.

4.18 Two identical particles A and B have velocities given by $\mathbf{v}_A = -20\mathbf{i}$ (m/s) and $\mathbf{v}_B = -20\mathbf{j}$ (m/s). They collide at the origin and, following the collision, ball A moves at a velocity $\mathbf{v}_A = +10\mathbf{i}$ (m/s). Determine the velocity of particle B, assuming that both particles are perfectly elastic.

4.19 A 0.25-lb baseball approaches a bat at a speed of 85 mph and, after impact, returns along the same line with the same speed. Determine the impulse the bat has exerted against the ball.

4.20 A 0.60-oz bullet is fired from a 10-lb gun. The bullet leaves the barrel at a speed of 2000 ft/s. Calculate the recoil speed of the gun.

4.21 A 10-kg block is moving to the left with a velocity of 2 m/s when it is hit by a 50-g bullet moving to the right at 1200 m/s. The bullet remains embedded in the block. Determine the velocity of the block (i.e., bullet + block) after the collision.

4.22 A 25-lb block is solidly fixed to the ground. It is hit by a 2-oz bullet traveling at 2000 ft/s. The bullet is brought to rest in 1 millisecond. Determine the direction and magnitude of the average impulsive force exerted by the bullet on the block.

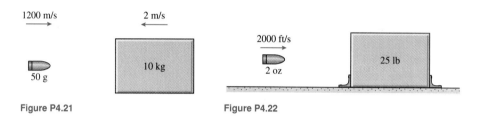

Figure P4.21   Figure P4.22

4.23 An alpha particle of mass 7×10^{-27} kg traveling at a speed of 5×10^4 m/s collides with a particle at rest. If the alpha particle is absorbed by the stationary particle and the combined mass moves in the same direction with a velocity of 3×10^3 m/s, determine the mass of the particle that the alpha particle collided with.

4.24 A star has a mass of 5×10^{32} kg and travels at a speed of 10^6 m/s when it overtakes another star of mass 5×10^{32} kg and traveling in the same direction at 5×10^5 m/s. The two stars join and stay together. Determine their final speed.

4.25 A 3000-lb truck traveling at 90 mph strikes a tree and comes to a stop in 0.15 s. Determine the average force on the truck during the crash.

4.26 Two boys, weighing 75 lb and 100 lb, respectively, are at rest on frictionless roller skates when the 100-lb boy pushes the 75-lb one, imparting to him a speed of 10 ft/s. Determine the final direction and speed of the big boy.

4.27 When a 10-g bullet is fired from a rifle, a recoil force of 5×10^9 dyne acts for a millisecond. Determine the velocity of the bullet.

4.28 A 0.2-kg hockey puck is approaching the stick of a player at a speed of 20 m/s. The player slaps the puck and sends it at 30 m/s in a direction making an angle of 30° with the line of approach. If the duration of contact between the stick and the puck has been 0.02 s, determine the magnitude and direction of the average force exerted by the stick on the puck during contact.

4.29 A 5-lb particle moves on a smooth horizontal plane with a velocity $\mathbf{v} = 10\mathbf{i}$ (ft/s). A steady force is suddenly applied to the particle for a period of 1 s. At

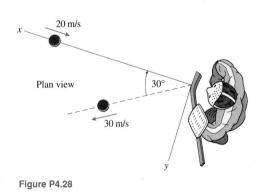

Figure P4.28

the end of this period the particle has a velocity of $\mathbf{v} = 10\mathbf{j}$ (ft/s). Determine the magnitude and direction of the applied force.

4.30 A 20-ton freight car collides at a speed of 8 ft/s with another freight car that is at rest and weighs 15 tons. After the collision, the two cars couple together. Determine (a) the common speed of the cars just after collision and (b) the average impulsive coupling force between the cars if the coupling duration is 0.2 s.

4.31 A 2000-lb car traveling east collided with a 3000-lb car traveling north. The wreckage of the two cars has a velocity given by $\mathbf{v} = 30\mathbf{i} + 20\mathbf{j}$ (ft/s). Determine the speed of each car prior to collision.

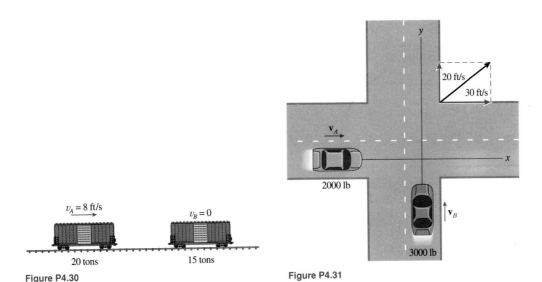

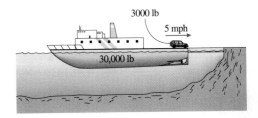

Figure P4.30   Figure P4.31

4.32 A neutron of mass 1.67×10^{-27} kg moving at a speed of 15^5 m/s collides with a stationary deuteron of mass 3.34×10^{-27} kg. The particles bounce away from each other without any loss of energy during the collision. Determine the postcollision velocities of the two particles.

4.33 A 10,000-lb airplane traveling at 500 mph collides with a bird flying in the opposite direction at 5 mph. If the bird weighs 5 lb and the collision period is approximately 10^{-3} s, determine the average force exerted by the bird on the plane.

4.34 If a radium atom at rest, with a mass of 226 atomic mass units (amu), suddenly emits an alpha particle with a mass of 4 amu and moving at 1.7×10^7 (m/s), determine the velocity of the remaining nucleus (called radon) just after the ejection of the alpha particle. (1 amu $= 1.67 \times 10^{-27}$ kg.)

4.35 A 3000-lb car is loaded on a 30,000-lb barge initially at rest. The car suddenly departs and leaves the barge with a velocity of 5 mph relative to it. Determine the velocity of the barge caused by the car's motion.

Figure P4.35

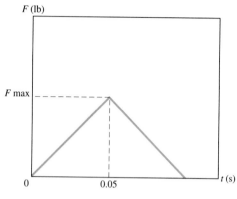

F (lb)

F max

0   0.05   t (s)

Figure P4.38

4.36 A golfer hits a golf ball giving it an initial velocity of $\mathbf{v} = 40\mathbf{i} + 10\mathbf{j}$ (m/s). If the mass of the golf ball is 25 g and the golf club and ball are in contact for 0.015 s, determine (a) the linear impulse on the ball, and (b) the average force exerted on the ball by the club.

4.37 A 2-kg shell is acted upon by an average force of 2×10^5 N while being fired from a cannon. If the shell resides within the gun barrel for 5×10^{-3} s, determine the velocity of the shell as it leaves the gun barrel.

4.38 A 0.6-lb billiard ball is pushed on a frictionless surface for a period of 0.1 s by a force F (lb) varying as shown. If the billiard ball's velocity at the end of the contact period is 10 ft/s, determine the maximum value of the force F that occurs at $t = 0.05$ s.

SECTION 4.5

4.39 A 2-kg particle impacts on a 3-kg particle as shown. The collision is direct central impact and the velocity of the 3-kg particle is 2 m/s before and 5 m/s after impact in the same direction. After impact the particles remain traveling along the original line of impact. If the coefficient of restitution is 0.50, and if the friction forces are negligible, determine (a) the initial and final velocities of the 2-kg particle, and (b) the kinetic energy lost during the collision.

4.40 Two freight cars are moving in the same direction as shown. Car A weighs 250,000 lb and moves at 5 ft/s. Car B, which precedes car A, weighs 500,000 lb and has a velocity of 2 ft/s. If the coefficient of restitution between the cars is 0.75, determine their velocities after impact.

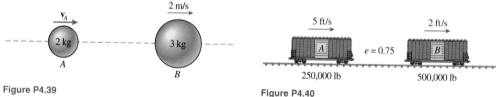

Figure P4.39   **Figure P4.40**

4.41 During a rear-end collision between two identical cars moving in the same direction, the car causing the collision had a speed of 55 mph before and 25 mph after impact. If the coefficient of restitution is 0.6, determine the initial and final velocities of the front car.

4.42 A pile driver consists of a ram (weight $= W_1$) which is dropped from a certain height (h) on a pile (weight $= W_2$) in order to drive the pile into the soil. Assuming that the coefficient of restitution between the ram and the pile is equal to 0.5, determine (a) the velocity of the ram before impact when $h = 5$ ft, and (b) the velocities of the ram and pile after impact for the following values: $W_1 = 1000$ lb, $W_2 = 250$ lb.

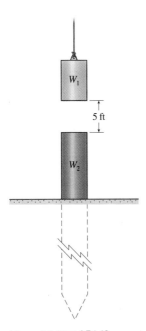

Figure P4.42 and P4.43

4.43 If the pile driver in the previous problem drives the pile 0.5 ft into the ground after each blow, determine the average resistance of the ground, assuming the impact to be perfectly plastic.

4.44 A ball of mass m approaches a smooth floor with a speed of v_i at an angle of θ_i and rebounds at a speed of v_f at an angle of θ_f. Show that the coefficient of restitution can be expressed as

$$e = \frac{\tan \theta_i}{\tan \theta_f}$$

4.45 An iron sphere is dropped from a height of 70 in. on a lead table in order to determine the coefficient of restitution between iron and lead. The sphere rebounds to a height of 1 in. Determine e.

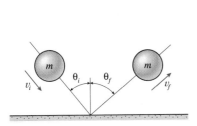

Figure P4.44

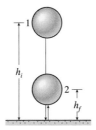

Figure P4.45

4.46   A 100-g sphere approaches a rough horizontal plane with a velocity of $v_i = 20$ m/s and rebounds as shown. If the coefficient of restitution is 0.75, determine (*a*) the velocity of rebound v_f, and (*b*) the linear impulse of the friction force acting on the sphere.

4.47   Two disks A and B, weighing 2 lb and 3 lb, respectively, slide on a *smooth* horizontal surface when they collide. Their positions and velocities just prior to impact are as shown. If the coefficient of restitution between the two disks is 0.70, determine their velocities after impact.

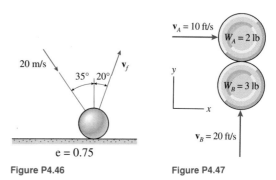

Figure P4.46   Figure P4.47

4.48   A 3-kg body makes a perfectly elastic collision with another body at rest and continues to move in the same direction at a third of its original speed. Determine the mass of the other body.

4.49   A 1-lb ball is attached to a 30-in.-long cord as shown. The horizontal cord and ball are released from rest. When the cord reaches a vertical position, the ball strikes a 5-lb steel block initially at rest on a frictionless surface. If the coefficient of restitution between the ball and the block is 0.9, determine (*a*) the speed of the ball before and after impact, and (*b*) the speed of the block just after impact.

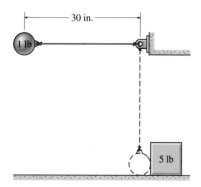

Figure P4.49

4.50   Two pendulums each of 100-g mass and attached by strings of 1-m length are initially positioned and at rest as shown. Pendulum A is released and strikes pendulum B. If the collision is completely inelastic, how high will the center of mass of the two spheres rise after the impact?

4.51   If the collision in the previous problem is elastic, with $e = 0.75$, $m_A = 2$ kg, $m_B = 5$ kg, and $\theta_1 = 60°$, determine the angular displacement θ_2 for the pendulum B, and θ_3 for the rebound angle of pendulum A.

4.52   A 2-lb sphere falls freely and impacts upon a 10-lb wedge with a velocity of 10 ft/s. Assuming all surfaces to be frictionless, and assuming elastic impact between the sphere and the wedge, determine the velocities of the sphere and of the wedge just after impact ($e = 0.75$).

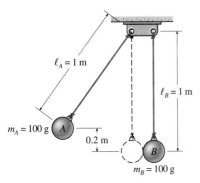

Figure P4.50

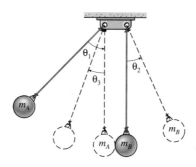

Figure P4.51

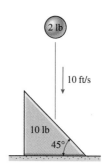

Figure P4.52

4.53 The sphere A of mass m_A has an initial velocity of $(v_A)_i$ when it collides centrally with a sphere B of mass m_B initially at rest. Right after impact the velocities of the spheres are $(v_A)_f$ to the left and $(v_B)_f$ to the right. If the coefficient of restitution is given as e, show that the net loss of kinetic energy is

$$\frac{1 - e^2}{2} \frac{m_A m_B}{m_A + m_B} (v_A)_i$$

SECTIONS 4.6 AND 4.7

4.54 At a given instant, three particles A ($m_A = 2$ kg), B ($m_B = 3$ kg), and C ($m_C = 4$ kg) are defined by their respective position vectors $\mathbf{r}_A = 3\mathbf{i} + 2\mathbf{j} - 7\mathbf{k}$ (m), $\mathbf{r}_B = -2\mathbf{i} - 4\mathbf{j} + 3\mathbf{k}$ (m), and $\mathbf{r}_C = \mathbf{i} - 2\mathbf{j} - 2\mathbf{k}$ (m), and velocities $\mathbf{v}_A = \mathbf{i} - 2\mathbf{j} - 3\mathbf{k}$ (m/s), $\mathbf{v}_B = 2\mathbf{j} + \mathbf{k}$ (m/s), and $\mathbf{v}_C = \mathbf{i} - 3\mathbf{k}$ (m/s). Determine the angular momentum of each particle about the origin of the Cartesian coordinate system.

4.55 Two particles A and B occupy positions defined by $\mathbf{r}_A = 2\mathbf{i} - \mathbf{j} - 3\mathbf{k}$ (m) and $\mathbf{r}_B = -\mathbf{i} + 2\mathbf{j} - \mathbf{k}$ (m), and their linear momenta are $5\mathbf{i} - 7\mathbf{j} + \mathbf{k}$ (kg · m/s) and $4\mathbf{i} + 3\mathbf{j}$ (kg · m/s), respectively. Determine the angular momentum of each particle about the origin.

4.56 A 2-lb particle passes through a point P defined by its position vector $\mathbf{r}_p = 3\mathbf{i} - 10\mathbf{j} - 4\mathbf{k}$ (ft) with a velocity of $\mathbf{v}_p = 2\mathbf{i} + 5\mathbf{j} + \mathbf{k}$ (ft/s). Determine the angular momentum $\mathbf{H}_A$ of the particle with respect to a point A defined by $\mathbf{r}_A = 2\mathbf{i} - 5\mathbf{j} - 2\mathbf{k}$ (ft).

4.57 A thin rod OA of negligible mass is rotating about the origin in the horizontal plane xy with an angular speed of 25 rpm as shown. A 5-kg sphere is sliding along the rod away from the origin O with a speed of 2 m/s. Determine the linear momentum $\mathbf{G}$ and the angular momentum $\mathbf{H}_O$ of the sphere with respect to the xyz Cartesian coordinate system.

4.58 A thin rod of negligible mass is rotating about the origin in the horizontal plane xy with an angular speed of 50 rpm as shown. A sphere weighing 25 lb is sliding along the rod toward the origin at 10 ft/s. Determine the torque that must be exerted about the vertical axis z to maintain the rod's angular speed at 50 rpm.

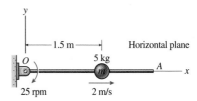

Figure P4.57

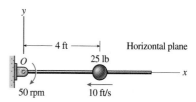

Figure P4.58

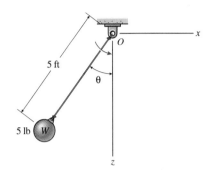

5 ft

5 lb W

Figure P4.59 and P4.60

4.59 A 5-lb sphere constitutes the weight of a pendulum attached by a 5-ft string to a ceiling as shown. The angle θ that the string makes with the vertical is decreasing at the rate of 0.1 rad/s when θ = 25°. The motion occurs within the vertical xz plane. Determine the linear momentum $\mathbf{G}$ and the angular momentum $\mathbf{H}_O$ of the sphere in polar and Cartesian coordinates.

4.60 Using the moment–rate of angular momentum equation, determine the tension in the string in Problem 4.59.

4.61 Two 5-kg spheres are mounted on two rigid rods of negligible mass and length L = 5 m and are rotating freely about a vertical shaft as shown. The vertical shaft is rotating at a speed of 120 rpm when θ = 60°. Determine the angular speed when θ = 45°.

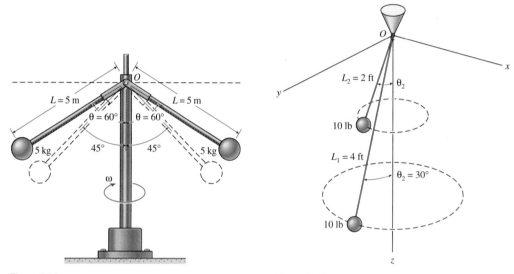

Figure P4.61   **Figure P4.62**

4.62 A conical pendulum consists of a 10-lb weight attached to a 4-ft-long string as shown. The ball swings at a constant angular speed in a horizontal circle with a cone half-angle θ = 30°. If the length of the string is shortened by half to 2 ft, determine the new cone half-angle.

4.63 A conical pendulum has a ball of 10-kg mass and a 2-m-long string. The ball is revolving in a horizontal circle at a constant speed. If the half-angle of the cone is equal to 40°, determine the tension in the string.

4.64 A 200-lb man stands on a horizontal turntable of negligible mass at a radial distance of 10 ft from the axis of the shaft as shown. The angular velocity of the turntable is 3 rad/s. If a moment of magnitude M = $2t$ lb · ft, where t is in seconds, is applied to the turntable in the direction opposing the motion, determine the time required to bring the turntable to rest.

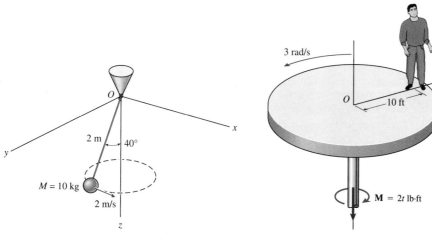

Figure P4.63

Figure P4.64

4.65 A small sphere of mass m is attached to an inextensible cord of negligible weight as shown. The sphere is situated at a radial distance r and is revolving clockwise at a constant angular velocity of ω rad/s on a smooth frictionless table. The cord passes through a hole in the table and is being pulled down by a force F. If F is increased until the radial distance r is reduced to half, and assuming that the radial acceleration is negligible, determine the new constant-angular velocity.

4.66 In Problem 4.65, determine the new force F' required to place the small sphere on a circular trajectory with a radius that is half the initial one.

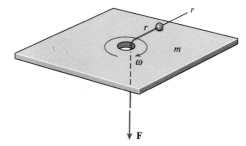

Figure P4.65 and P4.66

4.67 Two children weighing 70 lb each are seated at the opposite ends of a plank that is 9-ft long and of negligible mass. The plank rotates at an angular velocity of 8 rpm in a horizontal plane and about its midpoint. Determine the angular velocity when the children are seated 3 ft from the midpoint of the plank.

4.68 A 50-kg mass is attached to a weightless rigid 2-m-long rod rotating about point O in a vertical plane as shown. If, at the position shown ($\theta = 0$), the angular velocity of the rod is 0.5 rad/s, determine the moment necessary to accelerate the sphere at the rate of 1 rad/s^2.

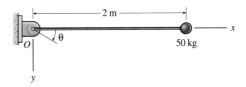

Figure P4.68

SECTION 4.8

4.69 An earth satellite will be injected into an elliptical orbit having an apogee at 5000 mi and a perigee at 500 mi from the surface of the earth. Determine the injection velocity if the free flight of the satellite begins at the perigee of the orbit.

4.70 An earth satellite is in circular orbit at an altitude of 300 mi above the surface of the earth. Determine the periodic time of the orbit.

4.71 For Problem 4.70, determine the boost in orbital velocity necessary to place the satellite into an elliptical orbit ($e = 0.5$).

4.72 Determine the semimajor axis length of an earth orbit having a periodic time of 95 min.

4.73 Show that for a satellite in elliptical orbit the semiminor axis is to be given by

$$b = [(r_{max})(r_{min})]^{1/2}.$$

4.74 A satellite is injected into orbit with a velocity of 20,000 mph parallel to the earth's surface and at an altitude of 560 miles above the surface of the earth. Determine (*a*) the equation of the orbit, and (*b*) the apogee distance to the surface of the earth.

4.75 A satellite is traveling in a circular orbit at an altitude of 900 miles above the earth. Determine (*a*) the velocity of the satellite, and (*b*) the apogee distance, after an elliptical orbit is achieved by boosting the satellite velocity to 20,000 mph.

4.76 If the apogee and perigee distances of an earth orbit are 20,000 and 7500 km, respectively, determine (*a*) the eccentricity of the orbit, and (*b*) the velocity at the perigee.

4.77 A satellite is in an elliptical orbit around the earth with an eccentricity $e = 0.20$. If the perigee is located at 3.5 miles above the earth, determine (*a*) the velocity at the perigee, and (*b*) the velocity at point P at the end of the semiminor axis of the orbit. (Hint: use the result developed in Problem 4.73.)

4.78 If the ratio of the maximum to minimum orbital velocity of a satellite is given, determine the ratio of its apogee and perigee altitudes. The satellite is orbiting around the earth.

4.79 A space vehicle is in circular orbit (radius 5500 km) around a planet (radius = 5000 km). The planet's gravitational acceleration is 3 m/s². Determine the escape velocity necessary to achieve parabolic orbit.

4.80 A central force field obeys the inverse third power law. The force is attractive and given by $F = -K\,m/r^3$. Determine the differential equation of the path.

KINETICS OF SYSTEMS OF PARTICLES

5.1 INTRODUCTION

The dynamics of engineering problems seldom involve a single particle. When we study the motion of a gear, a gyroscope, a propeller, or the jet flow out of a nozzle or the launch of a rocket, we are always dealing with the motion of a cluster of particles, called a *system*. It is therefore necessary to extend the concepts and the approach developed in the preceding chapters to a system of particles. Indeed it is the concepts and equations developed herein that will lay the foundation for the next chapter, in which we will study the kinetics of rigid bodies.

5.2 EQUATION OF MOTION FOR A SYSTEM OF PARTICLES

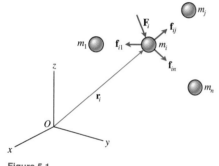

Figure 5.1

Consider a system of n particles, as shown in Figure 5.1, where the ith particle has a mass m_i and is acted upon by a net external force $\mathbf{F}_i$ and by $(n-1)$ internal forces $\mathbf{f}_{i1}, \mathbf{f}_{i2}, \ldots, \mathbf{f}_{i(i-1)}, \mathbf{f}_{i(i+1)}, \ldots, \mathbf{f}_{ij}, \ldots \mathbf{f}_{in}$ (since the internal force $\mathbf{f}_{ii}$ has no physical meaning). Applying the equation of motion to the ith particle, we obtain

$$\mathbf{F}_i + \sum_{j=1}^{n} \mathbf{f}_{ij} = m_i \mathbf{a}_i$$

where $\mathbf{a}_i$ is the absolute acceleration of the ith particle with respect to a fixed frame of reference xyz. Next, we write a similar equation for every particle of the system and we add them together, which yields

$$\sum_{i=1}^{n} \mathbf{F}_i + \sum_{i=1}^{n} \sum_{j=1}^{n} \mathbf{f}_{ij} = \sum_{i=1}^{n} m_i \mathbf{a}_i$$

The first term on the left-hand side of the above equation is the vector sum of all the external forces acting on all the particles, and the second term on the left represents the vector sum of all the internal forces acting and reacting mutually among the particles. Since the latter forces occur in pairs and cancel each other ($\mathbf{f}_{ij} = -\mathbf{f}_{ji}$), the term $\sum_{i=1}^{n} \sum_{j=1}^{n} \mathbf{f}_{ij}$ will be zero and the equation of motion will be reduced to $\sum_{i=1}^{n} \mathbf{F}_i = \sum_{i=1}^{n} m_i \mathbf{a}_i$. If the resultant of the external forces acting on all the particles of the system is given by $\mathbf{F}$ and the acceleration vector $\mathbf{a}_i$ of each particle is expressed in terms of its velocity vector $\mathbf{v}_i$, we can write the equation of motion as

$$\mathbf{F} = \sum_{i=1}^{n} m_i \mathbf{a}_i = \sum_{i=1}^{n} m_i \frac{d\mathbf{v}_i}{dt} \tag{5.1}$$

where $\mathbf{F} = \sum_{i=1}^{n} \mathbf{F}_i$. Furthermore, when particle mass m_i remains constant throughout, the above expression is reduced to

$$\mathbf{F} = \frac{d}{dt} \sum_{i=1}^{n} m_i \mathbf{v}_i \tag{5.2}$$

Recalling from statics the concept of first moment, we can now introduce it for a system of n particles as $\sum_{i=1}^{n} m_i \mathbf{r}_i$. The *center of mass* of the system of particles is thus defined by its position vector $\mathbf{r}_C$ (Figure 5.2), given as

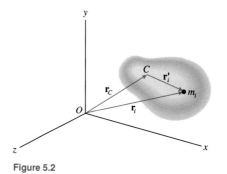

$$\mathbf{r}_C \sum_{i=1}^{n} m_i = \sum_{i=1}^{n} m_i \mathbf{r}_i$$

where $\sum_{i=1}^{n} m_i$ is the total mass m of the system. The final expression is

$$m\mathbf{r}_C = \sum_{i=1}^{n} m_i \mathbf{r}_i \qquad (5.3)$$

Figure 5.2

By taking the time derivatives of both sides of Equation (5.3) and recalling that the masses are constant, we obtain

$$m\mathbf{v}_C = \Sigma(m_i \mathbf{v}_i)$$

and

$$m\mathbf{a}_C = \Sigma(m_i \mathbf{a}_i)$$

and Equation (5.2) becomes

$$\mathbf{F} = = \frac{d}{dt}(m\mathbf{v}_C)$$

where $\mathbf{v}_C$ is the velocity at the center of mass of the system.
   Equation (5.1) now can be reduced to

$$\mathbf{F} = m\mathbf{a}_C \qquad (5.4)$$

We conclude that *the motion of the center of mass of a system of particles of constant mass m can be simulated by the motion of a single particle of mass m, located at the mass center of the system and subjected to a force, acting through the mass center, equal to the sum of all the external forces acting on the particles of the system.*
   We will next consider the moments, about an arbitrary and fixed point O, of the forces acting on the particles of a system. The sum of the moments of all internal forces will again be zero, since the internal forces will cancel in pairs. Taking the moment about O of the equation of motion of a particle i, we obtain

$$\mathbf{r}_i \times \mathbf{F}_i = \mathbf{r}_i \times m_i \mathbf{a}_i$$

and after writing similar equations for all the particles within the system and adding them together, we have

$$\sum_{i=1}^{n} \mathbf{r}_i \times \mathbf{F}_i = \sum_{i=1}^{n} \mathbf{r}_i \times m_i \mathbf{a}_i$$

$$\mathbf{M}_O = \sum_{i=1}^{n} \mathbf{r}_i \times m_i \mathbf{a}_i \tag{5.5}$$

We conclude that *the total moment* $\mathbf{M}_O$, *about a fixed origin O of all the external forces acting on a system of particles of constant mass is equal to the vector sum of the moments of the vectors* $m_i \mathbf{a}_i$ *of all the particles.*

EXAMPLE 5.1

A system consists of three particles with masses $m_1 = 1$ kg, $m_2 = 2$ kg, and $m_3 = 1$ kg. Their positions are defined by the vectors $\mathbf{r}_1 = 2t\mathbf{i}$ (m), $\mathbf{r}_2 = 3t^2\mathbf{j}$ (m), and $\mathbf{r}_3 = t\mathbf{k}$ (m). Determine the position, the velocity, and the acceleration vectors of the center of mass at time $t = 2$ s.

Solution The definition of the center of mass is expressed mathematically by the equation

$$\mathbf{r}_C \sum_{i=1}^{3} m_i = \sum_{i=1}^{3} m_i \mathbf{r}_i$$

Therefore we write

$$\mathbf{r}_C = \frac{1}{(1 + 2 + 1)}[1(2t)\mathbf{i} + 2(3t^2)\mathbf{j} + 1(t)\mathbf{k}]$$

$$\mathbf{r}_{C(t)} = 0.5t\mathbf{i} + 1.5t^2\mathbf{j} + 0.25t\mathbf{k}$$

$$\mathbf{r}_{C(t=2)} = \mathbf{i} + 6\mathbf{j} + 0.5\mathbf{k}\,(\text{m}) \blacktriangleleft$$

The velocity of the center of mass is given by

$$\mathbf{v}_C \sum m_i = \sum m_i \mathbf{v}_i = \sum m_i \dot{\mathbf{r}}_i$$

where $\dot{\mathbf{r}}_1 = 2\mathbf{i}$, $\dot{\mathbf{r}}_2 = 6t\mathbf{j}$, and $\dot{\mathbf{r}}_3 = \mathbf{k}$. Solving the above relationship, we obtain

$$\mathbf{v}_{C(t)} = \frac{1}{(1 + 2 + 1)}[2\mathbf{i} + 2(6t)\mathbf{j} + \mathbf{k}]$$

$$\mathbf{v}_{C(t=2)} = 0.5\mathbf{i} + 6\mathbf{j} + 0.25\mathbf{k}\,(\text{m/s}) \blacktriangleleft$$

The acceleration of the mass center is given by

$$\mathbf{a}_C \sum_{i=1}^{3} m_i = \sum_{i=1}^{3} m_i \mathbf{a}_i$$

and once again introducing the kinematic relationships $\mathbf{a}_i = \ddot{\mathbf{r}}_i$, we have

$$\mathbf{a}_C = \frac{1}{(1 + 2 + 1)}[(2)(0)\mathbf{i} + (2)(6)\mathbf{j} + (1)(0)\mathbf{k}] = 3\mathbf{j}$$

$$a_{C(t=2)} = 3\mathbf{j}\,(\text{m/s}^2) \blacktriangleleft$$

EXAMPLE 5.2

An observer from a fixed position measures the velocities of two particles A and B, weighing 5 lb and 10 lb, respectively, as $\mathbf{v}_A = 2\mathbf{i} + 3\mathbf{k}$ (ft/s) and $\mathbf{v}_B = \mathbf{j} - 2\mathbf{k}$ (ft/s). Determine the velocity of each particle relative to their common center of mass.

Solution The velocity of the center of mass can be evaluated from

$$\mathbf{v}_C \Sigma m_i = \Sigma m_i \mathbf{v}_i$$

Thus we have

$$\mathbf{v}_C = \frac{m_A \mathbf{v}_A + m_B \mathbf{v}_B}{m_A + m_B}$$

$$\mathbf{v}_C = \frac{32.2}{15}\left[\frac{5}{32.2}(2\mathbf{i} + 3\mathbf{k}) + \frac{10}{32.2}(\mathbf{j} - 2\mathbf{k})\right]$$

and the velocity of the mass center with respect to the fixed observer becomes

$$\mathbf{v}_C = \frac{2}{3}\mathbf{i} + \frac{2}{3}\mathbf{j} - \frac{1}{3}\mathbf{k}\,(\text{ft/s})$$

We derive the velocity of each particle relative to the center of mass using the principle of relative motion, given as

$$\mathbf{v}_{A/C} = \mathbf{v}_A - \mathbf{v}_C$$

$$\mathbf{v}_{A/C} = (2\mathbf{i} + 3\mathbf{k}) - \left(\frac{2}{3}\mathbf{i} + \frac{2}{3}\mathbf{j} - \frac{1}{3}\mathbf{k}\right)$$

$$\mathbf{v}_{A/C} = \frac{4}{3}\mathbf{i} - \frac{2}{3}\mathbf{j} + \frac{10}{3}\mathbf{k}\,(\text{ft/s})\quad\blacktriangleleft$$

$$\mathbf{v}_{B/C} = \mathbf{v}_B - \mathbf{v}_C$$

$$\mathbf{v}_{B/C} = (\mathbf{j} - 2\mathbf{k}) - \left(\frac{2}{3}\mathbf{i} + \frac{2}{3}\mathbf{j} - \frac{1}{3}\mathbf{k}\right)$$

$$\mathbf{v}_{B/C} = -\frac{2}{3}\mathbf{i} + \frac{1}{3}\mathbf{j} - \frac{5}{3}\mathbf{k}\,(\text{ft/s})\quad\blacktriangleleft$$

EXAMPLE 5.3

A 600-kg meteor traveling at 7500 m/s breaks into three parts A, B, and C at a point O as shown. The fragments move in the xy plane at $v_A = 8000$ m/s, $v_B = 10,000$ m/s, and $v_C = 2000$ m/s in the directions indicated. Determine the mass of each fragment.

Solution Considering the masses of the fragments, we write

$$m_A + m_B + m_C = 600 \qquad (a)$$

The mass of the meteor at the moment of breakup represents the total mass ($\Sigma m_i = 600$ kg) of the system, and the position O and velocity (7500 m/s) of the meteor can be viewed as the position and velocity of the center of mass of the three-particle system. We write the vector relationship

$$\mathbf{v}_O \Sigma m_i = \Sigma m_i \mathbf{v}_i$$

which, when written in the x direction, yields

$$600(7500) = m_A(8000)\cos 60° + m_B(10,000)$$

or, after simplifying,

$$2m_A + 5m_B = 2250 \qquad (b)$$

Applying the same vector relation in the y direction yields

$$600(7500)(0) = m_A(8000)\sin 60° - m_C(2000)$$

$$(4\sin 60°)m_A - m_C = 0 \qquad (c)$$

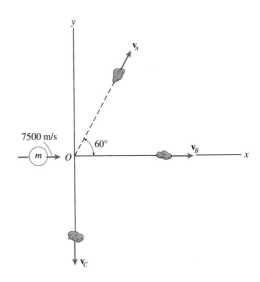

Equations (a), (b), and (c) will now yield

$$m_A = 36.9\text{ kg}\quad\blacktriangleleft$$

$$m_B = 435.2\text{ kg}\quad\blacktriangleleft$$

$$m_C = 127.8\text{ kg}\quad\blacktriangleleft$$

EXAMPLE 5.4

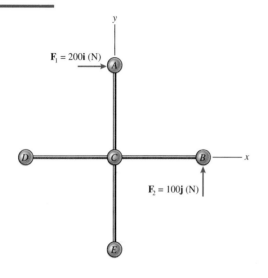

A system consists of five identical 5-kg spheres connected, as shown, by rigid bars having negligible masses. The system is initially at rest on a smooth horizontal plane. At time $t = 0$, two forces $\mathbf{F}_1 = 200\mathbf{i}$ (N) and $\mathbf{F}_2 = 100\mathbf{j}$ (N) begin to act on A and B, respectively. Determine the velocity of the mass center at $t = 2$ s.

Solution The equation of motion for a system of particles is given by Equation (5.4) as

$$\mathbf{F} = (\Sigma m_i)\mathbf{a}_C$$

where

$$\mathbf{F} = \Sigma \mathbf{F}_i = 200\mathbf{i} + 100\mathbf{j} \text{ (N)}$$

and

$$\Sigma m_i = 5(5) = 25 \text{ kg}$$

Thus we can write

$$\mathbf{a}_C = \frac{\Sigma \mathbf{F}_i}{\Sigma m_i} = \frac{1}{25}(200\mathbf{i} + 100\mathbf{j})$$

and since $\ddot{\mathbf{r}}_C = \mathbf{a}_C$,

$$\ddot{\mathbf{r}}_C = \mathbf{a}_C = 8\mathbf{i} + 4\mathbf{j} \text{ (m/s}^2)$$

Now, integrating once yields

$$\mathbf{v}_C = \dot{\mathbf{r}}_C = 8t\mathbf{i} + 4t\mathbf{j} + K$$

where $K = 0$, since initially $\mathbf{v}_{C(t=0)} = \mathbf{0}$. At $t = 2$, the velocity of the mass center becomes

$$\mathbf{v}_{C(t=2)} = 16\mathbf{i} + 8\mathbf{j} \text{ (m/s)} \blacktriangleleft$$

Alternate Solution By impulse-momentum we write

$$(\mathbf{v}_C)_1 \Sigma m_i + \Sigma \mathbf{F}_i \Delta t = (\mathbf{v}_C)_2 \Sigma m_i$$

$$0 + (200\mathbf{i} + 100\mathbf{j})2 = \mathbf{v}_C(25)$$

$$\mathbf{v}_C = 16\mathbf{i} + 8\mathbf{j} \text{ (m/s)} \blacktriangleleft$$

5.3 EQUATION OF WORK AND KINETIC ENERGY FOR A SYSTEM OF PARTICLES

Consider again a system of n particles subject to external forces $\mathbf{F}_i$ and internal forces $\mathbf{f}_{ij}$ as introduced in Figure 5.1. The work–kinetic energy equation when applied to the ith particle of mass m_i yields

$$(T_i)_A + (U_i)_{A \to B} = (T_i)_B$$

where $(U_i)_{A \to B}$ is the work done on the ith particle by all the forces ($\mathbf{F}_i$ and $\mathbf{f}_{ij}$) in order to bring it from its original space position indicated by the subscript A to its final space position given by the subscript B, and where $(T_i)_A$ and $(T_i)_B$ represent the kinetic energies of m_i when occupying the initial and final space positions respectively. Next, we write a similar equation for every particle within the system and add them together, to obtain

$$\sum_{i=1}^{n} (T_i)_A + \sum_{i=1}^{n} (U_i)_{A \to B} = \sum_{i=1}^{n} (T_i)_B$$

or simply

$$T_A + U_{A \to B} = T_B \qquad (5.6)$$

where U is the **total work** done by *all* forces on all the particles of the system to bring the system from its initial position indicated by the subscript A to its final position described by the subscript B, and where T_A and T_B are the kinetic energies of the total system of n particles at the initial and final positions, respectively. The **total kinetic energy** of the system, T, is given as

$$T = \sum_{i=1}^{n} T_i = \frac{1}{2} \sum_{i=1}^{n} m_i v_i^2 \qquad (5.7)$$

It must be noted that the total work done on the n particles of a system by *all* the forces must include the work of the internal forces $\mathbf{f}_{ij}$. Although these forces come in pairs of equal magnitude and opposite direction, equal displacement vectors are not necessarily associated with the particles involved. Therefore, the work of the internal force exerted by a particle upon another having a certain displacement may not cancel out with the work of the equal-but-opposite force exerted by the latter particle upon the former if the particles have different displacements.

However, if the system under consideration consists of particles that are joined together to form a rigid body or if several rigid bodies are connected by frictionless joints, the mutually interactive internal forces will not contribute to the total work. Then the expression for the total work may be written as

$$U_{A \to B} = \int_A^B \sum_{i=1}^{n} \mathbf{F}_i \cdot d\mathbf{r}_i$$

and the work–kinetic energy equation can now be expressed as

$$\left[\frac{1}{2} \sum_{i=1}^{n} m_i v_i^2 \right]_A + \int_A^B \sum_{i=1}^{n} \mathbf{F}_i \cdot d\mathbf{r}_i = \left[\frac{1}{2} \sum_{i=1}^{n} m_i v_i^2 \right]_B \qquad (5.8)$$

Special Case: Center of Mass as Reference Point

For certain engineering problems the judicious selection of an origin of co-ordinates may significantly simplify the analysis of the problem. Since the preceding analysis assumed that the frame of reference and its origin were fixed, we must now investigate the implications of a transformation of coordinates upon the work–kinetic energy relationship previously established. Here, the question will be limited to the case of a *translating* frame of reference with its origin located at the center of mass. A rotating frame of reference will be considered later, when we study rigid-body kinematics.

Consider in Figure 5.3 a fixed frame of reference xyz with origin at O. The ith particle of a system of n particles is located at a point P_i defined by its position vector $\mathbf{r}_i$. Assuming that the system has its center of mass C traveling at a velocity $\mathbf{v}_c$, let us write a transformation of coordinates that will relate the position and motion of the particles of the system to a new frame of reference $x'y'z'$ with its origin at C. We can now write

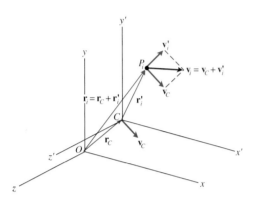

Figure 5.3

$$\mathbf{r}_i = \mathbf{r}_C + \mathbf{r}'_i \qquad \mathbf{v}_i = \mathbf{v}_C + \mathbf{v}'_i \tag{5.9}$$

The total kinetic energy T of the system of particles in the fixed frame of reference xyz is given as

$$T = \frac{1}{2}\sum m_i v_i^2 = \frac{1}{2}\sum m_i(\mathbf{v}_i \cdot \mathbf{v}_i)$$

Substituting $\mathbf{v}_i$ from Equation (5.9), we obtain

$$T = \frac{1}{2}\sum [m_i(\mathbf{v}_C + \mathbf{v}'_i) \cdot (\mathbf{v}_C + \mathbf{v}'_i)]$$

and, upon expansion of terms, we have

$$T = \frac{1}{2}\sum m_i(\mathbf{v}_C \cdot \mathbf{v}_C) + \frac{1}{2}\sum m_i(\mathbf{v}'_i \cdot \mathbf{v}'_i) + 2\left[\frac{1}{2}\sum m_i(\mathbf{v}_C \cdot \mathbf{v}'_i)\right]$$

$$T = \frac{1}{2}\left(\sum m_i\right)v_C^2 + \frac{1}{2}\sum(m_i v_i'^2) + \mathbf{v}_C \cdot \sum m_i \mathbf{v}'_i \tag{5.10}$$

From the definition of the center of mass of a system of n particles and realizing that $\mathbf{r}'_C = \mathbf{0}$, we have

$$\sum m_i \mathbf{r}'_i = (\sum m_i)\mathbf{r}'_C = m\mathbf{r}'_C = \mathbf{0}$$

where m is the total mass and $\mathbf{r}'_C$ the position vector of the center relative to itself and therefore equal to zero. Time differentiation of the above expression, for a constant mass system, will yield

$$\sum m_i \dot{\mathbf{r}}'_i = \sum m_i \mathbf{v}'_i = \mathbf{0}$$

The last term on the right-hand side of Equation (5.10) thus vanishes and we have

$$T = \frac{1}{2}\left(\sum_{i=1}^{n} m_i\right)v_C^2 + \frac{1}{2}\sum_{i=1}^{n}(m_i v_i'^2) \tag{5.11}$$

We conclude that *the total kinetic energy T of a system of particles is equal to the sum of the kinetic energy, relative to a fixed frame of reference, of the total mass* ($\sum_{i=1}^{n} m_i = m$), *assumed to be concentrated at the center of mass of the system, and the kinetic energies, relative to the center of mass, of all the individual particles forming the system.* The frame of reference attached to the mass center is assumed to be translating. Note that Equation (5.11) is not valid for a rotating frame of reference.

Conservation of Mechanical Energy

In Chapter 3, we established that the sum of the kinetic and potential energy of a particle (i.e., its total mechanical energy) is conserved if the particle is acted upon by conservative forces only. Now, if we consider the ith particle of a system of n particles and apply to it the relationship established in Chapter 3, Equation (3.22), we have

$$T_{iA} + V_{iA} = T_{iB} + V_{iB}$$

If we write the above expression for all n particles of the system and add them together, we obtain

$$\sum_{i=1}^{n} T_{iA} + \sum_{i=1}^{n} V_{iA} = \sum_{i=1}^{n} T_{iB} + \sum_{i=1}^{n} V_{iB}$$

or

$$T_A + V_A = T_B + V_B \tag{5.12}$$

which states that *the total mechanical energy of a system of particles, acted upon by conservative forces only, is conserved.*

EXAMPLE 5.5

The mass center of a system of spheres is moving within a horizontal plane as shown, with a velocity given as $v_C = 4\mathbf{i} - 3\mathbf{j}$ (ft/s), measured with respect to a fixed frame of reference Oxy. The four spheres weigh 5 lb each and are rigidly attached to the center C at the ends of four 10-ft-long slender bars of negligible mass. The whole system rotates at a constant angular speed $\omega = 25$ rpm. Determine the total kinetic energy of the system.

Solution The total kinetic energy is obtained by using Equation (5.11):

$$T = \frac{1}{2}\left(\sum_{i=1}^{4} m_i\right) v_C^2 + \frac{1}{2}\sum_{i=1}^{4} (m_i v_i'^2)$$

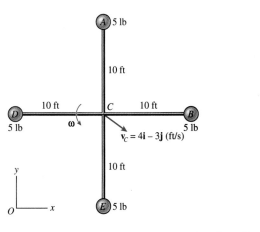

(continued)

EXAMPLE 5.5   (*concluded*)

where

$$v_C^2 = \mathbf{v}_C \cdot \mathbf{v}_C = (4\mathbf{i} - 3\mathbf{j}) \cdot (4\mathbf{i} - 3\mathbf{j})$$
$$= (4^2 + 3^2) = 25 \,(\text{m/s})^2$$

and

$$\Sigma m_i = \frac{(5 + 5 + 5 + 5)}{32.2} = 0.6211 \text{ slug}$$

From the relationship between the angular and linear velocities, we have for the velocities v_i' relative to the mass center C

$$v_i' = R_i \omega$$

which yields $v_A' = v_B' = v_C' = v_D' = 10\left[25\left(\dfrac{2\pi}{60}\right)\right] =$ 26.18 (ft/s). Thus we write

$$T = \frac{1}{2}\left[(4)\left(\frac{5}{32.2}\right)\right](5)^2 + \frac{1}{2}\left[(4)\left(\frac{5}{32.2}\right)\right](26.18)^2$$
$$= 7.76 + 212.85$$

The total kinetic energy of the system is

$$T = 221 \text{ lb} \cdot \text{ft} \blacktriangleleft$$

EXAMPLE 5.6

A system consists of three particles. Two of the particles have masses $m_1 = 2$ kg and $m_2 = 3$ kg. The particles move at speeds of $v_1 = 5$ m/s, $v_2 = 2$ m/s, and $v_3 = 5$ m/s. If the speed v_C of the mass center is 3 m/s and the kinetic energy of the system relative to the mass center is 32.5 J, determine the mass m_3 of the third particle.

Solution   The total kinetic energy of the system relative to a fixed frame of reference is, by Equation (5.7),

$$T_{\text{total}} = \frac{1}{2}\sum_{i=1}^{3} m_i v_i^2$$

which yields in this case

$$T_{\text{total}} = \frac{1}{2}[2(5)^2 + 3(2)^2 + m_3(5)^2] \qquad (a)$$

The total kinetic energy of the system can also be expressed with respect to a frame of reference attached to the mass center

$$T_{\text{total}} = \frac{1}{2}\left(\sum_{i=1}^{3} m_i\right)v_C^2 + \frac{1}{2}\sum_{i=1}^{3}(m_i v_i'^2)$$

$$T_{\text{total}} = \frac{1}{2}m v_C^2 + T_{\text{rel}}$$

where $v_C = 3$ m/s, $m = 5 + m_3$, and $T_{\text{rel}} = 32.5$ J. The above equation yields

$$T_{\text{total}} = \frac{1}{2}(5 + m_3)(3)^2 + 32.5 \qquad (b)$$

Equating Equations (a) and (b) and solving for m_3, we have

$$\frac{1}{2}(50 + 12 + 25m_3) = \frac{1}{2}(5 + m_3)(9) + 32.5$$

$$8m_3 = 24$$

$$m_3 = 3 \text{ kg} \blacktriangleleft$$

EXAMPLE 5.7

A six-car roller coaster moves along a horizontal stretch of track. Each car weighs 500 lb. Determine the height h of the rise from point A to point B that the train can clear if it is coasting at point A at a speed of 50 ft/s (a) if track friction is negligible, and (b) if losses due to rolling friction and drag, between A and B, is approximately equal to 10,000 ft · lb.

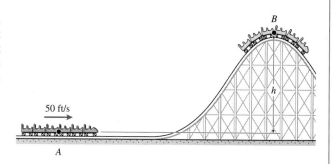

Solution

Part a.   The train will clear point B if the velocity of its mass center just becomes zero at B; thus, $v_B = 0$. Therefore the kinetic energy of the six-car system is, at A,

$$T_A = \frac{1}{2}\sum_{i=1}^{6} m_i v_i^2$$

$$T_A = \frac{1}{2}\sum_{i=1}^{6} \frac{W_i}{g}v_A^2 = \frac{1}{2}\left(\frac{6W}{g}\right)v_A^2$$

and at B ($v_B = 0$),

$$T_B = 0$$

The work done by the total weight of the system is

$$U_{A\rightarrow B} = -\left(\sum_{i=1}^{6} W_i\right)h = -6Wh$$

The equation of work–kinetic energy ($T_A + U_{A\rightarrow B} = T_B$) for the system becomes

$$\frac{1}{2}\left[6\left(\frac{W}{g}\right)\right]v_A^2 - 6Wh = 0$$

Eliminating W and solving for h,

$$h = \frac{v_A^2}{2g} = \frac{(50)^2}{2(32.2)} \qquad h = 38.8 \text{ ft} \blacktriangleleft$$

Part b.   The work done between A and B will also include the work of the frictional forces opposing the motion. Thus,

$$U_{A\rightarrow B} = -6Wh - 10,000$$

and the work–kinetic energy equation becomes

$$\frac{1}{2}\left[6\left(\frac{W}{g}\right)\right]v_A^2 - 6Wh - 10,000 = 0$$

and we find

$$h = \frac{v_A^2}{2g} - \frac{10,000}{6W} = \frac{(50)^2}{2(32.2)} - \frac{10,000}{6(500)}$$

$$h = 35.5 \text{ ft} \blacktriangleleft$$

EXAMPLE   5.8

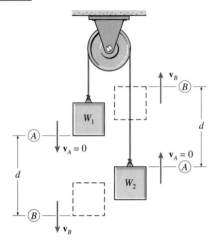

Two unidentical weights W_1 and W_2 ($W_1 > W_2$) are released from rest, as shown, and move in opposite directions. After the weights have moved through a distance d, the speed of the weights is v. Determine the value of the gravitational acceleration g based on the above conditions for W_1, W_2, d, and v. (Neglect the weight and axle friction of the pulley.)

Solution   The equation of work and kinetic energy applied to the system of the two weights is

$$(T_1 + T_2)_A + (U_{A \to B})_1 + (U_{A \to B})_2 = (T_1 + T_2)_B$$

where, in this case,

$$(T_1 + T_2)_A = \frac{1}{2}\left(\frac{W_1}{g} + \frac{W_2}{g}\right)(0)^2 = 0$$

$$(T_1 + T_2)_B = \frac{1}{2}\left(\frac{W_1}{g} + \frac{W_2}{g}\right)v^2$$

$$(U_{A \to B})_1 = W_1(d)$$

$$(U_{A \to B})_2 = W_2(-d)$$

Substituting the above terms into the work–kinetic energy equation yields

$$0 + (W_1 - W_2)d = \frac{1}{2}\left(\frac{W_1 + W_2}{g}\right)v^2$$

which gives for the gravitational acceleration

$$g = \frac{v^2}{2d}\frac{W_1 + W_2}{W_1 - W_2} \quad \blacktriangleleft$$

This apparatus is referred to as "Atwood machine" and is used to measure the gravitational acceleration, g.

5.4 EQUATION OF LINEAR IMPULSE AND MOMENTUM FOR A SYSTEM OF PARTICLES

The equation of motion for a system of particles was given in Equation (5.2) as

$$\mathbf{F} = \frac{d}{dt}\sum m_i \mathbf{v}_i$$

where $\mathbf{F} = \Sigma \mathbf{F}_i$. Introducing the concept of linear momentum as $\mathbf{G}_i = m_i \mathbf{v}_i$ and, after substituting $\mathbf{G} = \Sigma \mathbf{G}_i$, we obtain the relationship of force and rate of change of linear momentum as

$$\mathbf{F} = \dot{\mathbf{G}} \tag{5.13}$$

This equation states that *the resultant of all the external forces acting on a system of particles of constant mass is equal to the time rate of change of the linear momentum of the system.*

If we introduce the definition of the center of mass for a system of particles by writing

$$\mathbf{r}_C \Sigma m_i = \Sigma m_i \mathbf{r}_i$$

where Σm_i is the total constant mass of the system, time differentiation of the above expression will yield

$$m\dot{\mathbf{r}}_C = \Sigma m_i \dot{\mathbf{r}}_i$$

or

$$m\mathbf{v}_C = \Sigma m_i \mathbf{v}_i = \mathbf{G} \tag{5.14}$$

where $\mathbf{v}_C$ is the velocity of the mass center. Equation (5.14) states that *the linear momentum of a system of particles of constant mass is equivalent to the momentum of a single constant mass m located at the center of mass of the system.*

After differentiating $\mathbf{G}$ in Equation (5.14), Equation (5.13) can now be written as $\mathbf{F} = m\dot{\mathbf{v}}_C$ or

$$\mathbf{F} = m\mathbf{a}_C \tag{5.15}$$

where $\mathbf{a}_C$ is the acceleration of the mass center. Equation (5.15) is a restatement of the previously derived Equation (5.4). There is also another form of expressing the equation of motion for a system of particles. Considering Equation (5.2), we write

$$\mathbf{F} = \sum_{i=1}^{n} \mathbf{F}_i = \frac{d}{dt} \sum_{i=1}^{n} m_i \mathbf{v}_i$$

and integrating the above equation over a time interval $(t_2 - t_1)$, we obtain

$$\int_{t_1}^{t_2} \mathbf{F} \, dt = \sum_{i=1}^{n} (m_i \mathbf{v}_i)_2 - \sum_{i=1}^{n} (m_i \mathbf{v}_i)_1$$

or, after rearranging the terms,

$$\sum_{i=1}^{n} (m_i \mathbf{v}_i)_1 + \int_{t_1}^{t_2} \mathbf{F} \, dt = \sum_{i=1}^{n} (m_i \mathbf{v}_i)_2$$

and finally we have

$$\mathbf{G}_1 + \int_{t_1}^{t_2} \mathbf{F} \, dt = \mathbf{G}_2 \tag{5.16}$$

This is the linear impulse–momentum equation for a system of particles of constant mass. It states that the final linear momentum of a system is equal to its initial linear momentum plus the linear impulse acting on the system during the time interval under consideration.

Equation (5.16) can also be expressed in terms of the initial and final linear momenta of the mass center. Thus, we write

$$m(\mathbf{v}_C)_1 + \int_{t_1}^{t_2} \mathbf{F}\, dt = m(\mathbf{v}_C)_2 \qquad (5.17)$$

where $m = \Sigma m_i$ and $\mathbf{v}_C$ is the velocity of the mass center.

We conclude that the linear impulse–momentum equation can be applied to a system of particles of constant mass by considering the system as a single particle of constant mass $m = \Sigma m_i$, concentrated at the center of mass of the system. From Equation (5.17) we can see that if the linear impulse $\int_{t_1}^{t_2} \mathbf{F}\, dt$ is zero, the initial and final momenta are equal, and we have

$$\mathbf{G}_1 = \mathbf{G}_2 \qquad (5.18)$$

This equation represents the ***conservation of linear momentum*** for a system of particles of constant mass.

Special Case: Center of Mass as Reference Point

Referring to Figure 5.3 and introducing $\mathbf{r}_i = \mathbf{r}_C + \mathbf{r}_i'$ and $\mathbf{v}_i = \mathbf{v}_C + \mathbf{v}_i'$, we can write Equation (5.2) in the form

$$\mathbf{F} = \frac{d}{dt}\Sigma m_i(\mathbf{v}_C + \mathbf{v}_i')$$

or, after expanding the right-hand side of the above equation,

$$\mathbf{F} = \frac{d}{dt}(\Sigma m_i)\mathbf{v}_C + (\Sigma m_i)\mathbf{v}_i'$$

The second term on the right-hand side will vanish by definition of the center of mass [Equation (5.9)], and the final expression becomes identical to Equation (5.14) developed for the case of a fixed frame of reference as

$$\mathbf{F} = \dot{\mathbf{G}} = m\dot{\mathbf{v}}_C = m\mathbf{a}_C$$

EXAMPLE 5.9

A system of three particles, with masses $m_1 = 5$ kg, $m_2 = 6$ kg, and $m_3 = 10$ kg, moves under the action of forces $\mathbf{F}_1 = 500\mathbf{i} - 200\mathbf{j}$ (N), $\mathbf{F}_2 = -400\mathbf{i}$ (N), and $\mathbf{F}_3 = 300\mathbf{j}$ (N), as shown. The motion takes place in the vertical xy plane as shown. At a given instant the respective velocities of the particles are $\mathbf{v}_1 = 30\mathbf{i}$ (m/s), $\mathbf{v}_2 = 20\mathbf{j}$ (m/s), and $\mathbf{v}_3 = 5\mathbf{i} - 2\mathbf{j}$ (m/s). Determine (a) the total linear momentum of the system of particles, and (b) the rate of change of linear momentum.

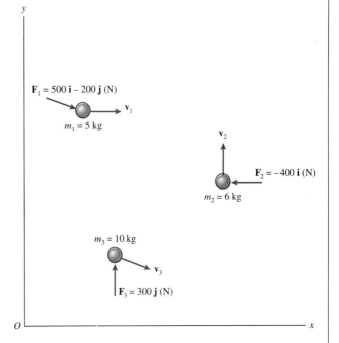

Solution

Part a.   The total linear momentum of the system is given by

$$\mathbf{G} = \Sigma m_i \mathbf{v}_i = 5(30\mathbf{i}) + 6(20\mathbf{j}) + 10(5\mathbf{i} - 2\mathbf{j})$$

$$= 150\mathbf{i} + 120\mathbf{j} + 50\mathbf{i} - 20\mathbf{j}$$

$$\mathbf{G} = 200\mathbf{i} + 100\mathbf{j}\,(\text{kg} \cdot \text{m/s}) \blacktriangleleft$$

Part b.   The relationship between the resultant force and the time rate of change of linear momentum is given by Equation (5.13), $\dot{\mathbf{G}} = \Sigma \mathbf{F}_i$. However, the sum $\Sigma \mathbf{F}_i$ of the external forces acting on the system must include, in addition to the three forces $\mathbf{F}_1$, $\mathbf{F}_2$, and $\mathbf{F}_3$, the weight forces $\mathbf{W}_1$, $\mathbf{W}_2$, and $\mathbf{W}_3$ of the particles. Therefore, we write

$$\mathbf{W}_1 = m_1 g(-\mathbf{j}) = -5(9.81)\mathbf{j} = -49.05\mathbf{j}\,(\text{N})$$

$$\mathbf{W}_2 = m_2 g(-\mathbf{j}) = -6(9.81)\mathbf{j} = -58.86\mathbf{j}\,(\text{N})$$

$$\mathbf{W}_3 = m_3 g(-\mathbf{j}) = -10(9.81)\mathbf{j} = -98.1\mathbf{j}\,(\text{N})$$

and the equation $\dot{\mathbf{G}} = \Sigma \mathbf{F}_i$ becomes

$$\dot{\mathbf{G}} = (500\mathbf{i} - 200\mathbf{j}) + (-400\mathbf{i}) + (300\mathbf{j}) + (-49.05\mathbf{j})$$

$$+ (-58.86\mathbf{j}) + (-98.1\mathbf{j})$$

$$\dot{\mathbf{G}} = 100\mathbf{i} - 106\mathbf{j}\,(\text{kg} \cdot \text{m/s}^2) \blacktriangleleft$$

EXAMPLE 5.10

A 5000-lb satellite reenters the atmosphere with a velocity $\mathbf{v}_{sat} = 1000(-\mathbf{i} - \mathbf{j} - \mathbf{k})$ (ft/s) and quickly disintegrates into three fragments A, B, and C. The fragments A and B, estimated to weigh 1000 lb and 2500 lb, respectively, are tracked with radar and observed to move with velocity $\mathbf{v}_A = 500\mathbf{i} - 375\mathbf{j}$ (ft/s) and $\mathbf{v}_B = -650\mathbf{j} + 800\mathbf{k}$ (ft/s) respectively. Neglecting the effect of gravity, determine the velocity of the fragment C right after disintegration.

Solution Neglecting the effect of gravity, the conservation of linear momentum of a system of particles, Equation (5.18), yields

$$(\Sigma m_i)\mathbf{v}_{sat} = m_A\mathbf{v}_A + m_B\mathbf{v}_B + m_C\mathbf{v}_C$$

and after introducing the velocity vectors and masses of the fragments A, B, and C, we obtain

$$\left(\frac{5000}{g}\right)[1000(-\mathbf{i} - \mathbf{j} - \mathbf{k})] = \left(\frac{1000}{g}\right)(-500\mathbf{i} - 375\mathbf{j}) +$$

$$\left(\frac{2500}{g}\right)(-650\mathbf{j} + 800\mathbf{k}) + \left(\frac{1500}{g}\right)(v_{C_x}\mathbf{i} + v_{C_y}\mathbf{j} + v_{C_z}\mathbf{k})$$

Simplifying in scalar form, we have

x direction:

$$-5000 = -500 + 1.5v_{C_x}$$

$$v_{C_x} = -3000 \text{ ft/s}$$

y direction:

$$-5000 = -375 - 1625 + 1.5v_{C_x}$$

$$v_{C_y} = -2000 \text{ ft/s}$$

z direction:

$$-5000 = -2000 + 1.5v_{C_z}$$

$$v_{C_z} = -2000 \text{ ft/s}$$

$$\mathbf{v}_C = -3000\mathbf{i} - 2000\mathbf{j} - 2000\mathbf{k} \text{ (ft/s)} \blacktriangleleft$$

EXAMPLE 5.11

Rigid bars with negligible mass connect four 100-kg particles A, B, C, and D, as shown. The system rotates in the vertical xy plane about the horizontal z axis with a constant angular velocity $\omega = 20$ rpm. At time $t = 0$, a constant force $\mathbf{F} = 800\mathbf{i}$ (N) begins to act upon particle B for a duration of 3 s. Determine the final velocity of the system's mass center located at O.

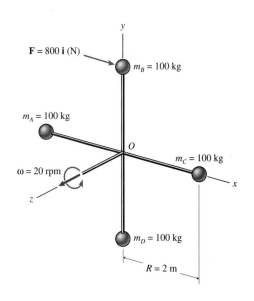

Solution The linear impulse–momentum equation for a system of particles can be expressed in terms of its mass center as

$$\left[\left(\sum_{i=1}^{n} m_i \right) \mathbf{v}_O \right]_1 + \int_{t_1}^{t_2} \mathbf{F}\, dt = \left[\left(\sum_{i=1}^{n} m_i \right) \mathbf{v}_O \right]_2$$

The center of mass of the system is at the origin and is initially at rest ($\mathbf{v}_O = 0$). From Equation (5.17) we have

$$\underbrace{\left[\left(\sum_{i=1}^{n} m_i \right) \mathbf{v}_O \right]_1}_{= \, 0} + \underbrace{\int_{t_1=0}^{t_2=3} 800\mathbf{i}\, dt}_{} = \underbrace{\left[\left(\sum_{i=1}^{n} m_i \right) \mathbf{v}_O \right]_2}_{}$$

Initial linear momentum of system   Impulse   Final linear momentum of system

$$800(3 - 0)\mathbf{i} = (400)\mathbf{v}_O$$

and solving for the final velocity of the center of mass,

$$\mathbf{v}_O = \left(\frac{2400}{400} \right)\mathbf{i} \qquad \mathbf{v}_O = 6\mathbf{i} \text{ (ft/s)} \blacktriangleleft$$

5.5 EQUATION OF ANGULAR IMPULSE AND MOMENTUM FOR A SYSTEM OF PARTICLES

The moment, about a fixed point O, of the momentum (i.e., the angular momentum) of the ith particle of a system of n particles of constant mass was developed in the previous chapter as

$$(\mathbf{H}_O)_i = \mathbf{r}_i \times m_i \mathbf{v}_i$$

After writing similar equations for all the particles of the system and adding them together, we obtain

$$\mathbf{H}_O = \sum_{i=1}^{n} (\mathbf{H}_O)_i = \sum_{i=1}^{n} (\mathbf{r}_i \times m_i \mathbf{v}_i) \tag{5.19}$$

Time differentiation of the above equation yields

$$\frac{d}{dt}(\mathbf{H}_O) = \Sigma(\dot{\mathbf{r}}_i \times m_i \mathbf{v}_i) + \Sigma(\mathbf{r}_i \times m_i \dot{\mathbf{v}}_i)$$

or

$$\dot{\mathbf{H}}_O = \Sigma m_i(\mathbf{v}_i \times \mathbf{v}_i) + \Sigma(\mathbf{r}_i \times m_i \mathbf{a}_i)$$

The first term on the right-hand side is zero, since $\mathbf{v}_i \times \mathbf{v}_i = \mathbf{0}$. The equation is thus reduced to

$$\dot{\mathbf{H}}_O = \Sigma(\mathbf{r}_i \times m_i \mathbf{a}_i)$$

Substituting the above expression into Equation (5.5), we obtain

$$\mathbf{M}_O = \dot{\mathbf{H}}_O \qquad (5.20)$$

This is the equation of moment and angular momentum; it states that *the moment, with respect to an arbitrary and fixed point, of the external forces acting on a system of particles of constant mass, is equal to the time rate of change of the angular momentum of the system.*

Equation (5.20) can now be integrated with respect to time, to yield

$$\int_{t_1}^{t_2} \mathbf{M}_O\, dt = (\mathbf{H}_O)_2 - (\mathbf{H}_O)_1$$

and, after rearranging the terms, we have

$$(\mathbf{H}_O)_1 + \int_{t_1}^{t_2} \mathbf{M}_O\, dt = (\mathbf{H}_O)_2 \qquad (5.21)$$

This relationship is the equation of angular impulse and momentum. It states that *the final angular momentum of a system of n particles about an arbitrary and fixed reference point O is equal to the sum of the initial angular momentum of the system and the angular impulse exerted on the system over the time interval considered.* From Equation (5.21) we can see that if the angular impulse $\int_{t_1}^{t_2} \mathbf{M}_O\, dt$ is zero, the initial and final angular momenta are equal. Thus we have

$$(\mathbf{H}_O)_1 = (\mathbf{H}_O)_2 \qquad (5.22)$$

and the angular momentum of the system is conserved.

Special Case: Center of Mass as Reference Point

Referring to Figure 5.4, we can now introduce the angular momentum (i.e., the moment of the linear momentum) of a system of n particles of constant mass, where the moment is taken with respect to the translating coordinate

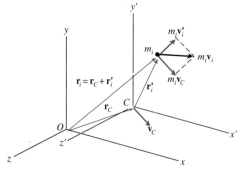

Figure 5.4

system centered at the mass center C. The linear momenta of the particles, however, can be expressed either in terms of the particle's absolute velocity $\mathbf{v}_i$ or its velocity $\mathbf{v}'_i$ relative to the mass center C. We will first define the angular momentum $\mathbf{H}_C$ using the absolute linear momenta $m_i \mathbf{v}_i$ as

$$(\mathbf{H}_C)_{\text{abs}} = \Sigma(\mathbf{r}'_i \times m_i \mathbf{v}_i)$$

Next, we will define the angular momentum of the system $\mathbf{H}_C$ (taken with respect to the mass center) in terms of relative linear momenta $m_i \mathbf{v}'_i$.

$$(\mathbf{H}_C)_{\text{rel}} = \Sigma(\mathbf{r}'_i \times m_i \mathbf{v}'_i)$$

We will now show that the above two expressions for the angular momentum $(\mathbf{H}_C)_{\text{abs}}$ and $(\mathbf{H}_C)_{\text{rel}}$ are identical. Substituting the expression $\mathbf{v}_i = \mathbf{v}_C + \mathbf{v}'_i$ into the expression for $(\mathbf{H}_C)_{\text{abs}}$, we obtain

$$(\mathbf{H}_C)_{\text{abs}} = \Sigma[\mathbf{r}'_i \times m_i(\mathbf{v}_C + \mathbf{v}'_i)]$$

$$(\mathbf{H}_C)_{\text{abs}} = \Sigma(\mathbf{r}'_i \times m_i \mathbf{v}_C) + \Sigma(\mathbf{r}'_i \times m_i \mathbf{v}'_i)$$

$$(\mathbf{H}_C)_{\text{abs}} = (\Sigma m_i \mathbf{r}'_i) \times \mathbf{v}_C + \Sigma(\mathbf{r}'_i \times m_i \mathbf{v}'_i)$$

By definition of the mass center we have $\Sigma m_i \mathbf{r}'_i = m\mathbf{r}'_C$, and since the mass center is the origin of the coordinate system we also have $\mathbf{r}'_C = \mathbf{0}$; thus the expression $\Sigma m_i \mathbf{r}'_C = m\mathbf{r}'_C = \mathbf{0}$ and the first term on the right-hand side of the above equation is zero, and we have

$$(\mathbf{H}_C)_{\text{abs}} = \Sigma \mathbf{r}'_i \times m_i \mathbf{v}'_i = (\mathbf{H}_C)_{\text{rel}} \qquad (5.23)$$

By differentiating both sides of the expression for $(\mathbf{H}_C)_{\text{rel}}$ we have

$$\dot{\mathbf{H}}_C = \Sigma(\dot{\mathbf{r}}'_i \times m_i \mathbf{v}'_i) + \Sigma(\mathbf{r}'_i \times m_i \dot{\mathbf{v}}'_i)$$

and since $\dot{\mathbf{r}}'_i = \mathbf{v}'_i$, we write

$$\dot{\mathbf{H}}_C = \Sigma(\mathbf{v}'_i \times m_i \mathbf{v}'_i) + \Sigma(\mathbf{r}'_i \times m_i \dot{\mathbf{v}}'_i)$$

The first term on the right is zero $(\mathbf{v}'_i \times \mathbf{v}'_i)$ and the expression is reduced to

$$\dot{\mathbf{H}}_C = \Sigma(\mathbf{r}'_i \times m_i \dot{\mathbf{v}}'_i) = \Sigma(\mathbf{r}'_i \times m_i \mathbf{a}'_i)$$

From Equation (5.5) we recognize that the term on the right in the above expression is the moment $\mathbf{M}_C$, about the mass center, of all the external forces acting on the system; thus we conclude

$$\mathbf{M}_C = (\dot{\mathbf{H}}_C)_{\text{rel}} \qquad \mathbf{M}_C = (\dot{\mathbf{H}}_C)_{\text{abs}} \qquad (5.24)$$

It must be emphasized that the above relationships are valid only with respect to the center of mass. From Equations (5.24) we conclude that, if the moment $\mathbf{M}_C$ or the angular impulse $\int_{t_1}^{t_2} \mathbf{M}_C \, dt$ is zero, $d/dt(\mathbf{H}_C) = 0$ and the initial and final angular momenta of a system, relative to its mass center, are equal and we have

$$(\mathbf{H}_C)_1 = (\mathbf{H}_C)_2 \qquad (5.25)$$

which states that the angular momenta of a system of particles of constant mass is conserved.

The transformation of coordinates, from the fixed xyz frame to the translating frame of reference $x'y'z'$, can now be analyzed and the relationships between $\mathbf{M}_O$ and $\mathbf{M}_C$ and between $\mathbf{H}_O$ and $\mathbf{H}_C$ developed.

From Equation (5.19) and referring to Figure 5.4 we write

$$\mathbf{H}_O = \Sigma(\mathbf{r}_i \times m_i\mathbf{v}_i) = \Sigma[(\mathbf{r}_C + \mathbf{r}'_i) \times m_i\mathbf{v}_i]$$

$$\mathbf{H}_O = \Sigma(\mathbf{r}_C \times m_i\mathbf{v}_i) + \Sigma(\mathbf{r}'_i \times m_i\mathbf{v}_i)$$

The last term on the right represents $\mathbf{H}_C$ and thus we obtain

$$\mathbf{H}_O = \Sigma(\mathbf{r}_C \times m\mathbf{v}_C) + \mathbf{H}_C \tag{5.26}$$

We next apply the transformation rules to the moment $\mathbf{M}_O$ about the fixed and arbitrary point O. Differentiating both sides of Equation (5.26) yields

$$\dot{\mathbf{H}}_O = \dot{\mathbf{r}}_C \times m\mathbf{v}_C + \mathbf{r}_C \times m\dot{\mathbf{v}}_C + \dot{\mathbf{H}}_C$$

and after introducing the expressions

$$\dot{\mathbf{r}}_C \times m\mathbf{v}_C = m(\mathbf{v}_C \times \mathbf{v}_C) = 0$$

$$\dot{\mathbf{v}}_C = \mathbf{a}_C$$

the above expression for $\dot{\mathbf{H}}_O$ becomes

$$\dot{\mathbf{H}}_O = \mathbf{r}_C \times m\mathbf{a}_C + \dot{\mathbf{H}}_C$$

When substituted into Equation (5.20), this yields

$$\mathbf{M}_O = (\mathbf{r}_C \times m\mathbf{a}_C) + \dot{\mathbf{H}}_C \tag{5.27}$$

EXAMPLE 5.12

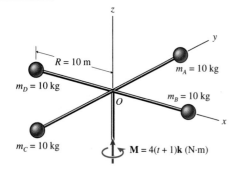

Rigid bars with negligible mass connect four 100-kg particles A, B, C, and D, as shown. The system, initially at rest, rotates in the horizontal xy plane about the vertical z axis under the action of a couple $\mathbf{M} = 4(t + 1)\mathbf{k}$ (N · m), where t is in seconds. Determine the speed of each of the particles at time $t = 10$ s.

Solution   The z component of the equation of angular impulse and momentum [Equation (5.21)] is

$$(H_O)_{1z} + \int_{t_1}^{t_2} (M_O)_z\, dt = (H_O)_{2z}$$

(continued)

EXAMPLE 5.12 (*concluded*)

where

$$(H_O)_{1z} = \left[\sum_{i=1}^{4} r_i \times m_i v_i\right]_z = 4[Rmv]_{1z} = 0$$

$$\int_{t_1=0}^{t_2=10} (M_O)_z \, dt = \int_0^{10} 4(t+1) \, dt = 4\left(\frac{t^2}{2} + t\right)\Big|_0^{10} = 240$$

$$(H_O)_{2z} = 4[Rmv]_{2z} = 4[2(10)v_2] = 80v_2$$

Solving for v_2, we find

$$80v_2 = 240 \qquad v_2 = 3 \text{ m/s} \blacktriangleleft$$

EXAMPLE 5.13

The masses, positions, and velocities of three particles and the forces acting on them are given as $m_1 = 3$ slug, $m_2 = 2$ slug, $m_3 = 5$ slug, $\mathbf{r}_1 = 2\mathbf{i} + 3\mathbf{j}$ (ft), $\mathbf{r}_2 = 2\mathbf{j} + 3\mathbf{k}$ (ft), $\mathbf{r}_3 = -\mathbf{i} - \mathbf{k}$ (ft), $\mathbf{v}_1 = 7\mathbf{j}$ (ft/s), $\mathbf{v}_2 = 5\mathbf{i}$ (ft/s), $\mathbf{v}_3 = 3\mathbf{k}$ (ft/s), $\mathbf{F}_1 = 20\mathbf{i}$ (lb), $\mathbf{F}_2 = 20\mathbf{i} - 20\mathbf{j}$ (lb), and $\mathbf{F}_3 = 20\mathbf{k}$ (lb). Determine (*a*) the total linear momentum and its time rate of change; (*b*) the total angular momentum of the system and its time rate of change about the origin of the frame of reference; and (*c*) the total angular momentum of the system about its center of mass.

Solution

Part a. Applying Equation (5.14), we write

$$\mathbf{G} = \sum_{i=1}^{3} m_i \mathbf{v}_i = 3(7\mathbf{j}) + 2(5\mathbf{i}) + 5(3\mathbf{k})$$

$$\mathbf{G} = 10\mathbf{i} + 21\mathbf{j} + 15\mathbf{k} \, (\text{lb} \cdot \text{s}) \blacktriangleleft$$

$$\dot{\mathbf{G}} = \sum_{i=1}^{3} \mathbf{F}_i = 20\mathbf{i} + (20\mathbf{i} - 20\mathbf{j}) + 20\mathbf{k}$$

$$\dot{\mathbf{G}} = 40\mathbf{i} - 20\mathbf{j} + 20\mathbf{k} \, (\text{lb}) \blacktriangleleft$$

Part b. For the angular momentum of the system, we use Equation (5.19); thus,

$$\mathbf{H}_O = \Sigma(\mathbf{r}_i \times m_i \mathbf{v}_i)$$

$$\mathbf{H}_O = (2\mathbf{i} + 3\mathbf{j}) \times 3(7\mathbf{j}) + (2\mathbf{j} + 3\mathbf{k}) \times 2(5\mathbf{i})$$

$$+ (-\mathbf{i} - \mathbf{k}) \times 5(3\mathbf{k})$$

$$\mathbf{H}_O = 45\mathbf{j} + 22\mathbf{k} \, (\text{lb} \cdot \text{ft} \cdot \text{s}) \blacktriangleleft$$

$$\dot{\mathbf{H}}_O = \mathbf{M}_O = \Sigma \mathbf{r}_i \times \mathbf{F}_i$$

$$= (2\mathbf{i} + 3\mathbf{j}) \times (20\mathbf{i}) + (2\mathbf{j} + 3\mathbf{k}) \times (20\mathbf{i} - 20\mathbf{j})$$

$$+ (-\mathbf{i} - \mathbf{k}) \times 20\mathbf{k}$$

$$\dot{\mathbf{H}}_O = 60\mathbf{i} + 80\mathbf{j} - 100\mathbf{k} \, (\text{lb} \cdot \text{ft}) \blacktriangleleft$$

Part c. Introducing the definition of the mass center we have

$$\left(\sum_{i=1}^{3} m_i\right)\mathbf{r}_C = \Sigma m_i \mathbf{r}_i$$

$$(3 + 2 + 5)\mathbf{r}_C = (3)(2\mathbf{i} + 3\mathbf{j}) + 2(2\mathbf{j} + 3\mathbf{k})$$

$$+ (5)(-\mathbf{i} - \mathbf{k})$$

$$\mathbf{r}_C = \frac{\mathbf{i} + 13\mathbf{j} + \mathbf{k}}{10} = 0.1\mathbf{i} + 1.3\mathbf{j} + 0.1\mathbf{k} \, (\text{ft})$$

We also have

$$\left(\sum_{i=1}^{3} m_i\right)\mathbf{v}_C = \Sigma m_i \mathbf{v}_i$$

$$m\mathbf{v}_C = 3(7\mathbf{j}) + 2(5\mathbf{i}) + 5(3\mathbf{k})$$

$$m\mathbf{v}_C = 10\mathbf{i} + 21\mathbf{j} + 15\mathbf{k} \, (\text{ft/s})$$

The total angular momentum relative to the mass center is

$$\mathbf{H}_C = \mathbf{H}_O - (\mathbf{r}_c \times m\mathbf{v}_c)$$

$$\mathbf{H}_C = (45\mathbf{j} + 22\mathbf{k}) - (0.1\mathbf{i} + 1.3\mathbf{j} + 0.1\mathbf{k})$$

$$\times (10\mathbf{i} + 21\mathbf{j} + 15\mathbf{k})$$

$$\mathbf{H}_C = 45\mathbf{j} + 22\mathbf{k} - \begin{vmatrix} \mathbf{i} & \mathbf{j} & \mathbf{k} \\ 0.1 & 1.3 & 0.1 \\ 10 & 21 & 15 \end{vmatrix}$$

$$\mathbf{H}_C = 45\mathbf{j} + 22\mathbf{k} - (17.4\mathbf{i} - 0.5\mathbf{j} - 10.9\mathbf{k})$$

$$\mathbf{H}_C = -17.4\mathbf{i} + 45.5\mathbf{j} + 32.9\mathbf{k} \, (\text{lb} \cdot \text{ft}) \blacktriangleleft$$

*5.6 SYSTEMS WITH STEADY MASS FLOW

In the preceding sections we have considered systems where all the constituent particles remain, at all times, part of the system; that is, no particle leaves the system and no new particle joins the system. These are commonly referred to as *closed systems*. Since we have also assumed that each particle's mass is constant, it follows that the mass within a closed system is constant with time. Acknowledging the contributions of Lagrange (French mathematician Joseph Louis Lagrange, 1736–1813) to the study of this problem, this approach of following a particular set of particles through their motion is often referred to as the *Lagrangian method*.

However, in many engineering applications, and especially when fluid flows into and out of a certain region of space, it is usually more satisfactory to select a particular volume in space—called the *control volume*—and describe the behavior of the fluid as it passes through this volume. This approach of focusing on a region in space rather than on a set of fluid particles is referred to as the *Eulerian method*, in honor of the Swiss mathematician Leonard Euler (1707–1783). Rather than being a system defined as an identified mass of fluid, a control volume (or open system) is simply a prescribed volume in space through which the fluid passes. Its size and shape may be arbitrarily chosen but must then be held constant. The bounding surface of the control volume is called the *control surface*.

A general relationship known as *Reynolds transport theorem*, in honor of British scientist Osborne Reynolds (1842–1912), is a powerful instrument relating the variation of any given property N of a system to the production, convection, and storage of N within and through the control volume associated with the system. The properties in question can be scalars such as mass or energy, or vectors such as linear or angular momenta. The Reynolds transport theorem[†] states that the time rate of increase (production) of a property N within a system is equal to the time rate of increase of the property N within the control volume (storage) plus the net rate of flux of N across the control surface (convection). The mathematical representation of the theorem can be expressed as (see Figure 5.5)

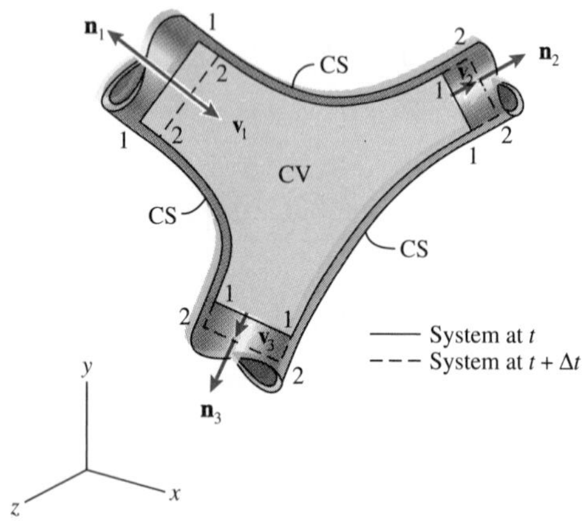

$$\frac{dN}{dt} = \frac{\partial}{\partial t}\int_{cv} \eta\rho \, dV + \int_{cs} \eta\rho(\mathbf{v} \cdot \mathbf{n})ds \qquad (5.28)$$

where η = property N per unit mass of fluid
   ρ = mass of fluid per unit volume (density)
   $\mathbf{v}$ = fluid flow velocity across the control surface
   $\mathbf{n}$ = unit normal on the control surface

— System at t
--- System at $t + \Delta t$

Figure 5.5

[†]For the derivation of Reynolds transport theorem, see an introductory fluid mechanics textbook for engineering students.

For systems where the total mass remains constant—that is, no mass is produced (or consumed) within the system—the left-hand side of the Reynolds
transport equation becomes (when $N = m$, then $\eta = m/m = 1$)

$$\frac{dm}{dt} = 0$$

The right-hand side of Equation (5.28) can now be written as

$$\frac{\partial}{\partial t} \int_{cv} \rho \, dV + \int_{cs} \rho(\mathbf{v} \cdot \mathbf{n}) ds$$

and the equation yields

$$\frac{\partial}{\partial t} \int_{cv} \rho \, dV + \int_{cs} \rho(\mathbf{v} \cdot \mathbf{n}) ds = 0 \qquad (5.29)$$

This is the *equation of continuity* for a control volume, and it states that the
time rate of increase of mass within a control volume (i.e., storage) is equal
to the net rate of mass flow into the control volume. When the mass flow is
steady, the mass within the control volume is not time-dependent and the
equation is further reduced to

$$\int_{cv} \rho(\mathbf{v} \cdot \mathbf{n}) ds = 0 \qquad (5.30)$$

Next, we will develop the linear momentum equation for a control volume by
using the linear momentum for the system along with the Reynolds transport
theorem, Equation (5.28). For a system, the equation of motion is given as

$$\Sigma \mathbf{F} = \frac{d(m\mathbf{v})}{dt} \qquad (5.31)$$

The right-hand side of this equation can be expressed in terms of the control
volume by appealing to Equation (5.28) and substituting for $N = m\mathbf{v}$, which
makes $\eta = m\mathbf{v}/m = \mathbf{v}$, and the linear momentum equation for the control
volume becomes

$$\Sigma \mathbf{F} = \frac{\partial}{\partial t} \int_{cv} \rho \mathbf{v} \, dV + \int_{cs} \rho \mathbf{v}(\mathbf{v} \cdot \mathbf{n}) ds \qquad (5.32)$$

Equation (5.32) states that the net force acting on a system is equal to the sum
of the time rate of increase (storage) of momentum within the control volume
and the net efflux of linear momentum leaving the control volume. When the
mass flow is steady, the momentum within the control volume is not time-
dependent, and the first term on the right-hand side is zero. The equation is

thus reduced to

$$\Sigma \mathbf{F} = \int_{cs} \rho \mathbf{v}(\mathbf{v} \cdot \mathbf{n})ds \tag{5.33}$$

With reference to Figure 5.5, Equations (5.30) and (5.33) can now be simplified and expressed for conduit flow. The control surface (cs) bounding the control volume is divided into three: areas (cs_1) through which flow is entering the control volume; areas (cs_2 and cs_3) through which flow is leaving the region; and areas across which no flow occurs, such as solid boundaries. Equation (5.30) can be rewritten as

$$\int_{cs_1} \rho_1(\mathbf{v}_1 \cdot \mathbf{n}_1)ds + \int_{cs_2} \rho_2(\mathbf{v}_2 \cdot \mathbf{n}_2)ds + \int_{cs_3} \rho_3(\mathbf{v} \cdot \mathbf{n}_3)ds = 0$$

Since the velocity vector and the unit normal vector are in the same direction at inflow sections but in opposite directions at outflow sections, we can write the above equation, after substituting $\mathbf{v}_1 \cdot \mathbf{n}_1 = -v_1$, $\mathbf{v}_2 \cdot \mathbf{n}_2 = +v_2$, and $\mathbf{v}_3 \cdot \mathbf{n}_3 = +v_3$, as

$$\int_{cs_1} \rho_1 v_1 \, ds + \int_{cs_2} \rho_2 v_2 \, ds + \int_{cs_3} \rho_3 v_3 \, ds = 0$$

Defining the average velocity V as $V \int ds = \int v \, ds$, and assuming that the density (mass per unit volume) remains constant across any given cross section, we obtain

$$\underbrace{\rho_1 V_1 A_1}_{\substack{\text{mass} \\ \text{inflow} \\ \text{rate}}} + \underbrace{\rho_2 V_2 A_2 + \rho_3 V_3 A_3}_{\substack{\text{mass} \\ \text{outflow} \\ \text{rate}}} = 0 \tag{5.34}$$

where A_1, A_2, and A_3 are the cross-sectional areas corresponding to control surfaces cs_1, cs_2, and cs_3, respectively. It is important to note that the selection of these areas must be such that the velocity vector remains constant across the section. Such regions of the flow are referred to as *zones of uniform flow*. We must therefore select judiciously the arbitrary boundaries of our control volume. This issue becomes important when one considers the impulse-momentum equation, which is a vector relationship and, as such, requires that we pay attention to the orientation of the incoming and outgoing momenta.

We can further simplify Equation (5.34) and generalize by introducing the concept of volume flow rate and defining it as $Q = VA$. We obtain

$$\underbrace{\sum_{i=1}^{n} \rho_i Q_i}_{\substack{\text{total mass} \\ \text{efflux}}} = \underbrace{\sum_{j=1}^{m} \rho_j Q_j}_{\substack{\text{total mass} \\ \text{influx}}} \qquad (5.35)$$

Equation (5.33) can also be simplified and adapted to the conduit flow represented in Figure 5.5. After using the substitutions introduced earlier for $(\mathbf{v} \cdot \mathbf{n})$ terms and noting that no flow takes place across solid boundaries, we write

$$\Sigma\mathbf{F} = -\int_{cs_1} \rho_1 v_1 \mathbf{v}_1 \, ds + \int_{cs_2} \rho_2 v_2 \mathbf{v}_2 \, ds + \int_{cs_3} \rho_3 v_3 \mathbf{v}_3 \, ds$$

By assuming that the densities are constant across the surfaces cs_1, cs_2, and cs_3, and by judiciously selecting the inflow and outflow areas to be located in regions of uniform flow, we can dispense with the surface integrals and write

$$\Sigma\mathbf{F} = [\rho_2 v_2 A_2 \mathbf{v}_2 + \rho_3 v_3 A_3 \mathbf{v}_3] - [\rho_1 v_1 A_1 \mathbf{v}_1]$$

After introducing $vA = Q$, the above equation can be generalized in the form

$$\Sigma\mathbf{F} = \underbrace{\sum_{i=1}^{n} \rho_i Q_i \mathbf{v}_i}_{\substack{\text{total linear} \\ \text{momentum efflux}}} \qquad \underbrace{\sum_{j=1}^{m} \rho_j Q_j \mathbf{v}_j}_{\substack{\text{total linear} \\ \text{momentum influx}}} \qquad (5.36)$$

This equation represents a boundary configuration where there would be n outflow sections and m inflow sections, each carrying an outflow of Q_i or an inflow of Q_j. Across each outlet or inlet section, the density of the fluid would be assumed constant and given by ρ_i or ρ_j, respectively.

EXAMPLE 5.14

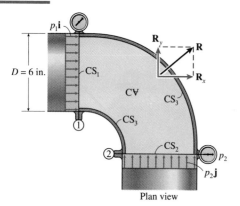

Plan view

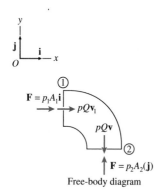

Free-body diagram

A 6-in.-diameter pipeline carries water at the rate of 1347 gpm (gallon/min). A horizontal elbow is to be anchored to the ground in order to stand the thrust of the water flow. The fluid pressures at sections (1) and (2) have been measured at 120 lb/in^2 and 110 lb/in^2, respectively. Determine the force exerted by the fluid (water density $\rho = 2$ slug/ft^3) on the elbow (1 ft^3/s $= 449$ gpm).

Solution The continuity equation, Equation (5.35), when applied to the free body of fluid shown, yields

$$Q_m = \rho_1 V_1 A_1 = \rho_2 V_2 A_2$$

and since $\rho_1 = \rho_2$, $D_1 = D_2$, and $A_1 = A_2$, it follows that $V_1 = V_2$, and the mass flow rate is

$$Q_m = \rho Q = 2\left(\frac{1347}{449}\right) = 6 \text{ slug/s}$$

The velocity is

$$V = \frac{Q}{A} = \frac{4Q}{\pi D^2} = \frac{4(3)}{\pi\left(\frac{1}{2}\right)^2} = \frac{48}{\pi} = 15.28 \text{ (ft/s)}$$

The linear momentum flux is found to be, in the x direction, the momentum influx of

$$Q_m \mathbf{v}_{\text{in}} = 6(15.28)\mathbf{i} = 92\mathbf{j}$$

and in the y direction, the momentum efflux of

$$Q_m \mathbf{v}_{\text{out}} = 6(15.28)(-\mathbf{j}) = -92\mathbf{j}$$

The right-hand side of Equation (5.36) can now be written as

$$\underbrace{(-92\mathbf{j})}_{\substack{\text{total linear} \\ \text{momentum efflux}}} \qquad \underbrace{(92\mathbf{i})}_{\substack{\text{total linear} \\ \text{momentum influx}}}$$

The left-hand side of Equation (5.36) can be written as

$$\Sigma \mathbf{F} = F_{p_1}\mathbf{i} + F_{p_2}\mathbf{j} + R_x\mathbf{i} + R_y\mathbf{j}$$

where F_{p_1} is the resultant pressure force acting on the entrance section (cs_1) as $p_1(\pi D^2/4)$; F_{p_2} is the resultant pressure force acting on the exit section (cs_2) as $p_2(\pi D^2/4)$; and R_x and R_y are the x and y components of the force exerted by the elbow upon the fluid-free body (cv) bounded by (cs_3).

(*continued*)

EXAMPLE 5.14 (*concluded*)

The equation of force and time rate of change of momentum thus becomes

$$p_1\left(\frac{\pi D^2}{4}\right)\mathbf{i} + p_2\left(\frac{\pi D^2}{4}\right)\mathbf{j} + R_x\mathbf{i} + R_y\mathbf{j} = -92\mathbf{i} - 92\mathbf{j}$$

where

$$p_1 = 120 \times 144 = 17{,}280\,\text{lb/ft}^2$$

$$p_1\left(\frac{\pi D^2}{4}\right) = 17{,}280\left(\frac{\pi}{4}\right)\left(\frac{1}{2}\right)^2 = 3{,}393\,\text{lb}$$

$$p_2 = 110 \times 144 = 15{,}840\,\text{lb/ft}^2$$

$$p_2\left(\frac{\pi D^2}{4}\right) = 15{,}840\left(\frac{\pi}{4}\right)\left(\frac{1}{2}\right)^2 = 3{,}110\,\text{lb}$$

In vector form, the equation is written as

$$3393\mathbf{i} + 3110\mathbf{j} + R_x\mathbf{i} + R_y\mathbf{j} = -92\mathbf{i} - 92\mathbf{j}$$

By equating the coefficients of **i** and **j**, we get, in the *x* direction:

$$3393 + R_x = -92 \qquad R_x = -3845\,\text{lb (to the left)}$$

and in the *y* direction:

$$3110 + R_x = -92 \qquad R_y = -3202\,\text{lb}\,(-y\,\text{direction})$$

The force components exerted by the elbow upon the fluid body are in the $-y$ direction and to the left; whereas the force components exerted by the fluid upon the elbow are to the right and in the $+y$ direction.

The magnitude of the force exerted upon the elbow by the fluid is

$$R = (3485^2 + 3202^2)^{1/2} = 4732.6\,\text{lb} \blacktriangleleft$$

and its direction is given by

$$\theta = \tan^{-1}\left(\frac{3202}{3485}\right) = 42.6° \blacktriangleleft$$

Since the weight of the fluid is acting in the *z* direction, which is normal to the plane of the figure, it has been ignored in the solution of this problem.

*5.7 SYSTEMS WITH VARIABLE MASS FLOW

When a system does not maintain a constant mass but instead gains or loses mass at a constant rate, the system is said to have *variable mass flow*, and the continuity equation developed in the preceding section is no longer valid. However, the Reynolds transport equation relating production, storage, and convection of mass or momentum can be used to develop the pertinent relationships applicable to a control volume.

Consider Equation (5.28) where the variation of property *N* of the system with time is given as

$$\frac{dN}{dt} = \frac{\partial}{\partial t}\int_{cv} \eta\rho\, dV + \int_{cs} \eta\rho(\mathbf{v}\cdot\mathbf{n})ds$$

Substituting for *N* the total linear momentum of the system at time *t* we write $\mathbf{N} = m\mathbf{v}$, where *m* is the mass within the system as well as inside the control volume at time *t*. Therefore, $d\mathbf{N}/dt$ will represent the time rate of change of the total linear momentum of the particles included within the control volume (*cv*) at the given instant *t*. This, by Newton's law of motion, must equal the total internal force $\Sigma\mathbf{F}$ applied to the mass within the control volume. Furthermore, if $\mathbf{N} = m\mathbf{v}$, then the linear momentum per unit mass $\boldsymbol{\eta} = \mathbf{N}/m =$

$m\mathbf{v}/m = \mathbf{v}$. Equation (5.28) becomes

$$\Sigma\mathbf{F} = \frac{\partial}{\partial t}\int_{cv}\rho\mathbf{v}\,dV + \int_{cs}\rho\mathbf{v}(\mathbf{v}_{rel}\cdot\mathbf{n})ds \tag{5.37}$$

The vector $\mathbf{v}_{rel}$, appearing in the integrand of the second term on the right, is the velocity vector, relative to the control surface, of the particles that are entering or leaving the control volume. Thus $\rho(\mathbf{v}_{rel}\cdot\mathbf{n})ds$ represents the rate at which particles are crossing the surface element ds, with a positive $(\mathbf{v}_{rel}\cdot\mathbf{n})$ referring to exiting native particles and a negative $(\mathbf{v}_{rel}\cdot\mathbf{n})$ referring to entering foreign particles. The resultant force $\Sigma\mathbf{F}$ on the left may include field forces as well as contact forces. However, such forces must be external to the control volume. Frictional forces caused by viscous effects do not enter the problem except when they contribute to surface drag forces along the boundary, that is, over the control surface.

An important application of the principles obtained for a system with variable mass flow is the rocket propulsion problem. The propulsion is achieved by means of reaction forces due to the ejection of mass. As a simplified example of the propulsion problem, let us consider the rocket system shown in Figure 5.6. We will ignore the pressure drag and skin drag forces acting on the rocket. The average absolute velocity of the exhaust gases is $\mathbf{u}$. Since the absolute velocity of the rocket at time t is $\mathbf{v}$, the exit velocity of the exhaust gases *relative to the rocket* and also to the control volume is $\mathbf{v}_{rel} = \mathbf{v} - \mathbf{u}$. The area of the nozzle exit is A_{exit} and the average pressure at the nozzle exit is p_{exit}. The mass of the rocket structure and the fuel together is initially equal to m_O. The rate at which fuel is burned and ejected from the rocket is usually assumed constant $(\dot{m}_{fuel} = K)$, so that, at any given instant t, the mass of the unburned fuel plus the mass of the rocket can be expressed as

$$m = m_O - Kt$$

where $K = \rho_{exit}(v_{rel}\cdot A_{exit})$. It follows that

$$\dot{m} = -K \tag{5.38}$$

We will now apply Equation (5.37) to the rocket propulsion problem. The control volume includes the rocket and moves with it. The total external force acting on the mass within the control volume is due to the exit pressure p_{exit} acting over the exit cross section A_{exit} and the weight of the rocket and fuel represented as (mg). Thus, the left-hand side of Equation (5.37) can be written as

$$\mathbf{F} = (p_{exit}\cdot A_{exit})\mathbf{i} - (mg)\mathbf{j} \tag{5.39}$$

Let us now evaluate the first term on the right-hand side of Equation (5.37). Since $\int_{cv}\rho\mathbf{v}\,dV$ represents the momentum of the mass within the control vol-

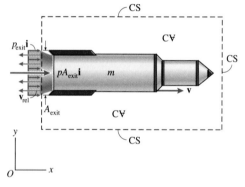

Figure 5.6

ume, we have, for the linear motion of the rocket,

$$\frac{\partial}{\partial t}\int_{cv}\rho\mathbf{v}\,dV = \frac{d}{dt}(m\mathbf{v})$$

$$= m\dot{\mathbf{v}} + \dot{m}\mathbf{v}$$

and since $\dot{m} = -K$, we write

$$\frac{\partial}{\partial t}\int_{cv}\rho\mathbf{v}\,dV = m\dot{\mathbf{v}} - K\mathbf{v}$$

$$\frac{\partial}{\partial t}\int_{cv}\rho\mathbf{v}\,dV = (m\dot{v} - Kv)\mathbf{i} \qquad (5.40)$$

Note that we have neglected the changes in the momentum of the jet relative to the rocket.

The second term on the right-hand side of Equation (5.37) can be expressed after considering the fact that the exhaust jet flow is the only area of the control surface across which we have mass efflux. Exhaust gases have a relative velocity of $\mathbf{v}_{rel}$, corresponding to an absolute velocity of $\mathbf{u} = (v - v_{rel})\mathbf{i}$, where v is the rocket velocity. Substituting for $[\rho_{exit} \cdot A_{exit} \cdot v_{rel}] = K$, we write

$$\int_{cs(exit)}\rho\,\mathbf{u}(\mathbf{v}_{rel} \cdot \mathbf{n})ds = [\rho_{exit}(v - v_{rel})v_{rel} \cdot A_{exit}]\mathbf{i}$$

$$= K(v - v_{rel})\mathbf{i} \qquad (5.41)$$

We can now evaluate the motion of a rocket experiencing a steady loss of mass through Equation (5.37) after introducing Equations (5.39), (5.40), and (5.41); thus,

$$(p_{exit} \cdot A_{exit})\mathbf{i} - (mg)\mathbf{j} = (m\dot{v} - Kv)\mathbf{i} + K(v - v_{rel})\mathbf{i} \qquad (5.42)$$

which becomes, after simplifying,

$$(pA)_{exit}\mathbf{i} - (mg)\mathbf{j} = (m\dot{v} - Kv_{rel})\mathbf{i}$$

Rearranging terms yields

$$(pA)_{exit}\mathbf{i} - (mg)\mathbf{j} + K\mathbf{v}_{rel} = (m\dot{v})\mathbf{i} \qquad (5.43)$$

For the case of a rocket positioned horizontally as shown in Figure 5.6, the x component of the equation of motion further simplifies as the gravitational effects are no longer a factor, and we can write in a scalar form along the thrust direction

$$(pA)_{exit} + Kv_{rel} = ma \qquad (5.44)$$

The above equation can also be expressed in the form

$$F_s = ma \qquad (5.45)$$

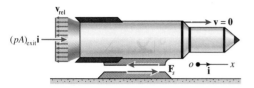

Figure 5.7

where $F_s = pA + Kv_{rel}$ is called the *static thrust* or simply the thrust of the rocket. Indeed the static thrust of a rocket is usually tested by firing the rocket while it is held fixed on a test stand as shown in Figure 5.7. The static thrust is the force transmitted to the ground by the test stand. An equal but opposite force acts upon the control volume to keep it in place. Since the rocket is stationary ($\mathbf{v} = \mathbf{0}$, $\dot{\mathbf{v}} = \mathbf{0}$), Equation (5.43) is reduced to

$$F_s \mathbf{i} - (pA)_{exit}\mathbf{i} + (Kv_{rel})\mathbf{i} = \mathbf{0}$$

and solving for F_s yields the static thrust as

$$F_s = pA + Kv_{rel} \qquad (5.46)$$

We conclude that the total force acting on the mass of the rocket and its unburned fuel consists of the exit pressure force $(pA)_{exit}$, and the jet reaction force Kv_{rel}.

In the above analysis we have assumed that, inside the rocket, the total momentum of the gases remained constant relative to the moving frame of reference (the rocket). In reality, however, the linear momentum of the total mass within the rocket is only *approximately* equal to $m\mathbf{v}$. Furthermore, we must remember that the pressure forces acting over the control surface will be zero if the pressure across the nozzle is the same as the atmospheric pressure on the rest of the control surface.

An alternative rocket configuration occurs when the rocket is in the vertical position and, therefore, all external forces (pressure forces and weight) are collinear. The modified Equation (5.43) can now be written as

$$(pA)_{exit}\mathbf{i} - mg\mathbf{i} = m\dot{v}\mathbf{i} - Kv_{rel}\mathbf{i}$$

where $m = (m_O - Kt)$ is the mass of rocket structure, payload, and leftover fuel at time t.

Since the above equation is in the vertical i direction, we can deal solely with scalar terms and write, after rearranging terms,

$$\frac{dv}{dt} = \frac{(pA)_{exit}}{m} + \frac{Kv_{rel}}{m} - g$$

Integrating, we find

$$\int_0^v dv = \int_0^t \left[\frac{(pA)_{exit} + Kv_{rel}}{m_O - Kt} - g \right] dt$$

$$v = [(pA)_{exit} + Kv_{rel}] \int_0^t \frac{dt}{m_O - Kt} - \int_0^t g\, dt$$

$$= (pA_{exit} + Kv_{rel})\left(-\frac{1}{K} \right) \ln(m_O - Kt) - gt$$

$$= \left(-\frac{pA}{K} - v_{rel} \right)[\ln(m_O - Kt) - \ln m_O] - gt$$

The velocity of the rocket at time t can now be expressed as

$$v = \left(v_{\text{rel}} + \frac{(pA)_{\text{exit}}}{K}\right)\ln\left(\frac{m_O}{m_O - Kt}\right) - gt \qquad (5.47)$$

EXAMPLE 5.15

A booster rocket initially weighing 56,000 lb (including rocket structure and fuel) is used to propel a 2,000-lb payload into earth orbit. The booster rocket's fuel load is 54,000 lb and the rocket consumes fuel at the rate of 600 lb/s. The exhaust gases leave the rocket at a constant speed of 10,000 ft/s relative to the exit nozzle. Determine the maximum speed of the rocket and payload after the rocket is fired vertically from the ground.

Solution   Substituting into Equation (5.47) the following values:

Exhaust gas velocity, relative to the rocket, $v_{\text{rel}} = 10,000$ ft/s

Burnout rate, $K = \dfrac{600}{g}$ slug/s

Total initial mass, $m_O = \dfrac{56,000 + 2000}{g} = \dfrac{58,000}{g}$ slug

Mass of fuel, $m_{\text{fuel}} = \dfrac{54,000}{g}$ slug

Burnout time, $t_B = \dfrac{m_{\text{fuel}}}{K} = \dfrac{54,000/g}{600/g} = 90$ s

and neglecting the pressure term across the exhaust section, we have

$$v = (10,000)\ln\frac{58,000}{58,000 - 600(90)} - 32.2(90)$$

$$v = (10,000)\ln 14.5 - 2898 = 26,741 - 2898$$

$$v = 23,843 \text{ ft/s} \blacktriangleleft$$

Note that the solution assumes the gravitational attraction to be constant (i.e., the altitude is considered to be small relative to the diameter of the earth).

5.8 SUMMARY

In this chapter, we have learned the following:

1. The equation of motion for a system of particles is

$$\sum_{i=1}^{n} \mathbf{F}_i = \sum_{i=1}^{n} m_i \mathbf{a}_i$$

2. The position, velocity, and acceleration of the mass center of a system of particles are written, respectively,

$$\left(\sum_{i=1}^{n} m_i \right) \mathbf{r}_C = \sum_{i=1}^{n} m_i \mathbf{r}_i$$

$$\left(\sum_{i=1}^{n} m_i \right) \mathbf{v}_C = \sum_{i=1}^{n} m_i \mathbf{v}_i$$

$$\left(\sum_{i=1}^{n} m_i \right) \mathbf{a}_C = \sum_{i=1}^{n} m_i \mathbf{a}_i$$

3. The equation of motion for the center of mass of a system of particles can be shown to be

$$\mathbf{F} = m\mathbf{a}_C \tag{5.4}$$

where $\mathbf{F} = \sum_{i=1}^{n} \mathbf{F}_i$ and $\mathbf{m} = \sum_{i=1}^{n} m_i$.

4. The kinetic energy of a system of particles is

$$T = \frac{1}{2} \sum_{i=1}^{n} m_i v_i^2 \tag{5.7}$$

$$T = \frac{1}{2} \left(\sum_{i=1}^{n} m_i \right) v_C^2 + \frac{1}{2} \sum_{i=1}^{n} (m_i v_i'^2) \tag{5.11}$$

where v_i are the velocities with respect to a fixed frame, and v_i' the velocities with respect to a translating frame of reference with its origin at the mass center.

5. For the equation of work and kinetic energy for a system of particles, we write

$$(\Sigma T_i)_A + \Sigma (U_i)_{A \to B} = (\Sigma T_i)_B$$

6. The conservation of mechanical energy is expressed

$$(\Sigma V_i)_A + (\Sigma T_i)_A = (\Sigma V_i)_B + (\Sigma T_i)_B$$

$$V_A + T_A = V_B + T_B$$

where V represents the potential energy of the system relative to a datum line.

7. The equation of force and rate of change of linear momentum for a system of particles is

$$\sum_{i=1}^{n} \mathbf{F}_i = \frac{d}{dt} \sum_{i=1}^{n} m_i \mathbf{v}_i$$

$$\mathbf{F} = \dot{\mathbf{G}} \tag{5.13}$$

8. The equation of linear impulse and momentum for a system of particles is written

$$\left(\sum_{i=1}^{n} m_i \mathbf{v}_i \right)_1 + \int_{t_1}^{t_2} \sum_{i=1}^{n} \mathbf{F}_i \, dt = \left(\sum_{i=1}^{n} m_i \mathbf{v}_i \right)_2$$

$$\mathbf{G}_1 + \int_{t_1}^{t_2} \mathbf{F} \, dt = \mathbf{G}_2 \tag{5.16}$$

and, in terms of the system's mass center at C,

$$m(\mathbf{v}_c)_1 + \int_{t_1}^{t_2} \mathbf{F} \, dt = m(\mathbf{v}_C)_2 \tag{5.17}$$

where $m = \sum_{i=1}^{n} m_i$, and $\mathbf{F} = \sum_{i=1}^{n} \mathbf{F}_i$.

9. Conservation of linear momentum for a system of particles

$$\mathbf{G}_1 = \mathbf{G}_2 \tag{5.18}$$

10. For the equation of moment of forces and rate of change of angular momentum for a system of particles,

$$\Sigma(\mathbf{r}_i \times \mathbf{F}_i) = \frac{d}{dt} \Sigma(\mathbf{r}_i \times m_i \mathbf{v}_i) = \Sigma \dot{\mathbf{H}}_{O_i} = \dot{\mathbf{H}}_O$$

$$\mathbf{M}_O = \dot{\mathbf{H}}_O \tag{5.20}$$

11. The equation of angular impulse and momentum for a system of particles is

$$[\Sigma(\mathbf{r}_i \times m_i \mathbf{v}_i)]_1 + \int_{t_1}^{t_2} \Sigma(\mathbf{r}_i \times \mathbf{F}_i) dt = [\Sigma(\mathbf{r}_i \times m_i \mathbf{v}_i)]_2$$

$$(\mathbf{H}_O)_1 + \int_{t_1}^{t_2} \mathbf{M}_O \, dt = (\mathbf{H}_O)_2 \tag{5.21}$$

12. The conservation of angular momentum of a system of particles gives

$$\Sigma(\mathbf{r}_i \times m_i \mathbf{v}_i)_1 = \Sigma(\mathbf{r}_i \times m_i \mathbf{v}_i)_2$$

$$(\mathbf{H}_O)_1 = (\mathbf{H}_O)_2 \tag{5.22}$$

13. The angular momentum of a system of particles about its center of mass is

$$(\mathbf{H}_C)_{abs} = (\mathbf{H}_C)_{rel} = \Sigma(\mathbf{r}'_i \times m_i \mathbf{v}'_i) \tag{5.23}$$

*14. For systems with steady mass flow, the equation of continuity is

$$\int_{cs} \rho(\mathbf{v} \cdot \mathbf{n})ds = 0 \tag{5.30}$$

and the equation of force and rate of change of linear momentum is

$$\Sigma\mathbf{F} = \int_{cs} \rho\mathbf{v}(\mathbf{v} \cdot \mathbf{n})ds \tag{5.33}$$

*15. For systems with variable mass flow, the equation of continuity is

$$\frac{\partial}{\partial t}\int_{cv} \rho\,dV + \int_{cs} \rho(\mathbf{v} \cdot \mathbf{n})ds = 0$$

and the equation of force and rate of change of linear momentum is

$$\Sigma\mathbf{F} = \frac{\partial}{\partial t}\int_{cv} \rho\mathbf{v}\,dV + \int_{cs} \rho\mathbf{v}(\mathbf{v} \cdot \mathbf{n})ds \tag{5.37}$$

KEY TERMS

center of mass *193*

closed system *212*

conservation of linear
  momentum *204*

continuity equation *213*

control surface *212*

control volume *212*

Eulerian method *212*

Lagrangian method *212*

steady mass flow *213*

system *192*

total kinetic energy *197*

total work *197*

variable mass (unsteady) flow *217*

PROBLEMS

SECTION 5.2

5.1 A system consists of three particles with masses $m_1 = 5$ kg, $m_2 = 10$ kg, and $m_3 = 15$ kg. Their positions are defined by the vectors $\mathbf{r}_1 = \mathbf{i} - 2\mathbf{j}$ (m), $\mathbf{r}_2 = 2\mathbf{i} + 3\mathbf{j}$ (m), and $\mathbf{r}_3 = -2\mathbf{i} + 3\mathbf{k}$ (m), respectively. Determine the position vector of the center of mass.

5.2 Three particles A, B, and C weighing 5 lb, 10 lb, and 20 lb, respectively, occupy positions defined by their respective position vectors $\mathbf{r}_A = t^2\mathbf{i} + 2t\mathbf{j}$ (ft), $\mathbf{r}_B = \mathbf{j} - 3t\mathbf{k}$ (ft), and $\mathbf{r}_C = 2t^2\mathbf{i} + 3t\mathbf{k}$ (ft), where t is in s. Determine the velocity vector of the mass center of the three-particle system at time $t = 5$ s.

5.3 A system consists of three particles A, B, and C, each with a mass of 10 kg. The velocities of the particles with respect to a fixed frame of reference are $v_A = 3i + 2j + k$ (m/s), $v_B = i - j + 2k$ (m/s), and $v_C = i - 2k$ (m/s). Determine the velocity of each particle relative to the mass center of the system.

5.4 The position vectors and velocities of the four particles shown are $r_1 = 2i + j$ (ft), $v_1 = 2i + j$ (ft/s); $r_2 = 2i + 2k$ (ft), $v_2 = i + k$ (ft/s); $r_3 = 2i + 3k$ (ft), $v_3 = i - j$ (ft/s); and $r_4 = 4i$ (ft), $v_4 = 8i$ (ft/s). Determine the position vector and velocity of the center of mass of the four-particle system. All four particles have equal weights of 20 lb.

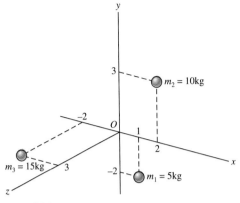

Figure P5.1

5.5 Four particles A, B, C, and D weighing respectively 10 lb, 12 lb, 20 lb, and 25 lb, form a system of particles. The particles' positions are defined by the position vectors $r_A = 3ti$ (ft), $r_B = 3t^2j$ (ft), $r_C = 2t^3k$ (ft), and $r_D = ti + 2tj$ (ft), where t is in s. Determine the position, velocity, and acceleration vectors of the system's mass center at time $t = 10$ s.

5.6 The three particles shown have masses $m_1 = 3$ kg, $m_2 = 4$ kg, $m_3 = 5$ kg and are accelerating in the directions shown at the same rate of 5 m/s². Determine the total force acting on the system.

5.7 The three particles shown have equal weights ($W = 10$ lb) and are subject to forces indicated in the figure. Determine the acceleration of the center of mass of the system.

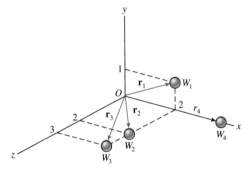

Figure P5.4

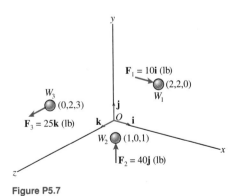

Figure P5.7

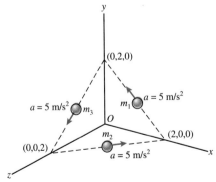

Figure P5.6

5.8 The motions of three particles A, B, and C, with masses $m_A = 5$ kg, $m_B = 10$ kg, and $m_C = 15$ kg, are defined by their position vectors $r_A = t^2i$ (ft), $r_B = 2t^2j$ (ft), and $r_C = 3t^2k$ (ft), where t is in seconds. Determine the total force acting on the three-particle system at $t = 5$ s.

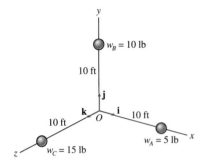

Figure P5.9

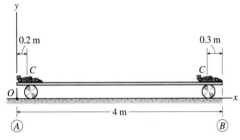

Figure P5.10

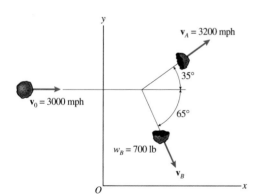

Figure P5.11

5.9 The three particles A, B, and C weighing 5 lb, 10 lb, and 15 lb, respectively, are moving with velocities $\mathbf{v}_A = 4\mathbf{i}$ (ft/s), $\mathbf{v}_B = 6\mathbf{j}$ (ft/s), and $\mathbf{v}_C = 3\mathbf{k}$ (ft/s). Determine the velocity of each particle relative to the center of mass of the three-particle system.

5.10 A 2-kg toy automobile starts from rest at the edge A of a 10-kg platform that is free to move on frictionless rollers as shown. Determine the final position of the edge A, relative to the coordinate origin O, when the toy automobile has reached the edge B of the platform. C is the center of mass of the toy car.

5.11 A 350-ton ferryboat is at rest along a dock when a 25-ton passenger bus starts from rest and moves its mass center C_2 from position A to position B. Determine the final position of the ferryboat's mass center C_1.

5.12 A meteor entering the earth's atmosphere at a speed of 3000 mph breaks into two parts as shown. The fragments remain within the xy plane. A radar tracks the disintegrating body and determines the speed of fragment A as $v_A = 3200$ mph. Fragment B is recovered on earth; it weighs $W_B = 700$ lb. Determine the total weight W of the meteor.

5.13 A rocket is reentering the earth's atmosphere at a speed of 10,000 km/h and at an angle of 10° with the x axis, as shown. The rocket breaks into two parts, both parts remaining within the xy plane. Upon recovery, the parts are determined to weigh $W_1 = 7500$ N and $W_2 = 5000$ N, respectively. If, at the moment of breakup, the fragments are observed to move along directions given by $\theta_1 = 10°$ and $\theta_2 = 15°$, determine the corresponding speeds v_1 and v_2 of the fragments.

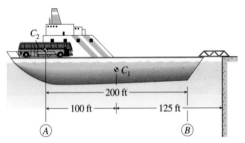

Figure P5.12

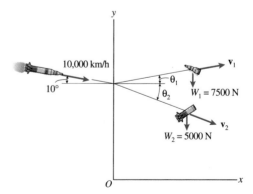

Figure P5.13

5.14 Assuming the pulleys shown to be frictionless and of negligible mass, determine the acceleration of the center of mass of the system consisting of four 10-lb weights.

5.15 The system of three 10-kg spheres slides on a smooth horizontal surface as shown. The spheres are linked by rigid slender bars of negligible mass. A force of $100\mathbf{i}$ (N) is applied at A. Determine the acceleration of the mass center of the system.

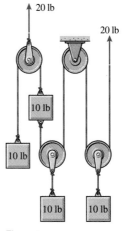

Figure P5.14

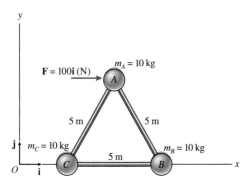

Figure P5.15

5.16 At a given instant two particles A and B of mass 10 kg and 5 kg, respectively, separated by a distance of 10 m, are moving as shown. Determine the position and velocity of their common mass center.

SECTION 5.3

5.17 A system consists of four particles each weighing 50 lb and moving on a horizontal surface xy at a speed of 20 ft/s as shown. Determine the total kinetic energy of the system relative to its mass center.

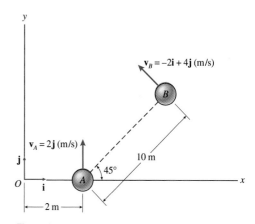

Figure P5.16

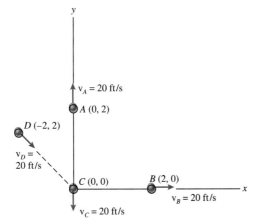

Figure P5.17

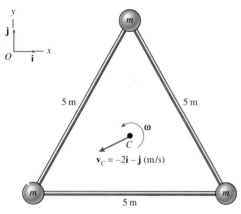

Figure P5.18

5.18 The mass center C of a system of three 10-kg spheres is moving within a horizontal plane xy with the velocity $\mathbf{v}_C = -2\mathbf{i} - \mathbf{j}$ (m/s). The spheres are rigidly connected to each other as shown by 5-m-long slender bars of negligible mass. In addition to translating with $\mathbf{v}_C$, the whole system is also rotating about its center of mass with a constant angular speed ω. If the total kinetic energy of the system is 100 N · m, determine the rotational speed ω.

5.19 The cars of a roller coaster train each weigh 2000 lb, including passengers. The train has five cars and a speed of 10 ft/s at A. Determine the speed of the train at the top of the loop at B, if the train is coasting from A to B.

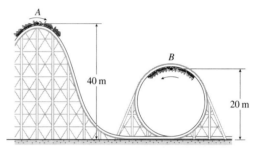

Figure P5.19

5.20 Four particles of masses $m_A = 20$ g, $m_B = 10$ g, $m_C = 10$ g, and $m_D = 20$ g are moving with constant velocities in the xy plane, as shown. Determine the total kinetic energy of the system. Compare your results with that obtained by using the velocity of the center of mass and the relative velocities of the particles with respect to the center of mass.

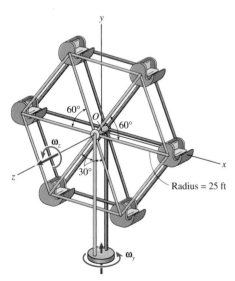

Figure P5.21

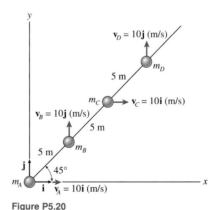

Figure P5.20

5.21 Each gondola of a six-gondola Ferris wheel weighs 600 lb with riders. The motion of the gondolas consists of a circular motion about the Oz axis in the vertical plane xy and a circular motion about the vertical axis Oy. Determine, for the position shown, the total kinetic energy of the six gondolas if $\omega_z = 0.25$ rad/s and $\omega_y = 0.10$ rad/s.

5.22 The Ferris wheel shown consists of five gondolas, each weighing 5000 N with riders. Neglecting the bearing friction and changes in elevation, determine the work required to start the Ferris wheel from rest and bring it to the angular speeds $\omega_z = 0.25$ rad/s and $\omega_y = 0.10$ rad/s in the directions shown.

5.23 A system consists of three particles A, B, and C with masses 3 kg, 2 kg, and 4 kg respectively. Particle A has a velocity of $5\mathbf{i}$ (m/s). Particle B is moving with the velocity $-6\mathbf{i} + 4\mathbf{j}$ (m/s). Find the velocity of particle C so that the center of mass of the system would remain at rest.

5.24 Block A with a mass of 75 kg is attached to block B with a mass of 50 kg by an inextensible cord as shown. If the system is released from rest, determine the velocity of each block after block A has moved to the right 0.75 m. The coefficient of friction on the horizontal surface is 0.18. Consider the pulley to be massless.

5.25 In the system shown, determine the mass of block B required to give it a velocity of 3 m/s after being released from rest and moving down a distance of 0.75 m.

5.26 Two blocks weighing 2 lb each move in smooth slots and are connected by a massless rod as shown. If the mechanism is released from rest in the position shown, determine the velocity of each block when the slope of the rod is 3 vertical to 4 horizontal.

5.27 If the mechanism is released from rest in the position shown, determine the velocity of each particle when the upper block reaches the bottom of the slot.

5.28 A 70-lb block is connected to an 80-lb block as shown. In its present position, the spring, which has a constant of 20 lb/in. is compressed 8 in. and the spring is not connected to the block. If the system is released from rest, determine the velocity of block B when it has moved down 10 in.

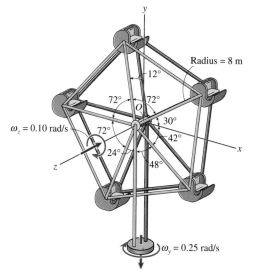

Figure P5.22

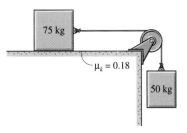

Figure P5.24 and P5.25

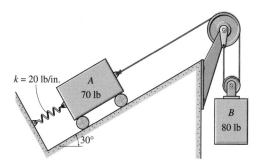

Figure P5.28

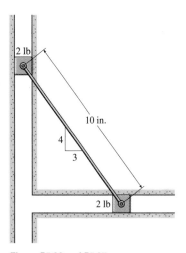

Figure P5.26 and P5.27

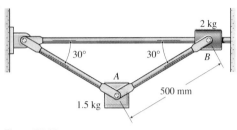

Figure P5.29

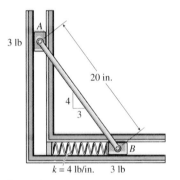

Figure P5.30

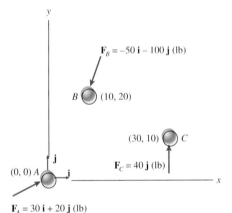

Figure P5.31

5.29 The mechanism shown is comprised of a 2-kg mass that slides on a smooth horizontal rod and a 1.5-kg mass that is connected to the horizontal rod and the 2-kg mass by massless links. The mechanism is released from rest in the position shown. Determine the velocity of mass B when the angle between the connecting links and the horizontal bar is 60°.

5.30 Two 3-lb blocks are connected by a massless bar. In the position shown, the spring is compressed 6 in. and is not attached to block B. If the system is released from rest, determine the velocity of each block when the slope of the rod is 3 vertical to 4 horizontal. The slots are smooth and the spring constant is 4 lb/in.

SECTION 5.4

5.31 A system of three particles A, B, and C, weighing $W_A = 10$ lb, $W_B = 15$ lb, and $W_C = 30$ lb, move under the action of forces $\mathbf{F}_A = 30\mathbf{i} + 20\mathbf{j}$ (lb), $\mathbf{F}_B = -50\mathbf{i} - 100\mathbf{j}$ (lb), and $\mathbf{F}_C = 40\mathbf{j}$ (lb), respectively. The motion takes place in the vertical plane xy as shown. At a given instant, the respective velocities of the particles are $\mathbf{v}_A = 100\mathbf{i}$ (ft/s), $\mathbf{v}_B = 50\mathbf{i} + 50\mathbf{j}$ (ft/s), and $\mathbf{v}_C = 15\mathbf{i} + 40\mathbf{j}$ (ft/s). Determine (a) the total linear momentum, and (b) the rate of change of linear momentum of the system.

5.32 A system of four 25-kg particles falls under gravitational attraction. Determine the change of linear momentum per unit time experienced by the system.

5.33 The total linear momentum of a system of three 15-kg masses is $1500\mathbf{i} + 1200\mathbf{j}$ (kg · m/s). Two of the masses have velocities of $50\mathbf{i}$ (m/s) and $50\mathbf{j}$ (m/s), respectively. Determine the velocity of the third particle.

5.34 If each particle of Problem 5.33 is acted upon by a force $\mathbf{F} = 400\mathbf{i}$ (N), find the rate of change of the total linear momentum of the system.

5.35 A satellite weighing 1000 lb and traveling with a velocity $\mathbf{v} = 2500\mathbf{i}$ (ft/s) disintegrates into three fragments A, B, C each weighing respectively 300, 400, and 300 lb. A radar station tracks two of the separated fragments and reports their positions two seconds after separation as $\mathbf{r}_A = 4000\mathbf{i} + 2500\mathbf{j} + 800\mathbf{k}$ (ft) and $\mathbf{r}_B = 1900\mathbf{i} - 1500\mathbf{j} - 600\mathbf{k}$ (ft), the position vectors being measured relative to the point of separation. Assuming that upon separation the fragments have traveled along straight lines, and neglecting the effects of gravity and air drag, determine the relative position of particle C after two seconds.

5.36 A satellite reenters the earth's atmosphere at an altitude of 10 km and a speed of 1200 km/h in the xz plane as shown, when it suddenly breaks into three equal parts A, B, and C. The broken parts hit the ground at the same instant under the influence of gravity. Two of them are reported found at locations given by their positions relative to the point of breakup, as $\mathbf{r}_A = 10{,}000\mathbf{i} + 1000\mathbf{j} - 10{,}000\mathbf{k}$ (m) and $\mathbf{r}_B = 12{,}000\mathbf{i} - 1600\mathbf{j} - 10{,}000\mathbf{k}$ (m), where $\mathbf{k}$ is the unit normal in the upward vertical direction. Neglecting air resistance, determine (a) the position of the mass center when all parts of the system hit the ground, and (b) the location where the part C was likely to have hit the ground.

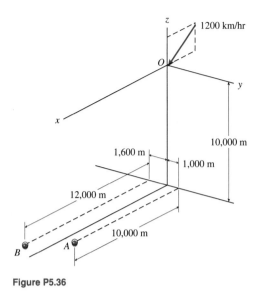

Figure P5.36

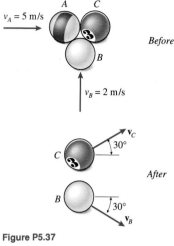

Figure P5.37

5.37 Two smooth billiard balls A and B, moving with velocities $\mathbf{v}_A = 5\mathbf{i}$ (m/s) and $\mathbf{v}_B = 2\mathbf{j}$ (m/s), strike each other and another smooth ball C which is at rest. After collision, the balls B and C move in the directions indicated, whereas ball A comes to rest. Determine the speed of balls B and C after a perfectly elastic collision. All balls have equal mass.

5.38 Six particles of equal weight ($W = 100$ lb) are connected by rigid rods having negligible mass. The system is rotating with a constant angular speed of 10 rad/s about the z axis as shown. Determine the linear momentum of the system if an impulse of $-100\mathbf{i}$ (lb · s) acts suddenly on the system at **B**.

5.39 A space vehicle is traveling at 5000 km/h with respect to the earth when the exhausted rocket motor is disengaged and sent backwards with a speed of 100 km/h with respect to the command module. Determine the speed of the command module after the separation if the mass of the motor is five times the mass of the module.

5.40 A machine gun fires 0.10-lb bullets at a speed of 3000 ft/s. The gunner, holding the machine gun in his hands, can exert an average force of 50 lb against the gun. Determine the maximum number of bullets he can fire per minute.

5.41 Two masses $m_A = 10$ kg and $m_B = 5$ kg are joined by a rigid bar of negligible mass and are at rest in the xy plane as shown. Suddenly the particles are subject to forces $\mathbf{F}_A = 8\mathbf{i}$ (N) and $\mathbf{F}_B = 6\mathbf{j}$ (N), respectively. Determine the total linear momentum of the system as a function of time.

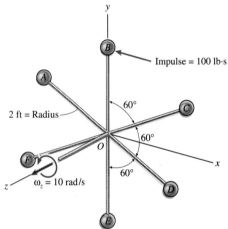

Figure P5.38

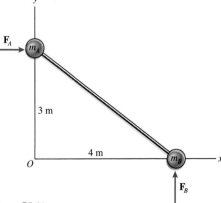

Figure P5.41

5.42 Two swimmers simultaneously dive off from the opposite ends of a 50-kg canoe at rest. If swimmer A has a mass of 80 kg and dives off at a velocity of $\mathbf{v}_A = 10\mathbf{i}$ (m/s) and swimmer B has a mass of 70 kg and dives off at a velocity of $\mathbf{v}_B = -5\mathbf{i}$ (m/s), determine the final velocity of the canoe.

5.43 A space vehicle has a mass of 2500 kg and is moving initially in space with an absolute velocity $\mathbf{v} = 750\mathbf{i} + 900\mathbf{j} + 1200\mathbf{k}$ (km/h). At a given instant the space vehicle launches three small probes A, B, and C, each with a mass of 500 kg. Their velocities are $\mathbf{v}_A = 500\mathbf{i}$ (km/h), $\mathbf{v}_B = 600\mathbf{j} + 700\mathbf{k}$ (km/h), and $\mathbf{v}_C = 750\mathbf{k}$ (km/h). Determine the final velocity vector of the space vehicle after it launches the three probes.

5.44 Consider a system of n particles, each having a mass m. If the system's center of mass C is moving with an absolute velocity $\mathbf{v}_C$, show that the linear momentum **G** of the system with respect to a fixed frame of reference xyz is given by

$$\mathbf{G} = \mathbf{G}_{\text{rel}} + (nm)\mathbf{v}_C$$

where $\mathbf{G}_{\text{rel}}$ represents the linear momentum of the system relative to a parallel frame of reference attached to C and translating with a velocity $\mathbf{v}_C$.

SECTION 5.5

5.45 A system consists of four particles, each having a mass of 10 kg. The particles are connected by slender rigid bars of negligible mass. The system, which is initially at rest, starts and remains in the xy plane. An impulse of $1000\mathbf{i} + 1000\mathbf{j}$ (kg · m/s) is applied at C as shown. Determine (a) the velocity of the center of mass, and (b) the angular speed ω of the system.

5.46 A system of particles is acted upon by external forces. The angular momentum of the system about a fixed point is $\mathbf{H}_1 = 5\mathbf{i} + 6\mathbf{j} - 7\mathbf{k}$ (kg · m²/s) at time $t = t_1$ seconds and $\mathbf{H}_2 = 5.2\mathbf{i} + 6.2\mathbf{i} - 6.8\mathbf{k}$ (kg · m²/s) at time $t_2 = t_1 + 0.1$ s. Determine the average resultant moment about the fixed point of all the forces acting on all particles during the interval $t_2 - t_1 = 0.1$ s.

5.47 Three particles A, B, and C with masses $m_A = m_B = 4$ kg and $m_C = 8$ kg are defined by their position vectors $\mathbf{r}_A = \mathbf{i} + \mathbf{j} + \mathbf{k}$ (m), $\mathbf{r}_B = 2\mathbf{i} + 3\mathbf{j} + 3\mathbf{k}$ (m), and $\mathbf{r}_C = 3\mathbf{i} - 2\mathbf{j} - 3\mathbf{k}$ (m) and their velocities $\mathbf{v}_A = 2\mathbf{i} + 2\mathbf{j} - \mathbf{k}$ (m/s), $\mathbf{v}_B = 3\mathbf{i} + 2\mathbf{j} + 2\mathbf{k}$ (m/s), and $\mathbf{v}_C = 2\mathbf{i} - 2\mathbf{j} - 2\mathbf{k}$ (m/s). Determine the angular momentum of the system about the origin of the fixed coordinate system.

5.48 100 small spheres with identical masses ($m = 500$ slug) are placed on a circular hoop of negligible mass. The hoop has a radius of 1 ft and is rotating at 4000 rpm about its fixed center. Determine the total angular momentum of the system about its center.

5.49 If two adjacent spheres fall off from the hoop of Problem 5.48, determine the total angular momentum of the system about the center of the hoop. Also determine the average torque necessary to stop the rotation of the hoop within 5 s.

5.50 The gondolas of a Ferris wheel (radius = 8 ft) each weigh 2000 lb with riders. For the position shown the wheel, with its five gondolas, rotates about the Oz axis in the vertical xy plane with the angular speed $\omega_z = 0.25$ rad/s as shown. The wheel also rotates about the y axis with the angular speed $\omega_y = 0.10$ rad/s. Determine the total angular momentum of the gondolas.

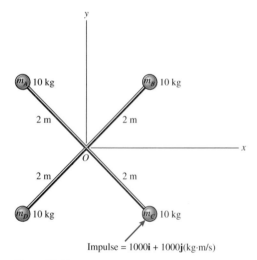

Impulse = 1000i + 1000j(kg·m/s)

Figure P5.45

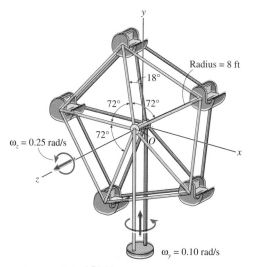

Figures P5.50 and P5.51

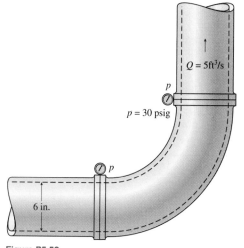

Figure P5.52

5.51 For the rotating system of Problem 5.50, determine the torques M_y and M_z necessary to bring the Ferris wheel to rest within 10 s.

*SECTION 5.6

5.52 A 6-in.-diameter horizontal pipeline bends through 90°. The water pressure in the 6-in. pipe is measured to be 30 psi when the flow rate is 5 ft³/s. Determine the magnitude and direction of the horizontal force exerted by the water on the bend.

5.53 A 30-cm-diameter horizontal pipeline is reduced to a 10-cm-diameter nozzle open to the atmosphere. At the 30-cm-diameter section, the water pressure is measured to be 720 kPa as shown and the flow rate is 0.30 m³/s. Determine the magnitude and direction of the horizontal force exerted by the water on the reduction.

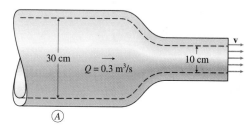

Figure P5.53

5.54 The drag force on a streamlined axisymmetric body is being determined through wind tunnel tests. The velocity profiles before and after the body are measured as indicated. Neglecting friction and air pressure forces, calculate the drag force on the body for the following data: $D = 2$ ft, $v_0 = 100$ ft/s.

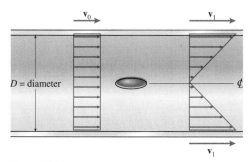

Figure P5.54

5.55 Water issues from a nozzle as shown with a velocity of 25 m/s. If the flow rate is 0.5 m³/s, determine the force F necessary to hold a plate in place against the impinging jet.

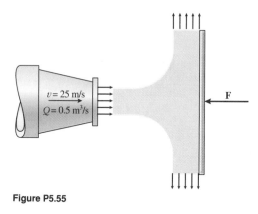

Figure P5.55

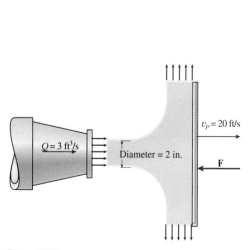

Figure P5.56

5.56 Water issues from a 2-in.-diameter nozzle at a rate of 3 ft³/s. The jet impinges upon a disk that is moving to the right with a velocity of 20 ft/s. Determine the force F necessary to hold the disk in place.

5.57 A jet engine is subject to a static thrust test. At the engine's exhaust section the air velocity is measured to be 550 m/s. The air flow passing through the engine is 50 m³/s. Assuming the approach velocity to be negligible, determine the thrust of the engine. The air density is 1.2 kg/m³.

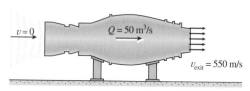

Figure P5.57

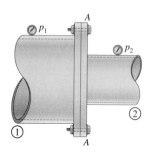

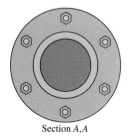

Section A,A

Figure P5.59

5.58 Determine the thrust of a jet engine drawing and expelling air at the rate of 200 lb/s when traveling at an absolute speed of 550 mph. The exhaust air velocity is 2000 ft/s relative to the engine and the air density is 0.076 lb/ft³.

5.59 Oil ($\rho = 1.75$ slug/ft³) flows through a horizontal pipe at the rate of 10 ft³/s. The pipe diameter (12 in.) is suddenly reduced to 4 in. If the pressures at sections 1 and 2 are 20 and 16 psi respectively, determine the tensile forces acting on the bolts holding the flanges together.

5.60 A vertical pipe 6 in. in diameter contains a conical expansion to 12-in. diameter; the expansion is 3 ft in length. The velocity of the water in the 6-in. pipe is 12 ft/s upward, and the pressure is 25 psig. Estimate the force exerted on the expansion if the pressure in the 12-in. pipe is 23.5 psig.

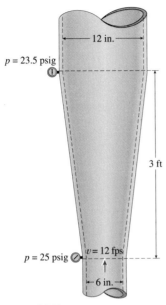

Figure P5.60

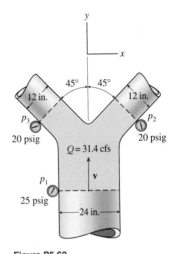

Figure P5.62

5.61 A jet-propelled motorboat draws 2 m³/s of water through ports in the boat's sides and discharges it through orifices with an effective area of 0.05 m² located in the rear of the boat. If the boat travels at 36 km/h, find the propulsive force.

5.62 Water flows into a branching pipe as shown. The Y is within a horizontal plane. Neglecting friction losses, determine the x and y components of the force needed to hold the Y in place.

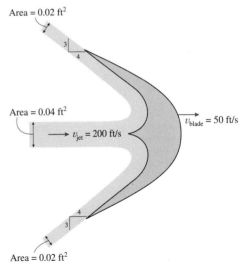

5.63 A turbine blade is moving at 50 ft/s when a water jet impinges on it with a velocity of $v_{jet} = 200$ ft/s as shown. Assuming that the magnitude of the velocity of the water relative to the blade is the same at all sections (1, 2, and 3) and neglecting friction forces, determine the power developed by the water jet on the turbine blade.

Figure P5.63

5.64   Water is flowing over a dam as shown at the rate of 60 ft³/s per linear foot of dam width. Determine the horizontal force due to water acting on the dam if the width of the dam is 10 ft.

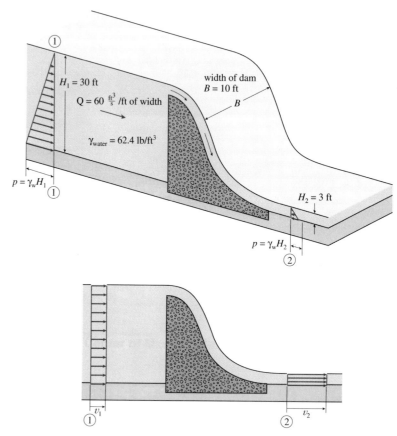

Figure P5.64

5.65   An elbow-nozzle assembly is located on the vertical xy plane as shown. The water issues out as a free jet from the nozzle. If the interior volume of the elbow-nozzle assembly downstream of section AA is equal to 0.25 m³, determine the total force on the assembly due to the presence of water.

5.66   Plate A is 2 ft in diameter and has a sharp-edged orifice at its center as shown. A water jet strikes the plate along the plate's axis with a speed of 200 ft/s. Determine the force needed to hold the plate in place.

*SECTION 5.7

5.67   Neglecting the drag force and the pressure across the exhaust section, and assuming that the fuel of a rocket decreases linearly with time, determine the vertical velocity of the rocket after a 75-s burnout if the thrust during burnout is 400 kN and the initial and final masses are 10,000 and 1000 kg, respectively.

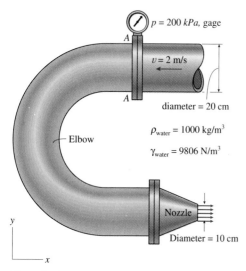

Figure P5.65

5.68 A vertical rocket initially weighs 10^6 lb, of which 700,000 lb is propellant. If the fuel consumption is at a constant rate, the initial thrust is 1.2×10^6 lb, and the exhaust jet velocity relative to the rocket is 10,000 ft/s, determine the burnout time for the rocket and the speed of the rocket at burnout time. (Neglect the air drag.)

5.69 A liquid-propellant rocket uses 30 lb of fuel and 300 lb of oxidant per second. The exhaust gases leave the rocket vertically at a relative speed of 2500 ft/s. Determine the thrust of the rocket.

5.70 A single-stage rocket initially weighs 12,000 lb, including 7500 lb of propellant fuel. It is fired vertically from rest. The speed of the exhaust gases relative to the rocket is 4500 ft/s and burnout time is 1 min. Neglecting air friction drag, determine the vertical velocity of the rocket at the time of burnout.

5.71 A rocket engine produces a thrust of 7.5×10^6 N when the exhaust gases have a velocity of 2500 m/s relative to the rocket. Determine the weight of the propellant fuel consumed at the end of 100 s.

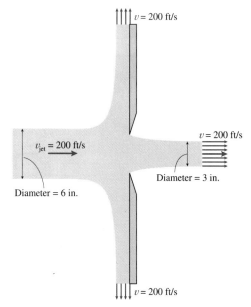

Figure P5.66

6

KINEMATICS
OF RIGID BODIES

6.1 INTRODUCTION

In this chapter we will extend the kinematics of particles to the kinematics of rigid bodies, by considering a rigid body as a system consisting of an infinite number of particles where the distance between any two particles remains constant. To study the kinematics of a rigid body, we determine the velocities and accelerations at any arbitrary location in the body and develop relationships that enable us to express the motion (displacement, velocity, and acceleration) at any point in the body when the motion is defined at some specified locations of the body. The concept of a rigid body—in which the distance between points remains unchanged—is an idealized model. In reality, when subjected to loads, all bodies deform. However, the concept is a very useful one that permits us to study the motion of bodies without concerning ourselves with their deformation. The various types of rigid-body motion are represented in Table 6.1. They are:

1. **Translation.** When any fixed-line segment of a rigid body remains parallel to itself during the motion, the rigid body is said to be translating. When the paths of all particles in the body are along straight lines, the motion is called *rectilinear translation*, as in Type 1a of the table. When the paths are along parallel curved lines, the motion is called *curvilinear translation*, as in Type 1b. Translation corresponds to any motion without rotation and hence is not restricted to planar motion.

2. **Rotation about a fixed axis.** When all particles of a body move along circular paths whose centers are on a fixed axis, the rigid body is said to be rotating about a fixed axis as in Type 2 of the table. The axis of rotation does not necessarily intersect with the rigid body.

3. **General *planar motion*.** When the movement of a rigid body corresponds to a planar motion that is neither pure translation nor fixed-axis rotation, the body is said to be subjected to general planar motion (Type 3). Such a rigid body would appear to be translating, with its points moving within planes parallel to a reference plane, and simultaneously rotating about a moving axis perpendicular to the reference plane.

4. **Spatial *motion* about a fixed point.** When a rigid body has a point fixed in space and moves freely about it, the body is said to be subjected to a *three-dimensional*, or *spatial*, motion about a fixed point (Type 4).

5. **General *spatial motion*.** This is the most general case, where the rigid body is not subject to any constraints and moves freely in space (Type 5).

Although the study of the first three motions calls for a two-dimensional analysis, we will always develop the pertinent kinematic relationships for the vector forms of the parameters and their three-dimensional components, thus maintaining the generality of the expressions until the special nature of a motion necessitates modifications. We will then pay attention to the simplifications inherent in the conversion of results to the special case of planar motion. The final two motions thus will be spared the necessity of redundant derivations, except where they are essential for a better grasp of the physical problem.

Table 6.1

Type of rigid-body motion	Schematic representation	Example
1. Pure translation 1a. Rectilinear		 Crate moving on a belt
1b. Curvilinear		 Swinging beam
2. Pure rotation (Planar motion) 2a. About a fixed axis passing through the body		 Swinging pendulum
2b. About a fixed axis passing outside the body		 Boat moving in a curved channel
3. General planar motion Translation plus rotation		 Rolling wheel
4. Spatial motion about a fixed point Rotation about a moving axis passing through a fixed point	 Moving axis — O — Fixed point	 Spinning top
5. General spatial motion	No constraint on the motion	 Spacecraft

6.2 TRANSLATION OF A RIGID BODY

Consider two points A and B in a rigid body in translation as in Figure 6.1. If a translating frame of reference xyz is attached to the body at A defined by its position vector $\mathbf{r}_A$, the relationship between the position vector $\mathbf{r}_B$ of point B and the position vector $\mathbf{r}_{B/A}$, measured relative to the translating frame xyz, is expressed in the form

$$\mathbf{r}_B = \mathbf{r}_A + \mathbf{r}_{B/A} \qquad (6.1)$$

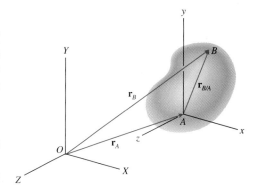

Figure 6.1

Both $\mathbf{r}_A$ and $\mathbf{r}_B$ are measured with reference to the fixed coordinate system XYZ.

The relationship between the corresponding velocities of points B and A can be derived by differentiating Equation (6.1) with respect to time. Since, in a rigid body in translation, the magnitude and direction between any two points of the body remains constant ($\mathbf{r}_{B/A}$ = constant), it follows that the derivative $\dot{\mathbf{r}}_{B/A}$ is zero and the differentiation of Equation (6.1) yields

$$\dot{\mathbf{r}}_B = \dot{\mathbf{r}}_A$$

or

$$\mathbf{v}_B = \mathbf{v}_A \qquad (6.2)$$

Since point B was chosen arbitrarily, we conclude that *in a rigid body in translation, all points move with the same velocity.*

By differentiating Equation (6.2) with respect to time, we obtain a similar result for the absolute-acceleration vectors of all points throughout the body:

$$\mathbf{a}_B = \mathbf{a}_A \qquad (6.3)$$

We conclude that, *in a rigid body in translation, all points accelerate at the same rate.* The velocity and the acceleration of any one point A of the body is thus sufficient to completely describe the motion of the whole rigid body. The results obtained in Chapter 1 for the kinematics of particle motion are thus applicable to the kinematics of the particles of a rigid body subjected to translation.

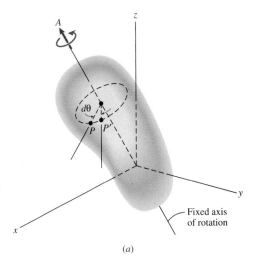

(a)

6.3 ROTATION OF A RIGID BODY ABOUT A FIXED AXIS

Consider a rigid body rotating about a fixed axis as shown in Figure 6.2. If the fixed axis of rotation is not aligned with any of the three Cartesian coordinate axes as indicated in Figure 6.2a, it is convenient to choose as one of the coordinate axes the fixed axis of rotation. An arbitrary point P of the body is defined by its position vector $\mathbf{r}$ making an angle ϕ with the axis of rotation

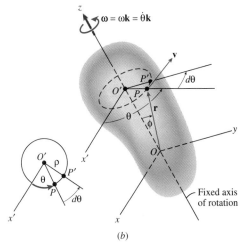

(b)

Figure 6.2

(z axis). The point P moves along a circular path (radius $\rho = r \sin \phi$) in a plane perpendicular to the axis of rotation. The *angular coordinate* θ, measured from an arbitrary reference line $O'x'$ to the radial line $O'P$, defines uniquely the position of the body.

The **angular velocity** vector $\boldsymbol{\omega}$ is the time rate of change of the angular position coordinate θ (i.e., angular displacement rate $d\theta/dt$) and is perpendicular to the plane of motion and thus *parallel* to the fixed axis of rotation of the motion. Its sense of direction is given by the right-hand rule when the hand is curled in the direction of rotation of the body. The magnitude of the angular velocity is usually measured in rad/s.

Choosing the fixed axis of rotation and the z axis to be collinear, we write

$$\boldsymbol{\omega} = \omega\mathbf{k} = \frac{d\theta}{dt}\mathbf{k} = \dot{\theta}\mathbf{k} \tag{6.4}$$

The **angular acceleration** vector $\boldsymbol{\alpha}$ is the time rate of change of the angular velocity vector $\boldsymbol{\omega}$. Differentiating Equation (6.4), we obtain

$$\boldsymbol{\alpha} = \alpha\mathbf{k} = \dot{\omega}\mathbf{k} \tag{6.5}$$

or

$$\boldsymbol{\alpha} = \ddot{\theta}\mathbf{k} \tag{6.6}$$

Thus, for the particular case of a body rotating about a *fixed axis*, the angular acceleration vector $\boldsymbol{\alpha}$ is collinear with the angular velocity vector $\boldsymbol{\omega}$, although its sense of direction will be determined by the increasing or decreasing magnitude of $\boldsymbol{\omega}$. When $\boldsymbol{\omega}$ is decreasing, $\boldsymbol{\alpha}$ is called an *angular deceleration*. Later on, we will see that for the general case of a rigid body rotating freely about a *fixed point* in space, $\boldsymbol{\omega}$ and $\boldsymbol{\alpha}$ will not be collinear.

The velocity $\mathbf{v}$ of point P in Figure 6.2b can be expressed by writing the time derivative of the position vector $\mathbf{r}$ as

$$\mathbf{v} = \frac{d\mathbf{r}}{dt} = \dot{\mathbf{r}}$$

Since point P is in a rigid body and because the origin lies on the same body, the position vector $\mathbf{r}$ of P is a constant magnitude vector that varies only in direction. It can be shown that the derivative vector $(d\mathbf{r}/dt)$ is a vector perpendicular to the position vector $\mathbf{r}$.[†] We conclude that the velocity vector $\mathbf{v}$ is perpendicular to $\mathbf{r}$. But since the angular velocity vector $\boldsymbol{\omega}$ is perpendicular to the plane of motion it is also normal to the velocity vector $\mathbf{v}$, which lies within this plane. Thus the velocity vector $\mathbf{v}$ is normal to both $\boldsymbol{\omega}$ and $\mathbf{r}$, and is tangent

---

[†]*Proof:* For a vector $\mathbf{r}$ of constant length, $|\mathbf{r}| = a$; thus, $\mathbf{r} \cdot \mathbf{r} = a^2$. Differentiating the scalar product $\mathbf{r} \cdot \mathbf{r}$ with respect to time yields $\mathbf{r} \cdot \dfrac{d\mathbf{r}}{dt} = 0$, which indicates the orthogonality of the two vectors $\mathbf{r}$ and $\dot{\mathbf{r}}$.

to the circle described by point P. Furthermore, the magnitude of $\mathbf{v}$ can be expressed as $r\omega \sin \phi$. But the vector cross product $\boldsymbol{\omega} \times \mathbf{r}$ too has a direction perpendicular to the plane defined by $\boldsymbol{\omega}$ and $\mathbf{r}$, and a magnitude of $r\omega \sin \phi$. After verifying that the vectors $\mathbf{v}$ and $\boldsymbol{\omega} \times \mathbf{r}$ have the same direction, we conclude that

$$\mathbf{v} = \boldsymbol{\omega} \times \mathbf{r} \tag{6.7}$$

Equation (6.7) can be applied to determine the velocity of any point of the rigid body. The angular velocity vector $\boldsymbol{\omega}$ is independent of the position of any point P and represents the angular velocity of the rigid body. Equation (6.7) is most useful in discussing the kinematics of rotating bodies; we will refer to it in subsequent sections. Since from Equation (6.7) we have $v = \omega \sin \theta$, in planar motion when $\mathbf{r}$ lies within the plane of motion, Equation (6.7) is further reduced into the scalar expression

$$v = \omega r$$

We can obtain the acceleration vector $\mathbf{a}$ of an arbitrary point P of the rigid body by writing the time derivative of the expression for the velocity as

$$\mathbf{a} = \frac{d\mathbf{v}}{dt} = \frac{d}{dt}(\boldsymbol{\omega} \times \mathbf{r})$$

$$\mathbf{a} = \boldsymbol{\omega} \times \dot{\mathbf{r}} + \dot{\boldsymbol{\omega}} \times \mathbf{r}$$

Next, we introduce $\mathbf{v} = \dot{\mathbf{r}}$ and $\boldsymbol{\alpha} = \dot{\boldsymbol{\omega}}$ and recall Equation (6.7) to obtain

$$\mathbf{a} = \boldsymbol{\omega} \times (\boldsymbol{\omega} \times \mathbf{r}) + \boldsymbol{\alpha} \times \mathbf{r} \tag{6.8}$$

With the position vector $\mathbf{r}$ lying in the plane of motion, the two terms on the right-hand side of Equation (6.8) can be seen to represent the normal $\mathbf{a}_n$ and tangential $\mathbf{a}_t$ components of the acceleration vector of P, and we write

$$\mathbf{a} = \mathbf{a}_n + \mathbf{a}_t$$

where

$$\mathbf{a}_n = \boldsymbol{\omega} \times (\boldsymbol{\omega} \times \mathbf{r}) \tag{6.9}$$

$$\mathbf{a}_t = \boldsymbol{\alpha} \times \mathbf{r} \tag{6.10}$$

In planar motion within the xy plane, the vector relationships above can now be reduced into scalar forms given by

$$\mathbf{a}_n = -\omega^2 \mathbf{r} \qquad a_n = \omega^2 r \tag{6.11}$$

$$\mathbf{a}_t = \boldsymbol{\alpha} \times \mathbf{r} \qquad a_t = \alpha r \tag{6.12}$$

Scalar Analysis of Planar Motion

Considering Equations (6.4), (6.5), and (6.6), we can note that since the vectors $\boldsymbol{\omega}$, $\boldsymbol{\alpha}$, and $\mathbf{k}$ are collinear, the vector relationships can be reduced into scalar equations relating the angular position, angular velocity, and angular acceleration by

$$\omega = \frac{d\theta}{dt} = \dot{\theta} \tag{6.13}$$

$$\alpha = \frac{d\omega}{dt} = \ddot{\theta} = \frac{d^2\theta}{dt^2} \tag{6.14}$$

By applying the chain rule of differentiaton, we have

$$\alpha = \frac{d\omega}{d\theta}\frac{d\theta}{dt} = \omega\frac{d\omega}{d\theta} \tag{6.15}$$

Equations (6.13), (6.14), and (6.15) are similar to those obtained in Chapter 1 for the rectilinear motion of a particle; that is, $v = ds/dt$, $a = dv/dt$, and $a = v(dv/ds)$.

SPECIAL CASES

1. Constant angular speed ($\omega = $ constant):   The angular acceleration α is zero and the angular coordinate θ is given by

$$\theta(t) = \omega t + \theta_0 \tag{6.16}$$

where $\theta_0 = \theta(t = 0)$.

2. Constant angular acceleration ($\alpha = $ constant):   From Equation (6.14), after integration, we obtain

$$\omega(t) = \alpha t + \omega_0 \tag{6.17a}$$

where $\omega_0 = \omega(t = 0)$. Integrating Equation (6.13) with respect to time, and introducing Equation (6.17a), we write

$$\theta(t) = \frac{1}{2}\alpha t^2 + \omega_0 t + \theta_0 \tag{6.17b}$$

Finally, after separating the variables in Equation (6.15), we integrate as $\int_{\omega_0}^{\omega} \omega \, d\omega = \int_{\theta_0}^{\theta} \alpha \, d\theta$ and obtain

$$\omega^2 = 2\alpha(\theta - \theta_0) + \omega_0^2 \tag{6.17c}$$

EXAMPLE 6.1

A wheel with a radius of 2 ft rotates about a fixed axis. Its angular speed increases uniformly from 10 rad/s when $t = 0$ to 25 rad/s when $t = 10$ s. Determine (a) the magnitude of the normal and tangential components of the acceleration of point P located at a radial distance of 1 ft from the axis of the wheel when $t = 5$ s, and (b) the total distance the point travels during the first 10 seconds.

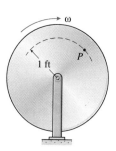

Solution

Part a. We must first determine the wheel's angular acceleration. Since the angular speed is increased *uniformly*, the angular acceleration is constant; using Equation (6.17a),

$$\omega_{t=10} = \alpha(10) + \omega_{t=0}$$

$$25 = 10\alpha + 10$$

$$\alpha = \frac{(25 - 10)}{10} = 1.5\,\text{rad/s}^2$$

At $t = 5$ s, the angular velocity of the body can be obtained by once again writing Equation (6.17a) as

$$\omega_{t=5} = \alpha(5) + \omega_{t=0} = 1.5(5) + 10$$

$$\omega_{t=5} = 17.5\,\text{rad/s}$$

Having established the angular velocity and angular acceleration of the wheel at a given instant ($t = 5$ s), we can now determine the linear acceleration components of the wheel from Equations (6.11) and (6.12), after considering the fact that the motion is planar and the radial distance $r = 1$ ft. Thus, we have

$$a_n = \omega^2 r = (17.5)^2(1.0)$$

$$a_n = 306.25\,\text{ft/s}^2 \blacktriangleleft$$

and

$$a_t = \alpha r = (1.5)(1.0)$$

$$a_t = 1.5\,\text{ft/s}^2 \blacktriangleleft$$

Part b. We determine the angular displacement of the point during the first 10 s through the use of Equation (6.17b):

$$\theta_{t=10} = \frac{1}{2}\alpha(10)^2 + \omega_{t=0}(10) + \theta_{t=0}$$

$$= \frac{1}{2}(1.5)(100) + 10(10) + 0$$

$$= 75 + 100 = 175\,\text{rad}$$

The total linear displacement s during the first ten seconds is related to the angular displacement θ through the relationship $s = r\theta$, which yields

$$s = (1.0)(175) \qquad s = 175\,\text{ft} \blacktriangleleft$$

EXAMPLE 6.2

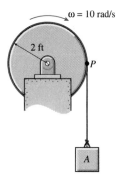

ω = 10 rad/s

2 ft

P

A

Block A is attached to a rope that is wrapped around a drum of radius 2 ft as shown. The drum's initial angular velocity is 10 rad/s clockwise and is increasing at a rate of $(t^2 + 2)$ rad/s². Determine the velocity and acceleration of block A at $t = 3$ s.

Solution   Angular velocity and angular acceleration at a given instant are related through Equation (6.14) as $\alpha = d\omega/dt$, which we can integrate to obtain the angular velocity ω; thus,

$$\int_{\omega_0}^{\omega} d\omega = \int_0^t \alpha\, dt$$

where

$$\alpha = t^2 + 2$$

$$\omega - \omega_0 = \int_0^t (t^2 + 2)dt$$

$$\omega = \omega_0 + \frac{t^3}{3} + 2t$$

Since the initial angular velocity $\omega_0 = 10$ rad/s, the angular velocity after $t = 3$ s will be

$$\omega = 10 + [9 + 2(3)] = 25\,\text{rad/s} \;\circlearrowright$$

The angular velocity ω of the drum is related to the linear velocity v_P along the rim at point P, by the relationship $v_P = \omega r$; thus,

$$v_P = 25(2) = 50\,\text{ft/s} \;\downarrow$$

Since the velocity at P is equal to the velocity at block A,

$$v_A = 50\,\text{ft/s} \;\downarrow \quad \blacktriangleleft$$

The angular acceleration α of the drum will relate to the tangential component of the acceleration of point P through the relationship $(a_P)_t = \alpha r_P$. With the given expression for angular acceleration, the acceleration of block A (and of point P) at time $t = 3$ s is

$$a_A = (a_P)_t = (t^2 + 2)r_P = (3^2 + 2)2$$

$$a_A = 22\,\text{ft/s}^2 \;\downarrow \quad \blacktriangleleft$$

EXAMPLE 6.3

A rigid, slender bar is rotating about its pin-connected support (*O*) with an angular speed of 5 rad/s clockwise. At the position shown, the angular speed of the bar is increasing at the rate of 3 rad/s². Determine the velocity and acceleration of the tip *A* of the bar at the given position.

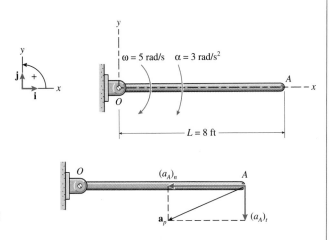

Solution   The velocity of a point *A* on a rigid body rotating about a fixed axis is given by $\mathbf{v} = \boldsymbol{\omega} \times \mathbf{r}$ [Equation (6.7)] or, for the case of a planar motion, by the scalar equation $v = \omega r$ where v is normal to the position vector *OA* and moving point *A* in the clockwise direction. Thus, we have

$$\mathbf{v}_A = \boldsymbol{\omega} \times \mathbf{r} = (-5\mathbf{k}) \times (8\mathbf{i})$$

$$\mathbf{v}_A = -40\mathbf{j} \qquad v_A = 40\,\text{ft/s}\,(\downarrow)\ \blacktriangleleft$$

The acceleration of point *A* can be obtained through $\mathbf{a} = \boldsymbol{\omega} \times (\boldsymbol{\omega} \times \mathbf{r}) + \boldsymbol{\alpha} \times \mathbf{r}$ [Equation (6.8)]. Thus, we have

$$\mathbf{a}_A = \boldsymbol{\omega} \times (\boldsymbol{\omega} \times \mathbf{OA}) + \boldsymbol{\alpha} \times (\mathbf{OA})$$

$$= (-5\mathbf{k}) \times [(-5\mathbf{k}) \times (8\mathbf{i})] + [(-3\mathbf{k}) \times (8\mathbf{i})]$$

$$= (-5\mathbf{k}) \times (-40\mathbf{j}) - 24\mathbf{j}$$

$$\mathbf{a}_A = -200\mathbf{i} - 24\mathbf{j}$$

Expressed in terms of components,

$$(a_A)_n = 200\,\text{ft/s}^2\,(\leftarrow)\ \blacktriangleleft$$

$$(a_A)_t = 24\,\text{ft/s}^2\,(\downarrow)\ \blacktriangleleft$$

6.4 GENERAL PLANAR MOTION RELATIVE TO A TRANSLATING FRAME OF REFERENCE

Having studied separately the translation and fixed-axis rotation of a rigid body, we will now consider the simultaneous presence of both these motions, which we will define as the general planar motion of a rigid body. That the planar motion of a body can be viewed as the superposition of two "component" motions—its translation and its rotation about an axis that moves with the body and is normal to the reference plane of motion—is illustrated in Figure 6.3. Consider a body subjected to a planar motion and two points *A* and *B* in the body. Assuming the *xy* coordinate plane to represent the plane within which the points *A* and *B* are displaced, the motion of the body from position 1 to position 2 can be represented either by a translation of B_1 to B_2 superimposed to a rotation about B_2, or by a rotation about A_1 superimposed by a translation of A_1 to A_2. The combination of simultaneous translation and

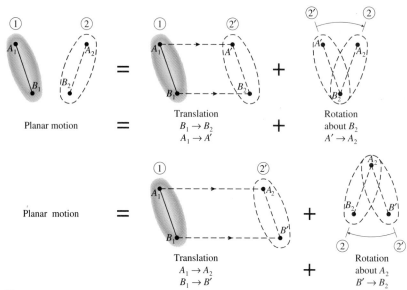

Figure 6.3

rotation will bring the body to its final position; the order in which they are executed is immaterial. We conclude that the most general motion of a rigid body is equivalent to a translation of the body following some arbitrary point of the body superimposed to a rotation of the body about an axis passing through the same point. This property is referred to as *Chasles' theorem*, after the 19th century French mathematician Michel Chasles (1793–1880). We will therefore analyze any general planar motion by studying its components—translation and rotation—and combine the kinematic parameters corresponding to each component motion to obtain the velocity or the acceleration of any arbitrary point on the body.

In the following sections we will study the velocity and acceleration of any arbitrary point of the body. We will distinguish between the *absolute* velocity or acceleration of the point as viewed by an observer on the fixed reference frame and the *relative* velocity or acceleration as viewed by an observer attached to the point. Since most often relative velocities and accelerations are more convenient to determine than their absolute counterparts, it is very useful to establish the kinematic equations relating the relative to the absolute velocity, and the relative to the absolute acceleration. These relationships require knowledge of the velocity and acceleration vectors at the point on the body where the observer is located. We will use two sets of coordinate axes: A *fixed* frame of reference *XYZ* will measure (Figure 6.4) *absolute* positions, velocities, and accelerations. Another frame of reference *xyz* with its origin at *A* will move with point *A*. It is important to distinguish between the motion of point

A (translation) and that of the body (translation and rotation). The frame of reference *xyz* is thus translating without rotating. The case of a rotating frame of reference will be considered in Section 6.8.

6.5 ABSOLUTE AND RELATIVE VELOCITIES

Consider a fixed frame of reference *XYZ* as in Figure 6.4. A rigid body is subjected to a general planar motion (translation and fixed-axis rotation). Assuming that the kinematic conditions prevailing at a given point *A* on a body are known, another set of coordinate axes *xyz* with its origin at *A* is introduced. The latter frame of reference will thus translate with *A*. The location of *A* is specified by its *absolute position vector* $\mathbf{r}_A$, whereas the location of any *arbitrary* point *B* on the rigid body will be defined by its absolute position vector $\mathbf{r}_B$. The position of point *B* relative to the translating coordinate system *xyz* is given by the relative position vector $\mathbf{r}_{B/A}$. The relationship between the *absolute* and *relative* positions of *B* is given from Equation (6.1) as

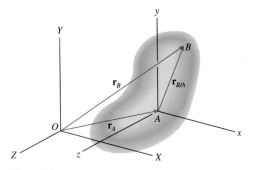

Figure 6.4

$$\mathbf{r}_B = \mathbf{r}_A + \mathbf{r}_{B/A}$$

The kinematic relationship between the absolute and relative velocities will be developed by time-differentiating the above equation. The result can be expressed in the form

$$\dot{\mathbf{r}}_B = \dot{\mathbf{r}}_A + \dot{\mathbf{r}}_{B/A}$$

or as

$$\mathbf{v}_B = \mathbf{v}_A + \mathbf{v}_{B/A} \tag{6.18}$$

The velocities $\mathbf{v}_B$ and $\mathbf{v}_A$ are **absolute velocities** with respect to the fixed frame of reference *XYZ*. The **relative velocity** $\mathbf{v}_{B/A}$ is measured relative to *xyz* and is therefore the contribution of the rotational movement ($\boldsymbol{\omega}$) of the body to the velocity at *B*. Referring to Equation (6.7), we can express this velocity as

$$\mathbf{v}_{B/A} = \boldsymbol{\omega} \times \mathbf{r}_{B/A}$$

Substituting Equation (6.7) into Equation (6.18) yields

$$\mathbf{v}_B = \mathbf{v}_A + \boldsymbol{\omega} \times \mathbf{r}_{B/A} \tag{6.19}$$

Equation (6.19) can be used to determine the velocity at any arbitrary point *B* on the body, given the velocity at a single point *A* and the angular velocity of the body. Recall that the angular velocity is not associated with any particular point on the rigid body. Indeed, it is a kinematic parameter describing the rotational motion of the body and is independent of our choice of point on the body.

EXAMPLE 6.4

A link CD is guided by two blocks A and B moving in slots as shown. Block A moves to the right at 5 m/s. Determine the velocity of the tip C of the link at the instant when $\theta = 35°$.

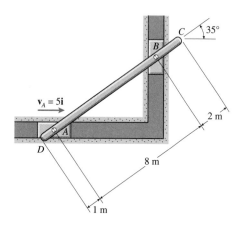

Solution   Since the motion of block A is completely defined as $\mathbf{v}_A = 5\mathbf{i}$, the velocity of point C can be expressed with Equation (6.18), writing

$$\mathbf{v}_C = \mathbf{v}_A + \mathbf{v}_{C/A}$$

$$\mathbf{v}_C = 5\mathbf{i} + \boldsymbol{\omega} \times \mathbf{r}_{C/A} \qquad\qquad (a)$$

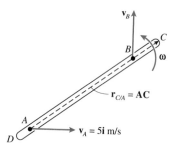

where $\mathbf{r}_{C/A} = (10\cos 35°)\mathbf{i} + (10\sin 35°)\mathbf{j}$

The angular velocity ω of the link will have to be determined by using the information provided about the motion of block B, which is constrained to move in the y direction. The velocity of block B can be expressed by writing

$$\mathbf{v}_B = \mathbf{v}_A + \mathbf{v}_{B/A}$$

$$\mathbf{v}_B = \mathbf{v}_A + \boldsymbol{\omega} \times \mathbf{r}_{B/A}$$

$$v_B\mathbf{j} = 5\mathbf{i} + \omega\mathbf{k} \times [(8\cos 35°)\mathbf{i} + (8\sin 35°)\mathbf{j}]$$

$$v_B\mathbf{j} = (5 - 8\omega\sin 35°)\mathbf{i} + (8\omega\cos 35°)\mathbf{j} \qquad (b)$$

Since the velocity of block B does not have an x component, we have from the y components

$$5 - 8\omega\sin 35° = 0$$

and solve for the angular velocity ω

$$\omega = \frac{5}{8\sin 35°} = 1.09 \,\text{rad/s}$$

$$\omega = 1.09\mathbf{k} \,(\text{rad/s})$$

Substituting ω into Equation (a) we obtain the velocity of point C as

$$\mathbf{v}_C = 5\mathbf{i} + 1.09\mathbf{k} \times [(10\cos 35°)\mathbf{i} + (10\sin 35°)\mathbf{j}]$$

$$= 5\mathbf{i} + (8.93\mathbf{j} - 6.25\mathbf{i})$$

$$= -1.25\mathbf{i} + 8.93\mathbf{j}$$

Thus the magnitude of the velocity of point C is

$$v_C = (1.25^2 + 8.93^2)^{1/2}$$

$$v_C = 9.02 \,\text{m/s} \blacktriangleleft$$

and it is directed at an angle θ measured up from the horizontal of

$$\theta = \tan^{-1}\left(\frac{1.25}{8.93}\right) = 8°$$

EXAMPLE 6.5

A crank CB is operated by the up-and-down motion of a piston A as shown. Determine the angular velocities of cranks AB and CB at the instant when $\theta = 20°$ and the piston moves downward at a speed $v_A = 10$ m/s.

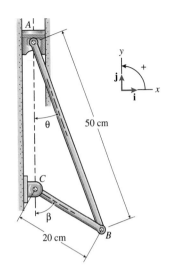

Solution From the geometry of the piston-crank system we have

$$\sin \beta = \frac{0.5 \sin 20°}{0.20}$$

$$\beta = 58.77°$$

The expression for the velocity of joint B using Equation (6.18) is $\mathbf{v}_B = \mathbf{v}_C + \boldsymbol{\omega}_{CB} \times \mathbf{r}_{B/C}$ where $\mathbf{v}_C = \mathbf{0}$ and

$$\mathbf{r}_{B/C} = (0.20 \sin 58.77°)\mathbf{i} + (-0.20 \cos 58.77°)\mathbf{j}$$

Thus, we write

$$\mathbf{v}_B = \omega_{CB}\mathbf{k} \times [(0.20 \sin 58.77°)\mathbf{i} + (-0.20 \cos 58.77°)\mathbf{j}]$$

$$\mathbf{v}_B = (0.1036\,\omega_{CB})\mathbf{i} + (0.1710\omega_{CB})\mathbf{j} \qquad \text{(a)}$$

Next, we express the velocity of joint B, by using the kinematics of piston A. Thus we write

$$\mathbf{v}_B = \mathbf{v}_A + \boldsymbol{\omega}_{AB} \times \mathbf{r}_{B/A}$$

where $\mathbf{v}_A = -10\mathbf{j}$ and $\mathbf{r}_{B/A} = (0.50 \sin 20°)\mathbf{i} + (-0.50 \cos 20°)\mathbf{j}$. Substituting the above expressions we obtain

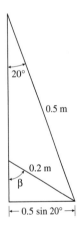

$$\mathbf{v}_B = -10\mathbf{j} + \omega_{AB}\mathbf{k} \times [0.50 \sin 20°\mathbf{i} - 0.50 \cos 20°\mathbf{j}]$$

$$\mathbf{v}_B = (0.4698\omega_{AB})\mathbf{i} + (0.171\omega_{AB} - 10)\mathbf{j} \qquad \text{(b)}$$

Equating the right-hand sides of Equations (a) and (b), we have

$$(0.1036\omega_{CB})\mathbf{i} + (0.171\omega_{CB})\mathbf{j} = (0.4698\omega_{AB})\mathbf{i} + (0.171\omega_{AB} - 10)\mathbf{j}$$

By equating $\mathbf{i}$ and $\mathbf{j}$ components from each side we obtain two simultaneous equations with two unknowns, ω_{CB} and ω_{AB}, which yield

$$0.1036\omega_{CB} = 0.4698\omega_{AB}$$

$$0.171\omega_{CB} = 0.171\omega_{AB} - 10$$

Solving the above equations simultaneously, the angular velocities are found to be

$$\omega_{AB} = 16.6\,\text{rad/s} \circlearrowright \blacktriangleleft$$

$$\omega_{CB} = 75.0\,\text{rad/s} \circlearrowright \blacktriangleleft$$

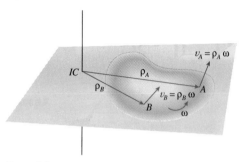

Figure 6.5

6.6 INSTANTANEOUS CENTER OF ZERO VELOCITY

In Section 6.5 we saw that the angular velocity $\boldsymbol{\omega}$ of a rigid body rotating about a fixed axis, together with the absolute velocity $\mathbf{v}_A$ of a given point on the body, define completely the instantaneous velocities of all other points. Since we earlier established that the linear speed v of a point P of a body rotating with an angular speed ω about an axis located at a radial distance r from P is given as $v = \omega r$, it is therefore possible to determine, at any given instant, a fixed axis intersecting the plane of motion at a point located at a distance $\rho_A = v_A/\omega$ from A along the perpendicular to $\mathbf{v}_A$, as in Figure 6.5. We will label such an axis an *instantaneous axis of rotation*, and its point of intersection with the plane to which it is normal, the *instantaneous center (IC) of rotation*. Since at a given instant the instantaneous center has zero velocity, the center is also called **instantaneous center of zero velocity**. Any other point B of the body will appear to rotate momentarily about the instantaneous center with a velocity v_B given as $v_B = \rho_B\omega$, where ρ_B is the distance from IC to point B. The direction of the velocity $\mathbf{v}_B$ would be perpendicular to the line joining IC to B.

It is important to note that the above kinematic analysis represents an instantaneous picture. The position of the instantaneous center of zero velocity may vary with time and with it the magnitude and direction of the velocity at any point of the body. The location of the IC may also be determined without a knowledge of the angular velocity ω of the body. If the directions of the velocities at two points A and B of a body are known, the IC is located at the intersection of the perpendiculars to $\mathbf{v}_A$ and $\mathbf{v}_B$, as in Figure 6.6a. However, if the velocities at A and B are parallel, then it is necessary to also know their magnitudes. In that case, the IC is located at the intersection of the line AB with the line joining the end points of the velocity vectors $\mathbf{v}_A$ and $\mathbf{v}_B$ (Figure 6.6b), provided the velocity vectors (and dimensions of the body, etc.) are drawn to scale. As one can observe from Figure 6.6, the IC may not necessarily lie at a point on the body, but rather on the extended plane over which the motion takes place.

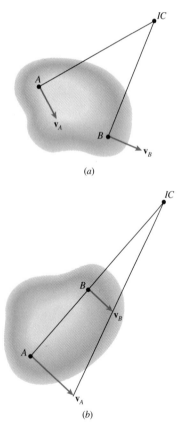

Figure 6.6

EXAMPLE 6.6

A crank CB is operated by the up and down motion of a piston A as shown. Determine the angular velocities of cranks AB and CB at the instant when $\theta = 20°$ and the piston moves downward with a speed $v_A = 10$ m/s.

Solution Refer to the figure of Example 6.5. The instantaneous center of zero velocity (IC) is established by drawing the perpendiculars to the velocity vectors at A and B, as shown.

From the triangle $ICAB$ we write

$$\frac{r_{A/IC}}{\sin 38.77°} = \frac{r_{B/IC}}{\sin 110°} = \frac{0.50}{\sin 31.23°}$$

Solving for $r_{A/IC}$ and $r_{B/IC}$ we obtain

$$r_{A/IC} = 0.6039 \text{ m} \qquad r_{B/IC} = 0.9062 \text{ m}$$

Next, we apply the relationship between the angular and linear velocities by writing

$$v_A = \omega_{AB} r_{A/IC} = 0.6039 \omega_{AB}$$

and since the piston is moving downward at $v_A = 10$ m/s, we have

$$10 = 0.6039 \omega_{AB}$$

$$\omega_{AB} = \frac{10}{0.6039}$$

$$\omega_{AB} = 16.56 \text{ rad/s} \circlearrowright \blacktriangleleft$$

The speed of joint B can be expressed in terms of the angular speed of the rod AB as

$$v_B = \omega_{AB} r_{B/IC}$$

and also in terms of the angular speed of the crank AB as

$$v_B = \omega_{CB} r_{B/C}$$

since crank CB is rotating about the pin C. Equating the two expressions yields

$$\omega_{AB} r_{B/IC} = \omega_{CB} r_{B/C}$$

Thus,

$$\omega_{CB} = \omega_{AB} \frac{r_{B/IC}}{r_{B/C}} = 16.56 \frac{0.9062}{0.20}$$

$$\omega_{CB} = 75.0 \text{ rad/s} \circlearrowright \blacktriangleleft$$

The results agree with the solution obtained in Example 6.5.

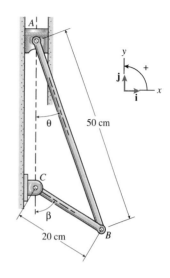

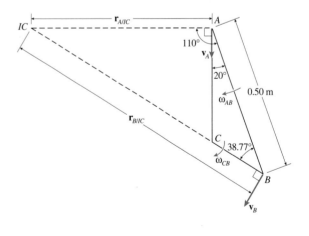

EXAMPLE 6.7

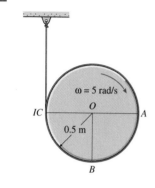

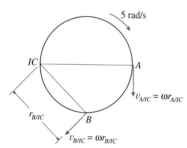

A cord wrapped around a disk (radius = 0.5 m) is attached to the ceiling as shown. The disk is moving downward as it rotates at the rate of 5 rad/s. Determine the velocities of points A and B.

Solution The motion is analogous to the disk rolling downward without slipping along the cord. The instantaneous center of zero velocity is at IC and we write

$$v_A = \omega r_{A/IC} \quad \text{and} \quad v_B = \omega r_{B/IC}$$

where
$$\omega = 5 \, \text{rad/s}$$
$$r_{A/IC} = 1.0 \, \text{m}$$
$$r_{B/IC} = (0.5^2 + 0.5^2)^{1/2} = 0.707 \, \text{m}$$

For the velocity of point A,

$$v_A = 5(1.0) \qquad v_A = 5 \, \text{m/s} \, (\downarrow) \quad \blacktriangleleft$$

and for the velocity of point B,

$$v_B = 5(0.707)$$
$$v_B = 3.54 \, \text{m/s} \, (\text{45°}) \quad \blacktriangleleft$$

EXAMPLE 6.8

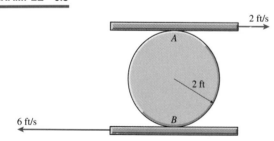

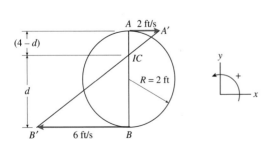

A 2-ft-radius disk is rolling without slipping between two parallel plates moving in opposite directions with 2-ft/s and 6-ft/s velocities as shown. Determine the angular velocity of the disk.

Solution

Scalar approach. The velocities of points A and B on the disk are also the velocities of the plates in contact with the disk at A or B. Thus we write

$$v_A = 2 \, \text{ft/s} \, (\rightarrow) \quad \text{and} \quad v_B = 6 \, \text{ft/s} \, (\leftarrow)$$

Next, we determine the location of the instantaneous center of rotation. Since the velocity vectors at A and B are parallel but their magnitudes are known, from the similarity of the triangles $AA'IC$ and $BB'IC$ we obtain

$$\frac{2}{4-d} = \frac{6}{d} \qquad d = 3 \, \text{ft}$$

(*continued*)

EXAMPLE 6.8 (*concluded*)

Finally, the angular velocity ω of the disk is related to v_B through the scalar expression $v_B = \omega r_{B/IC}$, where, in this case, $v_B = 6$ ft/s and $r_{B/IC} = 3$ ft. Hence, solving for the angular velocity,

$$\omega = \frac{v_B}{r_{B/IC}} = \frac{6}{3} \qquad \omega = 2\,\text{rad/s} \circlearrowright \blacktriangleleft$$

The same answer could have been obtained through the use of velocity $v_A = 2$ ft/s and $(r_{A/IC}) = 4 - d = 1$ ft.

$$\omega = \frac{v_A}{r_{A/IC}} = \frac{2}{1} = 2\,\text{rad/s}\circlearrowright$$

Vector approach. Since $\mathbf{v}_B = \boldsymbol{\omega} \times \mathbf{r}_{B/IC}$, where $\mathbf{v}_B = -6\mathbf{i}$, $\boldsymbol{\omega} = \omega\mathbf{k}$, and $\mathbf{r}_{B/IC} = -3\mathbf{j}$, we obtain

$$-6\mathbf{i} = (\omega)\mathbf{k} \times (-3)\mathbf{j}$$
$$(-6)\mathbf{i} = (+3\omega)\mathbf{i}$$
$$\omega = -2$$

thus

$$\omega = 2\,\text{rad/s}\circlearrowright \blacktriangleleft$$

EXAMPLE 6.9

The wheel A is rotating clockwise with an angular velocity $\omega = 5$ rad/s while connected through a rod to the collar B. At the instant shown, determine the velocity of the collar B.

Solution   The velocities of the two ends of the rod AB will enable us to determine its instantaneous center of zero velocity.
    The velocity of collar B is in the horizontal direction, whereas the velocity of the end A as shown is oriented at 45° over the horizontal. The perpendiculars B-IC and A-IC intersect to define the position of IC.
    Since the angular velocity of the wheel is given, the velocity of point A—on the wheel—can be determined from the equation $v_A = \omega_{\text{wheel}}(r_{A/O})$ by writing

$$v_A = 5(0.20) = 1\,\text{m/s}\ \angle^{45°}$$

Next, we consider point A as part of the rod AB and using the position of the instantaneous center of zero velocity (IC) of the rod AB, we determine the angular velocity ω_{AB} of the rod as

$$v_A = \omega_{AB}(r_{A/IC})$$
$$1.0 = \omega_{AB}(0.80)$$
$$\omega_{AB} = \frac{1.0}{0.80} = 1.25\,\text{rad/s}\circlearrowright$$

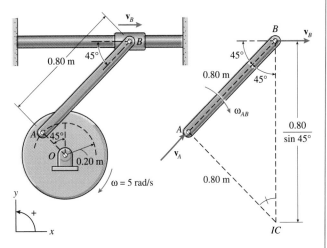

With the angular velocity ω_{AB} of the rod determined for the given instant and with the IC of zero velocity considered, we can now evaluate the velocity of collar B as

$$v_B = \omega_{AB}(r_{B/IC})$$
$$v_B = (1.25)(1.13)$$
$$v_B = 1.41\,\text{m/s}\rightarrow \blacktriangleleft$$

6.7 ABSOLUTE AND RELATIVE ACCELERATIONS

Next, we will develop the kinematic relations between the absolute and relative accelerations of an arbitrary point B of a body subjected to a general planar motion (translation and fixed-axis rotation). Let us assume that the kinematic conditions $(\mathbf{v}_A, \mathbf{a}_A)$ at a given point A are known, as well as the angular velocity $\boldsymbol{\omega}$ of the body. Once again, we will refer all *absolute* positions, velocities, and accelerations to a *fixed* frame of reference XYZ. The *relative* positions, velocities, and accelerations will be referred to the translating frame of reference xyz attached to point A of the body (Figure 6.7).

We have already established, in Equations (6.18) and (6.19), that the relationship between the absolute and relative velocities of a point in a body can be expressed as

$$\mathbf{v}_B = \mathbf{v}_A + \mathbf{v}_{B/A} \tag{6.18}$$

where $\mathbf{v}_{B/A} = \boldsymbol{\omega} \times \mathbf{r}_{B/A}$.

When Equation (6.18) is differentiated with respect to time, we obtain

$$\mathbf{a}_B = \mathbf{a}_A + \mathbf{a}_{B/A} \tag{6.20}$$

where

$$\mathbf{a}_{B/A} = \frac{d}{dt}(\boldsymbol{\omega} \times \mathbf{r}_{B/A})$$

The relative acceleration $\mathbf{a}_{B/A}$ can be expanded to yield

$$\mathbf{a}_{B/A} = \dot{\boldsymbol{\omega}} \times \mathbf{r}_{B/A} + \boldsymbol{\omega} \times \dot{\mathbf{r}}_{B/A}$$

$$\mathbf{a}_{B/A} = \dot{\boldsymbol{\omega}} \times \mathbf{r}_{B/A} + \boldsymbol{\omega} \times \mathbf{v}_{B/A}$$

Introducing $\boldsymbol{\alpha} = \dot{\boldsymbol{\omega}}$ as the angular acceleration of the rigid body, and recalling $\mathbf{v}_{B/A} = \boldsymbol{\omega} \times \mathbf{r}_{B/A}$, we have

$$\mathbf{a}_{B/A} = \boldsymbol{\alpha} \times \mathbf{r}_{B/A} + \boldsymbol{\omega} \times (\boldsymbol{\omega} \times \mathbf{r}_{B/A}) \tag{6.21}$$

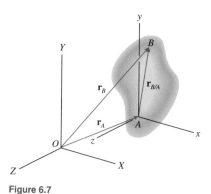

Figure 6.7

Substituting Equation (6.21) into Equation (6.20) yields

$$\mathbf{a}_B = \mathbf{a}_A + \underbrace{\boldsymbol{\alpha} \times \mathbf{r}_{B/A}}_{(\mathbf{a}_{B/A})_t} + \underbrace{\boldsymbol{\omega} \times (\boldsymbol{\omega} \times \mathbf{r}_{B/A})}_{(\mathbf{a}_{B/A})_n} \qquad (6.22)$$

Equation (6.22) relates the **absolute acceleration** of an arbitrary point B on the body to the acceleration of point B relative to the motion of point A. The **relative acceleration** represents the contribution of the rotational component of the motion to the absolute value of the acceleration vector $\mathbf{a}_B$. The tangential and normal components of the relative acceleration vector $\mathbf{a}_{B/A}$ are given in the form

Tangential:

$$(\mathbf{a}_{B/A})_t = \boldsymbol{\alpha} \times \mathbf{r}_{B/A}$$

or

$$|(\mathbf{a}_{B/A})_t| = \alpha r_{B/A}$$

Normal:

$$(\mathbf{a}_{B/A})_n = \boldsymbol{\omega} \times (\boldsymbol{\omega} \times \mathbf{r}_{B/A})$$

or

$$|(\mathbf{a}_{B/A})_n| = \omega^2 r_{B/A}$$

It is important to note that $\boldsymbol{\omega}$ and $\boldsymbol{\alpha}$ are independent of the choices of the points A and B. Indeed they represent kinematic parameters associated with all lines parallel to the plane of motion. The evaluation of the terms $\boldsymbol{\alpha} \times \mathbf{r}_{B/A}$ and $\boldsymbol{\omega} \times (\boldsymbol{\omega} \times \mathbf{r}_{B/A})$ requires that the position vectors be measured relative to the frame of reference attached to the body at A. The translational motion of the frame xyz is represented by the term $\mathbf{a}_A$, which is measured relative to the fixed frame XYZ. The final expression can be expressed as

$$\mathbf{a}_B = \underbrace{\mathbf{a}_A}_{\text{Translation}} + \underbrace{\underbrace{\boldsymbol{\alpha} \times \mathbf{r}_{B/A}}_{(\mathbf{a}_{B/A})_t} + \underbrace{\boldsymbol{\omega} \times (\boldsymbol{\omega} \times \mathbf{r}_{B/A})}_{(\mathbf{a}_{B/A})_n}}_{\text{Rotation}}$$

where
$\mathbf{a}_B$ = acceleration of point B (measured from XYZ)
$\mathbf{a}_A$ = acceleration of point A (measured from XYZ)
$\boldsymbol{\alpha}$ = angular acceleration of the rigid body
$\boldsymbol{\omega}$ = angular velocity of the rigid body
$\mathbf{r}_{B/A}$ = position vector of point B (measured from the origin A of xyz)

EXAMPLE 6.10

At a given instant, blocks A and B are moving in slots as shown. They are connected by a link AB. For the position shown, the velocity and acceleration of block A are 10 ft/s and 5 ft/s², respectively. Determine the acceleration of block B and the angular acceleration of the link AB at this instant.

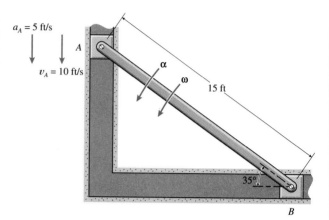

Solution The instantaneous center of zero velocity of the link AB is first determined by intersecting the lines perpendicular to the velocities v_A and v_B. From the geometry of the triangle A-IC-B we obtain the distance $r_{A/IC}$ as $15 \cos 35° = 12.287$ ft.

The angular velocity of the link AB is

$$\omega_{AB} = \frac{v_A}{r_{A/IC}} = \frac{10}{12.287} = 0.814 \,\text{rad/s} \,\circlearrowleft$$

Now, the acceleration $\mathbf{a}_B$ of block B and the angular acceleration $\boldsymbol{\alpha}$ of link AB can be obtained through Equation (6.22), which is given as

$$\mathbf{a}_B = \mathbf{a}_A + \boldsymbol{\alpha} \times \mathbf{r}_{B/A} + \boldsymbol{\omega}_{AB} \times (\boldsymbol{\omega}_{AB} \times \mathbf{r}_{B/A})$$

Since, from vector algebra, we have (for planar motion)

$$\boldsymbol{\omega}_{AB} \times (\boldsymbol{\omega}_{AB} \times \mathbf{r}_{B/A}) = -\omega_{AB}^2 \mathbf{r}_{B/A}$$

Equation (6.22) becomes

$$\mathbf{a}_B = \mathbf{a}_A + \boldsymbol{\alpha} \times \mathbf{r}_{B/A} - \omega_{AB}^2 \mathbf{r}_{B/A}$$

After substituting $\mathbf{a}_A = -5\mathbf{j}$ (ft/s), $\boldsymbol{\alpha} = \alpha\mathbf{k}$ (rad/s²), $\omega_{AB} = 0.814$ rad/s, and $\mathbf{r}_{B/A} = 15 \cos 35°\mathbf{i} - 15 \sin 35°\mathbf{j}$ (ft), the above equation becomes

$$a_B\mathbf{i} = -5\mathbf{j} + (\alpha\mathbf{k}) \times (15 \cos 35°\mathbf{i} - 15 \sin 35°\mathbf{j})$$
$$- (0.814)^2(15 \cos 35°\mathbf{i} - 15 \sin 35°\mathbf{j})$$

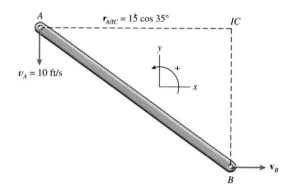

Collecting terms and equating components, we get for $\mathbf{i}$ components:

$$a_B = 15\alpha \sin 35° - 9.939 \cos 35° \qquad \text{(a)}$$

and for $\mathbf{j}$ components:

$$0 = -5 + 15\alpha \cos 35° + 9.939 \sin 35° \qquad \text{(b)}$$

The unknowns a_B and α can now be determined by the simultaneous solution of Equations (a) and (b). Equation (b) yields

$$\alpha = -0.057 \,\text{rad/s}^2$$

or

$$\alpha = 0.057 \,\text{rad/s}^2 \,\circlearrowright \,\blacktriangleleft$$

and substituting $\alpha = -0.057$ into Equation (a) we obtain

$$a_B = -8.63 \,\text{ft/s}^2$$

or

$$a_B = 8.63 \,\text{ft/s}^2 \,\circlearrowleft \,\blacktriangleleft$$

The negative sign on a_B indicates that at the given instant the block B is slowing down.

EXAMPLE 6.11

A wheel is rolling on a horizontal surface without slipping. The center of the wheel has a velocity of 50 ft/s and an acceleration of 5 ft/s² as shown. Determine the acceleration of points A, B, and C at the given instant.

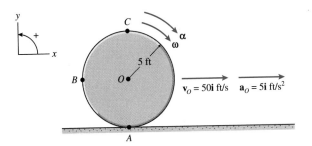

Solution   For a wheel rolling without slipping, the instantaneous center of zero velocity is located at A, and we write for the velocity of the center O of the wheel

$$v_O = \omega r_{O/A} \qquad \text{and} \qquad a_O = \alpha r_{O/A}$$

which yields

$$\omega = \frac{v_O}{r_{O/A}} = \frac{50}{5} = 10 \, \text{rad/s} \; \circlearrowright$$

or

$$\omega = -10\mathbf{k}$$

Also,

$$\alpha = \frac{a_O}{r_{O/A}} = \frac{5}{5} = 1 \, \text{rad/s}^2 \; \circlearrowright$$

and

$$\alpha = -\mathbf{k}$$

Equation (6.22) can now be expressed as

$$\mathbf{a}_A = \mathbf{a}_O + \alpha \times \mathbf{r}_{A/O} - \omega^2 \mathbf{r}_{A/O}$$

where $\mathbf{a}_O = 5\mathbf{i}$ (ft/s²), $\alpha = -\mathbf{k}$ (rad/s²), $\omega = 10$ rad/s, and $\mathbf{r}_{A/O} = -5\mathbf{j}$ (ft). After substituting, we have

$$\mathbf{a}_A = 5\mathbf{i} + (-\mathbf{k}) \times (-5\mathbf{j}) - (10)^2(-5\mathbf{j})$$
$$\mathbf{a}_A = 5\mathbf{i} - 5\mathbf{i} + 500\mathbf{j}$$
$$\mathbf{a}_A = 500\mathbf{j} \, (\text{ft/s}^2) \; \uparrow \; \blacktriangleleft$$

For point B, we will have to introduce $\mathbf{r}_{B/O} = -5\mathbf{i}$ into the expression, which gives

$$\mathbf{a}_B = 5\mathbf{i} + (-\mathbf{k}) \times (\mathbf{r}_{B/O}) - \omega^2 \mathbf{r}_{B/O}$$
$$= 5\mathbf{i} + (-\mathbf{k}) \times (-5\mathbf{i}) - (10)^2(-5\mathbf{i})$$
$$= 5\mathbf{i} + 5\mathbf{j} + 500\mathbf{i}$$
$$\mathbf{a}_B = 505\mathbf{i} + 5\mathbf{j} \, (\text{ft/s}^2) \; \nearrow \; \blacktriangleleft$$

For point C, $\mathbf{r}_{C/O} = +5\mathbf{j}$, and Equation (6.22) becomes

$$\mathbf{a}_C = 5\mathbf{i} + (-\mathbf{k}) \times (5\mathbf{j}) - \omega^2(5\mathbf{j})$$
$$\mathbf{a}_C = 5\mathbf{i} + 5\mathbf{i} - (10)^2(5\mathbf{j})$$
$$\mathbf{a}_C = 10\mathbf{i} - 500\mathbf{j} \, (\text{ft/s}^2) \; \searrow \; \blacktriangleleft$$

6.8 GENERAL PLANAR MOTION RELATIVE TO A ROTATING FRAME OF REFERENCE

In the preceding analyses all kinematic quantities were referred to *fixed* (absolute) and *translating* (relative) frames of reference. In what follows we will develop kinematic equations relating the absolute position, velocity, and acceleration of an arbitrary point B of a rigid body to the position, velocity, and acceleration of the same point B measured *relative* to a *translating and rotating* frame of reference attached to the body and subject to a planar motion. Since planar is a special case of the spatial motion, all derivations here will be carried out for the general spatial motion, which is the subject of Section 6.9.

An arbitrary point B is defined by its position vector $\mathbf{r}_B$ with respect to a fixed coordinate system XYZ. A moving frame of reference xyz translates with a linear velocity $\mathbf{v}_A$ and linear acceleration $\mathbf{a}_A$, and rotates, in the plane, with angular velocity $\boldsymbol{\Omega}$ and angular acceleration $\dot{\boldsymbol{\Omega}}$. The position of an arbitrary point B relative to the fixed frame XYZ can be related to its position relative to a translating and rotating frame xyz attached to XYZ at a given point A, as shown in Figure 6.8, by adding vectorially the respective position vectors in the form

$$\mathbf{r}_B = \mathbf{r}_A + \mathbf{r}_{B/A}$$

where all vectors are measured in the XYZ frame of reference. Differentiating the above equation with respect to time yields

$$\mathbf{v}_B = \mathbf{v}_A + (\dot{\mathbf{r}}_{B/A})_{XYZ} \tag{6.23}$$

where, once again, all vectors are measured in the fixed coordinate system XYZ. The second term on the right-hand side of Equation (6.23), $(\dot{\mathbf{r}}_{B/A})_{XYZ}$, can be obtained by first writing the position vector $\mathbf{r}_{B/A}$ in terms of its Cartesian components in the relative frame xyz as

$$\mathbf{r}_{B/A} = (r_{B/A})_x\mathbf{i} + (r_{B/A})_y\mathbf{j} + (r_{B/A})_z\mathbf{k} \tag{6.24}$$

where $\mathbf{i}$, $\mathbf{j}$, $\mathbf{k}$ are the unit vectors in the xyz frame. If now we differentiate Equation (6.24) with respect to time, with proper attention paid to the fact that the unit vectors $\mathbf{i}$, $\mathbf{j}$, $\mathbf{k}$ do not retain constant direction relative to the fixed XYZ frame, we can write

$$\begin{aligned}(\dot{\mathbf{r}}_{B/A})_{XYZ} = {}& [(\dot{r}_{B/A})_x\mathbf{i} + (\dot{r}_{B/A})_y\mathbf{j} + (\dot{r}_{B/A})_z\mathbf{k}] \\ & + [(r_{B/A})_x\dot{\mathbf{i}} + (r_{B/A})_y\dot{\mathbf{j}} + (r_{B/A})_z\dot{\mathbf{k}}]\end{aligned} \tag{6.25}$$

where $(\dot{\mathbf{r}}_{B/A})_{XYZ}$ is the second term on the right-hand side of Equation (6.23) and a vector measured in the XYZ frame. Next, we will interpret the terms within brackets on the right-hand side of Equation (6.25).

The term within the first bracket on the right-hand side of the equation can be expressed as

$$[(\dot{r}_{B/A})_x\mathbf{i} + (\dot{r}_{B/A})_y\mathbf{j} + (\dot{r}_{B/A})_z\mathbf{k}] = (\dot{\mathbf{r}}_{B/A})_{xyz} = (\mathbf{v}_{B/A})_{xyz}$$

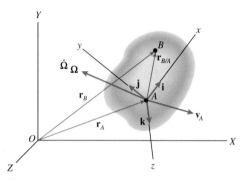

Figure 6.8

Equation (6.25) can now be written as

$$(\dot{\mathbf{r}}_{B/A})_{XYZ} = (\mathbf{v}_{B/A})_{XYZ} = (\mathbf{v}_{B/A})_{XYZ} + [(r_{B/A})_x\dot{\mathbf{i}} + (r_{B/A})_y\dot{\mathbf{j}} + (r_{B/A})_z\dot{\mathbf{k}}] \quad (6.26)$$

The term within the bracket on the right-hand side would be equal to the left-hand-side term $(\mathbf{v}_{B/A})_{XYZ}$ if the relative velocity $(\mathbf{v}_{B/A})_{xyz}$ becomes zero. At any given instant, for the velocity of any arbitrary point B relative to a reference frame rotating with an angular velocity Ω to be zero, the points B and A must be part of a rigid body rotating with the xyz frame. However, in this case, the velocity $\mathbf{v}_{B/A}$ measured with respect to a fixed frame would be equal to $\Omega \times (\mathbf{r}_{B/A})_{xyz}$ as given in Equation (6.7), and Equation (6.26) becomes

$$(\dot{\mathbf{r}}_{B/A})_{XYZ} = (\dot{\mathbf{r}}_{B/A})_{xyz} + \Omega \times (\mathbf{r}_{B/A})_{xyz} \quad (6.27)$$

Substitution of Equation (6.27) into Equation (6.23) yields

$$(\mathbf{v}_B)_{XYZ} = (\mathbf{v}_A)_{XYZ} + (\mathbf{v}_{B/A})_{xyz} + \Omega \times (\mathbf{r}_{B/A})_{xyz} \quad (6.28)$$

where $(\mathbf{v}_B)_{XYZ}$ = velocity of point B, measured from the fixed frame XYZ

$(\mathbf{v}_A)_{XYZ}$ = translational velocity of the origin A of the moving frame xyz, measured from the fixed frame XYZ

$(\mathbf{v}_{B/A})_{xyz}$ = velocity of point B relative to the origin of the moving frame xyz

Ω = instantaneous angular velocity of the rotating frame xyz measured from the fixed frame XYZ

$(\mathbf{r}_{B/A})_{xyz}$ = position vector of B measured from the origin A of the moving frame xyz.

The significance of Equation (6.27) cannot be overemphasized. Since point B was an arbitrarily chosen point, the vector $\dot{\mathbf{r}}_{B/A}$ can be viewed as any vector $\mathbf{v}$ expressed in the rotating frame xyz and we can write

$$\left(\frac{d\mathbf{v}}{dt}\right)_{XYZ} = \left(\frac{d\mathbf{v}}{dt}\right)_{xyz} + \Omega \times \mathbf{v} \quad (6.29)$$

where $(d\mathbf{v}/dt)_{XYZ}$ is the time rate of change of the vector $\mathbf{v}$ with respect to the XYZ frame and $(d\mathbf{v}/dt)_{xyz}$ the time rate of change of $\mathbf{v}$ with respect to the xyz frame rotating with the angular velocity Ω. The first term $(d\mathbf{v}/dt)_{xyz}$ on the right-hand side of Equation (6.29) represents the time rate of change of the magnitude of the vector $\mathbf{v}$, and the second term $(\Omega \times \mathbf{v})$ represents the time rate of change of the direction of the vector $\mathbf{v}$, which is expressed in terms of its xyz components.

Having thus established the procedure necessary to express the time derivative of a vector in a rotating frame, we will now appeal to Equation (6.29) to develop the kinematic equation for the acceleration vector $\mathbf{a}_B$.

The acceleration of B, measured from the fixed coordinate system XYZ, may be written, after time-differentiating Equation (6.28), as

$$\frac{d}{dt}[\mathbf{v}_B]_{XYZ} = \frac{d}{dt}[(\mathbf{v}_A)]_{XYZ} + \frac{d}{dt}[(\mathbf{v}_{B/A})_{xyz}]_{XYZ}$$

$$+ \frac{d}{dt}[\boldsymbol{\Omega} \times (\mathbf{r}_{B/A})_{xyz}]_{XYZ} \qquad (6.30)$$

where all derivative vectors are measured with respect to the XYZ frame, although $(\mathbf{r}_{B/A})_{xyz}$ and $(\mathbf{v}_{B/A})_{xyz}$ are with respect to the moving frame xyz. After expanding the last term above, we can rewrite the equation as

$$\frac{d}{dt}(\mathbf{v}_B)_{XYZ} = \frac{d}{dt}[(\mathbf{v}_A)]_{XYZ} + \frac{d}{dt}[(\mathbf{v}_{B/A})_{xyz}]_{XYZ} + \frac{d}{dt}(\boldsymbol{\Omega})_{XYZ}$$

$$\times (\mathbf{r}_{B/A})_{xyz} + (\boldsymbol{\Omega})_{XYZ} \times \frac{d}{dt}[(\mathbf{r}_{B/A})_{xyz}]_{XYZ} \qquad (6.31)$$

Each term of the expression above can now be rearranged, thus,

$$\frac{d}{dt}(\mathbf{v}_B)_{XYZ} = \mathbf{a}_B \qquad (6.32)$$

$$\frac{d}{dt}(\mathbf{v}_A)_{XYZ} = \mathbf{a}_A \qquad (6.33)$$

$$\frac{d}{dt}[(\mathbf{v}_{B/A})_{xyz}]_{XYZ} = \frac{d}{dt}[(\mathbf{v}_{B/A})_{xyz}]_{xyz} + \boldsymbol{\Omega} \times (\mathbf{v}_{B/A})_{xyz}$$

$$= (\mathbf{a}_{B/A})_{xyz} + \boldsymbol{\Omega} \times (\mathbf{v}_{B/A})_{xyz} \qquad (6.34)$$

using the last term from Equation (6.29); also,

$$\frac{d}{dt}[(\mathbf{r}_{B/A})_{xyz}]_{XYZ} = \frac{d}{dt}[(\mathbf{r}_{B/A})_{xyz}]_{xyz} + \boldsymbol{\Omega} \times (\mathbf{r}_{B/A})_{xyz}$$

$$= (\mathbf{v}_{B/A})_{xyz} + \boldsymbol{\Omega} \times (\mathbf{r}_{B/A})_{xyz} \qquad (6.35)$$

Substituting the above relationships (6.32), (6.33), (6.34), and (6.35) into Equation (6.31) yields

$$\mathbf{a}_B = \mathbf{a}_A + [(\mathbf{a}_{B/A})_{xyz} + \boldsymbol{\Omega} \times (\mathbf{v}_{B/A})_{xyz}] + \dot{\boldsymbol{\Omega}} \times (\mathbf{r}_{B/A})_{xyz}$$

$$+ \boldsymbol{\Omega} \times [(\mathbf{v}_{B/A})_{xyz} + \boldsymbol{\Omega} \times (\mathbf{r}_{B/A})_{xyz}]$$

and further expanding and rearranging terms, we have

$$\mathbf{a}_B = \mathbf{a}_A + (\mathbf{a}_{B/A})_{xyz} + \dot{\boldsymbol{\Omega}} \times (\mathbf{r}_{B/A})_{xyz}$$

$$+ \boldsymbol{\Omega} \times [\boldsymbol{\Omega} \times (\mathbf{r}_{B/A})_{xyz}] + 2\boldsymbol{\Omega} \times (\mathbf{v}_{B/A})_{xyz} \qquad (6.36)$$

where $\quad \mathbf{a}_B = $ acceleration of point B, measured from the fixed frame XYZ

$\mathbf{a}_A$ = linear acceleration of the origin A of the moving frame xyz, measured from the fixed frame XYZ

$\mathbf{a}_{B/A}$ = relative acceleration of B with respect to A, measured from the xyz frame

$\mathbf{v}_{B/A}$ = relative velocity of B with respect to A, measured from the xyz frame

$\mathbf{\Omega}$ = instantaneous angular velocity of the rotating frame xyz measured from the fixed frame XYZ

$\dot{\mathbf{\Omega}}$ = instantaneous angular acceleration of the rotating frame xyz measured from the fixed frame XYZ

$(\mathbf{r}_{B/A})_{xyz}$ = position vector of B measured from the origin A of the moving frame xyz.

Equation (6.36), when compared with the case of a purely translational motion, indicates that the presence of rotational motion of the coordinate system introduces three additional terms. The sum of the two terms

$$\dot{\mathbf{\Omega}} \times (\mathbf{r}_{B/A})_{xyz} + \mathbf{\Omega} \times [\mathbf{\Omega} \times (\mathbf{r}_{B/A})_{xyz}]$$

represents the acceleration component of B caused by the angular acceleration ($\dot{\mathbf{\Omega}}$) and angular velocity ($\mathbf{\Omega}$) of the rotating frame xyz (Figure 6.9). Indeed,

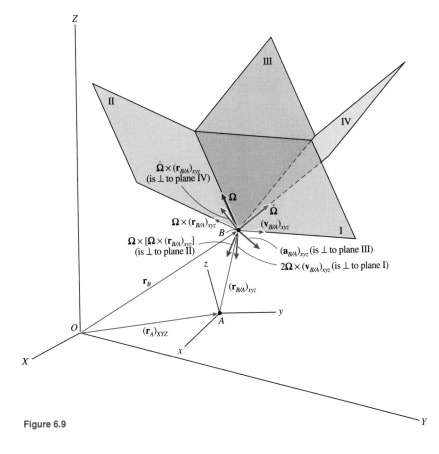

Figure 6.9

in the special case of planar motion, they represent the tangential and normal components of the acceleration vector developed in Equation (6.8). The term $\mathbf{\Omega} \times [\mathbf{\Omega} \times (\mathbf{r}_{B/A})_{xyz}]$ is called the *centripetal acceleration*; in curvilinear motion it is always directed towards the center of curvature. The third term $2\mathbf{\Omega} \times (\mathbf{v}_{B/A})_{xyz}$ is called the **complementary** or **Coriolis acceleration**, after the French engineer G. C. de Coriolis (1792–1843). It is always perpendicular to the angular velocity vector $\mathbf{\Omega}$ and to the relative velocity vector $\mathbf{v}_{B/A}$.

EXAMPLE   6.12

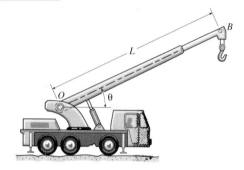

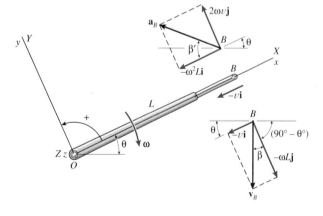

The operator of a crane, at a given instant, lowers the boom at a constant rate of $\dot{\theta} = \omega$ while at the same time retracting it at a constant rate of v. For the position shown, determine the velocity and acceleration of the end point B of the boom. The length of the boom is L.

Solution Both the fixed (XYZ) and rotating (xyz) frames of reference will have the pin at O as their common origin. At the instant under consideration the X axis of the fixed frame and the x axis of the moving frame of reference will be aligned with the boom axis. The moving frame of reference will follow the rotation of the boom as we *attach* the x axis to the axis of the boom.

The governing kinematic equations are Equations (6.28) and (6.36), expressed in terms of the velocity and acceleration of point B in the forms

$$\mathbf{v}_B = \mathbf{v}_O + (\mathbf{v}_{B/O})_{xyz} + \mathbf{\Omega} \times (\mathbf{r}_{B/O})_{xyz} \tag{a}$$

and

$$\mathbf{a}_B = \mathbf{a}_O + (\mathbf{a}_{B/O})_{xyz} + \dot{\mathbf{\Omega}} \times (\mathbf{r}_{B/O})_{xyz}$$
$$+ \mathbf{\Omega} \times [\mathbf{\Omega} \times (\mathbf{r}_{B/O})_{xyz}] + 2\mathbf{\Omega} \times (\mathbf{v}_{B/O})_{xyz} \tag{b}$$

where
$(\mathbf{r}_{B/O})_{xyz} = L\mathbf{i}$;
$\mathbf{v}_O = \mathbf{0}, \mathbf{a}_O = \mathbf{0}$, since the truck is assumed stationary;
$(\mathbf{v}_{B/O})_{xyz} = -v\mathbf{i}$
$(\mathbf{a}_{B/O})_{xyz} = \mathbf{0}$, since the rate at which the boom is retracted is constant
$\mathbf{\Omega} = -\omega\mathbf{k}$, since the boom is lowered and thus the rotation is clockwise (i.e., negative)

(*continued*)

EXAMPLE 6.12   (*concluded*)

Substituting the above values into Equation (a), the velocity of point B becomes

$$\mathbf{v}_B = \underbrace{\mathbf{v}_O}_{=\,0} - v\mathbf{i} - \omega\mathbf{k} \times L\mathbf{i}$$

$$\mathbf{v}_B = -v\mathbf{i} - \omega L\mathbf{j} \blacktriangleleft$$

The magnitude of the velocity vector of B can now be obtained from

$$v_B = (v^2 + \omega^2 L^2)^{1/2}$$

We evaluate the velocity vector's inclination from the horizontal by writing it as

$$(90° - \theta°) + \beta°$$

where $\beta = \tan^{-1}(v/\omega L)$.

Substituting the appropriate values of $\mathbf{r}_{B/O} = L\mathbf{i}$, $\mathbf{a}_O = \mathbf{0}$, $(\mathbf{v}_{B/O})_{xyz} = -v\mathbf{i}$, $(\mathbf{a}_{B/O})_{xyz} = \mathbf{0}$, $\boldsymbol{\Omega} = -\omega\mathbf{k}$, and $\dot{\boldsymbol{\Omega}} = \mathbf{0}$

into Equation (b), we obtain the acceleration vector of point B as

$$\mathbf{a}_B = \underbrace{\mathbf{a}_O}_{=\,0} + \underbrace{(\mathbf{a}_{B/O})_{xyz}}_{=\,0} + \underbrace{\dot{\boldsymbol{\Omega}}}_{=\,0} \times L\mathbf{i} - \omega\mathbf{k}$$
$$\times [-\omega\mathbf{k} \times L\mathbf{i}] + 2(-\omega\mathbf{k}) \times (-v\mathbf{i})$$
$$\mathbf{a}_B = -\omega^2 L\mathbf{i} + 2\omega v\mathbf{j} \blacktriangleleft$$

The magnitude of the acceleration vector becomes

$$a_B = [\omega^4 L^2 + 4\omega^2 v^2]^{1/2}$$

The acceleration vector's inclination from the horizontal is $(\beta' - \theta)$

where $\beta' = \tan^{-1}\left(\dfrac{2\omega v}{\omega^2 L}\right) = \tan^{-1}\left(\dfrac{2v}{\omega L}\right)$.

EXAMPLE 6.13

Collar A slides along a horizontal rod that is rotating as shown with an angular speed $\omega = 5$ rad/s and an angular acceleration $\alpha = 5$ rad/s^2. At a distance of 7 ft from the axis of rotation of the rod, the collar has a velocity of 10 ft/s and an acceleration of 4 ft/s^2 relative to the rod. Determine the velocity and acceleration of the collar at the instant shown.

Solution   The origin of both the fixed and moving frames of reference are at point O, with the x axis of the moving frame being attached to and moving with the horizontal rod OA.

The governing kinematic equations are Equations (6.28) and (6.36), written in terms of points O and A as

$$\mathbf{v}_A = \mathbf{v}_O + (\mathbf{v}_{A/O})_{xyz} + \boldsymbol{\Omega} \times (\mathbf{r}_{A/O})_{xyz} \qquad \text{(a)}$$

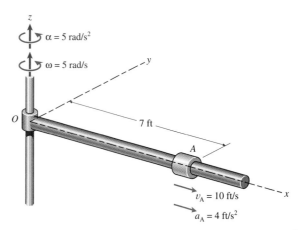

(continued)

EXAMPLE 6.13   *(concluded)*

and

$$\mathbf{a}_A = \mathbf{a}_O + (\mathbf{a}_{A/O})_{xyz} + \dot{\Omega} \times (\mathbf{r}_{A/O})_{xyz}$$
$$+ \, \Omega \times [\Omega \times (\mathbf{r}_{A/O})_{xyz}] + 2\Omega \times (\mathbf{v}_{A/O})_{xyz} \quad \text{(b)}$$

where $\mathbf{r}_{A/O} = 7\mathbf{i}\,(\text{ft})$ $\mathbf{a}_{A/O} = 4\mathbf{i}\,(\text{ft/s})$
           $\mathbf{v}_O = 0$ $\Omega = 5\mathbf{k}\,(\text{rad/s})$
           $\mathbf{v}_{A/O} = 10\mathbf{i}\,(\text{ft/s})$ $\dot{\Omega} = 5\mathbf{k}\,(\text{rad/s}^2)$
           $\mathbf{a}_O = 0$

Equation (a) will yield

$$\mathbf{v}_A = 0 + 10\mathbf{i} + [(5\mathbf{k}) \times (7\mathbf{i})]$$
$$\mathbf{v}_A = 10\mathbf{i} + 35\mathbf{j}\,(\text{ft/s}) \quad \blacktriangleleft$$

Substituting the data into Equation (b), we obtain

$$\mathbf{a}_A = 0 + 4\mathbf{i} + [(5\mathbf{k}) \times (7\mathbf{i})] + (5\mathbf{k}) \times [(5\mathbf{k}) \times (7\mathbf{i})]$$
$$+ \, 2(5\mathbf{k}) \times (10\mathbf{i})$$
$$\mathbf{a}_A = 4\mathbf{i} + 35\mathbf{j} - 175\mathbf{i} + 100\mathbf{j}$$

and after collecting terms, we have

$$\mathbf{a}_A = -171\mathbf{i} + 135\mathbf{j}\,(\text{ft/s}^2) \quad \blacktriangleleft$$

EXAMPLE 6.14

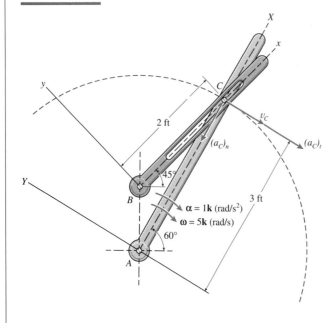

Link *AC* moves with an angular velocity of 5 rad/s and an angular acceleration of 1 rad/s². The angular motion of *AC* is transferred to link *BC* by a combination pin-slot, with the pin at *C* being attached to *AC* and moving within the slot of link *BC*. At the instant shown, determine the angular velocity and angular acceleration of link *BC*.

Solution   With the moving frame of reference attached to the shaft at *B*, the kinematic equations governing the motion of point *C* are given by Equations (6.28) and (6.36); thus,

$$\mathbf{v}_C = \mathbf{v}_B + (\mathbf{v}_{C/B}) + \Omega_{CB} \times (\mathbf{r}_{C/B}) \quad \text{(a)}$$

and

$$\mathbf{a}_C = \mathbf{a}_B + \mathbf{a}_{C/B} + \dot{\Omega}_{CB} \times \mathbf{r}_{C/B} + \Omega_{CB} \times (\Omega_{CB} \times \mathbf{r}_{C/B})$$
$$+ \, 2\Omega_{CB} \times \mathbf{v}_{C/B} \quad \text{(b)}$$

where $\mathbf{v}_B = 0$, $\mathbf{a}_B = 0$, $\Omega_{CB} = \Omega_{CB}\mathbf{k}$, $\dot{\Omega}_{CB} = \dot{\Omega}_{CB}\mathbf{k}$, and $\mathbf{r}_{C/B} = 2\mathbf{i}$. The motion of pin *C* can also be expressed with respect to the rotation ω_{AC} of link *AC* about point *A*, by writing

$$\mathbf{v}_C = (v_C)_x\mathbf{i} + (v_C)_y\mathbf{j}$$

where $(v_C)_x = [\omega_{AC}(r_{C/A})]\sin 15° = 5(3)\sin 15°$, and

$$(v_C)_y = -[\omega_{AC}(r_{C/A})]\cos 15° = -5(3)\cos 15°$$

(continued)

EXAMPLE   6.14   *(concluded)*

Also, we have

$$\mathbf{a}_C = (a_C)_x\mathbf{i} + (a_C)_y\mathbf{j}$$

where $(a_C)_x = (a_C)_t \sin 15° - (a_C)_n \cos 15°$
$(a_C)_y = (a_C)_t \cos 15° - (a_C)_n \sin 15°$
$(a_C)_t = \alpha_{AC}(r_{C/A}) = (1)3 = 3 \text{ ft/s}^2$
$(a_C)_n = \omega^2(r_{C/A}) = (5)^2(3) = 75 \text{ ft/s}^2$

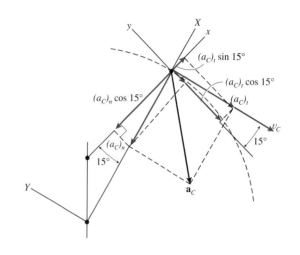

Thus, we write

$$\mathbf{v}_C = 15 \sin 15°\mathbf{i} - 15 \cos 15°\mathbf{j}$$

$$\mathbf{v}_C = 3.882\mathbf{i} - 14.489\mathbf{j}\,(\text{ft/s}) \tag{c}$$

and

$$\mathbf{a}_C = (3 \sin 15° - 75 \cos 15°)\mathbf{i}$$
$$+ (-3 \cos 15° - 75 \sin 15°)\mathbf{j}$$
$$\mathbf{a}_C = -71.668\mathbf{i} - 22.309\mathbf{j}\,(\text{ft/s}^2) \tag{d}$$

Recalling that the pin C is confined to move within the slot along the x axis, we write

$$\mathbf{a}_{C/B} = a_{C/B}\mathbf{i}$$

Substituting for $\mathbf{v}_C$ in Equation (a) from Equation (c) we obtain, since $\mathbf{v}_B = \mathbf{0}$,

$$(3.882\mathbf{i} - 14.489\mathbf{j}) = v_{C/B}\mathbf{i} + \Omega_{CB}\mathbf{k} \times 2\mathbf{i}$$

$$3.882\mathbf{i} - 14.489\mathbf{j} = v_{C/B}\mathbf{i} + 2\Omega_{CB}\mathbf{j}$$

Equating $\mathbf{i}$ and $\mathbf{j}$ components yields

$$v_{C/B} = 3.882 \text{ ft/s}$$
$$\Omega_{CB} = -7.245 \text{ rad/s} \circlearrowright \quad \blacktriangleleft$$

Next, substituting for $\mathbf{a}_C$ in Equation (b) from Equation (d) we have

$$-71.668\mathbf{i} - 22.309\mathbf{j} =$$
$$a_{C/B}\mathbf{i} + \dot{\Omega}_{CB}\mathbf{k} \times 2\mathbf{i} - (-7.245)^2\mathbf{r}_{C/B} + 2\mathbf{\Omega}_{CB} \times \mathbf{v}_{C/B}$$
$$-71.668\mathbf{i} - 22.309\mathbf{j} = a_{C/B}\mathbf{i} + 2\dot{\Omega}_{CB}\mathbf{j} - (52.49)(2\mathbf{i})$$
$$+ 2(-7.245\mathbf{k}) \times (3.882\mathbf{i})$$
$$-71.67\mathbf{i} - 22.31\mathbf{j} = (a_{C/B} - 104.98)\mathbf{i} + (2\dot{\Omega}_{CB} - 56.25)\mathbf{j}$$

Equating $\mathbf{i}$ and $\mathbf{j}$ components of the above equation we can solve for $a_{C/B}$ and $\dot{\Omega}_{CB}$ as

$$a_{C/B} = 33.31 \text{ ft/s}^2$$
$$\dot{\Omega}_{CB} = \alpha_{CB} = +16.97 \text{ rad/s}^2 \circlearrowright \quad \blacktriangleleft$$

*6.9 ROTATION OF A RIGID BODY ABOUT A FIXED POINT

In Section 6.3, when we considered the rotation of a rigid body about a fixed axis, we noted that the angular velocity $\boldsymbol{\omega}$ remains fixed in direction, varying only in magnitude with time. Now we are about to introduce a new concept of rotation. When a rigid body is free to *rotate about a fixed point*, the motion of the body will be considered to consist of a series of infinitesimal angular displacements $\Delta\boldsymbol{\theta}$ each about an *instantaneous axis of rotation*. The angular velocity vector $\boldsymbol{\omega}$ will no longer maintain a constant orientation but will, at any instant, be collinear with the angular displacement vector $\Delta\boldsymbol{\theta}$ and still be defined at any given instant as

$$\boldsymbol{\omega} = \lim_{\Delta t \to 0} \frac{\Delta\boldsymbol{\theta}}{\Delta t} = \frac{d\boldsymbol{\theta}}{dt} = \dot{\boldsymbol{\theta}}$$

It is important to note that the angular displacements ($\Delta\boldsymbol{\theta}$) and the angular velocities ($\boldsymbol{\omega}$) obey the vector addition laws. Indeed, from Figure 6.10 one can see that the addition of two infinitesimal rotations $d\boldsymbol{\theta}_A$ and $d\boldsymbol{\theta}_B$ of a rigid body about the corresponding axes OA and OB results in the displacement vector $[(d\boldsymbol{\theta}_A \times \mathbf{r}) + (d\boldsymbol{\theta}_B \times \mathbf{r})]$, irrespective of the order in which they are added. We conclude that the corresponding angular velocities $\boldsymbol{\omega}_A = \dot{\boldsymbol{\theta}}_A$ and $\boldsymbol{\omega}_B = \dot{\boldsymbol{\theta}}_B$ too may be added vectorially to obtain

$$\boldsymbol{\omega} = \boldsymbol{\omega}_A + \boldsymbol{\omega}_B \tag{6.37}$$

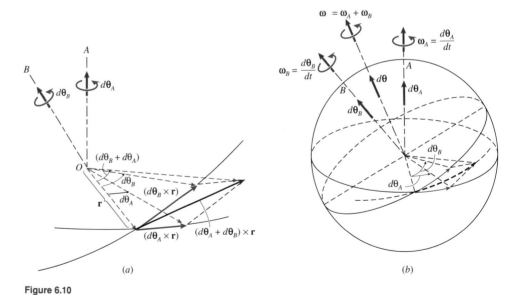

(a)   (b)

Figure 6.10

This conclusion can be applied to any case involving more than two rotations, since they can be combined into pairs until the final pair is reduced and combined to form a single rotation of the rigid body about an axis passing through the fixed point.

The above observation is known as *Euler's theorem* (Leonard Euler, Swiss scientist, 1707–1783). It states that at any given instant, *the motion of a rigid body about a fixed point O is equivalent to the rotation of the body about an axis through O*, called the *instantaneous axis of rotation*. This axis is collinear with the angular displacement vector $d\boldsymbol{\theta}$. The instantaneous velocity and acceleration of any given point of the body may now be obtained as in Section 6.3, by writing

$$\mathbf{v} = \dot{\mathbf{r}} = \boldsymbol{\omega} \times \mathbf{r} \qquad (6.38)$$

$$\mathbf{a} = \boldsymbol{\alpha} \times \mathbf{r} + \boldsymbol{\omega} \times (\boldsymbol{\omega} \times \mathbf{r}) \qquad (6.39)$$

where $\boldsymbol{\alpha}$ is the angular acceleration of the body and is given as the time derivative of the angular velocity vector $\boldsymbol{\omega}$:

$$\boldsymbol{\alpha} = \dot{\boldsymbol{\omega}} \qquad (6.40)$$

The major difference between planar motion—rotation about a fixed axis—and the motion of a rigid body about a fixed point is the relationship between the angular velocity $\boldsymbol{\omega}$ and the *angular acceleration* vector $\boldsymbol{\alpha}$. In planar motion they are collinear, whereas in three-dimensional motion—rotation about a fixed point—the angular velocity vector may change both in magnitude and direction and, in general, is not collinear with the instantaneous axis of rotation. The angular acceleration $\boldsymbol{\alpha}$ will change the magnitude *and* the direction of $\boldsymbol{\omega}$. Earlier, in discussing the time derivative of the position vector $\mathbf{r}$ in Section 6.3 (Figure 6.2), we saw that the operator $\left(\dfrac{d}{dt}\right)$ acting on the position vector

OP will yield the velocity vector representing the rate of displacement of the tip P of the vector **OP**. Hence, we conclude that, given $\boldsymbol{\alpha} = \dfrac{d}{dt}(\boldsymbol{\omega})$, the acceleration vector $\boldsymbol{\alpha}$ represents the velocity of the tip of the angular velocity vector $\boldsymbol{\omega}$, and if the vector $\boldsymbol{\omega}$ describes a curve in space (Figure 6.11) then $\boldsymbol{\alpha}$ is tangent to it at the tip of $\boldsymbol{\omega}$. As the rigid body rotates freely about a fixed point O, the instantaneous axis of rotation of the body assumes different orientations at every instant, always passing through O. The locus of points defined by the line of action of $\boldsymbol{\omega}$ generates a fixed cone, about the fixed frame of reference, called the **space cone**. However, if the line of action of $\boldsymbol{\omega}$ is viewed relative to the rotating body, the rotational axis generates another cone

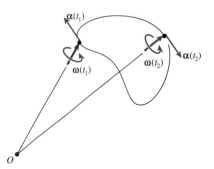

O

Figure 6.11

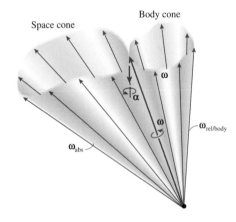

Figure 6.12

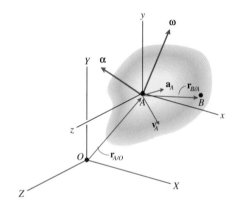

Figure 6.13

called the **body cone**. As shown in Figure 6.12, the body cone rolls on the space cone. When the body's rotation about an instantaneous axis is steady, the cones are right-circular cones; however, when the instantaneous axis has an unsteady rotation, the cones are no longer right-circular even though the body cone will still roll over the space cone.

*6.10 GENERAL SPATIAL MOTION RELATIVE TO A TRANSLATING FRAME OF REFERENCE

The most general motion to which a rigid body may be subjected is the three-dimensional or spatial motion involving translation and rotation in space. The velocity of a point B with respect to the fixed frame of reference XYZ (Figure 6.13) was developed in Section 6.5 in the form of Equation (6.18).

$$\mathbf{v}_B = \mathbf{v}_A + \mathbf{v}_{B/A}$$

where $\mathbf{v}_{B/A}$ is the velocity of B relative to the translating frame of reference xyz with its origin at A. The frame xyz is attached to the body at A, so the body's motion observed from the frame xyz will be that of a body rotating in space about a fixed point A. Thus, upon substituting for the relative velocity $\mathbf{v}_{B/A}$ the expression given by Equation (6.38), Equation (6.18) becomes

$$\mathbf{v}_B = \mathbf{v}_A + \boldsymbol{\omega} \times \mathbf{r}_{B/A} \tag{6.41}$$

where $\boldsymbol{\omega}$ is now the instantaneous angular velocity vector of the body.

The acceleration of point B with respect to the fixed frame of reference XYZ was developed in Section 6.7 as Equation (6.20) in the form

$$\mathbf{a}_B = \mathbf{a}_A + \mathbf{a}_{B/A}$$

where $\mathbf{a}_{B/A}$ is the acceleration of B relative to the translating frame of reference xyz (that is, having fixed orientation) and centered at A. The acceleration of point B, when observed from the translating frame, will appear to be that of a point on a body subjected to a spatial rotation about a point, which we established in Equation (6.39). Substituting for $\mathbf{a}_{B/A}$ from Equation (6.39) into Equation (6.20), we obtain

$$\mathbf{a}_B = \mathbf{a}_A + \boldsymbol{\alpha} \times \mathbf{r}_{B/A} + \boldsymbol{\omega} \times (\boldsymbol{\omega} \times \mathbf{r}_{B/A}) \tag{6.42}$$

where $\boldsymbol{\alpha}$ is now the instantaneous angular acceleration vector of the body.

We conclude, from Equations (6.41) and (6.42), that the most general spatial motion of a rigid body can be represented instantaneously as *the sum of a translationary motion and a rotationary motion about a fixed point*. This statement is a description of the motion at a given instant. Since the motion about the fixed point may call for the axis of rotation to change in direction constantly, the angular velocity **ω** and angular acceleration vector **α** are, in general, not collinear.

*6.11 GENERAL SPATIAL MOTION RELATIVE TO A ROTATING FRAME OF REFERENCE

In the preceding section we developed the kinematic relationships necessary when using a moving frame of reference attached to the body and allowed to translate throughout the motion of the rigid body. Such a moving coordinate system *xyz*, however, must maintain a fixed orientation; that is, *xyz* must remain parallel to the fixed coordinate axes *XYZ*. Sometimes, it is more convenient to allow the moving frame to rotate as well as translate. We will now discuss the use of such a frame and develop, once again, the pertinent kinematic relationships for the velocity and acceleration vectors. Recall that in Section 6.8, while developing the corresponding kinematic relationships for the general planar motion relative to a rotating frame of reference, we discussed the motion for the most general three-dimensional case, and the equations for the velocity and acceleration vectors were derived without limiting their applicabilities to the planar motion. The important distinction is to recognize that the expressions are developed for a given instant, and that the angular velocity **Ω** and angular acceleration **Ω̇** of the rotating frame of reference (*xyz*) will not have a common line of action (Figure 6.14).

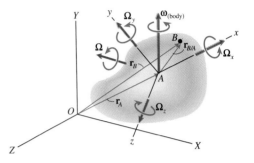

Figure 6.14

The position vector of any point *B*, relative to the fixed frame *XYZ*, will be expressed as

$$\mathbf{r}_B = \mathbf{r}_A + \mathbf{r}_{B/A} \tag{6.43}$$

where $\mathbf{r}_{B/A}$ is the position vector of *B*, relative to the moving frame *xyz* centered at *A*.

The velocity vector of any point *B* of the rigid body, relative to the fixed frame *XYZ*, will be identical to the expressions developed in Section 6.8 and given as Equation (6.28). We write

$$(\mathbf{v}_B)_{XYZ} = (\mathbf{v}_A)_{XYZ} + (\mathbf{v}_{B/A})_{xyz} + \mathbf{\Omega} \times (\mathbf{r}_{B/A})_{xyz} \tag{6.44}$$

where **Ω** is the instantaneous angular velocity of the rotating *xyz* frame of reference measured from the fixed frame *XYZ*.

The analysis carried out in Section 6.8 for the acceleration vector is applicable here too. The instantaneous absolute acceleration of any point *B* of the rigid body measured from a fixed frame *XYZ* was given in Equation (6.36) as

$$(\mathbf{a}_B)_{XYZ} = (\mathbf{a}_A)_{XYZ} + (\mathbf{a}_{B/A})_{xyz} + \mathbf{\dot{\Omega}} \times (\mathbf{r}_{B/A})_{xyz} + \mathbf{\Omega} \times [\mathbf{\Omega} \times (\mathbf{r}_{B/A})_{xyz}] \\ + 2\mathbf{\Omega} \times (\mathbf{v}_{B/A})_{xyz} \tag{6.45}$$

where $\dot{\boldsymbol{\Omega}}$ is the instantaneous angular acceleration of the rotating frame xyz measured from the fixed frame XYZ.

The significance of the various terms appearing in Equation (6.45) can be inferred from the discussion given in Section 6.8 about Equation (6.36). It must be noted that the last term on the right-hand side of Equation (6.45) (the Coriolis acceleration) is the result of a vector cross product. It is perpendicular to the vectors $\boldsymbol{\Omega}$ and $(\mathbf{v}_{B/A})_{xyz}$. In planar motion the vector $\boldsymbol{\Omega}$ is always perpendicular to the plane of motion and hence to $\mathbf{v}_{B/A}$. Thus, in planar motion, the magnitude of the Coriolis acceleration was equated to $[2\Omega(v_{B/A})]$. However, in spatial motion, the magnitude of the Coriolis acceleration is, in general, not equal to $2\Omega v_{B/A}$ since the two vectors may not be collinear.

It must also be noted that, when observed from the fixed and moving frames of reference, if the respective position vectors $\mathbf{r}_A$ and $\mathbf{r}_{B/A}$ have angular motions, then the computations of all kinematic variables involving differentiation of vector quantities must be performed using Equation (6.29), which will be given here again as

$$(\dot{\mathbf{v}})_{XYZ} = (\dot{\mathbf{v}})_{xyz} + \boldsymbol{\Omega} \times \mathbf{v} \qquad (6.46)$$

We conclude that the absolute and relative velocities $\mathbf{v}_A$ and $(\mathbf{v}_{B/A})_{xyz}$ will have to be evaluated respectively by computing $(\dot{\mathbf{r}}_A)$ and $(\dot{\mathbf{r}}_{B/A})_{xyz}$ according to Equation (6.46), and the absolute and relative accelerations $\mathbf{a}_A$ and $(\mathbf{a}_{B/A})_{xyz}$ will be obtained by calculating $(\ddot{\mathbf{r}}_A)$ and $(\ddot{\mathbf{r}}_{B/A})_{xyz}$ in a similar manner. For three-dimensional motion, $\dot{\boldsymbol{\Omega}}$ depends upon the variation of $\boldsymbol{\Omega}$ in both magnitude and direction and therefore it, too, must be evaluated by using Equation (6.46).

EXAMPLE   6.15

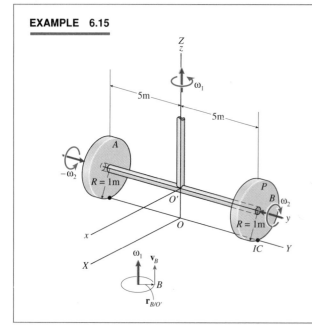

The wheels A and B (radius $R = 1$ m) roll without slipping on a horizontal surface as shown. The horizontal arm connecting the two wheels rotates counterclockwise about a vertical shaft at a constant angular speed of 5 rad/s. Determine the angular velocity and acceleration of the wheels and the acceleration of the point P on the rim of the wheel B at the instant shown.

Solution   We will consider the fixed (XYZ) and rotating (xyz) frames of reference to be coincident at the given instant. If the unit vectors of the rotating frame are $\mathbf{i}$, $\mathbf{j}$, and $\mathbf{k}$, we can express the angular velocity of the vertical shaft as $\boldsymbol{\omega}_1 = 5\mathbf{k}$ (rad/s). The end points of the horizontal arm (i.e., the centers of the wheels) thus move, from Equation (6.38), with velocities given by

$$\mathbf{v}_B = \boldsymbol{\omega}_1 \times \mathbf{r}_{B/O} = (5\mathbf{k}) \times (5\mathbf{j}) = -25\mathbf{i}\,(\text{m/s})$$

(continued)

EXAMPLE 6.15   (*concluded*)

Since wheel B rolls without slipping, at the instant shown, the instantaneous center of zero velocity IC yields, for the velocity of B,

$$\mathbf{v}_B = \boldsymbol{\omega}_2 \times \mathbf{r}_{B/IC}$$

$$\mathbf{v}_B = \omega_2 \mathbf{j} \times 1\mathbf{k} = \omega_2 \mathbf{i}$$

Equating the two expressions for $\mathbf{v}_B$, we write

$$\omega_2 \mathbf{i} = -25\mathbf{i}$$

or

$$\omega_2 = -25 \text{ rad/s (clockwise; the right-hand rule)}$$

Thus

$$\boldsymbol{\omega}_2 = -25\mathbf{j}$$

The instantaneous angular velocity vector $\boldsymbol{\omega}$ can now be expressed in terms of its two $\mathbf{i}$ and $\mathbf{j}$ components as

$$\boldsymbol{\omega} = \boldsymbol{\omega}_1 + \boldsymbol{\omega}_2 = 5\mathbf{k} - 25\mathbf{j}$$

$$\boldsymbol{\omega} = -25\mathbf{j} + 5\mathbf{k} \, (\text{rad/s}) \blacktriangleleft$$

The angular acceleration $\boldsymbol{\alpha}_B$ of the wheel, at the instant shown, is by definition the time derivative of the angular velocity $\boldsymbol{\omega}_2$ of the body, and is given from Equation (6.29) by adopting $\boldsymbol{\Omega} = \boldsymbol{\omega}_1$ and writing

$$\boldsymbol{\alpha}_B = \dot{\boldsymbol{\omega}}_2 = \boldsymbol{\omega}_1 \times \boldsymbol{\omega}_2$$

Thus, we have

$$\boldsymbol{\alpha}_B = (5\mathbf{k}) \times (-25\mathbf{j})$$

$$\boldsymbol{\alpha}_B = +125\mathbf{i} \, (\text{rad/s}^2) \, \circlearrowright \blacktriangleleft$$

The acceleration of a point P on the wheel can be evaluated from Equations (6.20) and (6.42). Thus, we write

$$\mathbf{a}_P = \mathbf{a}_B + \mathbf{a}_{P/B} \tag{a}$$

where

$$\mathbf{a}_B = \boldsymbol{\omega}_1 \times (\boldsymbol{\omega}_1 \times \mathbf{r}_{B/O}) \tag{b}$$

$$\mathbf{a}_{P/B} = (\boldsymbol{\alpha}_B \times \mathbf{r}_{P/B}) + \boldsymbol{\omega}_2 \times (\boldsymbol{\omega}_2 \times \mathbf{r}_{P/B}) \tag{c}$$

From Equation (b) we obtain

$$\mathbf{a}_B = (5\mathbf{k}) \times (5\mathbf{k} \times 5\mathbf{j}) = (5\mathbf{k}) \times (-25\mathbf{i})$$

$$\mathbf{a}_B = -125\mathbf{j} \, (\text{m/s}^2) \tag{d}$$

From Equation (c) we write

$$\mathbf{a}_{P/B} = (125\mathbf{i} \times 1\mathbf{k}) + [(-25\mathbf{j}) \times (-25\mathbf{j} \times 1\mathbf{k})]$$

$$\mathbf{a}_{P/B} = -125\mathbf{j} - 625\mathbf{k} \, (\text{m/s}^2) \tag{e}$$

Substituting $\mathbf{a}_B$ and $\mathbf{a}_{P/B}$ from Equations (d) and (e) respectively, Equation (a) becomes

$$\mathbf{a}_P = -250\mathbf{j} - 625\mathbf{k} \, (\text{m/s}^2) \blacktriangleleft$$

EXAMPLE 6.16

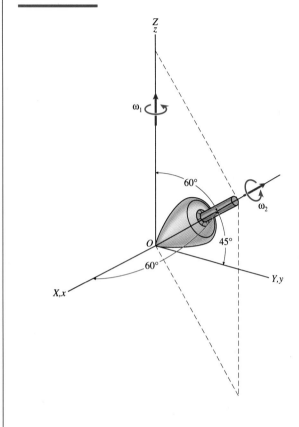

At the instant shown, a top is rotating about the z axis at a rate of 2 rad/s, while it is rotating about its own axis of symmetry at the rate of 5 rad/s. Determine the angular velocity and angular acceleration of the top at the instant shown.

Solution The angular velocity $\boldsymbol{\omega}$ of the top, when expressed in terms of its components $\boldsymbol{\omega}_1$ and $\boldsymbol{\omega}_2$, becomes

$$\boldsymbol{\omega} = \boldsymbol{\omega}_1 + \boldsymbol{\omega}_2$$

where
$$\boldsymbol{\omega}_1 = 2\mathbf{k}$$
$$\boldsymbol{\omega}_2 = 5(\cos 60°\mathbf{i} + \cos 60°\mathbf{j} + \cos 45°\mathbf{k})$$
$$= 2.5\mathbf{i} + 2.5\mathbf{j} + 3.536\mathbf{k}$$

Thus, we have

$$\boldsymbol{\omega} = 2.5\mathbf{i} + 2.5\mathbf{j} + 5.536\mathbf{k}\,(\text{rad/s}) \quad \blacktriangleleft$$

At the instant shown, the angular acceleration is $\boldsymbol{\alpha} = \dot{\boldsymbol{\omega}} = \dot{\boldsymbol{\omega}}_1 + \dot{\boldsymbol{\omega}}_2$. Considering the rotating axes xyz to have an angular velocity $\boldsymbol{\Omega} = \boldsymbol{\omega}_1$, we can evaluate the time derivatives $\dot{\boldsymbol{\omega}}_1$ and $\dot{\boldsymbol{\omega}}_2$ from Equation (6.29) as $\dot{\boldsymbol{\omega}}_1 = 0$, since $\boldsymbol{\omega}_1 = $ constant. Also,

$$\dot{\boldsymbol{\omega}}_2 = (\dot{\boldsymbol{\omega}}_2)_{xyz} + \boldsymbol{\omega}_1 \times \boldsymbol{\omega}_2$$
$$= 0 + (2\mathbf{k}) \times (2.5\mathbf{i} + 2.5\mathbf{j} + 5.536\mathbf{k})$$
$$\dot{\boldsymbol{\omega}}_2 = -5\mathbf{i} + 5\mathbf{j}$$

Substituting $\dot{\boldsymbol{\omega}}_1$ and $\dot{\boldsymbol{\omega}}_2$ into the expression for $\boldsymbol{\alpha}$, we obtain

$$\boldsymbol{\alpha} = -5\mathbf{i} + 5\mathbf{j}\,(\text{rad/s}^2) \quad \blacktriangleleft$$

EXAMPLE 6.17

At a given instant, the radar dish shown is rotating about the x and y axes with angular velocities of 5 and 3 rad/s, respectively. Both rates of rotation are, at the same instant, increasing at 5 rad/s^2. Determine the angular velocity and angular acceleration of the radar dish.

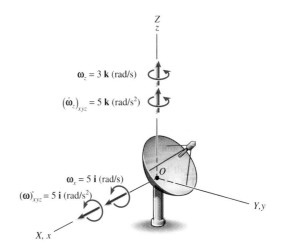

Solution Considering the fixed (XYZ) and rotating (xyz) coordinate frames to be coincident at the given instant, we can express the angular velocity of the dish in terms of its components as

$$\boldsymbol{\omega} = \boldsymbol{\omega}_z + \boldsymbol{\omega}_x \qquad \text{(a)}$$

where $\boldsymbol{\omega}_z = 3\mathbf{k}$ and $\boldsymbol{\omega}_x = 5\mathbf{i}$. Thus the instantaneous angular velocity of the radar dish is given by

$$\boldsymbol{\omega} = 5\mathbf{i} + 3\mathbf{k}\,(\text{rad/s}) \quad \blacktriangleleft$$

From Equation (a) we have

$$\boldsymbol{\alpha} = \dot{\boldsymbol{\omega}} = \dot{\boldsymbol{\omega}}_z + \dot{\boldsymbol{\omega}}_x \qquad \text{(b)}$$

By considering a rotating coordinate system (xyz) with $\boldsymbol{\Omega} = \boldsymbol{\omega}_z$ about the vertical axis, we can now determine the time derivatives $\dot{\boldsymbol{\omega}}_z$ and $\dot{\boldsymbol{\omega}}_x$ from Equation (6.29). We write

$$\dot{\boldsymbol{\omega}}_z = (\dot{\boldsymbol{\omega}}_z)_{xyz} + \boldsymbol{\omega}_z \times \boldsymbol{\omega}_z$$

where $(\dot{\boldsymbol{\omega}}_z)_{xyz} = 5\mathbf{k}$ and the second term on the right-hand side is zero from vector calculus. Thus we have

$$\dot{\boldsymbol{\omega}}_z = 5\mathbf{k} \qquad \text{(c)}$$

Next, we write from Equation (6.29),

$$\dot{\boldsymbol{\omega}}_x = (\dot{\boldsymbol{\omega}}_x)_{xyz} + (\boldsymbol{\omega}_z \times \boldsymbol{\omega}_x)$$

With $\boldsymbol{\Omega} = \boldsymbol{\omega}_z = 3\mathbf{k}$ and $(\dot{\boldsymbol{\omega}}_x)_{xyz} = 5\mathbf{i}$, we obtain

$$\dot{\boldsymbol{\omega}}_x = 5\mathbf{i} + (3\mathbf{k} \times 5\mathbf{i}) = 5\mathbf{i} + 15\mathbf{j} \qquad \text{(d)}$$

Substituting for $\dot{\boldsymbol{\omega}}_z$ and $\dot{\boldsymbol{\omega}}_x$ from Equations (c) and (d) into Equation (b) we obtain the instantaneous angular acceleration of the radar dish as

$$\boldsymbol{\alpha} = 5\mathbf{i} + 15\mathbf{j} + 5\mathbf{k}\,(\text{rad/s}^2) \quad \blacktriangleleft$$

EXAMPLE 6.18

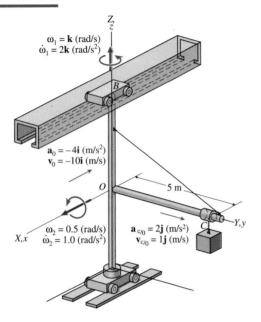

$\omega_1 = \mathbf{k}$ (rad/s)
$\dot{\omega}_1 = 2\mathbf{k}$ (rad/s²)

B

$\mathbf{a}_0 = -4\mathbf{i}$ (m/s²)
$\mathbf{v}_0 = -10\mathbf{i}$ (m/s)

O 5 m

$\omega_2 = 0.5$ (rad/s) $\mathbf{a}_{c/0} = 2\mathbf{j}$ (m/s²) Y,y
X,x $\dot{\omega}_2 = 1.0$ (rad/s²) $\mathbf{v}_{c/0} = 1\mathbf{j}$ (m/s) C

At a given instant, a crane moves along a track with a velocity of 10 m/s and accelerates at a rate of 4 m/s², while simultaneously it pivots about its vertical axis with an angular velocity of 1 rad/s and an angular acceleration of 2 rad/s², as shown. A boom OC, fastened through a horizontal pivot to the vertical post of the crane, supports a carriage C that moves outwardly along the boom with a relative speed of 1 m/s and a relative acceleration of 2 m/s². At the given instant, the boom is raised about its pivot O, as shown, with an angular velocity of 0.5 rad/s and an angular acceleration of 1 rad/s². Determine the velocity and acceleration of the carriage.

Solution   At the given instant, we will consider the fixed XYZ and rotating xyz coordinate axes to be coincident as shown. A judicious selection of the xyz frame can significantly reduce the computations, since the angular velocity can then be easily expressed in terms of its components. From the definition of the problem we note that, since z and Z axes are collinear, during the rotation of the vertical post of the crane the angular acceleration vector $\boldsymbol{\omega}_1$ will not change direction. But the angular velocity vector $\boldsymbol{\omega}_2$ *will* change direction under the action of $\boldsymbol{\omega}_1$. Thus we have $\boldsymbol{\Omega} = \boldsymbol{\omega}_1$ in Equation (6.44) to yield

$$\mathbf{v}_C = \mathbf{v}_O + (\mathbf{v}_{C/O})_{xyz} + [\boldsymbol{\omega}_1 \times (\mathbf{r}_{C/O})] \qquad \text{(a)}$$

where $\boldsymbol{\omega}_1 = \mathbf{k}$ (rad/s), $\mathbf{v}_O = -10\mathbf{i}$ (m/s), and $(\mathbf{r}_{C/O}) = +5\mathbf{j}$ (m). However, when observed from the moving frame of reference, $\mathbf{r}_{C/O}$ has an angular motion caused by $\boldsymbol{\omega}_2$; therefore, the kinematic parameters $(\mathbf{v}_{C/O})_{xyz}$ and $(\mathbf{a}_{C/O})_{xyz}$ describing the motion of the carriage with respect to the moving reference frame xyz must be determined by applying Equation (6.29). This means computing $\dot{\mathbf{r}}_{C/O}$ and $\mathbf{r}_{C/O}$ in the frame xyz which is rotating with $\boldsymbol{\omega}_2$ about the vertical Z axis.

Thus we write, from Equation (6.29), with $\boldsymbol{\Omega}_{C/O} = \boldsymbol{\omega}_2$,

$$(\mathbf{v}_{C/O})_{xyz} = (\dot{\mathbf{r}}_{C/O})_{xyz} = \frac{d}{dt}(\mathbf{r}_{C/O}) + \boldsymbol{\omega}_2 \times \mathbf{r}_{C/O}$$

$$= (\dot{\mathbf{r}}_{C/O})_{xyz} + \boldsymbol{\omega}_2 \times \mathbf{r}_{C/O} \qquad \text{(b)}$$

where $(\dot{\mathbf{r}}_{C/O})_{xyz} = (1.0)\mathbf{j}$ (m/s) and $\boldsymbol{\omega}_2 = 0.5\mathbf{i}$ (rad/s). Substituting for $(\dot{\mathbf{r}}_{C/O})_{xyz}$ and $\boldsymbol{\omega}_2$ from above, we obtain for Equation (b)

$$(\mathbf{v}_{C/O})_{xyz} = \mathbf{j} + (0.5\mathbf{i} \times 5\mathbf{j}) = \mathbf{j} + 2.5\mathbf{k}$$

(continued)

EXAMPLE   6.18   *(continued)*

Finally, Equation (a) is reduced to

$$\mathbf{v}_C = -10\mathbf{i} + (\mathbf{j} + 2.5\mathbf{k}) + (\mathbf{k} \times 5\mathbf{j})$$

$$= -10\mathbf{i} + \mathbf{j} + 2.5\mathbf{k} - 5\mathbf{i}$$

$$\mathbf{v}_C = -15\mathbf{i} + \mathbf{j} + 2.5\mathbf{k}\,(\text{m/s}) \blacktriangleleft$$

Next, we consider the instantaneous linear-acceleration vector of the carriage. From Equation (6.45) we write

$$\mathbf{a}_C = \mathbf{a}_O + (\mathbf{a}_{C/O})_{xyz} + \dot{\mathbf{\Omega}} \times (\mathbf{r}_{C/O}) + \mathbf{\Omega} \times [\mathbf{\Omega} \times (\mathbf{r}_{C/O})]$$
$$+ 2\mathbf{\Omega} \times (\mathbf{v}_{C/O})_{xyz}$$

Again, the *xyz* frame rotates about the *Z* axis of the fixed frame *XYZ* with $\mathbf{\omega}_1$. Thus in the above equation $\mathbf{\Omega} = \mathbf{\omega}_1$, and we write

$$\mathbf{a}_C = \mathbf{a}_O + (\mathbf{a}_{C/O})_{xyz} + (\dot{\mathbf{\omega}}_1 \times \mathbf{r}_{C/O}) + \mathbf{\omega}_1 \times (\mathbf{\omega}_1 \times \mathbf{r}_{C/O})$$
$$+ 2\mathbf{\omega}_1 \times (\mathbf{v}_{C/O})_{xyz} \tag{c}$$

However, the position vector ($\mathbf{r}_{C/O}$) of the carriage *C* has a rotational motion $\mathbf{\omega}_2$ about the *x* axis when observed from the vertically rotating *xyz* frame. It follows that the vector differentiations representing the kinematic parameters of the motion—its velocities and accelerations relative to the *xyz* frame—must be determined by applying Equation (6.29) to the computation of $(\mathbf{a}_{C/O})_{xyz}$, just as it was in calculating $(\mathbf{v}_{C/O})_{xyz}$. Thus we write for $(\mathbf{a}_{C/O})_{xyz}$ with $\mathbf{\omega}_2 = 0.5\mathbf{i}$ (rad/s) and $\dot{\mathbf{\omega}}_2 = (1.0)\mathbf{i}$ (rad/s²),

$$(\mathbf{a}_{C/O})_{xyz} = \frac{d}{dt}\left[\frac{d}{dt}(\mathbf{r}_{C/O})\right]_{xyz}$$

$$= \frac{d}{dt}[(\dot{\mathbf{r}}_{C/O})_{x'y'z'} + \mathbf{\omega}_2 \times (\mathbf{r}_{C/O})]_{xyz}$$

$$= \frac{d}{dt}[(\dot{\mathbf{r}}_{C/O})_{x'y'z'}]_{xyz} + \frac{d}{dt}[\mathbf{\omega}_2 \times (\mathbf{r}_{C/O})]_{xyz}$$

where *x'y'z'* represents a nonrotating frame of reference coincident with *xyz* at the given instant.

$$(\mathbf{a}_{C/O})_{xyz} = [(\ddot{\mathbf{r}}_{C/O}) + \mathbf{\omega}_2 \times (\dot{\mathbf{r}}_{C/O})]_{x'y'z'}$$
$$+ [(\dot{\mathbf{\omega}}_2 \times (\mathbf{r}_{C/O}) + (\mathbf{\omega}_2 \times (\dot{\mathbf{r}}_{C/O})_{xyz}]_{xyz}$$
$$= (\mathbf{a}_{C/O})_{x'y'z'} + (\mathbf{\omega}_2 \times \mathbf{v}_{C/O})_{x'y'z'}$$
$$+ (\dot{\mathbf{\omega}}_2 \times \mathbf{r}_{C/O}) + [\mathbf{\omega}_2 \times (\mathbf{v}_{C/O})_{xyz}]$$
$$(\mathbf{a}_{C/O})_{xyz} = 2\mathbf{j} + [0.5\mathbf{i} \times (1.0)\mathbf{j}] + (\mathbf{i} \times 5\mathbf{j})$$
$$+ [(0.5\mathbf{i}) \times (\mathbf{j} + 2.5\mathbf{k})]$$

Recall that we have already established that $(\mathbf{v}_{C/O})_{xyz} = \mathbf{j} + 2.5\mathbf{k}$. Expanding and rearranging terms, the expression above is reduced to

$$(\mathbf{a}_{C/O})_{xyz} = 0.75\mathbf{j} + 6\mathbf{k} \tag{d}$$

Now we can introduce Equation (d) into Equation (c) to obtain

$$\mathbf{a}_C = \mathbf{a}_O + (0.75\mathbf{j} + 6\mathbf{k}) + (\dot{\mathbf{\omega}}_1 \times \mathbf{r}_{C/O})$$
$$+ \mathbf{\omega}_1 \times (\mathbf{\omega}_1 \times \mathbf{r}_{C/O}) + 2\mathbf{\omega}_1 \times (\mathbf{v}_{C/O})_{xyz} \tag{e}$$

where $\mathbf{a}_O$ is the absolute acceleration of the origin of the *xyz* frame relative to the *XYZ* frame. Thus we write from Equation (6.45), when $\mathbf{\Omega} = \mathbf{\omega}_1$,

$$\mathbf{a}_O = \mathbf{a}_{O/XYZ} + \dot{\mathbf{\omega}}_1 \times \mathbf{r}_{O/XYZ} + \mathbf{\omega}_1 \times (\mathbf{\omega}_1 \times \mathbf{r}_{O/XYZ})$$
$$+ 2\mathbf{\omega}_1 \times (\mathbf{v}_{O/XYZ})$$
$$= -4\mathbf{i} + 2\mathbf{k} \times (-10\mathbf{i})$$
$$= -4\mathbf{i} - 20\mathbf{j} \tag{f}$$

Next we evaluate the term $(\dot{\mathbf{\omega}}_1 \times \mathbf{r}_{C/O})$ as

$$(\dot{\mathbf{\omega}}_1 \times \mathbf{r}_{C/O}) = (2\mathbf{k}) \times (5\mathbf{j}) = -10\mathbf{i} \tag{g}$$

The expression $\mathbf{\omega}_1 \times (\mathbf{\omega}_1 \times \mathbf{r}_{C/O})$ becomes

$$\mathbf{\omega}_1 \times (\mathbf{\omega}_1 \times \mathbf{r}_{C/O}) = \mathbf{k} \times (\mathbf{k} \times 5\mathbf{j}) = \mathbf{k} \times (-5\mathbf{i})$$
$$= -5\mathbf{j} \tag{h}$$

And we also have

$$2\mathbf{\omega}_1 \times (\mathbf{v}_{C/O})_{xyz} = 2\mathbf{k} \times (\mathbf{j} + 2.5\mathbf{k})$$
$$= -2\mathbf{i} \tag{i}$$

Now, introducing the expressions given by Equations (f), (g), (h), and (i) into Equation (e), we obtain

$$\mathbf{a}_C = (-4\mathbf{i} - 20\mathbf{j}) + (0.75\mathbf{j} + 6\mathbf{k}) - 10\mathbf{i} - 5\mathbf{j} - 2\mathbf{i}$$
$$\mathbf{a}_C = -16\mathbf{i} - 24.25\mathbf{j} + 6\mathbf{k}\,(\text{m/s}^2) \blacktriangleleft$$

Alternate approach.   These answers can also be obtained by observing that the rotational motion of the moving coordinate frame *xyz* consists of two components, which can be expressed as

$$\mathbf{\Omega} = \mathbf{\omega}_1 + \mathbf{\omega}_2 = \mathbf{k} + 0.5\mathbf{i}$$

The velocity of the carriage can, again, be given as

$$\mathbf{v}_C = (\mathbf{v}_{C/O})_{xyz} + \mathbf{\Omega} \times \mathbf{r}_{C/O} + \mathbf{v}_O$$

(continued)

EXAMPLE 6.18 *(concluded)*

However, when now observed from the moving frame of reference *xyz*, the position vector $\mathbf{r}_{C/O}$ of the carriage *does not* have an angular motion since $\boldsymbol{\omega}_2$ is included in the motion of *xyz*. This permits us to write $(\mathbf{v}_{C/O})_{xyz} = (1.0)\mathbf{j}$ (m/s), and the velocity $\mathbf{v}_C$ becomes

$$\mathbf{v}_C = (1.0)\mathbf{j} + (0.5\mathbf{i} + \mathbf{k}) \times (5\mathbf{j}) - 10\mathbf{i}$$

$$= \mathbf{j} + 2.5\mathbf{k} - 5\mathbf{i} - 10\mathbf{i}$$

$$\mathbf{v}_C = -15\mathbf{i} + \mathbf{j} + 2.5\mathbf{k} \text{ (m/s)} \blacktriangleleft$$

The acceleration of the carriage *C* can also be evaluated by considering the resultant rotational velocity $\boldsymbol{\Omega}$ as the summation of its two component vectors $\boldsymbol{\omega}_1$ and $\boldsymbol{\omega}_2$. We write

$$\boldsymbol{\Omega} = \boldsymbol{\omega}_1 + \boldsymbol{\omega}_2 = \mathbf{k} + 0.5\mathbf{i}$$

and

$$\dot{\boldsymbol{\Omega}} = \dot{\boldsymbol{\omega}}_1 + \dot{\boldsymbol{\omega}}_2 = 2\mathbf{k} + \mathbf{i}$$

The above expressions for $\boldsymbol{\Omega}$ and $\dot{\boldsymbol{\Omega}}$ will enable us to express the acceleration of *C* using Equation (6.45) by writing

$$\mathbf{a}_C = \mathbf{a}_O + (\dot{\boldsymbol{\Omega}} \times \mathbf{r}_{C/O}) + \boldsymbol{\Omega} \times (\boldsymbol{\Omega} \times \mathbf{r}_{C/O})$$
$$+ 2\boldsymbol{\Omega} \times (\mathbf{v}_{C/O})_{xyz} + (\mathbf{a}_{C/O})_{xyz}$$

where $\mathbf{a}_O = \mathbf{a}_{O/XYZ} = -4\mathbf{i} - 20\mathbf{j}\,(\text{m/s}^2)$ from Equation (f)
$\boldsymbol{\Omega} = \mathbf{k} + 0.5\mathbf{i}\,(\text{rad/s})$
$\dot{\boldsymbol{\Omega}} = 2\mathbf{k} + \mathbf{i}\,(\text{rad/s}^2)$
$\mathbf{r}_{C/O} = 5\mathbf{j}\,(\text{m})$
$(\mathbf{v}_{C/O})_{xyz} = 1\mathbf{j}\,(\text{m/s})$
$(\mathbf{a}_{C/O})_{xyz} = 2\mathbf{j}\,(\text{m/s}^2)$

Substituting the above into the expression for $\mathbf{a}_C$, we obtain

$$\mathbf{a}_C = (-4\mathbf{i} - 20\mathbf{j}) + [(2\mathbf{k} + \mathbf{i}) \times 5\mathbf{j}] + \{(\mathbf{k} + 0.5\mathbf{i})$$
$$\times [(\mathbf{k} + 0.5\mathbf{i}) \times 5\mathbf{j}]\} + 2(\mathbf{k} + 0.5\mathbf{i}) \times (\mathbf{j}) + 2\mathbf{j}$$

$$\mathbf{a}_C = -16\mathbf{i} - 24.25\mathbf{j} + 6\mathbf{k} \text{ (m/s}^2) \blacktriangleleft$$

which is identical to the answer obtained by the previous approach.

6.12 SUMMARY

In this chapter, we have learned the following:

1.   The velocity and acceleration of any arbitrary point *B* of a body subjected to a translation is completely defined by the motion of a single point *A* within the body.

$$\mathbf{v}_B = \mathbf{v}_A \tag{6.2}$$

$$\mathbf{a}_B = \mathbf{a}_A \tag{6.3}$$

2.   The kinematic equations governing the motion of any arbitrary point *P* (with position vector **r**) of a rigid body rotating about a fixed axis of rotation (with an angular velocity $\boldsymbol{\omega}$ and angular acceleration $\boldsymbol{\alpha}$) are

$$\mathbf{v} = \boldsymbol{\omega} \times \mathbf{r} \tag{6.7}$$

and

$$\mathbf{a} = \underbrace{\boldsymbol{\alpha} \times \mathbf{r}}_{\mathbf{a}_t} + \underbrace{\boldsymbol{\omega} \times (\boldsymbol{\omega} \times \mathbf{r})}_{\mathbf{a}_n} \tag{6.8}$$

3.   In planar rotational motion (within the *xy* plane), the kinematic equations given above are reduced into scalar expressions:

$$\mathbf{a}_n = \boldsymbol{\omega} \times (\boldsymbol{\omega} \times \mathbf{r}) = -\omega^2\mathbf{r} \qquad a_n = \omega^2 r \tag{6.11}$$

and

$$\mathbf{a}_t = \boldsymbol{\alpha} \times \mathbf{r} \qquad a_t = \alpha r \tag{6.12}$$

4. Relationships between the dependent variables of a planar rotational motion—angular position θ, angular velocity ω, and angular acceleration α—and the independent variable, time t, are given as

$$\omega = \frac{d\theta}{dt} = \dot{\theta} \tag{6.13}$$

$$\alpha = \frac{d\omega}{dt} = \frac{d^2\theta}{dt^2} = \ddot{\theta} \tag{6.14}$$

or

$$\alpha = \frac{d\omega\, d\theta}{d\theta\, dt} = \omega\frac{d\omega}{d\theta} \tag{6.15}$$

Special cases: If ω = constant,

$$\theta = \omega t + \theta_0 \tag{6.16}$$

where θ_0 is the initial angular coordinate at $t = 0$. If α = constant,

$$\omega = \alpha t + \omega_0 \tag{6.17a}$$

$$\theta = \frac{1}{2}\alpha t^2 + \omega_0 t + \theta_0 \tag{6.17b}$$

where ω_0 is the initial angular velocity at $t = 0$.

$$\omega^2 = 2\alpha(\theta - \theta_0) + \omega_0^2 \tag{6.17c}$$

5. The velocity $\mathbf{v}_B$ of a point B of a rigid body in general planar motion translating (with $\mathbf{v}_A$) and rotating (with $\boldsymbol{\omega}$) is

$$\mathbf{v}_B = \underbrace{\mathbf{v}_A}_{\text{translation}} + \underbrace{\boldsymbol{\omega} \times \mathbf{r}_{B/A}}_{\text{rotation}} \tag{6.19}$$

where $\mathbf{v}_A$ is the velocity of point A and defines the translation and $\mathbf{r}_{B/A}$ defines the position of point B relative to point A.

6. If the velocities $\mathbf{v}_A$ and $\mathbf{v}_B$ of two points A and B of a body in general planar motion are given, the location of the instantaneous center of zero velocity (*IC*) is at the intersection of the perpendiculars to $\mathbf{v}_A$ and $\mathbf{v}_B$ drawn from A and B. *IC* need not be located within the body.

7. The acceleration $\mathbf{a}_B$ of a point B of a rigid body in general planar motion translating (with $\mathbf{v}_A$ and $\mathbf{a}_A$ of a point A) and rotating (with $\boldsymbol{\omega}$ and $\boldsymbol{\alpha}$) is

$$\mathbf{a}_B = \underbrace{\underbrace{\mathbf{a}_A}_{\mathbf{a}_A}}_{\text{Translation}} + \underbrace{\underbrace{\boldsymbol{\alpha} \times \mathbf{r}_{B/A}}_{(\mathbf{a}_{B/A})_t} + \underbrace{\boldsymbol{\omega} \times (\boldsymbol{\omega} \times \mathbf{r}_{B/A})}_{(\mathbf{a}_{B/A})_n}}_{\text{Rotation}} \tag{6.22}$$

8.   At a given instant, the velocity $\mathbf{v}_B$ of a point B of a rigid body rotating in space about a fixed point O with an instantaneous angular velocity $\boldsymbol{\omega}$ is given as

$$\mathbf{v}_B = \boldsymbol{\omega} \times \mathbf{r}_{B/O}$$

9.   At a given instant, the acceleration $\mathbf{a}_B$ of a point B of a rigid body rotating in space about a fixed point O with an instantaneous angular velocity $\boldsymbol{\omega}$ and acceleration $\boldsymbol{\alpha}$ is given as

$$\mathbf{a}_B = \boldsymbol{\alpha} \times \mathbf{r}_{B/O} + \boldsymbol{\omega} \times (\boldsymbol{\omega} \times \mathbf{r}_{B/O})$$

where the instantaneous acceleration $\boldsymbol{\alpha}$ of the body is $\boldsymbol{\alpha} = \dot{\boldsymbol{\omega}}$.

10.   At a given instant, the velocity $\mathbf{v}_B$ of a point B of a rigid body translating in space (with $\mathbf{v}_A$) and rotating (with $\boldsymbol{\omega}$ and $\boldsymbol{\alpha}$) about a point A of the body is

$$\mathbf{v}_B = \mathbf{v}_A + \boldsymbol{\omega} \times \mathbf{r}_{B/A} \tag{6.41}$$

11.   At a given instant, the acceleration $\mathbf{a}_B$ of a point B of a rigid body translating in space (with $\mathbf{v}_A$ and $\mathbf{a}_A$) and rotating (with $\boldsymbol{\omega}$ and $\boldsymbol{\alpha}$) about a point A of the body is

$$\mathbf{a}_B = \mathbf{a}_A + \boldsymbol{\alpha} \times \mathbf{r}_{B/a} + \boldsymbol{\omega} \times (\boldsymbol{\omega} \times \mathbf{r}_{B/a}) \tag{6.42}$$

where $\boldsymbol{\omega}$ and $\boldsymbol{\alpha}$ are the instantaneous angular velocity and acceleration of the body, respectively.

12.   Kinematic equations governing the general motion of a rigid body relative to a rotating frame of reference are given as

$$(\mathbf{v}_B)_{XYZ} = (\mathbf{v}_A)_{XYZ} + (\mathbf{v}_{B/A})_{xyz} + \boldsymbol{\Omega} \times (\mathbf{r}_{B/A})_{xyz} \tag{6.44}$$

where XYZ and xyz are the fixed and moving frames of reference, respectively, and $\boldsymbol{\Omega}$ is the instantaneous angular velocity of the rotating frame xyz measured from the fixed frame XYZ; and as

$$\begin{aligned}(\mathbf{a}_B)_{XYZ} = (\mathbf{a}_A)_{XYZ} + (\mathbf{a}_{B/A})_{xyz} + \dot{\boldsymbol{\Omega}} \times (\mathbf{r}_{B/A})_{xyz} \\ + \boldsymbol{\Omega} \times [\boldsymbol{\Omega} \times (\mathbf{r}_{B/A})_{xyz}] + 2\boldsymbol{\Omega} \times (\mathbf{v}_{B/A})_{xyz}\end{aligned} \tag{6.45}$$

where $\dot{\boldsymbol{\Omega}}$ is the instantaneous angular acceleration of the rotating frame xyz measured from the fixed frame XYZ.

13.   The time derivatives of a vector $\mathbf{v}$ relative to a fixed XYZ and rotating xyz frame of reference (with $\boldsymbol{\Omega}$) are related by the equation

$$(\dot{\mathbf{v}})_{XYZ} = (\dot{\mathbf{v}})_{xyz} + \boldsymbol{\Omega} + \mathbf{v} \tag{6.46}$$

KEY TERMS

acceleration
  absolute *257*
  angular *242*
  Coriolis (or complementary) *264*

relative *257*
body cone *270*
instantaneous center of zero
  velocity *252*

PROBLEMS

SECTIONS 6.1, 6.2, AND 6.3

6.1 A wheel's angular speed is increased uniformly from zero to 1200 rpm in 3 s. Determine (*a*) the angular acceleration of the wheel, and (*b*) the number of revolutions the wheel executes in 3 s.

6.2 The rotation of the wheel shown is defined by the variation, with time, of the angular position coordinate θ of point P and is given by $\theta = 4t^3 - 2t^2 + 2$, where θ is in rad and t in s. The wheel starts from rest. Determine the angular acceleration of the wheel after 15 s.

6.3 The block A is attached to a rope that is wrapped around a drum as shown. The system is initially at rest. Assuming that the drum has an angular acceleration $\alpha = (2t^2 + 1)\ \text{rad/s}^2$, where t is in s, determine the magnitudes of the velocity and acceleration of block A at the end of 12 s.

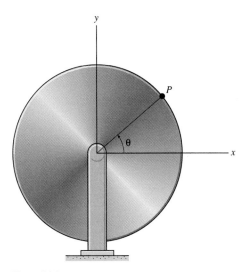

Figure P6.2

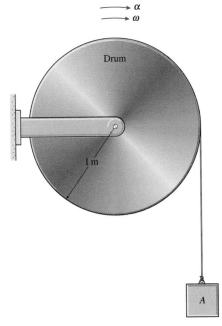

Figure P6.3

6.4 A uniform disk is eccentrically rotating, as shown, about a pin A at a constant rate of $\omega = 10$ rad/s. Determine the velocities and accelerations of points B and C for the position shown.

6.5 Solve Problem 6.4, assuming the disk has an initial angular velocity of 5 rad/s and an angular acceleration of 5 rad/s^2.

6.6 The disk shown rotates about point O as shown. The angular position of a point P on the disk is given by $\theta_P = (5t^2 + 2t)$ rad, where t is in min. Determine (a) the number of revolutions executed by the disk after 25 s, and (b) the angular velocity and angular acceleration of the disk when $t = 30$ s.

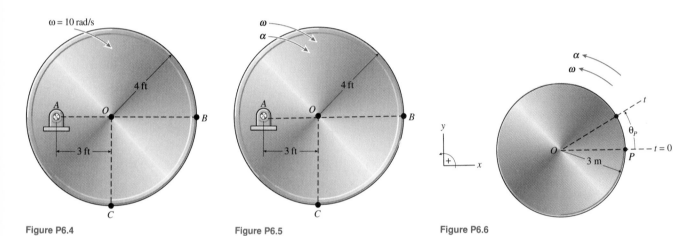

Figure P6.4

Figure P6.5

Figure P6.6

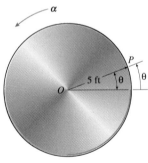

Figure P6.7

6.7 The angular acceleration of the disk shown is given by $\alpha = (5 + 0.2\theta)$ rad/s^2, where θ is in rad. Determine (a) the magnitudes of the velocity and acceleration of the point P on the rim of the disk, when $\theta = 5$ rad, and (b) the time needed to reach the angular position $\theta = 8$ rad. The initial angular coordinate of point P is $\theta_P = 0$, and the disk which is initially at rest rotates about C.

6.8 Four pulleys A, B, C, and D are linked by belts as shown. Pulleys B and C are fastened together so that they turn together. Pulley A has a constant angular acceleration of 3 rad/s^2 and is initially turning with an angular velocity of 10 rad/s. Determine the angular velocity of pulley D after it has turned 10 revolutions.

6.9 Two disks A and B are in contact with each other without slipping. Disk A (radius = 4 ft) starts from rest and rotates with a constant angular acceleration of 5 rad/s^2 as shown. Determine the angular velocity and angular acceleration of disk B just after disk A turns 5 revolutions.

6.10 Two wheels A and B are in contact without slipping. Wheel A (radius = 0.10 m) is initially rotating at an angular velocity of 10 rad/s when it begins to accelerate at the rate of $(0.1\theta^2 + 0.75)$ rad/s^2, where θ is in radians. Determine the angular velocity of wheel B just after wheel A has completed 15 revolutions.

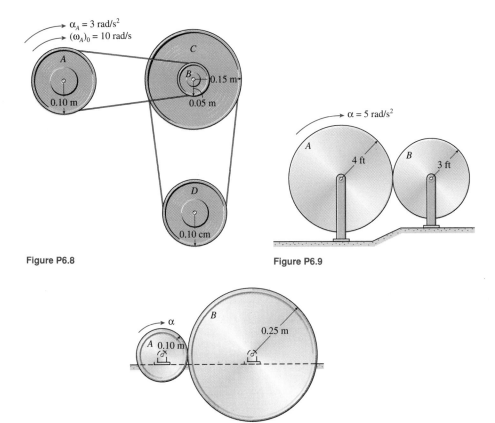

Figure P6.8

Figure P6.9

Figure P6.10

6.11 A wheel is rotating at an angular velocity $\omega = 15$ rad/s. Determine (a) the constant angular deceleration necessary to stop the wheel after three complete revolutions, and (b) the braking time t.

6.12 A wheel is rotating at an angular speed of 2500 rpm. Determine the constant angular deceleration necessary to stop the wheel in 50 s.

6.13 The sprockets of a chain drive are as shown. Starting from rest, sprocket A reaches a speed of 300 rpm in 15 s. Determine the constant angular acceleration necessary to be applied to sprocket B in order to achieve the desired speed on A.

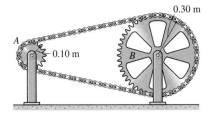

Figure P6.13

6.14 A record player has a turntable operated by a friction drive as shown. Determine the constant angular acceleration of the friction drive necessary to bring the turntable from rest to a speed of 33 rpm in 3 s.

6.15 A pulley initially at rest is operated through a gear A which is driven by a pinion gear B as shown. The maximum allowed vertical speed and acceleration of a load attached to the pulley are 6 m/s and 3 m/s^2, respectively. Determine (a) the maximum angular speed and angular acceleration of the pinion gear B, and (b) the number of revolutions it takes for gear B to reach its maximum speed.

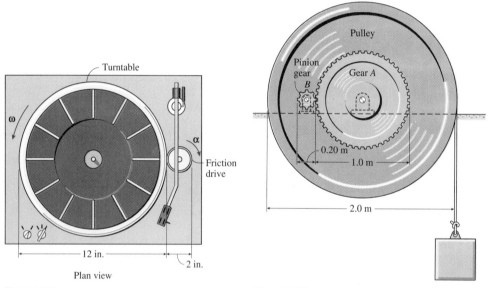

Figure P6.14

Figure P6.15

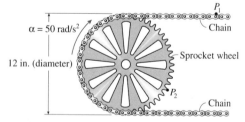

Figure P6.16

6.16 The sprocket wheel and chain shown are initially at rest. The wheel accelerates at a constant rate of 50 rad/s^2 in the direction indicated. Determine (a) the acceleration of a point P_1 along the chain, and (b) the normal and tangential components of the acceleration of a point P_2 along the rim of the wheel after 5 s.

6.17 Paper moves over a large drum at a speed of 20 m/s. The drum is moved by a pair of driving rollers as shown. Determine the angular speed of the rollers required to move the paper at the desired speed.

6.18 A double pulley serves as a hoisting mechanism. The rotating motion of the outer pulley is controlled by a cable connected to the inner pulley as shown. A point A along the cable has a constant acceleration of 1 ft/s^2, and an initial velocity of 1 ft/s, in the direction indicated. Determine (a) the number of revolutions executed by the double pulley in 5 s; (b) the vertical displacement of the load after 5 s; and (c) the normal and tangential components of the acceleration of point B located along the rim of the inner pulley after 5 s.

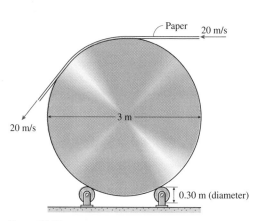

Figure P6.17

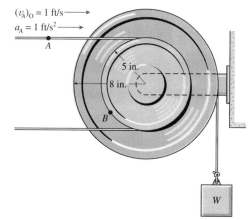

Figure P6.18

6.19 A disk is rotating at a speed of 1200 rpm when brakes are applied causing the disk to decelerate at a constant rate of 0.10 rad/s^2. Determine (a) the time required to stop the disk, and (b) the number of revolutions necessary to bring the disk to rest.

6.20 A disk starts from rest and accelerates at a constant rate. It reaches a speed of 1200 rpm after 120 revolutions. Determine the time it will take to attain the 1200-rpm speed.

SECTIONS 6.4 AND 6.5

6.21 The wheel shown rolls without slipping with its center moving to the right at a speed of 400 ft/s. Determine the velocities of points A, B, and C.

6.22 Collar A moves to the right at a constant speed of 10 m/s as shown. At the position given ($\theta = 45°$), determine (a) the angular velocity of rod AB, and (b) the velocity of point B.

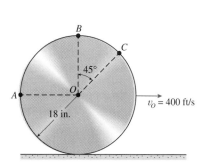

Figure P6.21

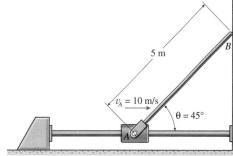

Figure P6.22

6.23   The crankshaft OA rotates clockwise with a constant angular velocity ω_{OA} = 2500 rpm. For the angular position θ = 90°, determine (*a*) the velocity of piston B, and (*b*) the angular velocity of the rod AB.

6.24   The crankshaft OA rotates counterclockwise with a constant angular velocity ω_{OA} = 1500 rpm. For the angular position θ = 0°, determine (*a*) the velocity of piston B, and (*b*) the angular velocity of the rod AB.

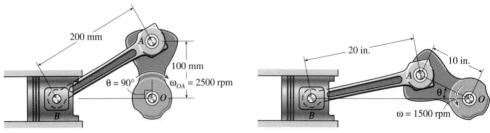

Figure P6.23   **Figure P6.24**

6.25   The crankshaft AB rotates clockwise with a constant angular velocity ω_{AB} = 25 rad/s. For the angular position θ = 30°, determine (*a*) the velocity of piston C, and (*b*) the angular velocity of the rod BC.

6.26   A link $ABCD$ is guided by two blocks at B and C moving in slots as shown. Block B moves downward at a constant speed v_B = 10 ft/s. Determine (*a*) the angular velocity of the link, and (*b*) the velocity of block C at the instant when θ = 35°.

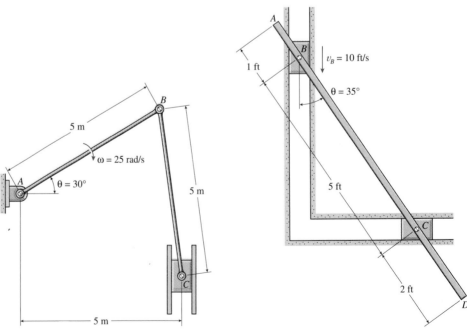

Figure P6.25   **Figure P6.26**

6.27 A link *ABCD* is guided by two blocks at *B* and *C* moving in slots as shown. Block *C* moves to the right at a constant speed $v_C = 3$ m/s. Determine (*a*) the angular velocity of the link, and (*b*) the velocity of tip *D* of the link when $\theta = 60°$.

6.28 The shaded area moves in the *xy* plane. At a given instant, the velocities of points *A* and *B* are given as $\mathbf{v}_A = 4\mathbf{i} + 3\mathbf{j}$ (ft/s) and $\mathbf{v}_B = -3\mathbf{i} - 4\mathbf{j}$ (ft/s), respectively. Determine, at the instant under consideration, (*a*) the angular velocity of the plate, and (*b*) the velocity of point *C*.

6.29 The shaded area *ABCD* moves in the *xy* plane. At a given instant the velocities of points *B* and *C* are shown. Determine (*a*) the angular velocity of the area, and (*b*) the velocities of points *A* and *D*.

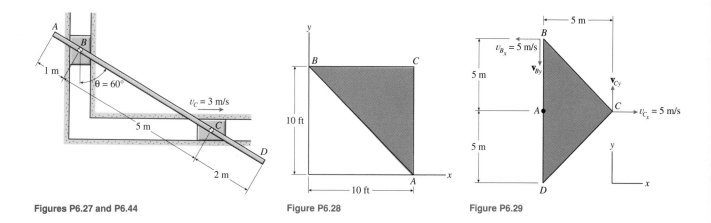

Figures P6.27 and P6.44   Figure P6.28   Figure P6.29

6.30 In the position shown, the bar *AB* rotates clockwise with a constant angular velocity of 5 rad/s. Determine the angular velocities of bars *BC* and *CD*.

6.31 In the position shown, bar *CD* rotates counterclockwise with a constant angular velocity of 10 rad/s. Determine the angular velocities of bars *AB* and *BC*.

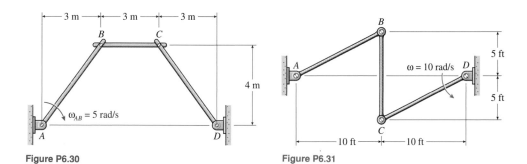

Figure P6.30   Figure P6.31

6.32 Two gears A and B are pinned at their centers to rod AB which rotates about pin A clockwise at a rate of 50 rpm. Determine the angular velocity of gear B if gear A rotates clockwise with a constant angular speed of 80 rpm. The shaft A is fixed.

6.33 A crankshaft AB is connected to the engine piston C by arm BC as shown. Determine the velocity of the piston C and the angular velocity of the arm BC for the instant shown, if the crank AB rotates clockwise with a constant angular velocity of 1200 rpm.

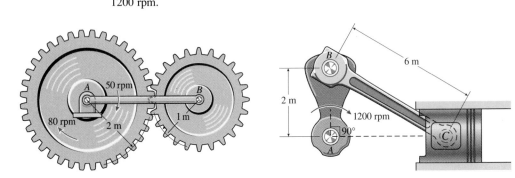

Figure P6.32   Figure P6.33

6.34 The slotted arm AOB is forced to rotate about O when pin A is moving along the horizontal track. For the position shown, establish the relationship between the velocity $\mathbf{v}_B$ of pin B and the velocity $\mathbf{v}_A$ of pin A.

6.35 The hydraulic mechanism of a dump truck is operated by a hydraulic cylinder that imparts an angular velocity ω_{AC} to the link AC as shown. At the position given, determine the angular velocity of the bed of the truck if $\omega_{AC} = 0.02$ rad/s clockwise.

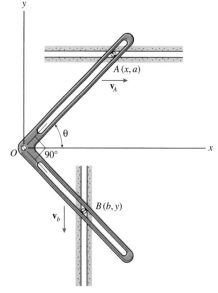

Figure P6.34

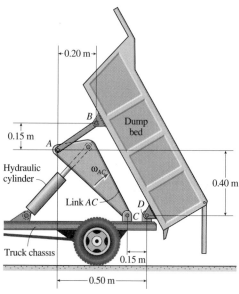

Figure P6.35

6.36 The gear shown rotates with an angular velocity of 4 rad/s counterclockwise about the fixed axis at O. A rack A slides along the wall, as shown, through the action of a pin B sliding in a slot in rack A. Determine the velocity of rack A and the velocity of pin B relative to the rack at the instant shown when points O, C, and B are aligned.

6.37 A boomerang is thrown in the direction shown with an angular velocity $\omega = 5$ rad/s and a mass-center velocity $v_C = 2$ ft/s. For the instant shown, determine the velocity of the tip P of the boomerang.

6.38 A pitcher throws a "curve ball" as shown with a forward speed v and a clockwise angular speed ω. If the diameter of the ball is d, determine the velocity on the surface of the ball at points A, B, and C.

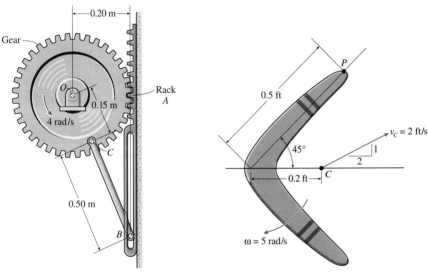

Figure P6.36

Figure P6.37

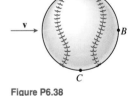

Figure P6.38

6.39 The forward speed of a helicopter is $v = 50$ m/s. If the major blades of the helicopter rotate at an angular speed $\omega = 180$ rad/s, determine the speed at points A, B, and C of the blades.

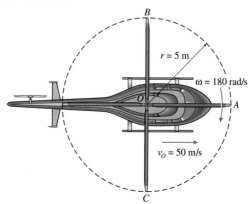

Figure P6.39

6.40 A car travels at a constant speed of 60 mph as shown. The tire diameter is 22 in. Determine the velocities of points A, B, C, and D on the rim.

6.41 A disk A (radius $= r_A$) rotates about a fixed shaft with angular speed ω_A as shown. A link (length $= L$) connects the disk to disk B (radius $= r_B$) rotating about a pin at B. For the position indicated, determine the expression for the angular speed of disk B.

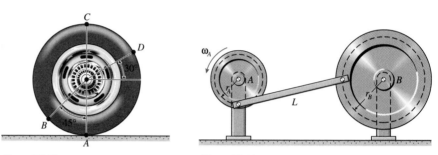

Figure P6.40   Figure P6.41

SECTION 6.6

6.42 Crankshaft AB rotates clockwise with a constant angular velocity $\omega = 1000$ rpm. For the angular position $\theta = 60°$, use the method of instantaneous center of zero velocity to determine (a) the velocity of piston C, and (b) the angular velocity of rod BC.

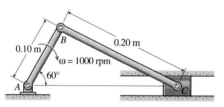

Figure P6.42

6.43 Bar $ABCD$ is guided by two blocks at B and C moving in slots as shown. Block B moves downward at a constant speed of $v_B = 10$ ft/s. Using the method of instantaneous center of zero velocity, determine (a) the angular velocity of the link, and (b) the velocity of block C at the instant when $\theta = 35°$.

6.44 Solve Problem 6.27 using the method of instantaneous center of zero velocity.

6.45 At a given instant, a disk is rotating clockwise at a constant angular speed of 120 rpm. A cord is wrapped around the disk and its end is attached to the ceiling. Determine the velocities of points A and B.

6.46 A cylinder is rolling clockwise and without slipping on a horizontal belt that is moving to the left at a constant speed of 6 m/s. If the angular speed of the cylinder is $\omega = 4$ rad/s, determine the velocities of points O and A at the instant given.

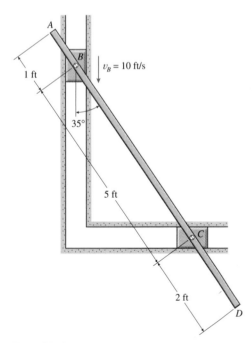

Figure P6.43

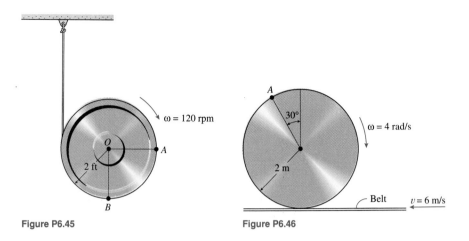

Figure P6.45

Figure P6.46

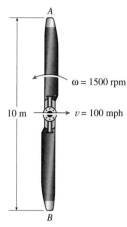

Plan view

Figure P6.47

6.47 A helicopter moves horizontally at 100 mph while the shaft of its blades rotates at an angular speed $\omega = 1500$ rpm as shown. Determine the absolute speed at the tips A and B of the blade in m/s.

6.48 A pitcher throws a curve ball at a forward speed of 120 km/h. The ball (diameter $= 10$ cm) rotates with an angular speed of 500 rpm. Determine the maximum and minimum speeds of points on the surface of the ball.

6.49 Arm AC rotates clockwise at the rate of 200 rpm. Using the method of instantaneous center of zero velocity, determine the angular speed of the slotted arm BD for the position shown.

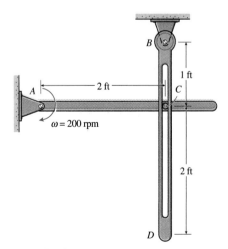

Figure P6.49

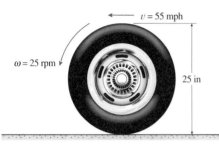

Figure P6.50

6.50 The tire of an automobile traveling at 55 mph has an angular speed of 25 rpm. The tire diameter is 25 in. Using the method of instantaneous center of zero velocity, determine the maximum absolute velocity along the rim of the tire.

SECTION 6.7

6.51 Link *AB* connects two blocks *A* and *B*. For the position shown, the velocity and acceleration of block *B* are 10 ft/s and 5 ft/s², respectively. Determine the acceleration of block *A* and the angular acceleration of link *AB* at the given instant.

6.52 Link *ABCD* connects two blocks *B* and *C*. For the position shown, the velocity and acceleration of block *C* are 10 m/s and 5 m/s², respectively. Determine (*a*) the acceleration of block *B*; (*b*) the angular acceleration of link *ABCD*; and (*c*) the acceleration of point *D*.

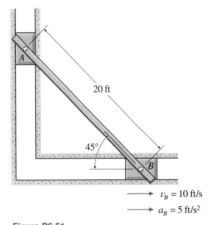

Figure P6.51

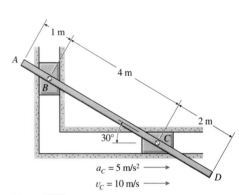

Figure P6.52

6.53 Crankshaft *OA* rotates clockwise at a constant angular speed of 16 rad/s. For the position shown, determine (*a*) the angular acceleration of rod *AB*, and (*b*) the acceleration of the piston.

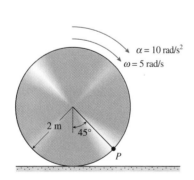

Figure P6.54

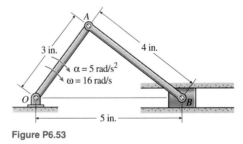

Figure P6.53

6.54 A wheel is rolling clockwise on a horizontal surface without slipping, with an angular velocity of 5 rad/s and an angular acceleration of 10 rad/s². Determine the acceleration of point *P* at the instant shown.

6.55 A wheel is rolling counterclockwise without slipping with an angular velocity of 2 rad/s and an angular acceleration of 5 rad/s². Determine the acceleration of point P at the instant shown.

6.56 If at a given instant crankshaft OA has the angular motion shown, determine the acceleration of piston P at this instant.

6.57 A gear A has its inner hub (dia. = 1 ft) in mesh with gear B (dia. = 1 ft) and its outer edge (dia. = 2 ft) in mesh with another gear C (dia. = 4 ft). Gears B and C rotate about point B while the center of gear A is free to move. If gears B and C have the angular motions shown, determine the angular acceleration of gear A.

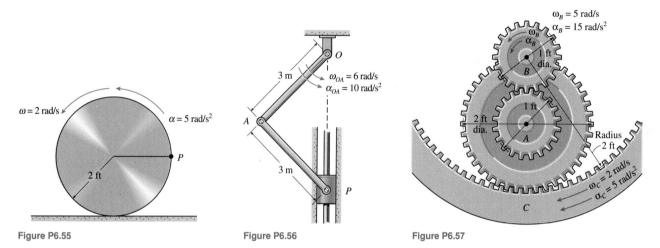

Figure P6.55   Figure P6.56   Figure P6.57

6.58 For the linkage indicated, determine the angular acceleration of BC and CD at the instant shown. The angular velocity of link AB is constant.

6.59 A disk with a 5-ft diameter is rolling on a surface without slipping. At the instant indicated, the disk is rotating clockwise at an angular speed of 5 rad/s and an angular deceleration of 5 rad/s². Determine the acceleration of point P at the instant shown.

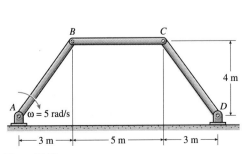

Figure P6.58

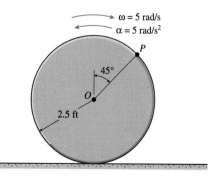

Figure P6.59

6.60   The inner spool (radius $= 1$ m) of a gear (radius $= 2$ m) rolling on a fixed gear rack is pulled at a constant speed of 10 m/s by a cord wrapped around it as shown. Determine the acceleration of point P.

6.61   The bar BC is supported by two arms AB and BC as shown. At the given instant the arm AB rotates clockwise with a constant angular velocity of 5 rad/s. Determine (a) the angular velocity of the bar BC; (b) the angular acceleration of BC; and (c) the acceleration of point G.

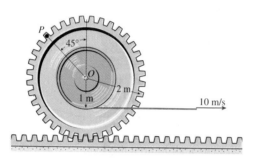

Figure P6.60

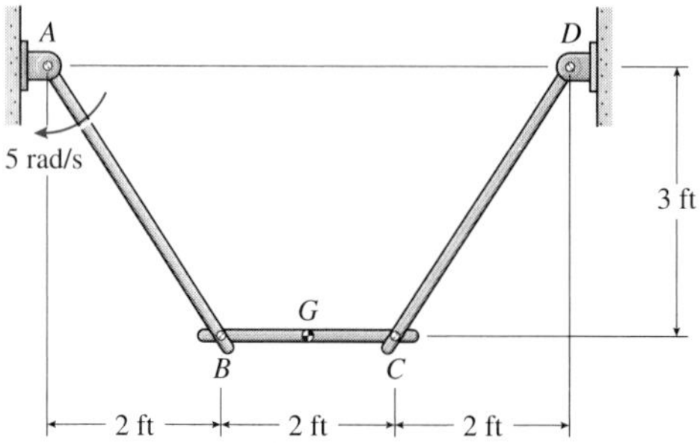

Figure P6.61

6.62   A wheel (radius $= 0.5$ m) rolls without slipping on a belt that moves to the right at a constant speed of 0.2 m/s. At the instant shown, the center O of the wheel has a velocity of 0.3 m/s to the left and a deceleration of 1 m/s² to the right. Determine the acceleration of point A.

SECTION 6.8

6.63   At a given instant, a collar C slides along a horizontal rod that is rotating counterclockwise with an angular speed $\omega = 10$ rad/s and an angular deceleration $\alpha = 20$ rad/s² as shown. At a distance of 5 m from the axis of rotation, the collar has a velocity of 10 m/s and a deceleration of 4 m/s² relative to the rod. Determine the absolute linear velocity and acceleration of the collar at the instant shown.

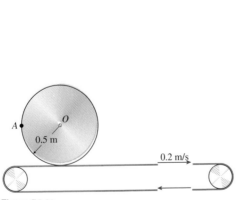

Figure P6.62

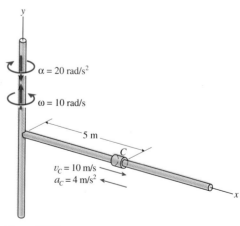

Figure P6.63

6.64 At the instant shown, rod OB rotates clockwise with an angular speed $\omega_{OB} = 2$ rad/s and an angular acceleration $\alpha_{OB} = 8$ rad/s². The collar C is pin-connected to a rod AC and slides over OB. Determine the angular velocity and angular acceleration of rod AC at the instant given.

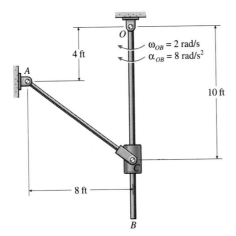

Figure P6.64

6.65 A collar C is pin-connected to a rod $O'C$ and slides over rod OB. At a given instant rod OB has the angular motion shown. Determine the angular velocity and angular acceleration of rod $O'C$.

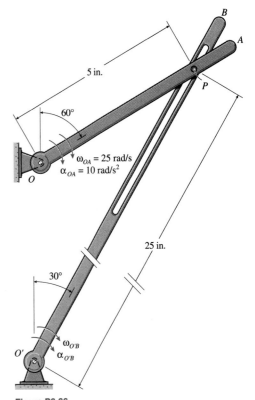

Figure P6.66

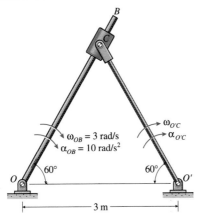

Figure P6.65

6.66 At a given instant, the crank arm OA has the angular motion shown. Determine the angular velocity and angular acceleration of the slotted arm $O'B$.

6.67 Pin P is rigidly attached to bar AB and slides in the slot of arm OC. The ends A and B of bar AB are fastened to two blocks moving in slots as shown. In the position indicated, block A moves to the right with a speed of 2 ft/s and a deceleration of 25 ft/s². Determine the angular velocity and the angular acceleration of the slotted arm OC.

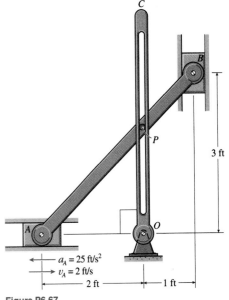

Figure P6.67

6.68 At a given instant, the crank arm *OA* has the angular motion shown. Determine the angular velocity and angular acceleration of the slotted arm *O'B*.

6.69 The arm of an amusement ride rotates clockwise at a constant angular speed of 2 rad/s, while the cabin itself turns counterclockwise relative to the arm at a constant angular speed of 1 rad/s. At the instant shown, determine the linear velocity and acceleration of point *P* along the rim of the cabin.

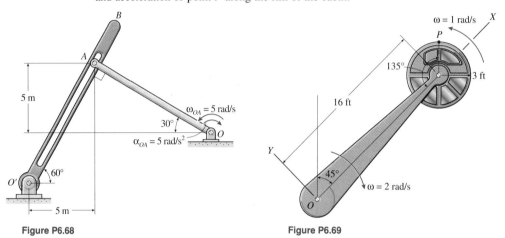

Figure P6.68   Figure P6.69

6.70 The arm of an amusement ride has the angular motion shown. The passenger cabin's angular motion, relative to the arm and at the same instant, is also shown. For the instant given, determine the linear velocity and acceleration of point *P*.

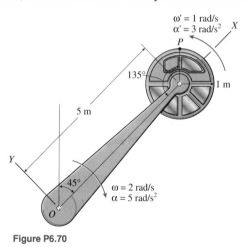

Figure P6.70

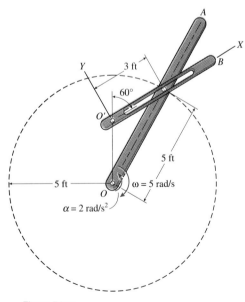

Figure P6.71

6.71 A link *OA* rotates clockwise with an angular speed of 5 rad/s and an angular deceleration of 2 rad/s². A combination pin-slot transfers the motion to the slotted arm *O'B*. At the instant shown, determine the angular velocity and angular acceleration of the slotted arm *O'B*.

6.72 At a given instant a boom is lowered at a constant angular speed $\omega = 0.1$ rad/s while its length is being increased at a constant rate of 100 mm/s. For $\theta = 40°$, determine the velocity and acceleration of the end point P of the boom.

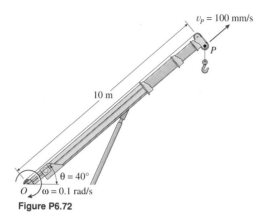

Figure P6.72

*SECTIONS 6.9, 6.10, AND 6.11

6.73 At a given instant, a fire truck ladder rotates about the vertical z axis with an angular velocity of $\omega_1 = 0.20$ rad/s, and an angular acceleration of $\alpha_1 = 0.5$ rad/s², while being raised upward at a constant angular velocity of $\omega_2 = 0.75$ rad/s as shown. Determine the velocity and acceleration of the end point P of the ladder at the instant shown.

6.74 The radar dish shown is rotating about the vertical z axis with an angular velocity $\omega_1 = 5$ rad/s and an angular acceleration $\alpha_1 = 3$ rad/s², while being tilted in the yz plane—about the x axis—from the position shown ($\theta = 45°$), with an angular velocity and acceleration of 3 rad/s and 5 rad/s², respectively. Determine the angular velocity and angular acceleration of the dish at the instant given.

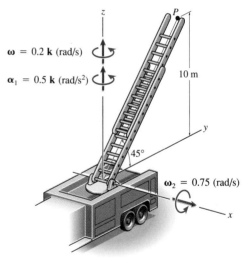

Figure P6.73

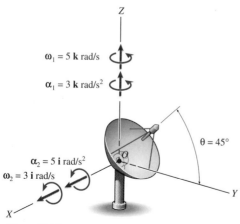

Figure P6.74

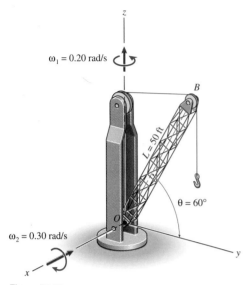

Figure P6.75

6.75 The 50-ft-long boom OB of a crane is rotating, as shown, about the vertical z axis at a constant rate $\omega_1 = 0.20$ rad/s while it is lowered downward by a rotation in the yz plane (about the x axis) with a constant angular speed of 0.30 rad/s. Determine the velocity and acceleration of the tip B of the boom at the given instant.

6.76 A rod AB has its ball-and-socket end points A and B attached to collars that move along two rods as shown. The collar A linking AB to the fixed vertical rod moves upward with a constant speed of 10 ft/s. Determine the speed of the collar B moving horizontally along the fixed rod CD as shown.

6.77 At the instant shown, a cone rolls without slipping along the horizontal plane surface xy, while rotating about the vertical axis with an angular velocity of 5 rad/s and an angular acceleration of 2 rad/s^2. Determine the velocity of point D at the instant shown.

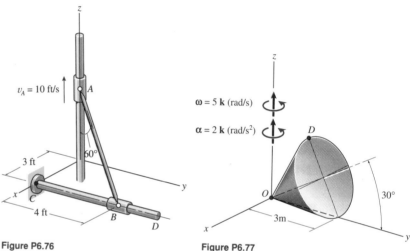

Figure P6.76   **Figure P6.77**

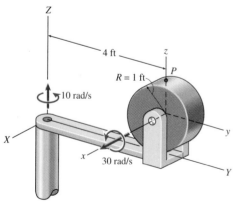

Figure P6.78

6.78 A circular disk with a radius of 1 ft is spinning about its own horizontal axis at a constant angular speed of 30 rad/s, while the frame supporting the disk is rotating about a vertical axis at a constant angular speed of 10 rad/s. Determine the angular acceleration α of the disk and the acceleration of a point P located at the top of the disk.

6.79 A circular disk with a radius of 0.5 m rotates about a horizontal axis (x) with a constant angular speed of 10 rad/s while its supporting arm OO' rotates about a vertical Z axis with a constant angular speed of 4 rad/s. Determine the velocities and accelerations of the points A, B, and C on the disk at the instant shown.

6.80 A rod is attached as shown to a disk and a collar by ball-and-socket joints. The disk has a radius of 2 ft and is rotating in the yz plane at a constant angular velocity of 4 rad/s about the horizontal x axis. Assuming that the angular velocity of the rod is directed perpendicular to its own axis, determine the velocity and acceleration of the collar at A at the instant given.

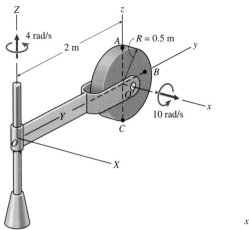

Figure P6.79

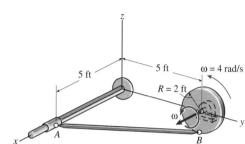

Figure P6.80

6.81 A turbine rotor has a constant angular speed of $\omega_R = 12{,}000$ rpm when its housing moves at a constant angular speed of $\omega_H = 3.6$ rad/s clockwise as shown. Determine the angular acceleration of the rotor.

6.82 A disk A with a radius of 200 mm rotates clockwise about the pin O at the constant rate of $\omega_1 = 4$ rad/s relative to its support frame B, which in turn rotates about the fixed shaft C at the constant angular speed of $\omega_2 = 10$ rad/s. Determine the angular velocity and the angular acceleration of the disk A at the instant shown.

6.83 At a given instant, the shaft AB is rotating, as shown, about the x axis with an angular velocity $\omega_{AB} = 5$ rad/s and an angular acceleration $\alpha_{AB} = 4$ rad/s^2. At the same instant, the link CD, which is pinned at C to AB, is rotating clockwise as shown, with an angular velocity $\omega_{CD} = 2$ rad/s and angular acceleration $\alpha_{CD} = 3$ rad/s^2. Determine the velocity and acceleration of the tip D of the link at the instant shown.

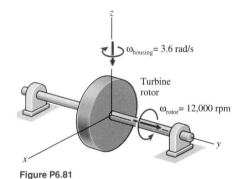

Figure P6.81

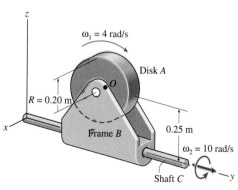

Figure P6.82

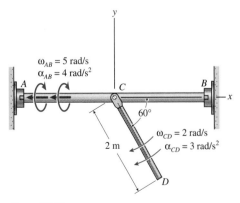

Figure P6.83

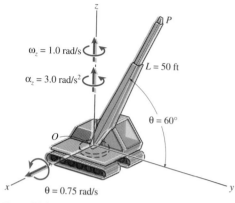

Figure P6.84

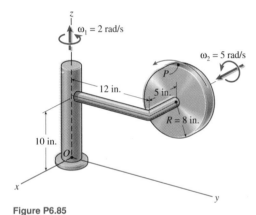

Figure P6.85

6.84 At a given instant the 50-ft-long boom of a crane is rotating about the vertical z axis with an angular velocity $\omega_z = 1$ rad/s and an angular acceleration $\alpha_z = 3$ rad/s^2 while at the same time it is rotating upward at a constant rate of 0.75 rad/s from the position shown. Determine the velocity and acceleration of the tip P of the boom at the given instant.

6.85 The disk shown has a radius of 8 in. and rotates at a constant angular speed $\omega_2 = 5$ rad/s relative to its support arm, which itself rotates at the constant angular speed $\omega_1 = 2$ rad/s about the vertical Z axis. Determine the angular acceleration of the disk and the velocity of point P.

6.86 The basket B used to raise a worker to higher elevations is attached to an arm AB as shown. The 5-m-long arm AB is, in turn, attached to another arm OA (4 m long) by a pivot at A. The entire system rotates around the vertical Z axis at a constant angular speed $\omega_1 = 0.2$ rad/s. The angle between the arm OA and the Y axis is held constant at $\theta = 30°$ and the angle between the arms OA and AB is, at the given instant, 60°, while the arm AB is rotated counterclockwise as shown about the pivot A at the constant angular speed $\omega_2 = 0.25$ rad/s. Determine the acceleration of the basket B at the instant shown.

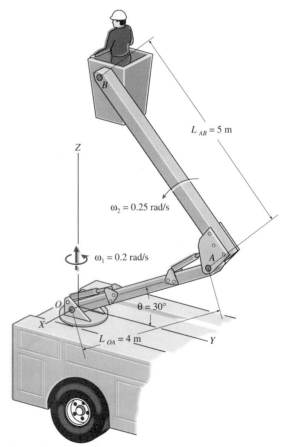

Figure P6.86

6.87 A football spins about its axis of symmetry at a rate of 100 rpm while its axis of symmetry rotates in turn about the horizontal axis Oy at a rate of 25 rpm as shown. Determine the angular acceleration of the football at the instant shown.

6.88 An amusement park ride consists of two cars rigidly fixed to supporting arms, which are free to rotate vertically about the pivot at O. The pivot is supported by a vertical post which at a given instant rotates at the constant angular speed $\omega_1 = 2$ rad/s. A passenger is seated in one of the cars at a location given by P. Determine the acceleration of the passenger at P, if the supporting arms are at the position shown ($\theta = 45°$) and rotating about pivot O at an angular velocity and angular deceleration $\omega_2 = 0.5$ rad/s and $\alpha_2 = 0.5$ rad/s², respectively.

6.89 At the instant shown, a rod rotates about its vertical axis with an angular velocity $\omega_1 = 10$ rad/s and an angular acceleration $\alpha_1 = 10$ rad/s², while the collar shown slides down the rod with a velocity of 5 m/s and acceleration of 2 m/s², both relative to the rod. Determine the collar's velocity and acceleration at the instant shown.

6.90 A disk with a radius of 0.2 m slides along the vertical shaft OA with a constant speed of 0.2 m/s and at the same instant rotates about it as shown. The shaft OA in turn rotates in the yz plane about the x axis. When in the position shown, the shaft OA rotates with $\omega_1 = 2$ rad/s and $\alpha_1 = 3$ rad/s². The angular velocity and acceleration of the disk relative to the shaft are 5 rad/s and 7 rad/s², respectively. Determine the angular acceleration of the disk and the velocity and acceleration of the point P on the disk.

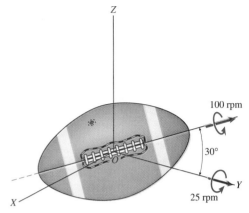

Figure P6.87

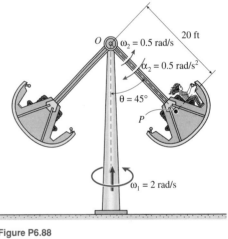

Figure P6.88

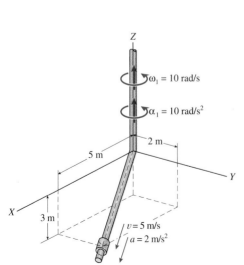

Figure P6.89

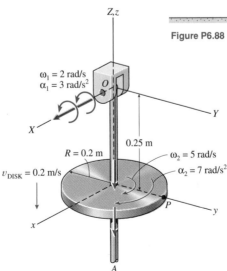

Figure P6.90

7

KINETICS OF RIGID BODIES IN PLANAR MOTION: FORCE, MASS, AND ACCELERATION

7.1 INTRODUCTION

In Chapter 6, we analyzed the motion of a rigid body without giving any consideration to the forces and moments causing the motion. In the present chapter, we will relate the forces and moments acting on a rigid body to its motion, through the use of Newton's second law. To do this we will appeal to the relationships developed in Chapter 5 between the forces acting on a system of n particles and the acceleration of the mass center of the system. By assuming the rigid body to be a system consisting of an infinite number of particles having invariant positions relative to each other, we will simply adapt the results presented in Chapter 5. Initially, the analysis of the motion will be carried out without any constraints as to the nature of the body and its motion. Later, we will focus on two-dimensional (planar) motion. During planar motion, all points of a rigid body move in parallel planes. The plane containing the mass center of the body is called the *plane of motion*. The motion of bodies symmetrical about their plane of motion and the movement of rigid bodies with a constant thickness (i.e., slabs) can be analyzed through the method developed herein.

7.2 GENERAL EQUATIONS OF PLANAR MOTION

Consider a rigid body upon which a force system $\Sigma\mathbf{F}$ is acting. The body is moving relative to a fixed (i.e., inertial) frame of reference (Figure 7.1). Applying the equation of motion established in Chapter 5, Equation (5.4), we write

$$\Sigma\mathbf{F} = m\mathbf{a}_C \qquad (7.1)$$

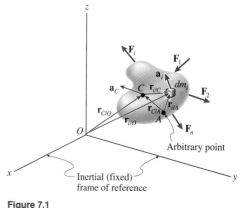

Figure 7.1

where $\Sigma\mathbf{F}$ is the resultant of all external forces acting on the body, m is the mass of the body, and $\mathbf{a}_C$ is the acceleration of the mass center. Equation (7.1) states that the resultant of all the external forces acting on a rigid body is equal to the mass of the body times the acceleration of its mass center.

Similarly, we can extend the moment equations developed for a system of particles [Equations (5.5) and (5.20)] to the case of a rigid body. Replacing the summations over n particles by an integration carried out throughout the body over the infinitesimally small elements, we write

$$\Sigma\mathbf{M}_O = \int_m (\mathbf{r}_{i/O} \times \mathbf{a}_i)\,dm_i = \dot{\mathbf{H}}_O \qquad (7.2)$$

where $\Sigma\mathbf{M}_O$ is the moment, with respect to an arbitrary and *fixed* point O, of all the external forces and external moments acting on a rigid body; and $\mathbf{r}_{i/O}$ is the position vector of an infinitesimal mass dm_i having an acceleration $\mathbf{a}_i$. The vector $\mathbf{H}_O$ is the angular momentum of the body about point O.

Equation (7.2) can be modified and expressed in terms of the position vector $\mathbf{r}_{C/O}$, acceleration vector $\mathbf{a}_C$, and angular momentum vector $\mathbf{H}_C$ of the mass center of the system of particles forming the rigid body by simply extending the analysis of Chapter 5, Equation (5.27), to yield

$$\Sigma \mathbf{M}_O = (\mathbf{r}_{C/O} \times m\mathbf{a}_C) + \dot{\mathbf{H}}_C \tag{7.3}$$

Special case: If the mass center of the rigid body is chosen as the arbitrary point about which moments are taken, then by extending the analysis carried out in Chapter 5, Equations (5.24a) and (5.24b), we obtain

$$\Sigma \mathbf{M}_C = (\dot{\mathbf{H}}_C)_{\text{rel}} = (\dot{\mathbf{H}}_C)_{\text{abs}} \tag{7.4}$$

In some cases, the motion of a rigid body may be more conveniently studied by taking moments about a point A which is neither fixed nor the mass center of the rigid body. In such a case, we can see through the application of the transfer-of-base-point rule (Figure 7.2)

$$\Sigma \mathbf{M}_A = \mathbf{r}_{C/A} \times m\mathbf{a}_C + \mathbf{M}_C$$

Substituting $\mathbf{M}_C = \dot{\mathbf{H}}_C$ we obtain from Equation (7.4),

$$\Sigma \mathbf{M}_A = \mathbf{r}_{C/A} \times m\mathbf{a}_C + \dot{\mathbf{H}}_C \tag{7.5}$$

where $\dot{\mathbf{H}}_C$ can be evaluated using either the absolute velocities or the velocities measured relative to the mass center C.

The moment equation (7.5) may also be expressed in terms of the rigid body's angular momentum about the arbitrary point A, that is, in terms of $\mathbf{H}_A$. The expression for $\mathbf{H}_A$ and the modified form of Equation (7.5) for $\mathbf{M}_A$ will be given here, but their derivations are left to the student as an exercise. Thus,

$$\mathbf{H}_A = \mathbf{H}_C + \mathbf{r}_{C/A} \times m\mathbf{v}_C \tag{7.6}$$

and

$$\mathbf{M}_A = [\mathbf{r}_{C/A} \times m(\mathbf{a}_A)_{\text{abs}}] + (\dot{\mathbf{H}}_A)_{\text{rel}} \tag{7.7}$$

In Equation (7.6), the velocity $\mathbf{v}_C$ and the angular momenta $\mathbf{H}_A$ and $\mathbf{H}_C$ can be expressed either with respect to a fixed (inertial) frame of reference or relative to a nonrotating frame attached to A. Note that Equation (7.7) will be reduced to the simpler form $\mathbf{M}_A = (\dot{\mathbf{H}}_A)_{\text{rel}}$ if the term within the bracket becomes zero—that is, if $\mathbf{r}_{C/A} = \mathbf{0}$, which corresponds to the case when A is the mass center [Equation (7.4)]; if $(\mathbf{a}_A)_{\text{abs}} = \mathbf{0}$, which makes point A move at a constant velocity; or if $\mathbf{r}_{C/A} \times (\mathbf{a}_A)_{\text{abs}} = \mathbf{0}$, which corresponds to the case when $(\mathbf{a}_A)_{\text{abs}}$ passes through the mass center.

Equations (7.1) through (7.7) are applicable to the most general motion of a rigid body. However, in this chapter we will focus on *planar motion* of rigid bodies. It is possible to express the angular momentum $\mathbf{H}_C$ and its derivative vector $\dot{\mathbf{H}}_C$ of the body for the special case, by recalling that, for the planar motion of a rigid body, the position vector $\mathbf{r}$ and the velocity vector $(\boldsymbol{\omega} \times \mathbf{r})$ of a point of the body are coplanar and in the plane of motion. We conclude that the cross product $[\mathbf{r} \times (\boldsymbol{\omega} \times \mathbf{r})]$ represents a vector normal to the plane

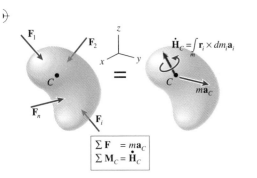

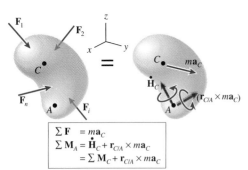

Figure 7.2

of motion, and we write

$$\mathbf{H}_C = \int_m \mathbf{r} \times (\boldsymbol{\omega} \times \mathbf{r})dm = \left(\int_m r^2\, dm \right)\boldsymbol{\omega} = \left(\int_m r^2\, dm \right)\omega\mathbf{k}$$

Since the term within parentheses represents the body's moment of inertia about its centroidal axis, we have

$$\mathbf{H}_C = I_C\boldsymbol{\omega}$$

and upon differentiation,

$$\dot{\mathbf{H}}_C = I_C\dot{\boldsymbol{\omega}} = I_C\boldsymbol{\alpha}$$

The final expression for the moment equation of a rigid body subjected to a planar motion becomes

$$\Sigma\mathbf{M}_A = (\mathbf{r}_{C/A} \times m\mathbf{a}_C) + I_C\boldsymbol{\alpha} \qquad (7.8)$$

Equation (7.8) can be modified and reduced further if the point A is chosen as a fixed point, or the center of mass:

1. In the case where A is a fixed point, the origin of the inertial frame of reference can be made to coincide with A and the equation is reduced to (Figure 7.2)

$$\Sigma\mathbf{M}_O = \mathbf{r}_C \times m\mathbf{a}_C + I_C\boldsymbol{\alpha} \qquad (7.9)$$

where $\mathbf{a}_C = \boldsymbol{\alpha} \times \mathbf{r}_C$. The above expression can thus be written as

$$\Sigma\mathbf{M}_O = [\mathbf{r}_C \times (\boldsymbol{\alpha} \times \mathbf{r}_C)]m + I_C\boldsymbol{\alpha} = (mr_C^2)\boldsymbol{\alpha} + I_C\boldsymbol{\alpha} = [I_C + mr_C^2]\boldsymbol{\alpha}$$

and, since $I_O = I_C + mr_C^2$, we write

$$\Sigma\mathbf{M}_O = I_O\boldsymbol{\alpha} \qquad (7.10)$$

2. If the arbitrary point A is the mass center C of the slab, then the relative position vector $\mathbf{r}_{C/A} = \mathbf{0}$ and Equation (7.8) becomes

$$\Sigma\mathbf{M}_C = I_C\boldsymbol{\alpha} \qquad (7.11)$$

In summary, we conclude from Equation (7.8) that the moment equation of a rigid body in planar motion will relate the moment summation $\Sigma\mathbf{M}_A$ about an arbitrary point A, of all external forces acting upon the rigid body, to the **acceleration** $\mathbf{a}_C$ of its mass center and to the **angular acceleration** $\boldsymbol{\alpha}$, the mass m and the centroidal moment of inertia I_C of the body.

The general planar motion of a rigid body will be governed by Equations (7.1) and (7.8). When expressed in terms of Cartesian coordinates, the equations become (Figure 7.3)

$$\Sigma F_x = m(a_C)_x \qquad \Sigma F_y = m(a_C)_y$$
$$\Sigma M_A = [(r_{C/A})_x m(a_C)_y + (r_{C/A})_y m(a_C)_x] + I_C \alpha \Bigg\} \qquad (7.12)$$

If the mass center C is chosen as the point about which moments are taken, $(r_C)_x = 0$ and $(r_C)_y = 0$, and the Equations (7.12) are reduced to

$$\Sigma F_x = m(a_C)_x \qquad \Sigma F_y = m(a_C)_y \qquad \Sigma M_C = I_C \alpha = 0 \qquad (7.13)$$

or, in terms of tangential and normal components,

$$\Sigma F_t = m(a_C)_t = m\alpha r_C \qquad \Sigma F_n = m(a_C)_n = m\omega^2 r_C \qquad \Sigma M_C = I_C \alpha \qquad (7.14)$$

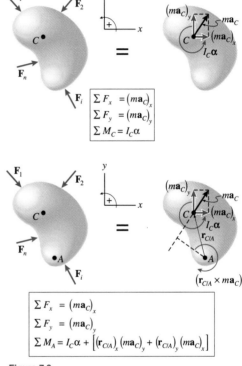

Figure 7.3

7.3 SPECIAL CASES

Frictional Rolling

The motion of a disk or wheel rolling on a plane surface is a special case of the planar motion discussed above. The two extreme limiting cases of the movement are:

Rolling (without sliding), which occurs nearly all the time a car or a bicycle
   moves.

Sliding (without rolling), which occurs when the driver locks the wheels
   with the brakes. In this case the problem is reduced to a translational
   motion.

Rolling and sliding is the third possibility.

When a wheel rolls without sliding, the magnitude F_μ of the friction force
is independent of the magnitude N of the normal force. Consequently, the
simultaneous solution of the equations of motion cannot be complemented
with an additional relationship since $F_\mu < \mu_s N$. The additional relationship
necessary for the solution of the simultaneous equations for the four unknowns
F_μ, N, a_C, and α can be secured if we take note of the fact that the point of
contact between the wheel and the plane surface is an instantaneous center of
zero velocity. Thus we have $a_C = \alpha r$, where a_C is the acceleration of the
wheel's mass center.

On the other hand, if a wheel rolls and slides, the contact point between
the wheel and the surface is no longer a point of zero velocity and we observe
relative motion between the point on the wheel and the surface on which the
wheel rolls. An important consequence is that the acceleration a_C of the mass
center C is now unrelated to the angular acceleration α of the wheel; that is,
$a_C \neq \alpha r$. However, in this case the magnitude F_μ of the friction force is now
dependent on the magnitude N of the normal force and is given as $F_\mu = \mu_k N$,
where μ_k is the coefficient of kinetic friction.

When we do not know whether the wheel's motion involves sliding, the
proper procedure is to first assume that the wheel rolls ''without'' sliding and
solve for the friction force F_μ, and thus verify that the inequality is satisfied.
If not, then the problem has to be solved anew, assuming rolling with sliding
and using the coefficient of kinetic friction μ_k.

Planar Motion of Connected Bodies

With problems involving the planar motion of several connected rigid bodies,
the analysis presented in Section 7.2 is still applicable. The proper procedure
first calls for the development of a schematic equation between the free-body
diagram and the kinetic diagram involving the terms $m\mathbf{a}$ and $I_c\boldsymbol{\alpha}$, for each
rigid body. The corresponding equations of motion can then be solved simul-
taneously.

However, it is not always necessary to develop separate diagrams for each
member of a system of rigid bodies, provided the composite free-body and
kinetic diagrams include all of the external forces and all the kinetic terms
represented by $m\mathbf{a}$ and $I_c\boldsymbol{\alpha}$. All internal forces, such as interaction forces between the parts of a composite body and tensile forces exerted by connecting

cables, occur in pairs of equal and opposite forces and thus cancel each other (Figure 7.4).

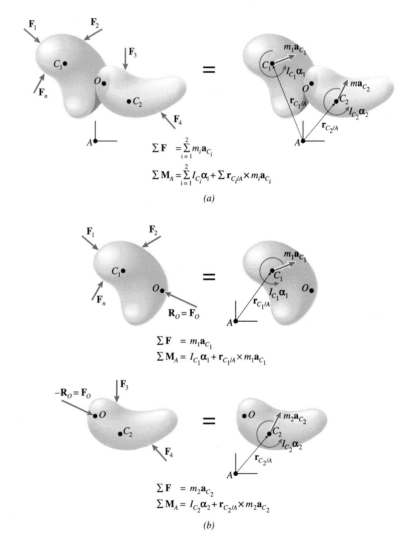

$$\sum \mathbf{F} = \sum_{i=1}^{2} m_i \mathbf{a}_{C_i}$$

$$\sum \mathbf{M}_A = \sum_{i=1}^{2} I_{C_i} \boldsymbol{\alpha}_i + \sum \mathbf{r}_{C_i/A} \times m_i \mathbf{a}_{C_i}$$

(a)

$$\sum \mathbf{F} = m_1 \mathbf{a}_{C_1}$$
$$\sum \mathbf{M}_A = I_{C_1} \boldsymbol{\alpha}_1 + \mathbf{r}_{C_1/A} \times m_1 \mathbf{a}_{C_1}$$

$$\sum \mathbf{F} = m_2 \mathbf{a}_{C_2}$$
$$\sum \mathbf{M}_A = I_{C_2} \boldsymbol{\alpha}_2 + \mathbf{r}_{C_2/A} \times m_2 \mathbf{a}_{C_2}$$

(b)

Figure 7.4

7.4 PURE TRANSLATIONAL MOTION

The movement of a rigid body, when limited to a ***translational motion*** within the plane of symmetry of the body, is a special case of the planar motion investigated in Section 7.2. Under ***translation*** all the particles of the body, including its mass center C, move with the same acceleration $\mathbf{a}_C = $ constant. When all points of a body move along the same direction, the angular acceleration $\boldsymbol{\alpha}$ of the rigid body is zero. The above considerations, when applied to Equations (7.1) and (7.8), yield

$$\Sigma\mathbf{F} = m\mathbf{a}_C \qquad \Sigma\mathbf{M}_A = \mathbf{r}_{C/A} \times m\mathbf{a}_C \qquad (7.15)$$

If the point A, about which the moments of the external forces and the moment of $m\mathbf{a}_C$ are taken, coincides with the body's center of mass (that is, $\mathbf{r}_C = \mathbf{0}$), the above equations can be reduced further to

$$\Sigma\mathbf{F} = m\mathbf{a}_C \qquad \Sigma\mathbf{M}_C = \mathbf{0} \qquad (7.16)$$

For the special case of *rectilinear translation*, the scalar equations become

$$\Sigma F_x = m(a_C)_x$$
$$\Sigma F_y = m(a_C)_y \qquad (7.17)$$
$$\Sigma M_C = 0$$

For the special case of *curvilinear translation*, the scalar equations are written

$$\Sigma F_n = m(a_C)_n$$
$$\Sigma F_t = m(a_C)_t \qquad (7.18)$$
$$\Sigma M_C = 0$$

7.5 PURE ROTATIONAL MOTION

The movement of a rigid body, when limited to a *rotational motion* about a fixed axis perpendicular to the plane of symmetry of the body, is another special case of the planar motion discussed in Section 7.2. Assuming that the *rotation* takes place about a fixed point O defined by the intersection of the fixed axis of rotation with the plane of symmetry of the body, we find that the angular velocity and angular acceleration are the result of the torque imparted to the body by the external force system acting on the body. Furthermore, the mass center C of the body will be moving in a circular path centered around the fixed point O. By taking the moments of the external forces about the fixed point O, Equations (7.1) and (7.10) can be applied to the rotational motion of a rigid body about a fixed point and we write again

$$\Sigma\mathbf{F} = m\mathbf{a}_C \qquad (7.1)$$
$$\Sigma\mathbf{M}_O = I_O\boldsymbol{\alpha} \qquad (7.10)$$

Equations (7.1) and (7.10) can be further expanded by introducing the appropriate components of the acceleration vector of the mass center (Figure 7.5) into the scalar forms of the equations of motion. Thus we have, in terms of Cartesian components,

$$\left. \begin{array}{ll} \Sigma F_x = m(a_C)_x & \Sigma F_y = m(a_C)_y \\ \Sigma M_C = I_C\alpha \quad \text{or} & \Sigma M_O = I_O\alpha \end{array} \right\} \tag{7.19}$$

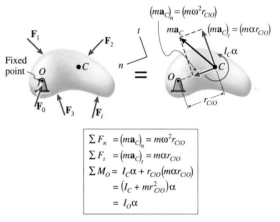

$$\Sigma F_n = (ma_C)_n = m\omega^2 r_{C/O}$$
$$\Sigma F_t = (ma_C)_t = m\alpha r_{C/O}$$
$$\Sigma M_O = I_C\alpha + r_{C/O}(m\alpha r_{C/O})$$
$$= (I_C + m r_{C/O}^2)\alpha$$
$$= I_O\alpha$$

Figure 7.5

or, in terms of tangential and normal components,

$$\left. \begin{array}{ll} \Sigma F_t = m(a_C)_t = m\alpha r_C & \Sigma F_n = m(a_C)_n = m\omega^2 r_C \\ \Sigma M_C = I_C\alpha \quad \text{or} & \Sigma M_O = I_O\alpha \end{array} \right\} \tag{7.20}$$

The equations of motion developed above can further be reduced if the rotational motion occurs about a fixed axis passing through the mass center C of the body. Then $r_C = 0$ and the motion, called **centroidal rotation**, is described by

$$\Sigma F_x = 0 \qquad \Sigma F_y = 0 \qquad \Sigma M_C = I_C\alpha \tag{7.21}$$

$$\Sigma F_t = 0 \qquad \Sigma F_n = 0 \qquad \Sigma M_C = I_C\alpha \tag{7.22}$$

EXAMPLE 7.1

A force of 50 lb is applied to the 100-lb box as shown. The weight of the box is uniformly distributed. The coefficient of kinetic friction between the box and the horizontal surface on which it rests is 0.30. Determine (a) if the box is sliding or tipping, and (b) the acceleration of the box.

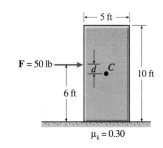

Solution   Let us assume that the crate slides. Once again, we will express the equations of motion in schematic form by equating the free-body diagram (where all external force vectors are shown) to the kinetic diagram (where the acceleration of the mass of the body caused by the external forces are illustrated). The pertinent equations, written in the Cartesian coordinate system, are

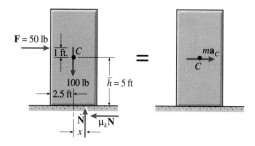

$$\xrightarrow{+}\ \Sigma F_x = m(a_C)_x \qquad F - \mu_k N = \frac{W}{g}(a_C) \qquad \text{(a)}$$

$$+\uparrow\ \Sigma F_y = m(a_C)_y \qquad N - W = 0 \qquad \text{(b)}$$

$$\stackrel{+}{\circlearrowleft}\ \Sigma M_C = 0 \qquad -Fd + Nx - \mu_k Nh = 0 \qquad \text{(c)}$$

where $d = 1$ ft, $h = 5$ ft, and $\mu_k = 0.30$. Substituting into Equations (a), (b), and (c), we get

$$50 - (0.30)N = \frac{100}{32.2}(a_C) \qquad \text{(d)}$$

$$N - 100 = 0 \qquad \text{(e)}$$

$$-50(1) + N(x) - 0.30N(5) = 0 \qquad \text{(f)}$$

From these we obtain

$$N = 100\,\text{lb}$$

$$x = 2 \text{ ft}$$

Thus *the box is sliding* (tipping would have resulted if $x > 2.5$ ft). From Equation (d) we obtain

$$a_C = 6.44 \,\text{ft/s}^2 \xrightarrow{\;} \quad \blacktriangleleft$$

EXAMPLE 7.2

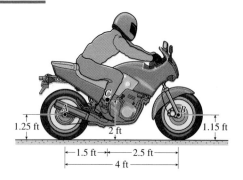

1.25 ft   2 ft   1.15 ft

1.5 ft   2.5 ft

4 ft

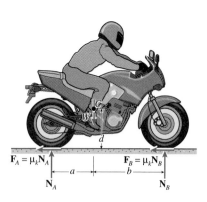

$F_A = \mu_k N_A$ $F_B = \mu_k N_B$

a b

N_A N_B

y $+$

x

$=$

$\alpha = 0$

$(W/g)a_C$

C

The collective weight of the motorcycle and its rider is 500 lb. When the brakes are suddenly applied, the motorcycle begins skidding along a straight line. The coefficient of kinetic friction between the tires and the ground is 0.6. Determine the acceleration of the motorcycle and the frictional forces acting on each wheel.

Solution The motorcycle is subjected to a pure translation, and the appropriate equations of motion are

$\xrightarrow{+} \Sigma F_x = m(a_C)_x$

$$-\mu_k N_A - \mu_k N_B = -\frac{W}{g}(a_C) \tag{a}$$

$\overset{+}{\uparrow} \Sigma F_y = m(a_C)_y$

$$N_A + N_B - W = 0 \tag{b}$$

$\overset{+}{\circlearrowright} \Sigma M_C = 0$

$$-F_A(d) - F_B(d) - N_A(a) + N_B(b) = 0 \tag{c}$$

where $W = 500$ lb, $\mu_k = 0.6$, $a = 1.5$ ft, $b = 2.5$ ft, and $d = 2$ ft. Substituting into Equations (a), (b), and (c) and rearranging terms, we have

$$0.6(N_A + N_B) = \frac{500}{g}(a_C) \tag{d}$$

$$N_A + N_B - 500 = 0 \tag{e}$$

$$N_A[2(0.6) + 1.5] + N_B[2(0.6) - 2.5] = 0 \tag{f}$$

Solving the simultaneous equations for N_A, N_B, and a_C, we obtain

$$N_A = 162.5 \text{ lb}, \qquad F_A = 97.5 \text{ lb} \blacktriangleleft$$
$$N_B = 337.5 \text{ lb}, \qquad F_B = 202.5 \text{ lb} \blacktriangleleft$$
$$a_C = 19.3 \text{ ft/s}^2 \overset{\leftarrow}{\circlearrowleft} \blacktriangleleft$$

EXAMPLE 7.3

A 500-kg bar BD is supported by flexible cords AB and DE of negligible mass and which rotate in the vertical plane $ABCDE$. The bar's mass is not distributed uniformly, as its mass center C is located at 4 m from B. At the instant shown, the speed of the mass center C is 12 m/s. Determine (a) the tension in each of the cords, and (b) the acceleration of the bar BD.

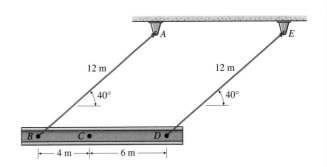

Solution All points of the bar BD move along circular paths, and the rigid bar is said to be subject to a curvilinear translation. Adopting a coordinate system with component directions tangential and normal to the curvilinear path of the mass center, the applicable relationships (Equation 17.18) become

$$\Sigma F_t = m(a_C)_t \qquad \Sigma F_n = m(a_C)_n \qquad \Sigma M_C = 0$$

where $(a_C)_t$ and $(a_C)_n$ represent the magnitudes of the tangential and normal components of the acceleration of the mass center C. From the kinematics of the circular motion, which has a radius of 12 m, we write

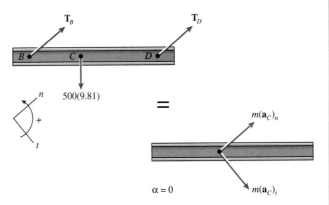

$$(a_C)_n = \frac{v_C^2}{\rho}$$

where $v_C = 12$ m/s and the radius of curvature $\rho = 12$ m. Thus $(a_C)_n = 12$ m/s^2. The remaining unknowns T_B, T_D, and $(a_C)_t$ can now be obtained by solving simultaneously the equations

$\xrightarrow{+} \Sigma F_t = m(a_C)_t$

$$mg \cos 40° = m(a_C)_t \qquad\qquad (a)$$

$\xuparrow{+} \Sigma F_n = m(a_C)_n$

$$-mg \sin 40° + T_B + T_D = m(12) \qquad\qquad (b)$$

$\circlearrowleft^{+} \Sigma M_C = 0$

$$6 \sin 40° T_D - 4 \sin 40° T_B = 0 \qquad\qquad (c)$$

From these three equations we obtain

$$(a_C)_t = 9.81 \cos 40° \qquad (a_C)_t = 7.51 \, \text{m/s}^2 \ \blacktriangleleft$$
$$T_B = 5491.8 \, \text{N} \ \blacktriangleleft$$
$$T_D = 3661.2 \, \text{N} \ \blacktriangleleft$$

EXAMPLE 7.4

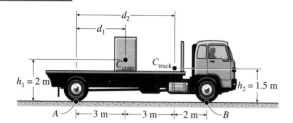

A rear-wheel-drive truck having a mass of 4000 kg carries, as shown, a crate (500 kg) while accelerating at $a = 0.2$ m/s^2. Assuming that the crate does not slip on the truck and the front wheels are rolling freely, determine the reaction forces exerted at each of the four tires.

Solution A   Since both crate and truck translate with the same acceleration, we can solve this problem by regarding the terms $(ma_C)_{\text{truck}}$ and $(ma_C)_{\text{crate}}$ as sliding vectors that are not passing through the point about which moments are taken, and apply Equations (7.12) to obtain

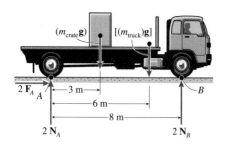

$$(+\uparrow)\,\Sigma F_y = [m(a_C)_y]_{\text{crate}} + [m(a_C)_y]_{\text{truck}} \qquad (a)$$

$$(\overset{+}{\rightarrow})\,\Sigma F_x = [m(a_C)_x]_{\text{crate}} + [m(a_C)_x]_{\text{truck}} \qquad (b)$$

$$(\circlearrowleft)\,\Sigma M_A = -(ma_C)_{\text{crate}}(h_1) - (ma_C)_{\text{truck}}(h_2) \qquad (c)$$

The left-hand sides of Equations (a), (b), and (c) can be expressed as

$$(+\uparrow)\,\Sigma F_y = 2N_A + 2N_B - (mg)_{\text{crate}} - (mg)_{\text{truck}}$$

$$(\overset{+}{\rightarrow})\,\Sigma F_x = 2F_A$$

$$(\circlearrowleft)\,\Sigma M_A = (3 + 3 + 2)2N_B - (mg)_{\text{crate}}(d_1) - (mg)_{\text{truck}}(d_2)$$

Equations (a), (b), and (c) can now be written in the form

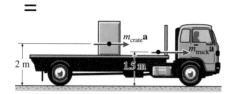

$$2N_A + 2N_B - (500)(9.81) - (4000)(9.81) = 0$$

$$2F_A = 500(0.2) + 4000(0.2)$$

$$8(2N_B) - 500(9.81)(3) - 4000(9.81)(6)$$
$$= -500(0.2)(2) - 4000(0.2)(1.5)$$

and solving for the unknowns yield

$$F_A = 450\,\text{N} \qquad N_A = 6525.5\,\text{N} \qquad N_B = 15{,}547\,\text{N} \blacktriangleleft$$

Solution B   We can determine the location of the center of mass of the combined mass (crate + truck) by appealing to the definition of the mass center of a system of particles as established in Chapter 5. Thus we have $\bar{d}\,\Sigma_{i=1}^{2}\,m_i = \Sigma_{i=1}^{2}\,d_i m_i$ and $\bar{h}\,\Sigma_{i=1}^{2}\,m_i = \Sigma_{i=1}^{2}\,h_i m_i$, where $\bar{d}$ and $\bar{h}$ define the location of the combined mass center.

$$\bar{d} = [3(500) + 6(4000)] \div [4000 + 500] = 5.6666\,\text{m}$$

and

$$\bar{h} = [2(500) + 1.5(4000)] \div [4000 + 500] = 1.5555\,\text{m}$$

(continued)

Example 7.4 (*concluded*)

The equations of motion thus become

$$\overset{+\uparrow}{\bigcirc} 2N_A + 2N_B - (4500)9.81 = 0 \qquad (a)$$

$$\overset{\rightarrow}{\bigcirc} 2F_A = 4500(0.2) \qquad (b)$$

$$\overset{+}{\bigcirc} 8(2N_B) - (4500)(9.81)(5.6666)$$
$$- (4500)(0.2)(1.5555) = 0 \qquad (c)$$

Solving Equations (a), (b), and (c) simultaneously yields

$$F_A = 450\,\text{N} \qquad N_A = 6525.5\,\text{N} \qquad N_B = 15{,}547\,\text{N} \; \blacktriangleleft$$

which is identical to the previous solution.

Solution C Having established the location of the center of mass $(\bar{d}, \bar{h})$ of the truck-crate system, we can apply the moment summation equation about the mass center C to obtain

$$\overset{+\uparrow}{\bigcirc} \Sigma F_y = 0$$

$$2N_A + 2N_B - (4500)9.81 = 0 \qquad (a)$$

$$\overset{\rightarrow}{\bigcirc} \Sigma F_x = (\Sigma m)a_C$$

$$2F_A = 4500(0.2) \qquad (b)$$

$$\overset{+}{\bigcirc} \Sigma M_C = 0$$

$$-\bar{d}N_A + \bar{h}F_A + (8 - \bar{d})N_B = 0 \qquad (c)$$

Substituting $\bar{d} = 5.666$ m and $\bar{h} = 1.555$ m, we have for Equation (c)

$$-5.666N_A + 1.555F_A + (8 - 5.666)N_B = 0$$

The simultaneous solution of these equations once again yields

$$F_A = 450\,\text{N} \qquad N_A = 6525.5\,\text{N} \qquad N_B = 15{,}547\,\text{N} \; \blacktriangleleft$$

EXAMPLE 7.5

A 1000-lb weight is attached by a cable to a 3-ft-radius drum. The weight falls freely as the cable unwinds from the rotating drum. The weight of the drum and cable is 2000 lb. Neglecting friction, determine (*a*) the angular acceleration of the drum, and (*b*) the tension in the cable. The centroidal radius of gyration of the drum is 2 ft.

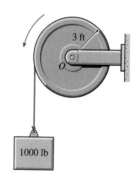

3 ft

O

1000 lb

(*continued*)

Example 7.5   *(concluded)*

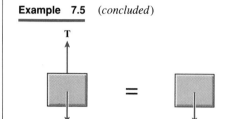

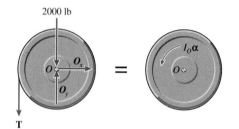

Solution   Since the weight-drum system consists of two masses linked by a cable, we will consider each free body separately. The weight is subjected to a *rectilinear translation*. The pertinent equations are reduced to

$$(+\uparrow y)\ \Sigma F_y = -ma$$

where $a = \alpha r_{\text{drum}} = 3\alpha$. Substituting, we have

$$-1000 + T = -\frac{1000}{32.2}(3\alpha) \qquad \text{(a)}$$

The drum is subjected to a *centroidal rotation*. The pertinent equations are

$$(\uparrow +)\ \Sigma F_y = 0 \qquad\qquad O_y - 2000 - T = 0 \qquad \text{(b)}$$

$$(\xrightarrow{+})\ \Sigma F_x = 0 \qquad\qquad O_x = 0 \qquad\qquad\qquad \text{(c)}$$

$$(\circlearrowleft +)\ \Sigma M_O = I_O\alpha \qquad\qquad 3T = I_O\alpha \qquad\qquad \text{(d)}$$

where

$$I_O = mk_O^2 = \frac{2000}{32.2}(2)^2$$

Equations (a) and (d) solved simultaneously for T and α yield

$$T = 470.6\,\text{lb} \ \blacktriangleleft$$

$$\alpha = 5.68\,\text{rad/s}^2\,(\circlearrowright) \ \blacktriangleleft$$

EXAMPLE 7.6

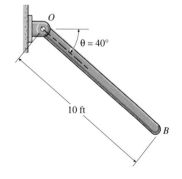

A slender uniform 30-lb bar (10 ft long) is released from rest at the position shown. Determine, for the instant after release, the angular acceleration of the bar and the reaction force at the hinge O.

(continued)

Example 7.6   *(concluded)*

Solution A For a body subjected to a purely rotational motion about a fixed axis, the applicable equations are

$$\Sigma F = ma_C \qquad \Sigma M_O = I_O \alpha$$

where $m = 30/32.2$ slug and $I_O = ml^2/3 = (30/32.2)[(10)^2/3]$ $= 31.1 \text{ ft}^4$. Since the bar is released from rest, at the instant after release $\omega = 0$, and we have

$$\mathbf{a}_C = \alpha \times \mathbf{r}_C = -\alpha \mathbf{k} \times 5(\cos 40° \mathbf{i} - \sin 40° \mathbf{j})$$

$$\mathbf{a}_C = -5(\cos 40°)\alpha \mathbf{j} + 5(\sin 40°)\alpha(-\mathbf{i})$$

$$= \underbrace{-3.21\alpha \mathbf{i}}_{(a_C)_x} \underbrace{-3.83\alpha \mathbf{j}}_{(a_C)_y} (\text{ft/s}^2)$$

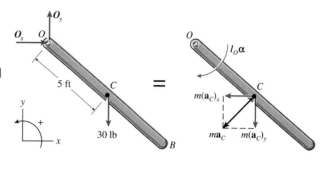

From Equations (7.19) (in Cartesian coordinates) we have

$$\xrightarrow{+} \Sigma F_x = m(a_C)_x \qquad O_x = \frac{30}{32.2}(-3.21\alpha) \qquad \text{(a)}$$

$$+\!\!\uparrow \Sigma F_y = m(a_C)_y$$

$$O_y - 30 = \frac{30}{32.2}(-3.83\alpha) \qquad \text{(b)}$$

$$\circlearrowleft \Sigma M_O = I_O(-\alpha)$$

$$-30(5\cos 40°) = -31.1\alpha \qquad \text{(c)}$$

Solving Equation (c) for α, we obtain the angular acceleration:

$$\alpha = +3.70 \text{ rad/s}^2 \circlearrowright \blacktriangleleft$$

The positive sign indicates that the initial assumption of a clockwise rotation was correct. Substituting α into Equations (a) and (b) and solving for O_x and O_y, respectively, we have

$$O_x = -11.08 \text{ lb} \qquad \text{or} \qquad O_x = 11.08 \text{ lb} \circlearrowleft \blacktriangleleft$$

$$O_y = +16.80 \text{ lb} \qquad \text{or} \qquad O_y = 16.80 \text{ lb} \uparrow \blacktriangleleft$$

Solution B Considering the moment summation equation about the mass center C of the bar, we write the pertinent equations of motion in the form

$$\xrightarrow{+} \Sigma F_x = m(a_C)_x \qquad O_x = \frac{30}{32.2}(-3.21\alpha) \qquad \text{(a)}$$

$$+\!\!\uparrow \Sigma F_y = m(a_C)_y$$

$$O_y - 30 = \frac{30}{32.2}(-3.83\alpha) \qquad \text{(b)}$$

$$\circlearrowleft \Sigma M_C = I_C \alpha$$

$$-O_x(5\sin 40°) - O_y(5\cos 40°) = \left[\frac{1}{12}\left(\frac{30}{32.4}\right)(10)^2\right]\alpha \quad \text{(c)}$$

Solving Equations (a), (b), and (c) simultaneously yields

$$\alpha = +3.69 \text{ rad/s}^2 \circlearrowright \blacktriangleleft$$

$$O_x = -11.04 \qquad \text{or} \qquad O_x = 11.04 \text{ lb} \circlearrowleft \blacktriangleleft$$

$$O_y = +16.83 \qquad \text{or} \qquad O_y = 16.83 \text{ lb} \uparrow \blacktriangleleft$$

Solution C Moment summation equation taken about the tip B of the slender bar would yield the following equations of motion [Equations (7.12)]

$$\xrightarrow{+} \Sigma F_x = m(a_C)_x \qquad O_x = \frac{30}{32.2}(-3.21\alpha) \qquad \text{(a)}$$

$$+\!\!\uparrow \Sigma F_y = m(a_C)_y$$

$$O_y - 30 = \frac{30}{32.2}(-3.83\alpha) \qquad \text{(b)}$$

$$\circlearrowleft \Sigma M_B = m(a_C)_x(5\sin 40°) + m(a_C)_y(5\cos 40°) + I_C\alpha \quad \text{(c)}$$

The left-hand side of Equation (c) becomes

$$\Sigma M_B = 30(5\cos 40°) - O_x(5\sin 40°) - O_y(5\sin 40°)$$

and the right-hand side can be written in the form

$$\frac{30}{32.2}(-3.21\alpha)(5\sin 40°) + \frac{30}{32.2}(-3.83\alpha)(5\cos 40°)$$

$$+ \left[\frac{1}{12}\left(\frac{30}{32.4}\right)(10)^2\right]\alpha$$

It is apparent from the above equation (c) that method C is not the most efficient procedure for solving for α.

EXAMPLE 7.7

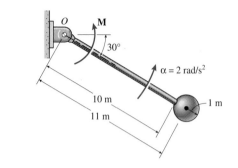

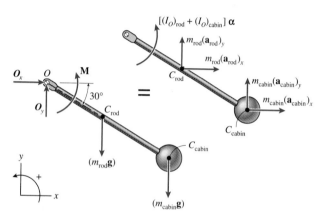

The swinging arm of an amusement ride consists of a slender uniform 100-kg rod (10 m long) and a 400-kg cabin (2-m diameter) as shown. For the position shown, determine (a) the magnitude of the torque **M** necessary to cause a counterclockwise angular acceleration of 2 rad/s² if, at the instant shown, $\omega = 0$, and (b) the reaction forces at the hinge O.

Solution The rod-cabin system is subjected to a purely rotational motion about a fixed axis through O. The applicable equations of motion are

$$\sum \mathbf{F} = \sum_{i=1}^{2} m_i \mathbf{a}_i \qquad \sum \mathbf{M}_O = \left[\sum_{i=1}^{2} (I_O)_i \right] \alpha$$

where $m_1 = 100$ kg, $m_2 = 400$ kg, $(I_O)_1 = \frac{1}{3} m_1 l_1^2$, $l_1 = 10$ m, $(I_O)_2 = \frac{2}{5} m_2 r_2^2 + m_2 l_2^2$, $r_2 = 1$ m, and $l_2 = 11$ m. Since, at the instant shown $\omega = 0$, the acceleration vectors of the mass centers of the rod and the cabin are given as

$$\mathbf{a}_1 = \alpha \times \mathbf{r}_{C_1} = \alpha \mathbf{k} \times 5(\cos 30° \mathbf{i} - \sin 30° \mathbf{j})$$

$$= 5(\cos 30°)\alpha \mathbf{j} - 5(\sin 30°)\alpha(-\mathbf{i})$$

$$= (2.5\alpha)\mathbf{i} + (4.33\alpha)\mathbf{j}$$

$$(a_1)_x = 2.5\alpha \qquad (a_1)_y = 4.33\alpha$$

$$\mathbf{a}_2 = \alpha \times \mathbf{r}_{C_2} = \alpha \mathbf{k} \times 11(\cos 30° \mathbf{i} - \sin 30° \mathbf{j})$$

$$= 11(\cos 30°)\alpha \mathbf{j} - 11(\sin 30°)\alpha(-\mathbf{i})$$

$$= (9.53\alpha)\mathbf{i} + (5.5\alpha)\mathbf{j}$$

$$(a_2)_x = 9.53\alpha \qquad (a_2)_y = 5.5\alpha$$

The equations of motion, when expressed in Cartesian coordinates, are

$$\overset{\rightarrow}{+}\ O_x = 100(2.5\alpha) + 400(9.53\alpha)$$

$$O_x = 4062\,\alpha \tag{a}$$

$$\overset{\uparrow}{+}\ O_y - 100(9.81) - 400(9.81) = 100(4.33\alpha)$$

$$+ 400(5.5\alpha)$$

$$O_y = 2633\alpha + 4905 \tag{b}$$

$$\overset{+}{\circlearrowleft}\ M - [100(9.81)](5 \cos 30°) - [400(9.81)](11 \cos 30°)$$

$$= [\tfrac{1}{3}(100)(10^2)](\alpha) + \left[\begin{array}{c} \frac{2}{5}(400)(1.0)^2 \\ +48{,}400 \end{array} \right](\alpha)$$

$$M = 51{,}893.33\alpha + 41{,}629 \tag{c}$$

For $\alpha = 2$ rad/s², we obtain

$$M = 145{,}415.7\,\text{N} \cdot \text{m} \,\circlearrowleft \ \blacktriangleleft$$

$$O_x = 8{,}124\,\text{N} \rightarrow \qquad O_y = 10{,}171\,\text{N} \uparrow \ \blacktriangleleft$$

EXAMPLE 7.8

Two weights ($W_1 = 70$ lb and $W_2 = 50$ lb) are connected as shown by a cord passing without slipping through a 2-ft-radius pulley. Neglecting the mass of the cord and treating the pulley as a 40-lb uniform disk, determine the acceleration of the weights.

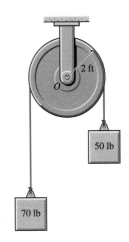

Solution Since the moment summation is taken about O, the vectors $m_1\mathbf{a}$ and $m_2\mathbf{a}$ will have to be considered, in addition to $I_O\alpha$, when writing the rotational equation. Thus we have

$$\circlearrowleft \Sigma M = (m_1 + m_2)a(2) + I_O\alpha \qquad \text{(a)}$$

where

$$\Sigma M = 70(2) - 50(2) = 40$$

$$I_O = \frac{1}{2}\left(\frac{40}{32.2}\right)(2)^2 = 2.48 \text{ slug} \cdot \text{ft}^2 \text{ (or lb} \cdot \text{ft} \cdot \text{s}^2\text{)}$$

and $a = \alpha(2)$. Substituting these expressions into Equation (a), we obtain

$$40 = \left(\frac{70 + 50}{32.2}\right)(2\alpha)2 + (2.48)\alpha = 14.91\alpha + 2.48\alpha = 17.39\alpha$$

which we can then solve for α:

$$\alpha = \frac{40}{17.39} = 2.30 \text{ rad/s}^2$$

$$a = \alpha r = (2.30)(2) = 4.60 \text{ ft/s}^2$$

$$a_1 = 4.60 \text{ ft/s}^2 \,\,\downarrow \quad \blacktriangleleft$$

$$a_2 = 4.60 \text{ ft/s}^2 \,\,\uparrow \quad \blacktriangleleft$$

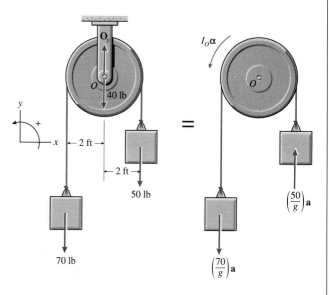

EXAMPLE   7.9

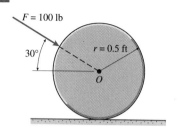

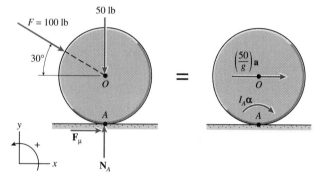

A 50-lb uniform disk (1-ft diameter) rolls without slipping along a horizontal surface under the action of an inclined force $F = 100$ lb as shown. Determine the linear acceleration of the disk.

Solution   The instantaneous center of zero velocity, at the given position, is at point A. By taking the moment summation about A, we write

$$\circlearrowleft \Sigma M_A = I_A \alpha$$

where $I_A = \left[\dfrac{1}{2}\left(\dfrac{50}{32.2}\right)(0.5)^2 + \left(\dfrac{50}{32.2}\right)(0.5)^2\right] = 0.582.$

The above equation becomes

$$-100(\cos 30°)(0.5) = -(0.582)\alpha$$

Solving for α and a,

$$\alpha = 74.40 \text{ rad/s}^2 \circlearrowleft \qquad a = \alpha r = (74.40)0.5$$

$$a = 37.20 \text{ ft/s}^2 \rightarrow \blacktriangleleft$$

EXAMPLE   7.10

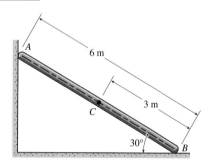

A 50-kg slender bar starts sliding along a smooth floor and wall as shown. Determine (a) the initial angular acceleration of the bar, and (b) the corresponding floor and wall reactions.

(*continued*)

Example 7.10 (*concluded*)

Solution The bar will be subjected to a translational and a rotational motion. Since the surfaces along which the body is sliding are smooth, no frictional forces will be involved. The equations of motion applicable to the case are

$$\xrightarrow{+} \Sigma F_x = m(a_C)_x \qquad N_A = 50(a_C)_x \qquad \text{(a)}$$

$$\uparrow^{+} \Sigma F_y = m(a_C)_y$$

$$N_B - 50(9.81) = 50(a_C)_y \qquad \text{(b)}$$

$$\circlearrowright^{+} \Sigma M_C = I_C \alpha$$

$$-N_A(3 \sin 30°) + N_B(3 \cos 30°) = \left[\frac{1}{12}(50)(6)^2\right]\alpha \qquad \text{(c)}$$

where N_A, N_B, a_C, and α are the four unknowns. The fourth equation necessary for the solution of the problem is the kinematic relationship between a_C and α. And if we recognize that the bar rotates instantaneously about the instantaneous center of zero velocity at IC, the acceleration of the mass center C can be expressed as

$$\mathbf{a}_C = \boldsymbol{\alpha} \times \mathbf{r}_C$$

since $\boldsymbol{\omega} = \mathbf{0}$ when the body starts from rest. Thus, we write

$$\mathbf{a}_C = \alpha \mathbf{k} \times (-3 \cos 30°\mathbf{i} - 3 \sin 30°\mathbf{j})$$

$$= -3\alpha \cos 30°\mathbf{j} + 3\alpha \sin 30°\mathbf{i}$$

$$\mathbf{a}_C = 1.5\alpha \mathbf{i} - 2.6\alpha \mathbf{j}$$

$$(a_C)_x = 1.5\alpha \qquad (a_C)_y = -2.6\alpha \qquad \text{(d)}$$

Substituting Equations (d) into Equations (a), (b), and (c) we have

$$N_A = 75\alpha \qquad N_B = -130\alpha + 490.5$$

$$-1.5N_A + 2.6N_B = 150\alpha$$

The simultaneous solution of these three equations yields

$$\alpha = 2.12 \text{ rad/s}^2 \, \circlearrowleft \; \blacktriangleleft$$

which, when substituted into Equation (d), gives

$$\mathbf{a}_C = 1.5(2.12)\mathbf{i} - 2.6(2.12)\mathbf{j} = 3.18\mathbf{i} - 5.51\mathbf{j} \, (\text{m/s}^2)$$

Also,

$$N_A = 75(2.12)$$

$$N_A = 159 \text{ N} \xrightarrow{} \; \blacktriangleleft$$

$$N_B = 490.5 - 130(2.12)$$

$$N_B = 214.9 \text{ N} \uparrow \; \blacktriangleleft$$

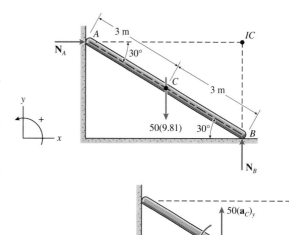

EXAMPLE 7.11

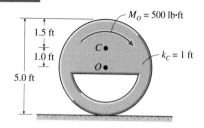

$M_O = 500$ lb·ft

1.5 ft
1.0 ft
5.0 ft

$C\bullet$
$O\bullet$
$k_C = 1$ ft

An unbalanced wheel (5-ft diameter) weighs 300 lb and has a mass radius of gyration k_C with respect to an axis through its mass center C of 1 ft. A 500-lb · ft moment is applied on the wheel as shown. If the coefficient of static friction between the horizontal floor and the wheel is 0.50, determine, for the position shown, the magnitude of the maximum angular velocity of the wheel that will not cause slippage.

Solution The wheel is translating and rotating. Since the body's mass center is not coincident with its center of rotation, the applicable equations of motion are

$$\Sigma F_x = m(a_C)_x \qquad \Sigma F_y = m(a_C)_y$$
$$\Sigma M_C = I_C\alpha$$

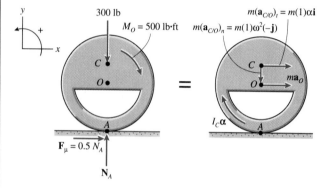

300 lb
$M_O = 500$ lb·ft
$m(\mathbf{a}_{C/O})_t = m(1)\alpha\mathbf{i}$
$m(\mathbf{a}_{C/O})_n = m(1)\omega^2(-\mathbf{j})$
ma_O
$I_C\alpha$
$F_\mu = 0.5 N_A$
N_A

The additional relationship needed to solve for the unknowns is the kinematic equation relating the linear acceleration vector $\mathbf{a}_C$ of the mass center to the angular velocity and acceleration of the wheels. To this effect we write

$$\mathbf{a}_C = \mathbf{a}_O + \mathbf{a}_{C/O} \qquad (a)$$

and since the instantaneous center of zero velocity is at A, we have

$$\mathbf{a}_O = (2.5\alpha)\mathbf{i} \qquad (b)$$
$$\mathbf{a}_{C/O} = (a_{C/O})_n\mathbf{j} + (a_{C/O})_t\mathbf{i} \qquad (c)$$

where

$$(a_{C/O})_n = -(\overline{OC})\omega^2 = -(1)\omega^2 \qquad (d)$$
$$(a_{C/O})_t = (\overline{OC})\alpha = (1)\alpha \qquad (e)$$

Substituting the acceleration terms from (b), (c), (d), and (e) into Equation (a), we obtain

$$\mathbf{a}_C = [(2.5\alpha) + \alpha]\mathbf{i} - \omega^2\mathbf{j} = 3.5\alpha\mathbf{i} - \omega^2\mathbf{j}$$
$$(a_C)_x = 3.5\alpha \qquad (a_C)_y = -\omega^2$$

The governing equations of motion can now be expressed

$\xrightarrow{+} \Sigma F_x = m(a_C)_x$

$$0.5N_A = \left(\frac{300}{32.2}\right)(3.5\alpha) = 32.6\alpha \qquad (f)$$

$\circlearrowleft \Sigma M_C = I_C\alpha$

$$-500 + (3.5)(0.5)N_A = \left[\left(\frac{300}{32.2}\right)(1.0)^2\right]\alpha \qquad (g)$$

(continued)

Example 7.11   (*concluded*)

where $I_C = mk_C^2$. Equations (f) and (g) can be solved simultaneously for N_A and α to yield

$$\alpha = 4.77 \text{ rad/s}^2 \;\circlearrowright \qquad N_A = 311.13 \text{ lb} \;\uparrow$$

The angular velocity ω is determined through the force equation along the y axis:

$$\overset{+\uparrow}{} \Sigma F_y = m(a_C)_y$$

$$311.13 - 300 = \left(\frac{300}{32.2}\right)(-\omega^2)$$

$$\omega^2 = 1.195$$

$$\omega = -1.093 \text{ rad/s} \qquad \omega = 1.093 \text{ rad/s} \;\circlearrowright \;\blacktriangleleft$$

7.6 SUMMARY

In this chapter, we have learned the following:

1. The equations of general planar motion are

$$\Sigma \mathbf{F} = m\mathbf{a}_C \tag{7.1}$$

$$\Sigma \mathbf{M}_A = (\mathbf{r}_{C/A} \times m\mathbf{a}_C) + I_C\boldsymbol{\alpha} \tag{7.8}$$

where $\mathbf{M}_A$ represents the moment summation of all external forces acting on the slab, $\mathbf{r}_{C/A}$ is the position vector of the mass center relative to A, and I_C is the mass moment of inertia of the slab about the mass center.

In scalar form we have, in Cartesian coordinates,

$$\left.\begin{array}{l} \Sigma F_x = m(a_C)_x \qquad \Sigma F_y = m(a_C)_y \\ \Sigma M_A = [(r_{C/A})_x m(a_C)_y + (r_{C/A})_y m(a_C)_x] + I_C\alpha \end{array}\right\} \tag{7.12}$$

2. The equations of motion for the translational motion of a slab having a mass m are

$$\Sigma \mathbf{F} = m\mathbf{a}_C \qquad \Sigma \mathbf{M}_C = \mathbf{0} \tag{7.16}$$

where $\Sigma \mathbf{F}$ is the resultant of all external forces acting upon the body and $\mathbf{a}_C$ is the acceleration of the mass center. $\Sigma \mathbf{M}_C$ represents the summation of the moments of the external forces about the mass center of the slab. In scalar form (Cartesian coordinates) we have

$$F_x = m(a_C)_x \qquad F_y = m(a_C)_y \qquad M_C = 0 \tag{7.17}$$

3. The equations for the rotational motion about a fixed point O of a slab, having a mass m:

$$\Sigma \mathbf{F} = m\mathbf{a}_C \tag{7.1}$$

$$\Sigma \mathbf{M}_O = I_O\boldsymbol{\alpha} \tag{7.10}$$

where $\Sigma \mathbf{M}_O$ represents the summation of the moments of the external forces about the fixed point O, I_O is the mass moment of inertia of the slab about O, and $\boldsymbol{\alpha}$ is the angular acceleration of the slab.

In scalar form we have (in tangential and normal coordinates)

$$\Sigma F_t = m(a_C)_t = m\alpha r_C \qquad \Sigma F_n = m(a_C)_n = m\omega^2 r_C \qquad \Sigma M_O = I_O\alpha \qquad (7.20)$$

For the case of *centroidal rotation*, the equations are

$$\Sigma F_x = 0 \qquad \Sigma F_y = 0 \qquad \Sigma M_C = I_C\alpha \qquad (7.21)$$

$$\Sigma F_t = 0 \qquad \Sigma F_n = 0 \qquad \Sigma M_C = I_C\alpha \qquad (7.22)$$

KEY TERMS

angular acceleration *305*

acceleration vector *304*

planar motion *304*

rotation *309*

   centroidal *310*

rotational motion *309*

translation *308*

   curvilinear *309*

   rectilinear *309*

translational motion *308*

PROBLEMS

ALL SECTIONS

7.1 A 100-kg crate rests on a horizontal floor. A force $F = 1000$ N is applied to the crate as shown. If the coefficient of kinetic friction between crate and floor is $\mu_k = 0.3$, determine the crate's initial acceleration. Assume that the crate slides and verify the assumption.

7.2 A loaded shopping cart weighs 100 lb and its mass center is at C. A force of $F = 30$ lb is applied, as shown, to the handle. Neglecting the rolling resistance and the mass of the wheels, determine the normal reactions at each of the wheels.

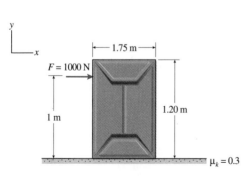

Figure P7.1

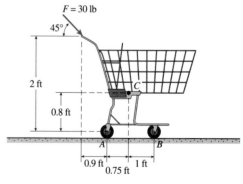

Figure P7.2

7.3 A loaded shopping cart has a mass of 150 kg and its mass center is at C as shown. Neglecting the rolling resistance and the mass of the wheels, determine the magnitude of the smallest force F that will cause the front wheels of the cart to leave the ground.

7.4 A 16-ft-long wooden post (2 in. × 4 in.) is loaded on a trailer pulled by a car. Determine the maximum acceleration which the trailer can have before the post pivots about the point A and leaves the trailer's edge at B.

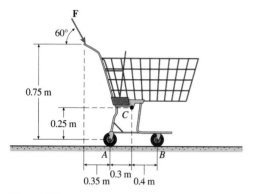

Figure P7.3

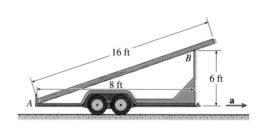

Figure P7.4

7.5 A 200-kg bar is supported by flexible cords as shown. The mass center C of the bar is not at its geometric center. If, at the instant shown, the speed of the mass center is 20 m/s; determine the acceleration of the bar.

7.6 A car has a weight of 3000 lb and its center of mass is located at C_1. A load of 1000 lb with its mass center at C_2 is placed on top of the car as shown. The car is traveling at 55 mph when suddenly the driver applies the brakes to all four wheels and causes them to lock and slip. If the coefficient of kinetic friction $\mu_k = 0.25$, determine the distance the car skids before coming to a full stop. Neglect the mass of the wheels and the aerodynamic drag forces, and assume the skid is along a straight line.

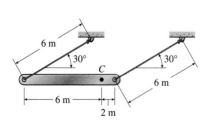

Figure P7.5

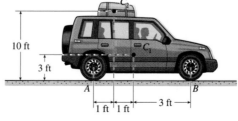

Figure P7.6

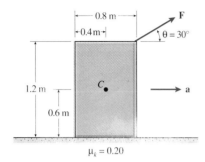

Figure P7.7

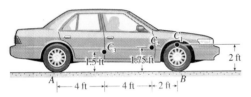

Figure P7.8

7.7 A force $F = 200$ N moves the 40-kg box as shown. The coefficient of kinetic friction between the box and the floor is $\mu_k = 0.20$. Determine the acceleration of the box.

7.8 A front-wheel-drive car's total weight of 4000 lb is distributed, as shown, between its 800-lb engine with its mass center at C_1, its 500-lb transmission with its mass center at C_2, and the remaining 2700 lb of the body and frame acting at C_3. If the rear wheels are rolling freely, and the coefficient of static friction between the wheels and the road is $\mu_s = 0.5$, and ignoring the mass of the wheels and driver, determine the shortest time it takes for the car to reach 55 mph, starting from rest.

7.9 A 60-kg bicycle rider has his mass center located at C_1. The bicycle has a mass of 10 kg and its mass center is at C_2 as shown. The rider suddenly applies the brakes to the rear wheel which becomes locked. Neglecting the mass of the wheels and assuming that the front wheel is rolling without sliding, determine the deceleration of the rider and the reactions on the tires. The coefficient of kinetic friction at the rear tire is $\mu_k = 0.75$.

7.10 A bicycle and rider together weigh 180 lb. The center of mass of the system is located at C as shown. The rider suddenly applies the brakes to the front wheel which becomes locked. Neglecting the mass of the wheels, determine the minimum coefficient of kinetic friction between the pavement and the wheel to cause the rear wheel to lift off the ground.

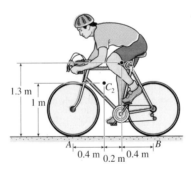

Figure P7.9

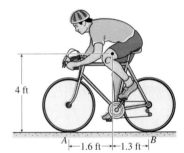

Figure P7.10

7.11 Block A and counterweight B weigh 400 lb and 50 lb, respectively, and are connected by a cable as shown. Determine the acceleration of block A and the reaction against A of the smooth surface along which block A is sliding. Neglect the mass of the pulley.

7.12 A 40-kg homogeneous flat disk is pulled along a rough surface as shown. If the disk is accelerating at 2 m/s^2 over the surface by sliding without rotating, determine the coefficient of friction μ_k between disk and ground and the force T of the cord.

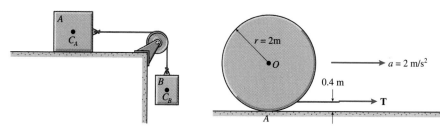

Figure P7.11

Figure P7.12

7.13 A 120-lb homogeneous flat disk is pulled along a pavement by a cable AB, which is attached to the frame of a truck through a pulley. If, at the instant shown, the acceleration of point B is 3 ft/s² as shown, determine the tension in the cable and the angle θ, if the coefficient of kinetic friction between the disk and the pavement is $\mu_k = 0.25$.

7.14 A 2000-lb car is coasting freely downhill as shown. If the mass of the wheels and the rolling resistance are negligible, determine the acceleration of the vehicle and the reaction forces between the road and tires.

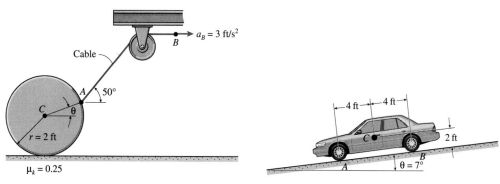

Figure P7.13

Figure P7.14

7.15 The 40-kg uniform triangular plate is released from rest at $\theta = 40°$. The rigid bars connecting the plate to the hinges A and B have negligible masses. For the position shown, determine the tension in each bar and the acceleration of the mass center of the triangular plate.

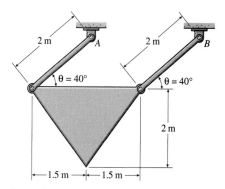

Figure P7.15

7.16 A jet aircraft during landing has a speed of 130 mph and within 1000 ft reduces its speed uniformly to 50 mph by reversing its jet thrusts, which develop a force of T lb. If the total weight of the plane is 300,000 lb and the mass center is located at C, determine the normal reaction force developed under the nose wheel at the instant when the speed of the plane has been reduced to 50 mph. Neglect the aerodynamic lift and drag forces acting on the aircraft.

7.17 A 70-Mg twin-jet aircraft's engines provide, during takeoff, a total thrust T of 600 kN as shown. Neglecting the mass of the wheels and the aerodynamic forces, determine the acceleration of the aircraft and the normal reactions developed under the nose wheel and each of the two wing wheels.

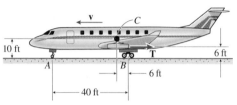

Figure P7.16

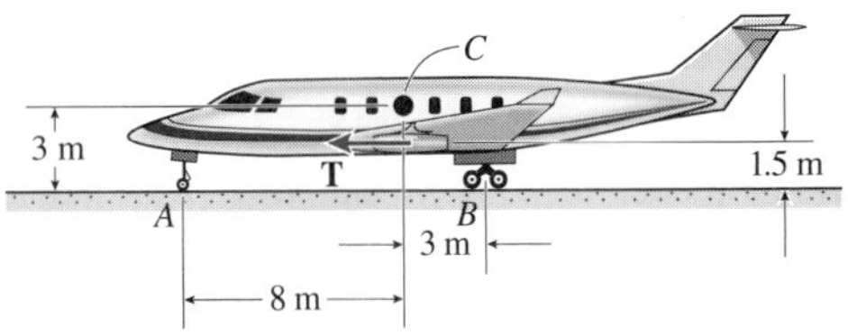

Figure P7.17

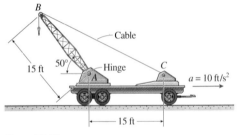

Figure P7.18

7.18 The 100-lb boom AB is fastened to the trailer by a cable BC and a hinge at A. The trailer starts from rest and accelerates at 10 ft/s². Assuming the weight of the boom is uniformly distributed, determine the reaction force acting at the hinge A.

7.19 A 1200-kg front-wheel-drive car is accelerated from rest. The mass center of the car is located at C. Determine the velocity of the car after it has covered a distance of 200 m. Neglect the mass of the wheels which are assumed to be rolling without slipping. Assume an effective coefficient of friction between the driving tires and the pavement of $\mu = 0.4$.

7.20 A 2500-lb automobile is accelerated on a flat horizontal pavement as shown. Determine the acceleration of the car, if the driven rear-wheels are about to slip. The coefficient of static friction between each driven tire and the pavement is 0.50. Neglect the mass of the wheels, and the rolling resistance of the undriven front wheels.

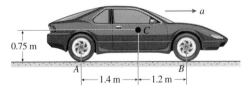

Figure P7.19

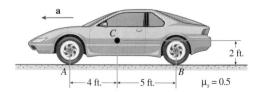

Figure P7.20

7.21   The 75-lb disk of 2-ft radius is pin-supported at its center O and a cord is wrapped around its periphery. A constant force $F = 5.0$ lb and a constant moment $M = 5$ lb · ft are applied to the cord and the disk respectively. Neglecting the mass of the cord, determine the reactions at the pin and the disk's angular acceleration.

7.22   The 75-kg disk (radius $= 0.2$ m) shown is pin-supported at its center O and a cord of negligible mass is wrapped around its periphery. The cord is attached to a 75-kg crate. If the crate is released from rest, determine the reactions at the pin and the disk's angular acceleration.

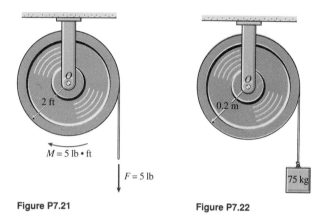

Figure P7.21   Figure P7.22

7.23   A 100-lb spool shown is pin-supported at its center O and a cord of negligible mass is wrapped around its periphery. The cord is attached to a weight of 20 lb. The spool's radius of gyration about its centroidal axis is $k_O = 1.5$ ft. Determine the spool's angular velocity 5 s after the release of the crate from rest.

7.24   Determine the angular velocity of the spool of Problem 7.23 after the crate has descended 5 ft.

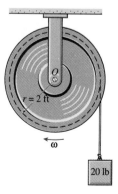

Figure P7.23 and P7.24

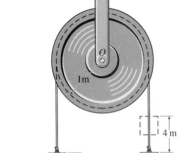

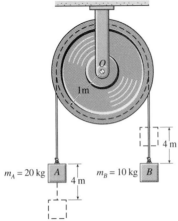

$m_A = 20$ kg A $m_B = 10$ kg B

Figure P7.25

7.25 Two weights A and B are attached as shown to the ends of a cord of negligible mass which passes over a 5-kg pulley having a mass radius of gyration $k_O = 0.4$ m. Assuming no cord slippage on the pulley, determine the speed of the weights A and B, just after they have moved, in opposite directions, by 4 m.

7.26 A 25-lb wheel is subjected to a constant moment $M = 100$ lb · ft as shown. The wheel has a mass radius of gyration $k_O = 1.25$ ft. Determine the angular acceleration of the wheel and the reactions which the pin at O exerts on the wheel.

7.27 The 20-lb slender rod (length $= 5$ ft) is pin-connected at O and, at the position shown, has an angular velocity $\omega = 5$ rad/s. Determine the reaction that the pin support at O exerts on the rod at the instant shown.

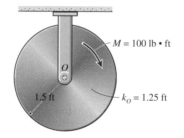

Figure P7.26

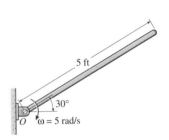

Figure P7.27

7.28 A composite body consists of a uniform 10-lb sphere (radius $= 2$ ft) and a 3-lb slender rod having a length of 4 ft. If, at the instant shown, the angular velocity of the body is $\omega = 2$ rad/s clockwise, determine the magnitude of the torque M necessary to cause a counterclockwise angular deceleration of 3 rad/s². Also, determine at the same instant the reaction forces at the hinge O.

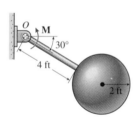

Figure P7.28

7.29 The rod-sphere system shown consists of a uniform 25-kg sphere (radius 1.0 m) and a 10-kg slender rod (length 5 m). If, at $\theta = 0$, the system is at rest, determine its angular velocity when $\theta = \pi/2$. Also determine the horizontal and vertical components of the reaction at the pin O, when $\theta = \pi/2$.

7.30 Two blocks A and B are linked by a cord of negligible mass wrapped around a pulley C (radius $= 1.0$ ft) as shown. The blocks A and B and the pulley C weigh 50 lb, 60 lb, and 15 lb, respectively, and the mass radius of gyration of the pulley is $k_C = 0.70$ ft. Assuming no cord slippage on the pulley, determine the tensile force in the horizontal and vertical segments of the cord. The coefficient of kinetic friction between the block A and the table top is $\mu_k = 0.20$.

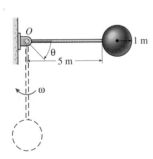

Figure P7.29

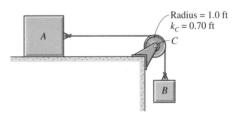

Figure P7.30

7.31 The 50-kg plate (2 m × 2 m) is pin-supported at A as shown. When released from rest at this position, determine the initial reaction force at A.

7.32 The 120-lb disk (radius = 3 ft) is pin-supported at A, as shown, and is rotating clockwise with $\omega = 0.3$ rad/s, when $\theta = 20°$. Determine the horizontal and vertical components of the reaction force at A, when $\theta = 0$.

7.33 A constant force $F = 1200$ N is applied on a cord wrapped around drum A, which, in turn, rotates drum B, elevating the weight C, as shown. Drums A and B are rigidly fastened together and turn about their common mass center O. The two drums have a combined mass of 250 kg and a radius of gyration $k_o = 300$ mm. Determine the upward acceleration of the weight C and the reaction force at O.

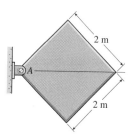

Figure P7.31

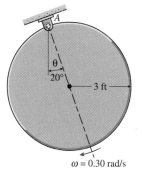

Figure P7.32

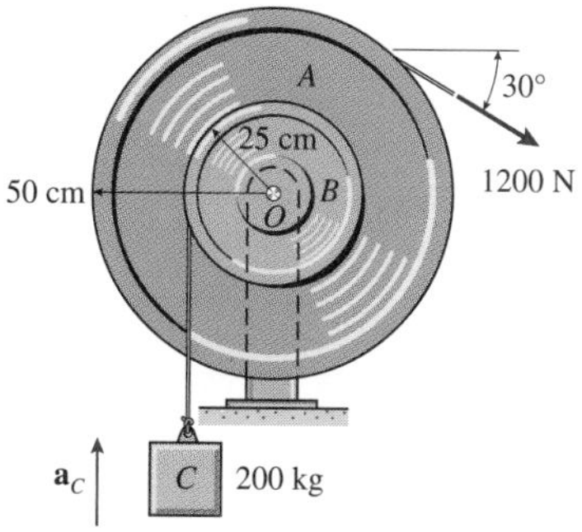

Figure P7.33

7.34 The 50-kg block shown slides on the smooth horizontal surface under the pull of a 100-kg block. The blocks are joined to each other by a cord of negligibie mass. There is no slipping between the cable and the pulley which has a mass moment of inertia of 5 kg · m² and a radius of 1.0 m. Determine the angular acceleration of the pulley and the tensile forces along the horizontal and vertical segments of the cord.

7.35 The chain-drive shown consists of a 5-kg sprocket A (radius = 100 mm) and a 2-kg sprocket B (radius = 20 mm). If sprocket A is driven by torque $M = 50$ N · m, as shown, determine the angular acceleration of sprocket B. (Assume A and B are disks.)

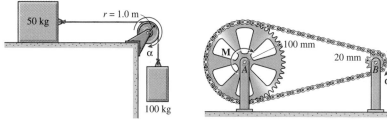

Figure P7.34

Figure P7.35

7.36 The 50-kg slender uniform rod shown is pin-supported at O and is released from rest. It rotates clockwise under its own weight in the vertical plane. Determine the angular acceleration of the rod at the instant shown.

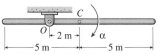

Figure P7.36

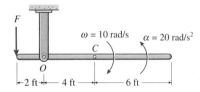

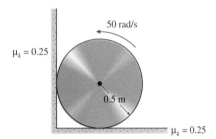

Figure P7.37

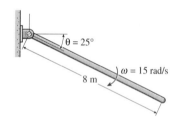

Figure P7.38

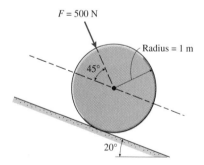

Figure P7.40

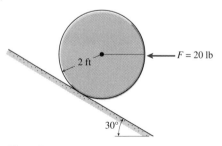

Figure P7.41

7.37 The 50-lb slender rigid bar rotates clockwise in the vertical plane about the horizontal axis through O, with an angular velocity of 10 rad/s clockwise as shown. At the position shown, determine the force F necessary to decelerate the bar at the rate of 20 rad/s². Also, determine the components of the pin reactions at O for the position given.

7.38 At a given instant, the 40-kg uniform disk is rotating counterclockwise with an angular velocity of 50 rad/s. If the coefficient of kinetic friction between the disk and the horizontal and vertical surfaces is 0.25, determine the time required for the disk to come to rest.

7.39 The 15-lb uniform slender rod is initially at rest in the position shown. A horizontal force $F = 50$ lb is applied at the tip of the rod. Determine, for the position shown: the distance (d) for which the horizontal component of the pin reaction at O is zero and the angular acceleration of the rod.

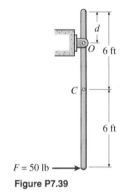

Figure P7.39

7.40 At the instant shown when $\theta = 25°$, the 10-kg uniform slender rod has an angular speed of 15 rad/s clockwise. Determine for the instant given: the angular acceleration of the rod; the horizontal and vertical components of the reaction at pin O.

7.41 A 50-kg uniform disk rolls without slipping down a slope under the action of a force $F = 500$ N as shown. Determine the acceleration of the disk's center.

7.42 A 100-lb uniform disk rolls without slipping down a 30° slope. A horizontal force $F = 20$ lb acts opposite the motion as shown. Determine the acceleration of the disk's center.

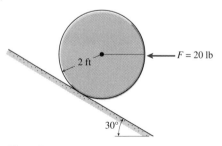

Figure P7.42

7.43 A 75-N · m couple moment is applied to the 50-kg disk shown. Determine whether slipping occurs. Also, find the acceleration of the disk's center. The coefficients of static and kinetic friction between the wheel and the floor are $\mu_s = 0.3$ and $\mu_k = 0.2$, respectively.

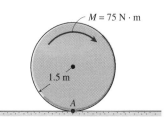

Figure P7.43

7.44 A 150-lb unbalanced wheel has its mass center at C and a radius of gyration $k_c = 1.4$ with respect to its centroidal axis through C. If the wheel is released from rest in the position shown, determine the angular acceleration of the wheel at the instant given. The coefficients of static and kinetic friction between the wheel and the surface at A are $\mu_s = 0.40$ and $\mu_k = 0.30$, respectively.

7.45 The 30-kg semicircular disk shown is released from rest from the position shown. If the coefficients of static and kinetic friction between the disk and the surface are $\mu_s = 0.45$ and $\mu_k = 0.25$, respectively, determine the angular acceleration of the disk and the normal and frictional forces exerted by the floor on the disk at the instant shown.

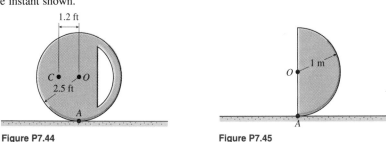

Figure P7.44   **Figure P7.45**

7.46 The 75-lb semicircular disk is rotating with an angular velocity $\omega = 5$ rad/s at the position shown. Assuming that the disk does not slip as it rolls, determine, for the position shown, the normal and the frictional forces exerted by the floor on the disk.

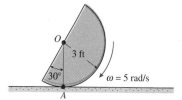

Figure P7.46

7.47 The 75-kg spool and wire assembly is acted upon by a force $F = 300$ N as shown. If the spool-wire assembly has a centroidal radius of gyration $k_c = 350$ mm, and the coefficients of static and kinetic friction between the spool and the floor at A are $\mu_s = 0.25$ and $\mu_k = 0.20$, respectively, determine the angular acceleration of the spool-wire assembly.

7.48 The spool-wire assembly weighs 250 lb and has a centroidal radius of gyration $k_C = 2.5$ ft. It is acted upon by a vertical force $F = 100$ lb as shown. If the coefficients of static and kinetic friction at A are $\mu_s = 0.35$ and $\mu_k = 0.3$, determine the angular acceleration of the spool and the normal and frictional forces at A.

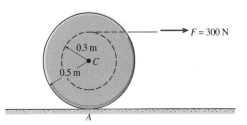

Figure P7.47

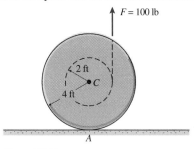

Figure P7.48

7.49   A 40-kg slender bar starts sliding along a floor and wall as shown. If the coefficient of kinetic friction between wall and floor surfaces and the end points of the bar is $\mu_k = 0.20$, determine the initial angular acceleration of the bar and the normal and frictional forces exerted on the bar at A and B.

7.50   The 200-lb slender bar is originally at rest, being supported by two cables, as shown. Determine the initial angular acceleration of the bar and the tension in cable A, if the other is suddenly broken.

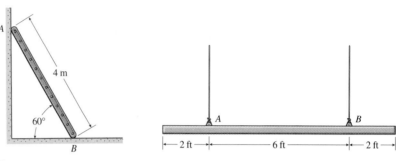

Figure P7.49

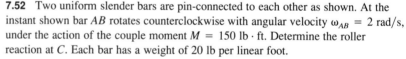

Figure P7.50

7.51   The 10-kg slender rod is supported by a pin and a cord as shown. When the cord suddenly fails, determine the initial angular acceleration of the bar and the reactions at C.

7.52   Two uniform slender bars are pin-connected to each other as shown. At the instant shown bar AB rotates counterclockwise with angular velocity $\omega_{AB} = 2$ rad/s, under the action of the couple moment $M = 150$ lb · ft. Determine the roller reaction at C. Each bar has a weight of 20 lb per linear foot.

7.53   The uniform 50-kg beam is being raised from rest upward by two cables, each moving at different rates, as shown. At the instant shown, determine the tension in each cable.

7.54   The 5-kg crank arm AB is rotating counterclockwise at a constant rate of 2000 rpm. It is pin-connected to the 7.5-kg piston rod BC, which is pin-connected to the 10-kg piston C. Determine the pin reactions at C. (Rod BC may be assumed to be a slender rod and its weight neglected.)

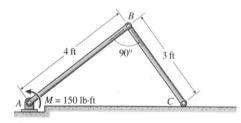

Figure P7.51

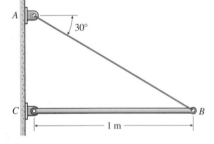

Figure P7.52

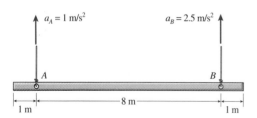

Figure P7.53

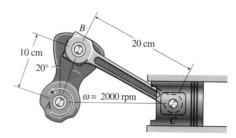

Figure P7.54

7.55 The 40-lb slender rod is hanging from a pin fixed to a 40-lb carriage at rest as shown. The rod is released from rest when $\theta = 30°$. Determine the acceleration a of the carriage and the angular acceleration α of the rod, at the instant shown. Neglect frictional forces.

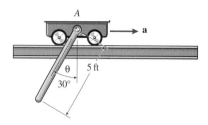

Figure P7.55

7.56 The 50-kg panel swings about a pivot A, which is attached to a carriage. The carriage and the panel are initially at rest ($\theta = 0°$). When the carriage suddenly accelerates at 2 m/s², the panel swings clockwise as shown. The panel's centroidal radius of gyration $k_C = 0.6$ m and its mass center C is located at a distance $r_C = 1.0$ m from the pin A. Determine the angular velocity of the panel at the instant when $\theta = 15°$.

7.57 The two 150-lb uniform slender bars are 20-ft long each and are pin-connected at B to each other. At the instant shown, the 150-lb bar BC under the action of the couple moment M has an angular velocity of 3 rad/s and an angular acceleration of 5 rad/s², as indicated. Determine the normal and frictional reactions exerted on the bar at C as well as the pin reactions at B. The coefficient of kinetic friction as C is $\mu_k = 0.2$.

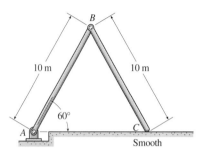

Figure P7.58

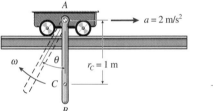

Figure P7.56

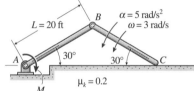

Figure P7.57

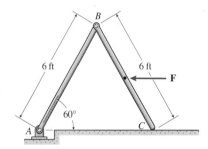

Figure P7.59

7.58 The two 10-kg slender bars (10-m long each) are released from rest in the position shown. Assuming the floor to be smooth, determine the angular acceleration of the bar AB, right after release.

7.59 The two 25-lb slender bars (6-ft long each) are subjected to a force F acting at the midpoint of bar BC. The force causes the end point C of the bar to move on the smooth surface to the left with a constant velocity 5 ft/s. Determine the magnitude of the force F at the instant shown.

7.60 The homogeneous 5-kg disk (radius = 0.40 m) rolls without slipping in the vertical plane along the circular path shown. In the position indicated by $\theta = 40°$, the disk's mass center has a speed of 7 m/s. Determine the reaction which the path exerts on the disk and the disk's angular acceleration, at this position.

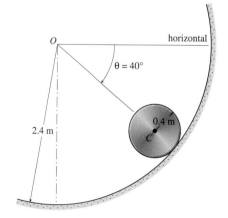

Figure P7.60

7.61 A 15,000-kg rocket 20-m long is moving upward with an acceleration of 20 m/s² under the thrust of two rocket engines, as shown. Determine (*a*) the thrust produced by each engine, and (*b*) assuming that one engine suddenly fails, the acceleration of the mass center of the rocket and its angular acceleration. The rocket can be approximated as a slender cylinder 20 m long (dia. = 2m).

7.62 The 500-lb unbalanced wheel (radius = 3 ft) rolls and slips on the horizontal surface under the action of the couple moment *M*, as shown. The centroidal radius of gyration of the wheel is 0.75 ft. In the position shown, the velocity of the center *O* is 10**i** (ft/s), the wheel's angular velocity $\boldsymbol{\omega} = -5\mathbf{k}$ (rad/s), and angular acceleration $\boldsymbol{\alpha} = -5\mathbf{k}$ (rad/s²). The coefficient of kinetic friction between the wheel and the floor is 0.25. Determine the magnitude *M* of the moment.

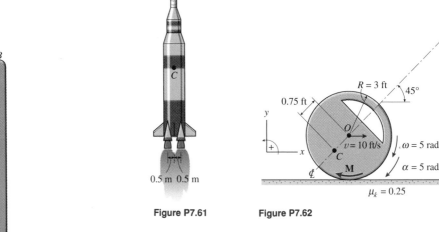

Figure P7.61   Figure P7.62

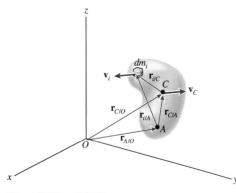

Figure P7.63

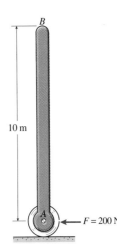

7.63 The 100-kg slender uniform bar *AB* (length = 10 m) is balanced in the vertical position when a horizontal force *F* = 200 N is applied as shown. Determine the bar's initial angular acceleration and the acceleration of its end point *B*.

7.64 Show that, if the angular momentum of a rigid body about an arbitrary point *A* is given as

$$\mathbf{H}_A = \int_m \mathbf{r}_{i/A} \times dm_i(\mathbf{v}_i)$$

where $\mathbf{r}_{i/A}$ and $\mathbf{v}_i$ are the position (relative to *A*) and velocity vectors, respectively, of a particle of mass dm_i, as shown, the angular momentum vector $\mathbf{H}_A$ can be expressed by Equation (7.6). Introduce the definition of the mass center *C* in the form

$$\int_m dm_i(\mathbf{v}_i) = \mathbf{v}_C \int_m dm_i = m\mathbf{v}_C$$

where $\mathbf{v}_C$ is the velocity of the mass center.

7.65 Show that introducing Equation (7.6) into Equation (7.5) yields Equation (7.7).

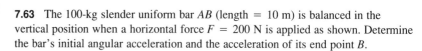

Figure P7.64 and P7.65

7.66   A rocket of uniform mass m and length L is launched vertically as shown. The rocket's trajectory is altered when the thrust T acts at an angle θ to the vertical. Express the variation of the bending moment M developed along the length of the rocket in terms of the distance y from the tail of the rocket. (The rocket can be treated as an L-long slender bar.)

7.67   For the 700-lb rocket shown calculate its angular acceleration α and the x- and y-components of the acceleration $\mathbf{a}_C$ of its mass center C. The thrust of the rocket is $T = 1000$ lb and is directed as shown. The rocket's centroidal radius of gyration is $k_C = 5$ ft.

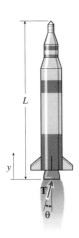

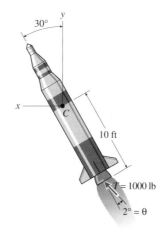

Figure P7.66   Figure P7.67

7.68   The centroidal radius of gyration of a rocket of uniform mass m and length L is k_C. If a thrust T is applied to the rocket at an angle θ to the vertical, determine the angular acceleration of the rocket and the acceleration of its tip point P.

7.69   A car door of mass m opens and swings about its hinge as shown when the brakes are applied and the car is decelerated at a rate a. If the door's radius of gyration about the hinge is k_O derive an expression for the door's angular velocity ω and the hinge reaction O_x and O_y in terms of the angle θ.

7.70   A car door weighing 80 lb is fully open when the car suddenly accelerates at a rate of 7.5 ft/s². If the door's centroidal radius of gyration is 1 ft, determine the door's angular velocity at the moment when it is fully shut. ($\overline{OC} = 2$ ft)

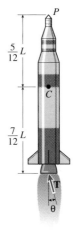

Figure P7.68

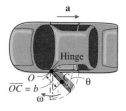

Figure P7.69

Figure P7.70

7.71 The mass center C of a car is located at 2 ft above ground and at 4 ft behind the front wheel axle as shown. If the coefficient of static friction between the tires and road is 0.60, compare the maximum possible accelerations for a front-wheel drive and a rear-wheel drive car.

7.72 The car shown weighs W and travels on a curved, banked road at a speed v. Determine the bank angle θ necessary for equalizing the normal forces on all wheels. The road's radius of curvature is R and the car's mass center is located at $\bar{h}$ above the road. The coefficient of static friction is μ_s.

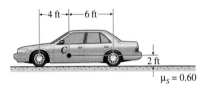

Figure P7.71

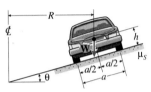

Figure P7.72

7.73 Gears A and B have masses of 50 kg and 15 kg respectively. A torque of 100 N · m is applied to the shaft of gear A. If the centroidal radii of gyration of the gears A and B are 150 mm and 50 mm respectively, determine the angular acceleration of gear B.

7.74 A 5-kg cylinder (diameter = 100 mm, length = 200 mm) rests on a conveyor belt as shown. Determine the angular acceleration of the cylinder when the belt starts from rest with an acceleration of 2 m/s². The coefficients of static and kinetic friction are $\mu_s = 0.35$ and $\mu_k = 0.25$ respectively.

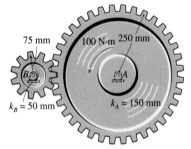

Figure P7.73

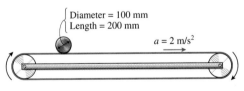

Figure P7.74

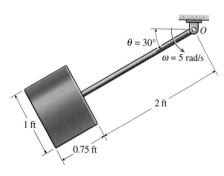

Figure P7.75

7.75 A pendulum consists of a uniform 10-lb plate and a 3-lb slender rod, the whole system swinging around a pin at O as shown. At the instant shown ($\theta = 30°$) the pendulum has a counterclockwise angular velocity of 5 rad/s. Determine the pin reactions at O.

7.76 The centroidal radius of gyration of a 50-kg cylinder is $k_C = 500$ mm. The cylinder is hanging from a rope and subjected to a horizontal force $F = 200$ N as shown. Determine the initial angular acceleration of the cylinder.

7.77 Determine the tensile force developed in the supporting cable OA of Problem 7.76.

7.78 A motorcycle weighs 300 lb and its mass center is at C_1. The rider weighs 180 lb and his mass center is at C_2. Determine the acceleration of the cycle and the minimum coefficient of friction μ_s necessary to lift the front wheel of the motorcycle off the ground as it starts moving forward.

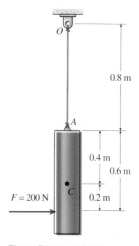

Figure P7.76 and P7.77

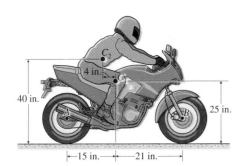

Figure P7.78

7.79 A slider-crank mechanism ABO is shown. The angular speed of the crank OB (length $= 1.25$ ft) is $\omega = 500$ rpm clockwise. A 3-ft long slender bar AB weighing 10 lb connects the crank to the 6-lb piston. Neglecting all friction forces and the weights of all members, determine the force on the piston pin at A when $\theta = 0°$.

7.80 A bowling ball is released by a bowler with a velocity of 5 m/s but without any angular velocity as shown. Determine the distance traveled by the ball along the alley floor before it begins to roll without slipping if the coefficient of friction between the ball and the floor is 0.25. The bowling ball has a diameter of 220 mm and weighs 100 N. Its radius of gyration is 85 mm.

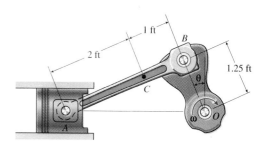

Figure P7.79

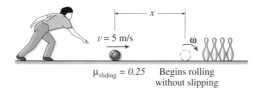

Figure P7.80

8

KINETICS OF RIGID BODIES IN PLANAR MOTION: WORK–ENERGY AND IMPULSE–MOMENTUM METHODS

8.1 INTRODUCTION

In the preceding chapter, we analyzed the planar motion of a rigid body by using the fundamental equation of motion (Newton's second law) relating the external forces acting upon the body to its mass and acceleration. The kinematic parameters of velocity and displacement vectors for any point of the rigid body were obtained by first solving for the acceleration vector and then proceeding with the integration of the acceleration-velocity-displacement relationships.

When the primary focus of our attention is *not* the acceleration vector, it is possible to adopt work–energy or impulse–momentum methods to solve certain classes of problems without involving the calculation of the acceleration vector. Rigid body motion caused by the effect of forces acting through distances is best studied by applying the *principle of work and energy*, and rigid body motion resulting from the effects of forces acting over a certain period of time is best dealt with by applying the *principle of impulse and momentum*. These will be the subject of this chapter.

8.2 WORK–KINETIC ENERGY RELATIONSHIP FOR A RIGID BODY IN PLANAR MOTION

In Chapter 5, we developed the work–kinetic energy relationship for a system of n particles joined together to form a rigid body, and expressed it in the form

$$\left(\sum_{i=1}^{n} T_i\right)_1 + \left(\sum_{i=1}^{n} U_i\right)_{1\rightarrow2} = \left(\sum_{i=1}^{n} T_i\right)_2$$

where

$$\sum_{i=1}^{n} T_i = \frac{1}{2}\sum_{i=1}^{n} m_i v_i^2$$

This represents the kinetic energy of the total system. The expression

$$\left(\sum_{i=1}^{n} U_i\right)_{1\rightarrow2} = \sum_{i=1}^{n} \int_{1}^{2} \mathbf{F}_i \cdot d\mathbf{r}_i$$

is the total work done by all *external* forces acting on all the particles of the system to bring it from its initial to its final position. The above relationship can thus be written in the familiar form

$$T_1 + \Sigma U_{1\rightarrow2} = T_2 \tag{8.1}$$

where T_1 and T_2 are the kinetic energies of the rigid body at its initial and final positions, respectively, and $\Sigma U_{1\rightarrow2}$ represents the algebraic sum of the works done by all of the external forces acting upon the rigid body during its displacement from initial to final position. In what follows, we will first establish the methods necessary for determining the work and energy terms appearing in Equation (8.1).

The Work Done by a Force

The *work* done by a force $\mathbf{F}$ acting on a rigid body follows the definition given earlier for the case of a force acting on a particle. Thus, we write

$$U_{1 \to 2} = \int_1^2 \mathbf{F} \cdot d\mathbf{r}$$

where $d\mathbf{r}$ is the infinitesimal displacement vector of the point of application of $\mathbf{F}$. Using the definition of scalar (dot) product, the above equation can now be expressed in the form

$$U_{1 \to 2} = \int_1^2 \mathbf{F} \cdot d\mathbf{r} = \int_1^2 F \cos \theta \, ds \tag{8.2}$$

where θ is the angle between $\mathbf{F}$ and the local tangent $d\mathbf{r}$ to the path and ds the magnitude of $d\mathbf{r}$. The computation of the work done by certain types of forces will now be discussed.

Work Done by a Force of Constant Magnitude and Direction   Applying Equation (8.2), and referring to (Figure 8.1*a*), we can write

$$U_{1 \to 2} = \mathbf{F} \cdot \int_1^2 d\mathbf{r} = \mathbf{F} \cdot (\mathbf{r}_2 - \mathbf{r}_1)$$

$$U_{1 \to 2} = \mathbf{F} \cdot \mathbf{R} = FR \cos \theta \tag{8.3}$$

where $\mathbf{R}$ is the resultant displacement vector of the point P of the body, upon which the force $\mathbf{F}$ acts during the motion of the rigid body from 1 to 2, and θ is the angle between the positive directions of $\mathbf{F}$ and $\mathbf{R}$.

Work Done by the Weight $W = mg$ of a Rigid Body in Planar Motion   Referring to Figure 8.1*b* and the vector form of Equation (8.2), we introduce $\mathbf{F} = -W\mathbf{j}$, to write

$$U_{1 \to 2} = \int_1^2 (-mg\mathbf{j}) \cdot (dx_C\mathbf{i} + dy_C\mathbf{j} + dz_C\mathbf{k})$$

$$U_{1 \to 2} = -\int_{(y_C)_1}^{(y_C)_2} (mg)dy = -(mg)[(y_C)_2 - (y_C)_1]$$

$$U_{1 \to 2} = -mg[(y_C)_2 - (y_C)_1]$$

$$U_{1 \to 2} = -W\Delta y_C \tag{8.4}$$

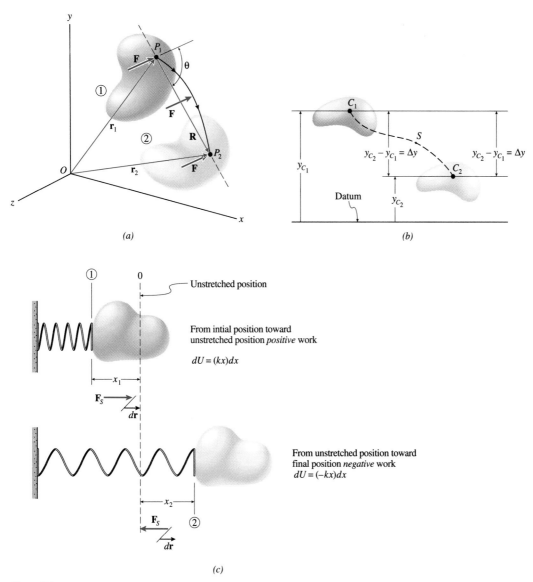

Figure 8.1

Work Done by a Spring Force Acting on a Rigid Body   The force exerted by a linear elastic spring attached to a rigid body (Figure 8.1*c*) can be expressed in the form

$$\mathbf{F}_s = kx\mathbf{i}$$

where x is measured from the spring's unstretched position and k is the spring constant.

Substituting the force $\mathbf{F}_s$ into Equation (8.2) yields

$$U_{1\to2} = \int_1^2 \mathbf{F}_s \cdot d\mathbf{r} = \int_{-x_1}^0 kx\,dx + \int_0^{x_2}(-kx)dx$$

$$U_{1\to2} = -\frac{k}{2}(x_2^2 - x_1^2) \tag{8.5}$$

This expression takes note of the fact that initially, the spring is compressed and, as a result, during the relaxation of the spring from its position at 1 to its unstretched position 0, the force exerted by the spring and the displacement vector are in the same direction and the work done is positive. However, from its unstretched position 0 to its position at 2, the spring opposes the movement of the rigid body—therefore, the work done by the spring force on the body is negative.

The Work Done by a Couple

Figure 8.2

We can now express the work done by a couple moment M acting on a rigid body, with the help of what we have already established regarding the work of a force. In Chapter 7, the general motion of a rigid body was described in terms of its translational and rotational components. Since the translational displacements of all particles of a rigid body are identical, the work done by a pair of noncollinear and opposite parallel forces—that is, a **couple**—acting on a rigid body will not have a component resulting from the translational motion. The work of a couple acting on a rigid body undergoing a general motion will thus be reduced to the work of the couple acting on the body under rotation. Consider in Figure 8.2 a body subjected to a couple with a magnitude of $M = Fd$. Under a differential angular displacement $d\theta$ of the body about the axis of rotation, which is perpendicular to the plane of the couple and intersects it at O, we can write, for a planar motion, the differential work done by the couple moment M

$$dU_M = F(r + d)d\theta - F(r)d\theta = Fd\,d\theta$$
$$dU_M = M\,d\theta$$

Note that in planar motion, the couple moment $\mathbf{M}$ and the infinitesimal angular displacement vector $d\boldsymbol{\theta}$ have parallel lines of action and the work of the couple is positive or negative depending on whether $\mathbf{M}$ and $d\boldsymbol{\theta}$ are in the same or opposite directions, respectively.

Therefore, when the rigid body undergoes a planar rotation and its angular position goes from θ_1 to θ_2,

$$U_{1\to2} = \int_1^2 dU_M = \int_{\theta_1}^{\theta_2} M\,d\theta \tag{8.6}$$

and, if the couple M has a constant magnitude,

$$U_{1\rightarrow 2} = M(\theta_2 - \theta_1) = M\,\Delta\theta \qquad (8.7)$$

The same sign convention must apply to M and θ.

Nonworking Forces

A careful review of Equation (8.2) will show that under certain circumstances the work done by a force will be zero. If the point of application of a force is not subject to any displacement ($d\mathbf{r} = \mathbf{0}$) or if the displacement is in a direction perpendicular to the force, that is, if the angle θ between $\mathbf{F}$ and $d\mathbf{r}$ is 90° ($\cos\theta = 0$), then the dot product ($\mathbf{F} \cdot d\mathbf{r}$) is zero and the force will do no work. For example, when a body rotates about a frictionless pin, the reaction forces at the pin will do no work. Similarly, when a body moves along a frictionless surface, the reaction force perpendicular to the surface will do no work. An important case when the friction force does no work is the ***rolling without sliding*** of a rigid body. Since, at any given instant, the point of contact P between body and surface is an instantaneous center of zero velocity ($v_P = 0$), the point of contact is not under the influence of the friction force.

The Kinetic Energy of a Rigid Body in Planar Motion

The ***kinetic energy*** of a rigid body is the sum of the kinetic energies of all its particles. In Chapter 5, the kinetic energy of a system of particles was expressed in Equation (5.11) as the sum of the kinetic energy, relative to a fixed frame of reference, of the total mass ($\Sigma m_i = m$) of the system—assumed to be concentrated at its center of mass—and the kinetic energies, relative to the center of mass, of all the individual particles of the system. For a rigid body, Equation (5.11) can be expressed as

$$T = \frac{1}{2}mv_C^2 + \frac{1}{2}\int_m dm\, v_{i/C}^2 \qquad (8.8)$$

where v_C is the absolute velocity of the mass center and $v_{i/C}$ represents the velocity field within the rigid body, relative to the mass center (Figure 8.3).

Since, in planar motion, $v_{i/C} = \omega r_{i/C}$, where ω is the angular velocity of the planar body or slab, Equation (8.8) can now be expressed as

$$T = \frac{1}{2}mv_C^2 + \frac{1}{2}\left(\int_m dm\, r_{i/C}^2\right)\omega^2$$

The term within parentheses is the mass moment of inertia I_C of the planar rigid body about its centroidal axis, which is perpendicular to the plane of motion. The kinetic energy of a rigid body in planar motion is now reduced

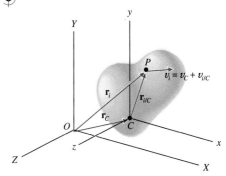

Figure 8.3

to

$$T = \frac{1}{2}mv_C^2 + \frac{1}{2}I_C\omega^2 \qquad (8.9)$$

Equation (8.9) states that the total kinetic energy of a rigid body subjected to a planar motion consists of a component—the ***translational kinetic energy***—resulting from the translational motion v_C of the body, and another—the ***rotational kinetic energy***—due to its rotational motion ω. From Equation (8.9) it follows that if the body is subjected to a pure translation, the kinetic energy of the body is reduced to the translational kinetic energy given as

$$T = \frac{1}{2}mv_C^2 \text{ (Translation only)} \qquad (8.10)$$

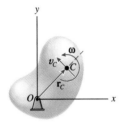

Figure 8.4

If, however, the rigid body is subjected to a rotation about an arbitrary fixed axis at O, then we can see from Figure 8.4 that the translational velocity v_C of the mass center can be expressed in terms of the angular velocity of the body, by writing $v_C = \omega r_C$, where r_C is measured relative to an origin at the point of rotation O. Thus we write

$$T = \frac{1}{2}m(\omega r_C)^2 + \frac{1}{2}I_C\omega^2$$

and after collecting terms

$$T = \frac{1}{2}(I_C + mr_C^2)\omega^2$$

Using the parallel-axis theorem, we see that the term within parentheses represents the mass moment of inertia of the body about the axis through O. Thus, the kinetic energy of a body rotating about a fixed axis is reduced to the rotational kinetic energy given as

$$T = \frac{1}{2}I_O\omega^2 \text{ (Rotation only)} \qquad (8.11)$$

The Equation of Work and Kinetic Energy

Having thus established above the methods for obtaining the terms for work ($U_{1\to2}$) and kinetic energy (T_1, T_2) appearing in Equation (8.1), we will now discuss the application of the principle of work and kinetic energy to the solution of dynamics problems involving velocities and displacements—angular and linear—without the necessity of calculating the acceleration vector.

The work–kinetic energy equation for a rigid body in planar motion given in Equation (8.1) as

$$T_1 + \Sigma U_{1\rightarrow2} = T_2$$

states that, as a rigid body moves under the influence of external forces and moments, its initial kinetic energy (T_1) is modified by the addition or subtraction of the work ($\Sigma U_{1\rightarrow2}$) done by all the external forces and moments. In the above equation we have

T_1 = initial kinetic energy of the body
T_2 = final kinetic energy of the body
$\Sigma U_{1\rightarrow2}$ = total work of all external forces and moments acting
on the body undergoing translational and
rotational displacement from position 1 to 2

Special Case When several rigid bodies are involved in what is often termed a *system*, there are two ways of approaching the problem. Either we consider each rigid body as a separate case and apply to them the equations of work and kinetic energy, or we consider *all* rigid bodies together and apply the principle of work and kinetic energy to the system as a whole. In the latter case T represents the arithmetic sum of the kinetic energies of the various rigid bodies and $U_{1\rightarrow2}$ represents the algebraic sum of the works of all the forces and moments external to the system and acting on the various rigid bodies.

EXAMPLE 8.1

The uniform 20-lb bar shown is moved from its initial position where $\theta = 0°$, to a position where $\theta = 60°$, under the action of a 50-lb force F which always acts perpendicular to the bar as shown. If the initial angular velocity ω_1 of the bar is counterclockwise and equal to 5 rad/s, determine the bar's angular velocity when $\theta = 60°$.

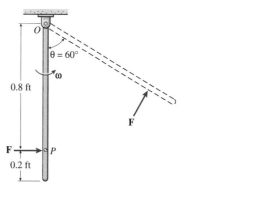

(*continued*)

EXAMPLE 8.1   (*concluded*)

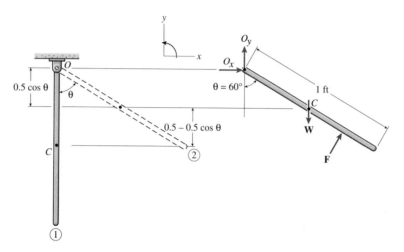

Solution   We apply the equation of work and kinetic energy, Equation (8.1), between the initial ($\theta = 0°$) and final ($\theta = 60°$) angular positions. We consider the body's kinetic energy with reference to the fixed point of rotation O by writing, from Equation (8.11),

$$T_1 = \frac{1}{2}I_O\omega_1^2 = \frac{1}{2}\left[\frac{1}{3}\left(\frac{20}{32.2}\right)(1.0)^2\right](5)^2 = 2.588 \text{ ft} \cdot \text{lb}$$

$$T_2 = \frac{1}{2}\left[\frac{1}{3}\left(\frac{20}{32.2}\right)(1.0)^2\right]\omega_2^2 = 0.1035\omega_2^2$$

The external forces acting on the bar consist of the reactions at O, the weight $W = 20$ lb and the force $F = 60$ lb. Their total work $\Sigma U_{1\rightarrow2}$ is computed from

$$\Sigma U_{1\rightarrow2} = (U_{1\rightarrow2})_{Ox} + (U_{1\rightarrow2})_{Oy} + (U_{1\rightarrow2})_W + (U_{1\rightarrow2})_F$$

Since the pin at O does not move during the motion of the bar, the work terms $(U_{1\rightarrow2})_{Ox}$ and $(U_{1\rightarrow2})_{Oy}$ are zero. The work done by the weight is negative, since the upward displacement

of the mass center of the bar is opposite to the downward direction of the weight. The vertical displacement of the mass center is

$$\Delta y = OC - OC \cos \theta = 0.5(1 - \cos 60°) = 0.25 \text{ ft}$$

and the work of the weight becomes

$$(U_{1\rightarrow2})_W = -W(\Delta y) = -20(0.25) = -5 \text{ lb} \cdot \text{ft}$$

Since the force F is at all times tangent to the path described by its point of application P, the work term becomes

$$(U_{1\rightarrow2})_F = F\left[\frac{60}{360}(2\pi r)\right] = 50\left[\frac{1}{6}(2\pi)(0.8)\right] = 41.89 \text{ lb} \cdot \text{ft}$$

The equation of work and kinetic energy can now be expressed as $T_1 + \Sigma U_{1\rightarrow2} = T_2$, and upon substituting the expressions for T_1, T_2, and $\Sigma U_{1\rightarrow2}$, we find

$$2.588 + (-5.00 + 41.89) = 0.1035\omega_2^2$$

$$\omega_2 = 19.5 \text{ rad/s} \circlearrowleft \blacktriangleleft$$

EXAMPLE 8.2

The 50-kg disk shown is at rest as it is originally held in equilibrium by a spring having a spring constant $k = 1000$ N/m. A couple of moment $M = 700$ N $\cdot$ m is suddenly applied to the disk causing the disk to roll without slipping from position 1 to position 2, as shown. Determine the angular velocity of the disk when it is at position 2.

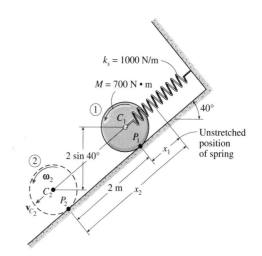

Solution   We must first determine the spring force acting on the disk and holding it in equilibrium at its initial position. The initial tension force F_s in the spring can be determined from

$$\circlearrowleft \Sigma M_{P_1} = 0$$

$$F_s(0.5) - [(50)(9.81)\sin 40°](0.5) = 0$$

$$F_s = 315.29 \text{ N}$$

The initial elongation of the spring from its unstretched position can be deduced from the spring constant $k = 1000$ N/m by writing

$$x_1 = \frac{F_s}{k} = \frac{315.29}{1000} = 0.315 \text{ m}$$

Thus, the final position s_2 of the stretched spring, after a displacement of 2 m of the disk, becomes

$$x_2 = 0.315 + 2 = 2.315 \text{ m}$$

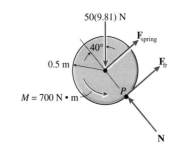

Now, to utilize the work–kinetic energy equation and evaluate the various terms, we have $T_1 + \Sigma U_{1 \to 2} = T_2$ where $T_1 = 0$, since the disk is initially at rest.

$$T_2 = \frac{1}{2}mv_{C_2}^2 + \frac{1}{2}I_C\omega_2^2$$

Since the disk is rolling without slipping, the instantaneous center of zero velocity is at P_2 and the velocity of the mass center at C_2 becomes

$$v_{C_2} = \omega_2 r = 0.5\omega_2$$

where ω_2 is assumed counterclockwise.
   The kinetic energy T_2 of the disk at its final position can now be calculated from

$$T_2 = \frac{1}{2}(50)(0.5\omega_2)^2 + \frac{1}{2}\left[\frac{1}{2}(50)(0.5)^2\right]\omega_2^2$$

$$= (6.25 + 3.125)\omega_2^2 = 9.375\omega_2^2$$

(continued)

EXAMPLE 8.2   *(concluded)*

The work done by the couple of moment M necessitates the evaluation of the angular displacement $(\theta_1 - \theta_2) = \Delta\theta$ corresponding to an arc length of 2 m. We have

$$r(\Delta\theta) = 2 \text{ m}$$

$$\Delta\theta = \frac{2}{0.5} = 4 \text{ rad}$$

Thus we obtain

$$(U_{1\rightarrow2})_M = +M(\Delta\theta) = 700(4) = 2800 \text{ N} \cdot \text{m}$$

The work of the spring force will be negative, since the spring opposes the motion, and we have

$$(U_{1\rightarrow2})_{sp} = -\frac{1}{2}k(x_2^2 - x_1^2)$$

where $x_2 = 2.315$ m and $x_1 = 0.315$ m. Thus we have

$$(U_{1\rightarrow2})_{sp} = -\frac{1}{2}(1000)(2.315^2 - 0.315^2) = -2630 \text{ N} \cdot \text{m}$$

We evaluate the work done by the weight force as

$$(U_{1\rightarrow2})_W = +mg[(C_1C_2) \sin 40°] = +50(9.81)[2 \sin 40°]$$

$$= 630.6 \text{ N} \cdot \text{m}$$

Now we can obtain the total work done by all the external forces acting on the disk:

$$\Sigma U_{1\rightarrow2} = (U_{1\rightarrow2})_M + (U_{1\rightarrow2})_{sp} + (U_{1\rightarrow2})_W$$

$$= 2800 - 2630 + 630.6 = 800.6 \text{ N} \cdot \text{m}$$

and using the work–kinetic energy equations, we solve for ω_2, writing

$$0 + 800.6 = 9.375\omega_2^2$$

$$\omega_2 = 9.24 \text{ rad/s} \circlearrowleft \blacktriangleleft$$

The counterclockwise rotation of the disk is in the assumed positive direction.

EXAMPLE 8.3

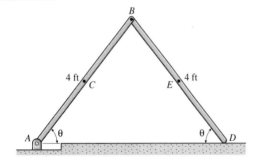

The linkage shown consists of two 30-lb slender bars (length = 4 ft) released from rest at $\theta = 60°$. Determine their angular velocities at the instant when $\theta = 30°$. The end of the bar BD at D slides on a smooth floor.

Solution   Before applying the work–kinetic energy equation we need to determine the velocity of the mass center of each bar as well as the kinematic relationship between the angular velocities of the bars.

The bar AB rotates clockwise about pin A. Thus, we can write the velocity (v_B) of point B as

$$v_B = (\omega_{AB})(AB) = 4\omega_{AB} \qquad \text{(a)}$$

The kinematics of the motion of bar BD reveals that, since D moves along the horizontal AD and the point B rotates about A, at any given instant the bar BD rotates counterclockwise about an instantaneous center of zero velocity located at IC as shown. We conclude that the velocity v_B of point B can also be

(continued)

EXAMPLE 8.3   (*concluded*)

expressed as

$$v_B = \omega_{BD}(IC - B) = +4\omega_{BD} \qquad (b)$$

Equating Equations (a) and (b) yields

$$\omega_{AB} = \omega_{BD} \qquad (c)$$

Note that these angular velocities are in opposite directions. Thus, we can write the velocity v_C of the mass center C of bar AB as

$$v_C = 2\omega_{AB} \qquad (d)$$

and the velocity v_E of the mass center E of bar BD becomes

$$v_E = \omega_{BD}(IC - E) = (4 \sin 60°)\omega_{BD}$$
$$v_E = 3.464\omega_{AB} \qquad (e)$$

We now write the work–kinetic energy equation [after introducing Equations (d) and (e)] as $T_1 + \Sigma U_{1\rightarrow2} = T_2$, where

$T_1 = 0$, since the linkage is released from rest

$$T_2 = \frac{1}{2}\underbrace{\left(\frac{1}{3}mL^2\right)}_{I_A}\omega_{AB}^2 + \frac{1}{2}\underbrace{\left(\frac{1}{12}mL^2\right)}_{I_E}\omega_{BD}^2 + \frac{1}{2}m(v_E)^2$$

since $v_A = 0$. Substituting known values,

$$T_2 = \frac{1}{2}\left[\frac{1}{3}\left(\frac{30}{32.2}\right)(4)^2\right]\omega_{AB}^2 + \frac{1}{2}\left[\frac{1}{12}\left(\frac{30}{32.2}\right)(4)^2\right]\omega_{AB}^2$$

$$+ \frac{1}{2}\left(\frac{30}{32.2}\right)(3.464\,\omega_{AB})^2$$

$$T_2 = (2.48 + 0.62 + 5.59)\omega_{AB}^2 = 8.69\omega_{AB}^2$$

$$\Sigma U_{1\rightarrow2} = 2W\,\Delta y_C = 2(30)\left[\frac{4}{2}(\sin 60° - \sin 30°)\right] = 43.92 \text{ lb} \cdot \text{ft}$$

Thus, after substituting for T_1, T_2, and $\Sigma U_{1\rightarrow2}$,

$$0 + 43.92 = 8.69\omega_{AB}^2$$

$$\omega_{AB} = 2.25 \text{ rad/s} \circlearrowright \qquad \omega_{BD} = 2.25 \text{ rad/s} \circlearrowleft \quad \blacktriangleleft$$

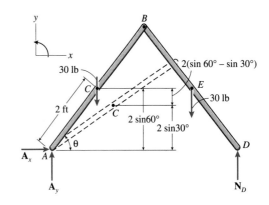

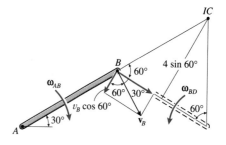

EXAMPLE 8.4

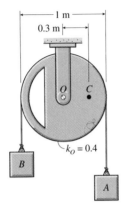

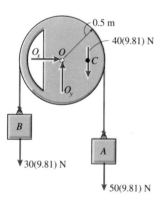

Two blocks A (50 kg) and B (30 kg) are supported by a cord which is wrapped around an unbalanced drum (40 kg) as shown. The mass radius of gyration of the drum with respect to its axis of rotation is 0.40 m. In the position shown, the drum is moving clockwise with an angular velocity of 5 rad/s. Determine the angular velocity of the drum after it has completed one full revolution.

Solution The work–kinetic energy equation applied to the blocks-drum system becomes $T_1 + \Sigma U_{1\to 2} = T_2$, where

$$T_1 = \frac{1}{2}m_A(v_A)_1^2 + \frac{1}{2}m_B(v_B)_1^2 + \frac{1}{2}(I_O)_{\mathrm{dr}}\omega_1^2$$

$$T_1 = \frac{1}{2}m_A(\omega_1 r)^2 + \frac{1}{2}m_B(\omega_1 r)^2 + \frac{1}{2}(I_O)_{\mathrm{dr}}\omega_1^2$$

$$T_2 = \frac{1}{2}m_A(\omega_2 r)^2 + \frac{1}{2}m_B(\omega_2 r)^2 + \frac{1}{2}(I_O)_{\mathrm{dr}}\omega_2^2$$

and

$$\Sigma U_{1\to 2} = (m_A g)(2\pi r) - (m_B g)(2\pi r)$$

since the work done by the weight of the drum through one full revolution (equal and opposite displacements of the mass center) is zero.

Substituting for $(I_O)_{\mathrm{dr}} = m_{\mathrm{dr}}k_0^2 = 40(0.4)^2$ and for $\omega_1 = 5$ rad/s, we have

$$\underbrace{\left\{\begin{array}{c}\frac{1}{2}(50)[(5)(0.5)]^2 \\ + \\ \frac{1}{2}(30)[(5)(0.5)]^2 \\ + \\ \frac{1}{2}(40)(0.4)^2(5)^2\end{array}\right\}}_{T_1} + \underbrace{\left\{\left[\begin{array}{c}(50)(9.81) \\ - \\ (30)(9.81)\end{array}\right](2\pi)(0.5)\right\}}_{\Sigma U_{1\to 2}} = \underbrace{\left\{\begin{array}{c}\frac{1}{2}(50)(0.5)^2 \\ + \\ \frac{1}{2}(30)(0.5)^2 \\ + \\ \frac{1}{2}(40)(0.4)^2\end{array}\right\}}_{T_2}\omega_2^2$$

which yields $\omega = 8.47$ rad/s ◄

8.3 CONSERVATION OF MECHANICAL ENERGY

In Chapter 5, the conservation of energy theorem applied to a system of particles subjected only to *conservative* forces led to the expression

$$\sum_{i=1}^{n} (T_i)_1 + \sum_{i=1}^{n} (V_i)_1 = \sum_{i=1}^{n} (T_i)_2 + \sum_{i=1}^{n} (V_i)_2$$

Considering a rigid body as a system where the particles' positions relative to each other remain invarient, we can extend the above relationship to a rigid body and write

$$T_1 + V_1 = T_2 + V_2 \tag{8.12}$$

where T_1 and V_1 are the rigid body's initial kinetic and potential energy, and T_2 and V_2 are the rigid body's final kinetic and potential energies. Equation (8.12) states that a rigid body's kinetic energy plus its potential energy—commonly referred to as its mechanical energy—remain constant when the body moves from one position to another. Equation (8.12) is referred to as the *equation of **conservation of mechanical energy*** for a body subjected only to conservative forces. The equation can be used to solve problems involving displacements and velocities of rigid bodies undergoing motions due to conservative forces. However, it cannot be applied when considering physical problems where friction and drag forces or elastic deformations are encountered. In such cases, there is an irreversible transfer of energy from kinetic into heat or noise rather than into potential. The two most common forms of potential energy pertinent to the above discussion are the gravitational potential energy of a body and the elastic potential energy of a spring.

Gravitational Potential Energy The *gravitational potential energy* of a body is the body's potential to do work under the action of its weight. If the displacements are measured with respect to a reference line (such as the datum line of Figure 8.5) the gravitational potential energy of a body, when at position 1, can be expressed as

$$(V_g)_1 = W(y_C)_1 \tag{8.13}$$

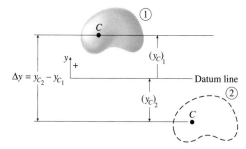

Figure 8.5

The potential energy is in this case positive, for the work done by the weight W of the body during its displacement from 1 to the datum line would have been positive. However, if a body is positioned at 2, then clearly its weight does not have the potential to do work while the body goes from 2 to the datum line. In fact, one has to do work to raise the body by $(y_C)_2$. Thus, the gravi-

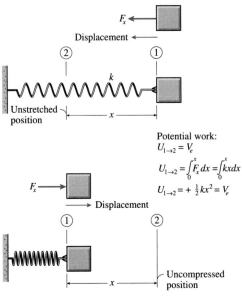

Figure 8.6

tational potential energy of the body, in this case, will be negative, and can be expressed as

$$(V_g)_2 = W(y_C)_2$$

where $(y_C)_2$ is a negative quantity.

Elastic Potential Energy   A linear elastic spring, when either stretched or compressed from its undeformed position, develops a conservative force that will tend to move the end of the spring toward its initial position (see Figure 8.6). The potential of a spring to do work can thus be expressed in terms of a potential function that is equated to the magnitude of the work as

$$V_e = + \int_{x=0}^{x} kx\,dx = +\frac{1}{2}kx^2 \tag{8.14}$$

8.4 POWER

The definition of *power*, as discussed in Chapter 3 for the motion of particles subjected to forces and experiencing displacements, is also valid for rigid-body motion. But we must now consider the fact that in addition to transla-tional movement, rigid bodies might experience rotational motion that necessitates consideration of rotational kinetic energy, in addition to the kinetic energy of translation. The time rate of change of the kinetic energy of translation ($T_{\text{trans}} = \frac{1}{2}m\mathbf{v}_C \cdot \mathbf{v}_C$) is the net power supplied to or withdrawn from a rigid body of mass m translating with $\mathbf{v}_C$. We can write

$$\text{Power} = \frac{dU}{dt} = \frac{\Sigma \mathbf{F} \cdot d\mathbf{r}}{dt} = \Sigma \mathbf{F} \cdot \frac{d\mathbf{r}}{dt} = \Sigma \mathbf{F} \cdot \mathbf{v}_C$$

or

$$\text{Power} = \frac{d}{dt}(T_{\text{trans}}) = \frac{d}{dt}\left(\frac{1}{2}m\mathbf{v}_C \cdot \mathbf{v}_C\right) = m\mathbf{a}_C \cdot \mathbf{v}_C = \Sigma \mathbf{F} \cdot \mathbf{v}_C$$

where the velocity of translation $\mathbf{v}_C$ is also equal to the velocity of the mass center C.

Consider, however, a rigid body of mass m subjected to a rotational motion $\boldsymbol{\omega}$ about a fixed axis under the action of a constant couple moment $\mathbf{M}$, with a direction parallel to the axis of rotation of $\boldsymbol{\omega}$. The net power supplied to or withdrawn from the rigid body will be equal to the time rate of change of the kinetic energy of rotation ($T_{\text{ro}} = \frac{1}{2}I_C\omega^2$).

$$\text{Power} = \frac{d}{dt}(T_{\text{ro}}) = \frac{d}{dt}\left(\frac{1}{2}I_C\omega^2\right) = \frac{d}{dt}\left[\frac{1}{2}I_C(\boldsymbol{\omega} \cdot \boldsymbol{\omega})\right]$$

$$= \frac{1}{2}I_C(\dot{\boldsymbol{\omega}} \cdot \boldsymbol{\omega} + \boldsymbol{\omega} \cdot \dot{\boldsymbol{\omega}}) = \frac{1}{2}I_C(2\boldsymbol{\alpha} \cdot \boldsymbol{\omega})$$

$$= (I_C\boldsymbol{\alpha})\omega = M\omega$$

This follows since $\mathbf{M}$, $\boldsymbol{\alpha}$, and $\boldsymbol{\omega}$ are all collinear. The above expression can also be given in the form

$$\text{Power} = \frac{dU}{dt} = M\frac{d\theta}{dt} = M\omega$$

In addition, the power supplied to or withdrawn from a rigid body may be used to modify the rigid body's potential energies. In sum, the total power supplied to a system to increase its translational and rotational kinetic energies and its potential energies (gravitational and elastic) can be expressed as

$$\text{Power} = \frac{d}{dt}\underbrace{(T_{\text{trans}} + T_{\text{ro}} + V_{\text{gr}} + V_{\text{el}})}_{\text{mechanical energy}}$$

The energy terms when considered as input to the body's mechanical energy level are positive; they are negative if they represent energy withdrawal (output) from the system. The units of power are watts (J/s) in SI units and lb · ft/s or horsepower in the U.S. Customary units system.

EXAMPLE 8.5

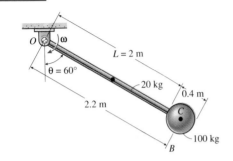

The 100-kg sphere (radius $=$ 0.2 m) is attached to the 20-kg slender rod (length $=$ 2.0 m) OB and the system swings about a pin at O. At the instant shown ($\theta = 60°$) the pendulum system has an angular velocity of $\omega_1 = 2$ rad/s clockwise. Determine the angular velocity of the pendulum when $\theta = 0°$.

Solution We can evaluate the mass moment of inertia of the sphere-rod system about the pin O from

$$I_O = \underbrace{\left(\frac{2}{5}m_{sp}R^2 + m_{sp}d^2\right)}_{\underbrace{(I_C)_{sphere}}_{(I_O)_{sphere}}} + \underbrace{\left(\frac{1}{3}m_{rod}L^2\right)}_{(I_O)_{rod}}$$

$$I_O = \frac{2}{5}(100)(0.2)^2 + (100)(2.2)^2 + \frac{1}{3}(20)(2.0)^2$$

$$= 512.27 \text{ kg} \cdot \text{m}^2$$

The conservation of mechanical energy theorem applied to the system between the initial (1) and final (2) positions is written

$$T_1 + V_1 = T_2 + V_2$$

where, since the body rotates about O,

$$T_1 = \frac{1}{2}I_O\omega_1^2 = \frac{1}{2}(512.27)(2)^2 = 1024.54 \text{ N} \cdot \text{m}$$

$$T_2 = \frac{1}{2}I_O\omega_2^2 = 256.14\omega_2^2$$

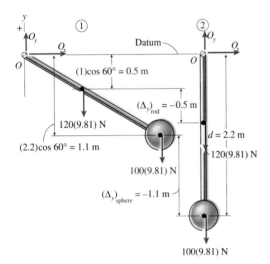

Also, we have

$$V_1 = (V_1)_{sphere} + (V_1)_{rod}$$
$$= (mg)_{sph}(-y_E)_1 + (mg)_{rod}(-y_C)_1$$
$$V_1 = [(100)(9.81)](-1.1) \text{ J} + [(20)(9.81)](-0.5) \text{ J} = -1177.20 \text{ J}$$
$$V_2 = [(100)(9.81)](-2.2) \text{ J} + [(20)(9.81)](-1.0) = -2354.4 \text{ J}$$

Thus, the conservation of mechanical energy theorem will yield

$$(1024.54) + (-1177.20) = (256.14\omega_2^2) + (-2354.40)$$
$$\omega_2 = 2.93 \text{ rad/s} \quad \circled{2} \quad \blacktriangleleft$$

EXAMPLE 8.6

The spool shown has a weight of 100 lb and a mass radius of gyration of $k_O = 1.5$ ft. A 50-lb cylinder suspended from the spool is released from rest. Neglecting the mass of the cord, determine the velocity of the cylinder after it has descended 5 ft.

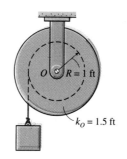

Solution We calculate the mechanical energy of the cylinder-spool system for its initial and final positions. The initial kinetic energy of the system is

$$T_1 = \frac{1}{2}m_{cyl}(v_{cyl})_1^2 + \frac{1}{2}I_O(\omega_{spool})_1^2 = 0$$

Since the system is released from rest and $v_{cyl} = \omega_{spool} = 0$.

$$T_2 = \frac{1}{2}\left(\frac{50}{32.2}\right)(v_{cyl})_2^2 + \frac{1}{2}\left[\left(\frac{100}{32.2}\right)(1.5)^2\right]\left(\frac{v_P}{1.0}\right)^2$$

since $I_O = (m_{spool})k_O^2$, and $\omega_{spool} = v_P/r$. Because $v_P = v_{cyl}$, the above expression for T_2 becomes

$$T_2 = \frac{1}{2}\left[\left(\frac{50}{32.2}\right) + \left(\frac{100}{32.2}\right)(1.5)^2\right]v_{cyl}^2$$

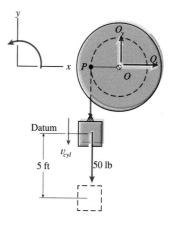

The initial and final potential energies of the system are those of the cylinder. When measured relative to a datum line attached to the initial position of the cylinder, we can express them as

$$V_1 = V(y_1) = 0$$

since $y_1 = 0$, and

$$V_2 = (50)(-5) = -250 \text{ lb} \cdot \text{ft}$$

The conservation of mechanical energy theorem $(T_1 + V_1 = T_2 + V_2)$ can now be applied to the spool-cylinder system

$$(0) + (0) = \frac{1}{2}\left[\left(\frac{50}{32.2}\right) + \left(\frac{100}{32.2}\right)(1.5)^2\right]v_{cyl}^2 + (-250)$$

Solving for v_{cyl}, we obtain

$$v_{cyl} = 7.65 \text{ ft/s}\, (\downarrow) \quad \blacktriangleleft$$

EXAMPLE 8.7

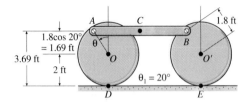

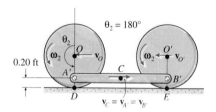

Two 20-lb uniform disks (radius $= 2$ ft) are linked by a 50-lb rod as shown. The disks roll counterclockwise and without sliding on a horizontal surface. In the position shown ($\theta_1 = +20°$) the linkage is released from rest. Determine the angular velocity of the disks when $\theta_2 = 180°$.

Solution   First we will analyze the kinematics of the linkage. Because the disks are rolling without slippage, the points D and E are the instantaneous centers of zero velocity of the disks. As the disks start from rest we have, for the initial conditions,

$$(v_O)_1 = (v_{O'})_1 = 0 \qquad (v_{A'B'})_1 = 0 \qquad \omega_1 = 0$$

and for the final conditions,

$$(v_O)_2 = (v_{O'})_2 = (DO)\omega_2 = (2.0)\omega_2$$

$$(v_C)_2 = (v_{A'})_2 = (v_{B'})_2 = (DA')\omega_2 = (0.2)\omega_2$$

The mass moment of inertia of the disk about its mass center O is given as $I_O = I_{O'} = \frac{1}{2}(m)_{\text{disk}}r^2$. Thus we have

$$I_O = I_{O'} = \frac{1}{2}\left(\frac{20}{32.2}\right)(2.0)^2$$

The initial and final kinetic-energy terms are

$$T_1 = 0 \quad \text{(since the system is initially at rest)}$$

$$T_2 = \frac{1}{2}m_{\text{rod}}(v_C)_2^2 + 2\left[\frac{1}{2}(m)_{\text{disk}}(v_O)_2^2 + \frac{1}{2}I_O\omega_2^2\right]$$

$$= \frac{1}{2}\left(\frac{50}{32.2}\right)(0.2\omega_2)^2 + 2\left[\frac{1}{2}\left(\frac{20}{32.2}\right)(2\omega_2)^2\right.$$

$$\left. + \frac{1}{2}\frac{1}{2}\left(\frac{20}{32.2}\right)(2.0)^2\omega_2^2\right] = 3.76\omega_2^2$$

The initial and final potential energy terms are

$$V_1 = W_{\text{rod}}(1.69) = 50(1.69) = 84.5 \text{ lb} \cdot \text{ft}$$

$$V_2 = W_{\text{rod}}(-1.8) = 50(-1.8) = -90 \text{ lb} \cdot \text{ft}$$

The conservation of mechanical energy $T_1 + V_1 = T_2 + V_2$ is now expressed by

$$0 + 84.5 = 3.76\omega_2^2 - 90 \qquad 3.76\omega_2^2 = 174.5$$

$$\omega_2^2 = 46.41 \text{ and } \omega_2 = 6.81 \text{ rad/s} \circlearrowleft \blacktriangleleft$$

8.5 IMPULSE–MOMENTUM RELATIONSHIPS FOR A RIGID BODY IN PLANAR MOTION

The principle of linear impulse and momentum developed in Chapter 4 for the motion of a particle was later extended, in Chapter 5, to the motion of a system of particles of constant mass and expressed in the form of Equation (5.17) as

$$m(\mathbf{v}_C)_1 + \sum \int_{t_1}^{t_2} \mathbf{F}\,dt = m(\mathbf{v}_C)_2$$

where m is the total mass of the system and $\mathbf{v}_C$ the velocity of the mass center of the system.

The above equation can be extended once again, to the dynamics of a rigid body by considering it as a system of particles with the mass concentrated at its center of mass. For a rigid body,

$$\mathbf{G}_1 + \sum \int_{t_1}^{t_2} \mathbf{F}\,dt = \mathbf{G}_2 \qquad (8.15)$$

where $\mathbf{G} = m\mathbf{v}_C$ is the linear momentum of the rigid body and $\displaystyle\sum \int_{t_1}^{t_2} \mathbf{F}\,dt$ is the total linear impulse due to all the external forces acting on the body during the time interval from t_1 to t_2.

Similarly, the angular impulse–momentum equation developed in Chapter 4 for the motion of a particle was later extended, in Chapter 5, to the motion of a system of particles of constant mass and expressed in the form of Equation (5.21). Equation (5.21) can be applied to the motion of a rigid body of constant mass, by considering the rigid body to consist of a finite number of particles rigidly attached to each other. The appropriate equation of angular impulse and momentum for a rigid body is thus expressed in the form

$$(\mathbf{H}_O)_1 + \sum \int_{t_1}^{t_2} \mathbf{M}_O\,dt = (\mathbf{H}_O)_2 \qquad (8.16)$$

where $\mathbf{H}_O$ is the angular momentum of the rigid body about an arbitrary and *fixed* reference point O, and $\displaystyle\sum \int_{t_1}^{t_2} \mathbf{M}_O\,dt$ represents the angular impulse ex-
erted on the body over the time interval considered by all the external forces and moments. It must be noted that the motion described above is given relative to an inertial (fixed) frame of reference. We shall next develop the methods necessary to determine the linear and angular impulse and momentum terms appearing in Equations (8.15) and (8.16), limiting our discussion to rigid bod-

ies subjected to planar motion. Therefore, the slabs under consideration will be symmetrical about the plane of motion.

Linear and Angular Impulse

Again, the **linear impulse** acting on a rigid body during a time interval from t_1 to t_2 can be determined from the expression

$$\sum_{i=1}^{n} \int_{t_1}^{t_2} \mathbf{F}_i \, dt$$

where $\mathbf{F}_i$ represents the external forces acting on the body.

The **angular impulse** exerted on a rigid body during a time interval from t_1 to t_2 can be determined from the expression

$$\sum_{i=1}^{n} \int_{t_1}^{t_2} (\mathbf{M}_i)_O \, dt$$

where the moments $(\mathbf{M}_i)_O$ of all the external forces acting on the body are taken about an arbitrary and fixed reference point O.

Linear and Angular Momentum

The **linear momentum** of a rigid body is the vectorial sum of the linear momenta of all the particles forming the rigid body, and can be expressed as

$$\mathbf{G} = \int_m (dm)\mathbf{v} = \mathbf{v}_C \int_m dm = m\mathbf{v}_C$$

$$\mathbf{G} = m\mathbf{v}_C \tag{8.17}$$

where m is the mass of the rigid body and $\mathbf{v}_C$ is the velocity of its mass center.

By extension, we obtain the **angular momentum** H_O of a rigid body about an arbitrary and *fixed* reference point O from Equation (5.26) as

$$\mathbf{H}_O = (\mathbf{r}_{C/O} \times m\mathbf{v}_C) + \mathbf{H}_C \tag{8.18}$$

where $\mathbf{H}_C$ is the angular momentum of the rigid body taken with respect to its mass center (see Figure 8.7) and expressed as

$$\mathbf{H}_C = \int_m \mathbf{r}_{i/C} \times \mathbf{v}_{i/C} \, dm = \int_m \mathbf{r}_{i/C} \times (\boldsymbol{\omega} \times \mathbf{r}_{i/C}) dm$$

since, from Equation (6.7), $\mathbf{v}_{i/C} = \boldsymbol{\omega} \times \mathbf{r}_{i/C}$. However, limiting the discussion to a slab in planar motion, the above expression for $\mathbf{H}_C$ is reduced to

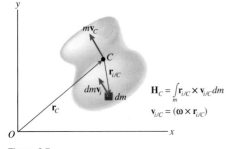

Figure 8.7

$$\mathbf{H}_C = \left(\int_m r_{i/C}^2 \, dm \right) \boldsymbol{\omega}$$

since the velocity vector ($\boldsymbol{\omega} \times \mathbf{r}_{i/C}$) and the position vector ($\mathbf{r}_{i/C}$) are coplanar (in the xy plane). The term within parentheses represents the mass moment of inertia I_C of the slab with respect to its centroidal axis normal to its plane of symmetry. Thus we write

$$\mathbf{H}_C = I_C \boldsymbol{\omega} \tag{8.19}$$

Substituting Equation (8.19) into Equation (8.18) gives

$$\mathbf{H}_O = (\mathbf{r}_{C/O} \times m\mathbf{v}_C) + I_C \boldsymbol{\omega} \tag{8.20}$$

The first term on the right-hand side of Equation (8.20), after considering that $\mathbf{v}_C = \boldsymbol{\omega} \times \mathbf{r}_{C/O}$, can be expressed as

$$\mathbf{r}_{C/O} \times m\mathbf{v}_C = m[\mathbf{r}_{C/O} \times (\boldsymbol{\omega} \times \mathbf{r}_C)]$$

and for the case of a slab in a planar motion the expression is further reduced to

$$(\mathbf{r}_{C/O} \times m\mathbf{v}_C) = (m r_C^2) \boldsymbol{\omega} \tag{8.21}$$

Equation (8.21) introduced into Equation (8.20) yields

$$\mathbf{H}_O = m r_C^2 \boldsymbol{\omega} + I_C \boldsymbol{\omega}$$
$$\mathbf{H}_O = (I_C + m r_C^2) \boldsymbol{\omega} \tag{8.22}$$

The term within parentheses, from the parallel-axis theorem, represents the mass moment of inertia I_O of the slab about the arbitrary and fixed axis perpendicular to the slab at O. The expression (8.20) is finally reduced to

$$\mathbf{H}_O = I_O \boldsymbol{\omega} \tag{8.23}$$

Equations (8.21), (8.22), and (8.23) are valid for fixed-axis rotation about point O.

Equation of Linear Impulse and Momentum

We can now formulate the linear impulse–momentum relationship by introducing Equation (8.17) into Equation (8.15). The equation becomes

$$(m\mathbf{v}_C)_1 + \sum \int_{t_1}^{t_2} \mathbf{F} \, dt = (m\mathbf{v}_C)_2 \tag{8.24}$$

and states that the final linear momentum of a rigid body subjected to external forces during a period from t_1 to t_2 is equal to the vectorial sum of the initial linear momentum of the body and the total linear impulse created by all the external forces acting on the body.

Equation of Angular Impulse and Momentum

For a body in general planar motion, the equation of angular impulse and momentum will now be formulated by combining Equation (8.23) with Equation (8.16). This yields

$$(I_O\boldsymbol{\omega})_1 + \sum \int_{t_1}^{t_2} \mathbf{M}_O \, dt = (I_O\boldsymbol{\omega})_2 \qquad (8.25)$$

The above equation states that the final angular momentum, about a fixed point O, of a rigid slab in planar motion and subjected to external forces and moments during a period from t_1 to t_2 is equal to the vectorial sum of the initial angular momentum about O and the total angular impulse created by all the external forces and moments acting on the slab.

If we consider, instead, angular momenta and moments about the centroidal axis of the slab by introducing Equation (8.19) into Equation (8.24), we obtain

$$(I_C\boldsymbol{\omega})_1 + \sum \int_{t_1}^{t_2} \mathbf{M}_C \, dt = (I_C\boldsymbol{\omega})_2 \qquad (8.26)$$

For a rigid body subjected to planar motion the linear impulse–momentum equation (8.24) yields two scalar equations which, in Cartesian coordinates, become

$$
\begin{aligned}
m(v_{Cx})_1 + \sum \int_{t_1}^{t_2} F_x \, dt = m(v_{Cx})_2 \\
m(v_{Cy})_1 + \sum \int_{t_1}^{t_2} F_y \, dt = m(v_{Cy})_2
\end{aligned}
\qquad (8.27)
$$

whereas the angular impulse–momentum equation (8.26) would yield the z component of the vector relationship in the form

$$(I_C\omega)_1 + \sum \int_{t_1}^{t_2} M_C \, dt = (I_C\omega)_2 \qquad (8.28)$$

EXAMPLE 8.8

The 200-kg rectangular plate is at rest on a smooth horizontal surface. For 10 seconds the plate is acted upon by the forces F_1, F_2, and F_3 as shown. The directions of the forces remain constant with respect to a fixed frame of reference. Determine the final angular velocity of the plate and the velocity of its mass center.

Solution The linear impulse–momentum relationship shown in the kinetic diagram below yields two scalar equations along the x and y directions:

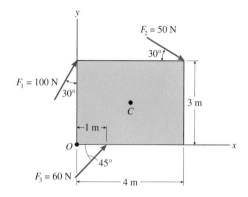

$$\overset{\rightarrow}{+}\; m(v_{Cx})_1 + \sum \int_{t_1}^{t_2} F_{ix}\, dt = m(v_{Cx})_2$$

$$0 + (100 \sin 30° + 50 \cos 30° + 60 \cos 45°)(10 - 0)$$

$$= (200)(v_{Cx})_2$$

$$1357.3 = 200(v_{Cx})_2 \qquad (v_{Cx})_2 = 6.79 \text{ m/s}$$

$$\overset{+}{\uparrow}\; m(v_{Cy})_1 + \sum \int_{t_1}^{t_2} F_{iy}\, dt = m(v_{Cy})_2$$

$$0 + (100 \cos 30° - 50 \sin 30° + 60 \sin 45°)(10)$$

$$= (200)(v_{Cy})_2$$

$$1040.3 = 200(v_{Cy})_2 \qquad (v_{Cy})_2 = 5.20 \text{ m/s}$$

The velocity of the mass center becomes

$$\mathbf{v}_C = 6.79\mathbf{i} + 5.20\mathbf{j} \ (\text{m/s}) \ \blacktriangleleft$$

To determine the final angular velocity of the plate, we appeal to the equation of angular impulse and momentum,

which when written about the centroidal axis of the plate yields

$$\overset{+}{\circlearrowleft}\; I_C\omega_1 + \sum \int_{t=0}^{t=10} M_C\, dt = I_C\omega_2$$

$$0 + \left[\begin{array}{l} -(100 \cos 30°)(2) - (100 \sin 30°)(1.5) \\ -(50 \cos 30°)(1.5) - (50 \sin 30°)(2) \\ +(60 \cos 45°)(1.5) - (60 \sin 45°)(1.0) \end{array} \right](10 - 0) = I_C\omega_2$$

where

$$I_C = \frac{1}{12}(200)[(4)^2 + (3)^2] = 416.67 \text{ kg} \cdot \text{m}^2$$

The equation yields

$$-3419.44 = 416.67\omega_2$$

$$\omega_2 = 8.21 \text{ rad/s} \ \circlearrowleft \ \blacktriangleleft$$

EXAMPLE 8.9

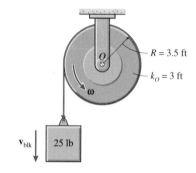

The 25-lb block is attached to a cord that is wrapped around a 100-lb spool with a radius of 3.5 ft and a mass radius of gyration k_o of 3 ft as shown. The block is initially descending with a speed of 3 ft/s. Neglecting the mass of the cord, determine the speed of the block after 1 s.

Solution The equation of angular impulse and momentum will be applied to the free-body diagram of the spool, whereas the y component of the equation of linear impulse and momentum will be applied to the free-body diagram of the block. Hence, for the spool,

$$\circlearrowright I_O\boldsymbol{\omega}_1 + \sum \int_{t=0}^{t=1} \mathbf{M}_O\, dt = I_O\boldsymbol{\omega}_2$$

where

$$I_O = m(k_o)^2 = \left(\frac{100}{32.2}\right)(3)^2 = 27.95 \text{ slug} \cdot \text{ft}^2$$

$$(27.95)\omega_1 + 3.5T(1 - 0) = (27.95)\omega_2$$

The kinematics of the problem yields $v_{\text{block}} = \omega_{\text{spool}}R$. Thus, we can write

$$\omega_1 = \frac{v_1}{3.5} = \frac{3.0}{3.5} = 0.857 \text{ rad/s} \quad \text{and} \quad \omega_2 = \frac{(v_{\text{blk}})_2}{3.5}$$

Hence,

$$(27.95)(0.857) + 3.5T = (27.95)\frac{(v_{\text{blk}})_2}{3.5}$$

$$7.99(v_{\text{blk}})_2 - 3.5T = 23.95 \qquad (a)$$

The y component of the equation of linear impulse and momentum when applied to the 25-lb block yields

$$\uparrow) m_{\text{blk}}(v_{\text{blk}})_1 + \sum \int_{t=0}^{t=1} F_{iy}\, dt = m_{\text{blk}}(v_{\text{blk}})_2$$

$$-\left(\frac{25}{32.2}\right)(3) + [T(1) - 25(1)] = -\left(\frac{25}{32.2}\right)(v_{\text{blk}})_2$$

$$0.776(v_{\text{blk}})_2 + T = 27.33 \qquad (b)$$

Solving equations (a) and (b) simultaneously for $(v_{\text{blk}})_2$, we obtain

$$(v_{\text{blk}})_2 = 11.18 \text{ ft/s} \downarrow \quad \blacktriangleleft$$

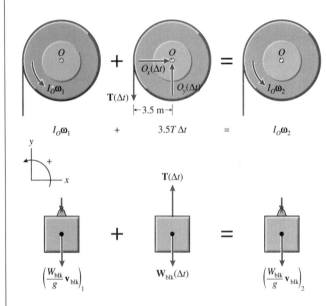

EXAMPLE 8.10

The 100-lb uniform rod OA (length = 5 ft) rests in the vertical position shown. At a given instant a sudden blow of $P = 2000$ lb is administered at the end of the rod. The impulse time interval is 0.004 s. Determine the angular velocity of the rod after the impulse has been applied. Also, find the horizontal component of the pin reaction at O.

Solution The free-body diagram involves four external forces, three of which are concurrent at O. Thus, by applying the angular impulse–momentum equation about the fixed pin O, we obtain

$$\circlearrowright\; I_O\omega_1 + \int \mathbf{M}_O\, dt = I_O\omega_2$$

where $I_O = \frac{1}{3}mL^2$. Thus,

$$0 + \int_0^{0.004} 5(2000)\,dt = \left[\left(\frac{1}{3}\right)\left(\frac{100}{32.2}\right)(5)^2\right]\omega_2$$

$$10{,}000(0.004 - 0) = 25.88\omega_2$$

$$\omega_2 = \frac{40}{25.88} = 1.55 \text{ rad/s} \;\circlearrowright \;\blacktriangleleft$$

Next, we apply the x component of the linear impulse–momentum equation to determine the x component of the pin reaction.

$$\overset{\rightarrow}{+}\; m(v_{Cx})_1 + \sum \int_0^{0.004} F_x\, dt = m(v_{Cx})_2$$

where $(v_{Cx})_2 = \omega_2 r_C$. Hence,

$$\left(\frac{100}{32.2}\right)(0) + \int_0^{0.004} (O_x + P)\,dt = \left(\frac{100}{32.2}\right)[(\omega_2)(r_C)]$$

where $r_C = 2.5$ ft and $\omega_2 = 1.55$ rad/s. Thus, assuming that O_x remains constant during Δt, we can reduce the equation and solve for O_x:

$$O_x(0.004) + 2000(0.004) = \frac{100}{32.2}[(1.55)(2.5)]$$

$$O_x = 1007.5 \text{ lb} \;\circlearrowright \;\blacktriangleleft$$

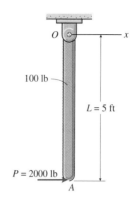

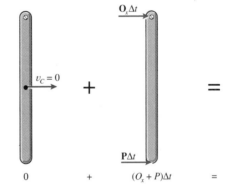

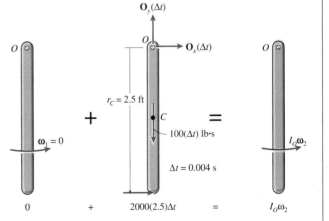

EXAMPLE 8.11

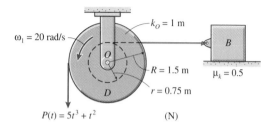

$\omega_1 = 20$ rad/s

$k_O = 1$ m

B

O

$R = 1.5$ m

$\mu_k = 0.5$

$r = 0.75$ m

D

$P(t) = 5t^3 + t^2$ (N)

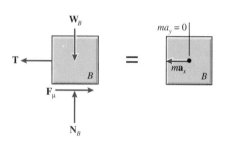

W_B

$T \leftarrow$ $\qquad = \qquad$ $ma_y = 0$

B ma_x

F_μ B

N_B

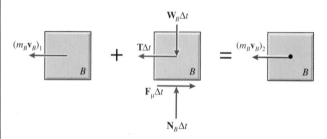

$(m_B v_B)_1$ $+$ $T\Delta t$ $W_B \Delta t$ $=$ $(m_B v_B)_2$

B B B

$F_\mu \Delta t$

$N_B \Delta t$

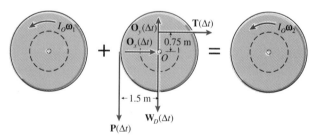

$I_O \omega_1$ $+$ $O_y(\Delta t)$ $T(\Delta t)$ $=$ $I_O \omega_2$

$O_x(\Delta t)$ 0.75 m

O

$\leftarrow 1.5$ m $\rightarrow$

$W_D(\Delta t)$

$P(\Delta t)$

The 200-kg drum D (radius $= 1.5$ m, mass radius of gyration $k_o = 1.0$ m) is activated by a variable force $P(t) = 5t^3 + t^2$ (newtons) where t is in seconds. The inner hub of the drum (radius $= 0.75$ m) pulls a 50-kg block B as shown. The coefficient of kinetic friction between block B and the horizontal surface is $\mu_k = 0.5$. If the initial angular velocity of the drum is 20 rad/s counterclockwise, determine the velocity of block B when $t = 5$ s.

Solution The free-body diagram for the block B yields the equation of motion in the y direction as

$$(+\uparrow) \Sigma F_y = m(a_y = 0) = 0$$

$$N_B - 50(9.81) = 0 \qquad N_B = 50(9.81) = 490.5 \text{ N} (\uparrow)$$

$$F_\mu = \mu_k N_B = 0.5(490.5) = 245.25 \text{ N} (\rightarrow)$$

The linear impulse–momentum equation for the block B is

$$(\overset{+}{\rightarrow}) -m_B(v_{Bx})_1 + \int_{t=0}^{t=5} (-T + F_\mu)dt = -m_B(v_{Bx})_2$$

The velocity v_{Bx} of the block is equal to the tangential velocity at the rim of the inner hub ($r = 0.75$ m), which has an angular velocity ω; thus, $v_B = \omega r$. Substituting this expression into the linear impulse–momentum equation and recalling that $\omega_1 = 20$ rad/s, we obtain

$$(\overset{+}{\rightarrow}) -50(0.75)(20) - T(5) + 245.25(5) = -50(0.75)\omega_2$$

$$37.5\omega_2 - 5T = -476.25 \qquad\qquad \text{(a)}$$

Next, we apply the angular impulse–momentum relationship to the free-body diagram for the drum D and write

$$I_O(\omega_1) + \Sigma \int_{t=0}^{t=5} M_O \, dt = I_O(\omega_2)$$

where $I_O = m_D k_O^2$. Hence,

$$[(200)(1.0)^2](20) + \int_{t=0}^{t=5} (1.50)[P(t)]dt - \int_{t=0}^{t=5} (0.75)(T)dt$$

$$= [200(1.0)^2]\omega_2$$

$$200\omega_2 + 3.75T = 1.5 \int_{t=0}^{t=5} (5t^3 + t^2)dt + 4000$$

$$200\omega_2 + 3.75T = 5234.38 \qquad\qquad \text{(b)}$$

(continued)

EXAMPLE   8.11   (*concluded*)

Solving Equations (a) and (b) simultaneously for ω_2 gives

$$\omega_2 = 21.38 \text{ rad/s} \circlearrowright$$

And since we have $v_B = r\omega \doteq (0.75)\omega$, the velocity of the

block when $t = 5$ s, can now be evaluated from

$$(v_B)_2 = 0.75(\omega)_2 = 0.75(21.38)$$

$$(v_B)_2 = 16.0 \text{ m/s} \circlearrowleft \blacktriangleleft$$

8.6 CONSERVATION OF MOMENTUM

Conservation of Linear Momentum

Considering the equation of linear impulse and momentum (8.24), we observe that if the impulse term $\Sigma \int_{t_1}^{t_2} \mathbf{F} \, dt = 0$ then the initial and final linear momenta of the rigid body are equal, and we write the equation for the ***conservation of linear momentum*** as

$$(m\mathbf{v}_C)_1 = (m\mathbf{v}_C)_2 \tag{8.29}$$

Equation (8.29) is a natural extension of the principle developed in Chapter 5 for a system of particles, Equation (5.18); it is also applicable to a system of interconnected rigid bodies. It is important to recall that the scalar expressions corresponding to Equation (8.24) and given in Equations (8.27) could yield a linear-momentum conservation in one direction (if $\Sigma \int F_x \, dt = 0$) while the linear momentum may not be conserved in the other direction (if $\Sigma \int F_y \, dt \neq 0$). In fact, the problem of oblique central impact discussed in Chapter 4 [Equation (4.21)] illustrates this case. Furthermore, in many dynamics problems the impulsive forces—those forces acting on the body over a very short period of time—may produce very large impulses in comparison to the impulses generated over the same period of time by nonimpulsive forces, such as the weight of a body. As a result, the impulses due to such nonimpulsive forces may be neglected without introducing any significant error in the computations carried out using Equation (8.29).

Conservation of Angular Momentum

Considering the equation of angular impulse and momentum (8.25 or 8.26) we observe that if the angular impulse term $\Sigma \int_{t_1}^{t_2} \mathbf{M}_O \, dt = \mathbf{0}$, then the initial and final angular momenta (moments of the linear momenta) of the rigid body are equal and we write the equation of the ***conservation of angular momentum*** as

$$(I_O\omega)_1 = (I_O\omega)_2 \tag{8.30}$$

Equation (8.30) states that if the sum of all the angular impulses caused by the external forces acting on a rigid body, over a period of time, is zero, the angular momentum of the body is conserved.

It must be noted that in Equation (8.30) the subscripts 1 and 2 apply to the moment of inertia as well as to the angular velocity. The body's moment of inertia may vary during the time interval $t_2 - t_1$. However, if the moment of inertia of the rigid body about O does remain constant during the time interval $t_2 - t_1$, then from Equation (8.30) we conclude that the angular velocity of the body must also remain constant.

Equations (8.25) and (8.26) are vector relationships and therefore can also be expressed in terms of their scalar components in the three Cartesian coordinate directions.

Here too, although the angular impulse term $\Sigma \int_{t_1}^{t_2} \mathbf{M}_O \, dt$ may be other than zero, any one of its components along the corresponding coordinate direction may be zero—therefore, the angular momentum component in the direction of zero moment will be conserved, although the total angular momentum $\mathbf{H}_O$ will not be conserved. Furthermore, the reader is reminded that if $\Sigma \int_{t_1}^{t_2} \mathbf{M}_O \, dt = \mathbf{0}$, it *does not* necessarily follow that we also have $\Sigma \int_{t_1}^{t_2} \mathbf{M}_C \, dt = \mathbf{0}$.

Therefore, the conservation of angular momentum principle may hold about a fixed point O but not necessarily about the mass center C of the rigid body, *and vice versa.* Thus,

$$(I_O\omega)_1 = (I_O\omega)_2 \quad \text{or} \quad (I_C\omega)_1 = (I_C\omega_2) \tag{8.31}$$

Finally, we must be aware of the fact that there is no linkage between the conservation of linear momentum and the conservation of angular momentum. If all external forces pass through the fixed point O or if the sum of the angular impulses of the external forces about O is zero, then the term $\Sigma \int \mathbf{M}_O \, dt$ is zero. However, this situation does not necessarily require that the resultant of *all the external forces* be zero. For example, in problems involving central forces (Chapter 4, Section 4.8), the moment about a fixed point O of every external force is zero even though the forces are nonzero. In planetary motion the gravitational forces acting on the planets are concurrent and pass through the center of the sun, *and* the angular momenta of the planets are conserved.

EXAMPLE 8.12

The 50-kg uniform slender rod (length = 4 m) rotates in a horizontal plane about a vertical axis passing through O as shown. At a given instant when the rod has an angular velocity ω = 5 rad/s counterclockwise, a 0.1-kg bullet moving at a velocity of 500 m/s and directed as shown strikes the rod and becomes embedded in it. Determine the angular velocity of the rod just after the impact of the bullet. Also, determine the average impulsive reactions O_x and O_y at the pin support O, if the duration of impulse is Δt = 0.04 s.

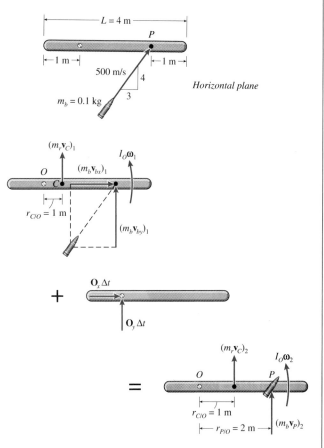

Horizontal plane

Solution The impulsive force exerted upon the rod by the bullet is equal and opposite to the impulsive reaction force exerted by the rod upon the bullet. Hence, considering each free body separately and applying the angular impulse–momentum theorem to it, we obtain two equations with two unknowns— the impulse of the bullet and the angular velocity of the rod. However, if we consider the bullet-rod system together, the external forces acting on it are the reactions O_x and O_y and the weights of the bullet and of the rod. Since the moments of O_x and O_y about the pin O are zero and since the weights of the bullet and rod are normal to the horizontal plane and therefore parallel to the axis about which the rod rotates, the moments, about O, of all external forces will be zero, and the angular momentum of the system will be conserved.

$$\Sigma(\mathbf{H}_O)_1 = \Sigma(\mathbf{H}_O)_2$$

$$\circlearrowleft \ \begin{Bmatrix} I_O\omega_1 \\ + \\ [m_{\text{bullet}}(v_B)_1(\tfrac{4}{5})](2) \end{Bmatrix} = \begin{Bmatrix} I_O\omega_2 \\ + \\ [m_{\text{bullet}}(v_B)_2(2)] \end{Bmatrix} \qquad \text{(a)}$$

where

$$(I_O)_{\text{rod}} = (I_C)_{\text{rod}} + m_{\text{rod}}(r_{C/O})^2$$

$$= \frac{1}{12}(m_{\text{rod}})(L)^2 + (m_{\text{rod}})(r_{C/O})^2$$

$$= \frac{1}{12}(50)(4)^2 + (50)(1)^2 = 116.67 \text{ kg} \cdot \text{m}^2$$

The kinematic analysis of the bar's horizontal movement yields

$$(v_C)_1 = \omega_1 r_{C/O} = (5)(1) = 5 \text{ m/s}$$
$$(v_C)_2 = \omega_2(r_{C/O}) = \omega_2(1) = \omega_2 \text{ m/s}$$
$$(v_B)_1 = 500 \text{ m/s}$$
$$(v_B)_2 = \omega_2(r_{B/O}) = \omega_2(2) = 2.0\omega_2 \text{ m/s}$$

(*continued*)

EXAMPLE 8.12 *(concluded)*

Substituting into Equation (a) gives

$$\left\{\begin{matrix} (116.67)5 \\ + 0.1(500)(\frac{4}{5})(2) \end{matrix}\right\} = \left\{\begin{matrix} 116.67 \\ + 0.1(2)(2) \end{matrix}\right\}\omega_2$$

and solving for the final angular velocity of the bar,

$$\omega_2 = 5.67 \text{ rad/s} \circlearrowleft \blacktriangleleft$$

To determine the average impulsive reactions at O we apply the x and y component of the linear impulse–momentum equation to the bullet-rod system.

$$\overset{+}{\rightarrow} (m_b v_{bx})_1 + \int_{t=0}^{t=0.04} O_x \, dt = m_r (v_{Cx})_2 + m_b (v_{Px})_2 \quad \text{(a)}$$

where v_P is the velocity on the rod of the point P where the bullet is lodged.

$$\overset{+}{\uparrow} m_b (v_{by})_1 + m_r (v_{Cy})_1 + \int_{t=0}^{t=0.04} O_y \, dt$$
$$= m_r (v_{Cy})_2 + m_b (v_{Py})_2 \quad \text{(b)}$$

From Equation (a) we have

$$(0.1)[(\tfrac{3}{5})500] + O_x(0.04) = 50(0) + 0.10(0)$$
$$O_x = 750 \text{ N} \overset{\leftarrow}{} \blacktriangleleft$$

From Equation (b) we obtain

$$(0.1)[(\tfrac{4}{5})500] + (50)[(\omega_1)r_{C/O}] + O_y(0.04)$$
$$= 50[(\omega_2)r_{C/O}] + 0.1[(\omega_2)r_{P/O}]$$

where $\omega_1 = 5$ rad/s and $\omega_2 = 5.67$ rad/s and

$$r_{C/O} = 1 \text{ m} \qquad r_{P/O} = 2 \text{ m}$$

Now, solving the above for O_y, $\qquad O_y = 134.2 \text{ N} \downarrow \blacktriangleleft$

EXAMPLE 8.13

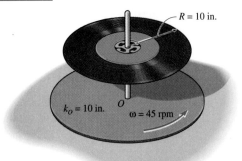

R = 10 in.

k_O = 10 in.   *O* ω = 45 rpm

The 2-lb turntable (mass radius of gyration $k_O = 10$ in.) of a record player is turning freely at an angular velocity $\omega_1 = 45$ rpm when a record (radius $R = 10$ in.) weighing 0.10 lb is suddenly dropped on it as shown. After a short period during which the record slips on the turntable, the two objects move together. Determine the final angular velocity of the record-turntable system.

Solution The angular momentum of the record-turntable system is conserved. We have $(H_O)_1 = (H_O)_2$, where O is the center of rotation (and mass center) of the system. Initially the record is at rest; hence it has no angular momentum and the left-hand side of the above equation becomes

$$(H_O)_1 = (I_O)_T \omega_1 = [(m_T)k_O^2]\omega_1$$

where $\quad m_T = \dfrac{2 \text{ lb}}{32.2} = 0.062$ slugs

$$k_O = \frac{10}{12} = 0.833 \text{ ft}$$

$$\omega_1 = \left[\frac{45(2\pi)}{60}\right] = 4.71 \text{ rad/s}$$

The final angular momentum will involve the mass moment of inertia of the system. Hence, we write

$$(H_O)_2 = [(I_O)_T + (I_O)_R]\omega_2$$

(continued)

EXAMPLE 8.13 (concluded)

where $(I_O)_R = \dfrac{1}{2} m_R R^2$ $\quad (I_O)_T = m_T k_O^2$

$$m_R = \left[\dfrac{0.10}{32.2} \right] = 0.003 \text{ slugs}$$

$$R = \left(\dfrac{10}{12} \right) = 0.833 \text{ ft}$$

The theorem of conservation of angular momentum can now be expressed as

$[(0.062)(0.833)^2](4.71)$

$$= [(0.062)(0.833)^2 + \dfrac{1}{2}(0.003)(0.833)^2]\omega_2$$

and solving for ω_2 we obtain

$$\omega_2 = 0.976(4.71) = 4.60 \text{ rad/s}$$

$$\omega_2 \approx 43.9 \text{ rpm} \blacktriangleleft$$

The turntable would have a 2.4% less angular speed.

8.7 ECCENTRIC IMPACT

In Section 4.5, problems of *central impact* involving the collision between two deformable bodies were shown to be particularly well suited to solution by the method of linear impulse and momentum. In contrast problems of **eccentric impact** necessitate, in addition, the introduction of the kinematic parameters describing the angular motion of the bodies. The principle of angular impulse and momentum thus becomes the *second* relationship essential to the solution of such eccentric impact problems. The following analysis is essentially similar to the discussion of the central impact of two deformable bodies.

Consider two colliding bodies 1 and 2 as shown in Figure 8.8. The two

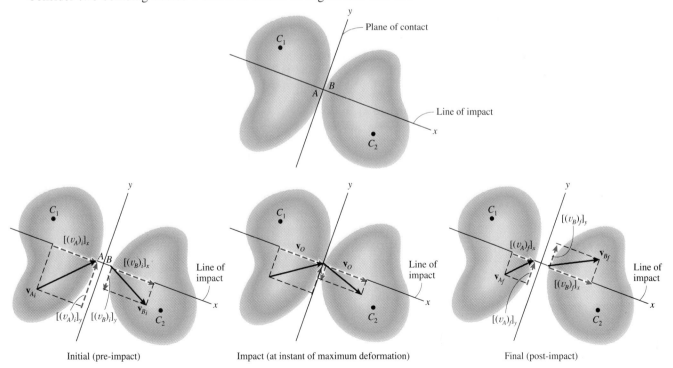

Initial (pre-impact)   Impact (at instant of maximum deformation)   Final (post-impact)

Figure 8.8

points of contact A and B on the respective bodies will have, prior to impact, velocities $(v_A)_i$ and $(v_B)_i$ respectively. The period of impact consists of a period of *deformation*, followed by a period of *restitution*. At the instant of maximum deformation, the velocity components of the contact points A and B along the line of impact will be equal ($v_A = v_B = v_0$). The dynamic condition called impact comes to an end when the two bodies move apart. Each body acquires a new velocity and momentum, the direction and magnitude of which will be determined from the initial momenta of the bodies and the energy they have lost during impact.

Writing, for each body, the linear impulse–momentum equations for the deformation ($0 - t_0$) and restitution ($t_0 - t$) periods, we would obtain, for the components of the equations along the line of impact [from Equation (8.27)] for body 1,

Deformation period:

$$m_1(v_C)_i - \int_{t=0}^{t_0} F_d \, dt = m_1(v_C)_0 \tag{8.32a}$$

Restitution period:

$$m_1(v_C)_0 - \int_{t_0}^{t} F_r \, dt = m_1(v_C)_f \tag{8.32b}$$

F_d and F_r are the impulsive forces exerted on body 1 during the deformation and restitution periods respectively. The minus signs are due to the fact that F_d and F_r are in the negative x direction. The subscripts i and f indicate the initial and final values of the velocity of the mass center.

Next, we consider the angular impulse–momentum equation [Equation (8.28)] and apply it to body 1 for the deformation and restitution periods. Assuming that the moment of inertia of the body does not change during impact we have, for body 1,

Deformation period:

$$I_{C_1}(\omega)_i + \int_{t=0}^{t_0} (M_C)_d \, dt = I_{C_1}(\omega)_0 \tag{8.33a}$$

Restitution period:

$$I_{C_1}(\omega)_0 + \int_{t_0}^{t} (M_C)_r \, dt = I_{C_1}(\omega)_f \tag{8.33b}$$

where $(M_C)_d$ and $(M_C)_r$ represent the moments about C_1 of the impulsive forces acting on body 1 during the deformation and restitution periods respectively.

Equations (8.33a) and (8.33b) can also be expressed as

$$I_{C_1}\omega_i - r\int_{t=0}^{t_0} F_d \, dt = I_{C_1}\omega_0 \tag{8.34a}$$

$$I_{C_1}\omega_0 - r\int_{t_0}^{t} F_r \, dt = I_{C_1}\omega_f \tag{8.34b}$$

where r is the normal distance from C_1 to the line of impact. In writing the above equations it is assumed that the bodies are *smooth*.

Recalling that the coefficient of restitution e was defined in Chapter 4, Equation (4.12) as

$$e = \frac{\displaystyle\int_{t_0}^{t} F_r \, dt}{\displaystyle\int_{t=0}^{t_0} F_d \, dt}$$

we can solve Equations (8.32a) and (8.32b) for $\int F_r \, dt$ and $\int F_d \, dt$ respectively to obtain

$$e = \frac{(v_C)_0 - (v_C)_f}{(v_C)_i - (v_C)_0} \tag{8.35}$$

Next, we solve Equations (8.34a) and (8.34b) for the same two impulses and get

$$e = \frac{(\omega)_0 - (\omega)_f}{(\omega)_i - (\omega)_0} \tag{8.36}$$

Equations (8.35) and (8.36) can now be rearranged and combined to yield the expression

$$e = \frac{(v_C + \omega r)_0 - (v_C + \omega r)_f}{(v_C + \omega r)_i - (v_C + \omega r)_0} = \frac{(v_A)_0 - (v_A)_f}{(v_A)_i - (v_A)_0} \tag{8.37}$$

where v_A is the velocity of the contact point and r the distance from A to C_1.

An identical analysis carried out for body 2 will yield the expression

$$e = \frac{(v_B)_0 - (v_B)_f}{(v_B)_i - (v_B)_0} \tag{8.38}$$

Since at the end of the deformation period (at $t = t_0$) the velocity components along the line of impact of the two bodies are identical, $(v_A)_0 = (v_B)_0$, we can combine Equations (8.37) and (8.38) and after eliminating $(v_A)_0$ and $(v_B)_0$ we obtain for the coefficient of restitution e

$$e = \frac{(v_B)_f - (v_A)_f}{(v_A)_i - (v_B)_i} \tag{8.39}$$

Equation (8.39) is identical to the expression obtained for central impact: Equation (4.15). However, the coefficient of restitution for eccentric impact is expressed in terms of the ratio of the relative velocity of *separation* of the *points of contact* just after impact to the relative velocity of *approach* of the *points of contact* immediately prior to impact (all velocities representing the components along the line of impact of the contact points).

We must note that Equation (8.39) has been derived for the case when the x components of the initial velocities, which we referred to as $(v_A)_i$ and $(v_B)_i$, are in the same direction. Should the bodies 1 and 2 move toward each other the signs of the velocity terms would be affected accordingly. In fact a more descriptive expression for the coefficient of restitution can be written in the form

$$e = \frac{\left| \begin{array}{c} \text{relative velocity of separation} \\ \text{of the contact points} \end{array} \right|}{\left| \begin{array}{c} \text{relative velocity of approach} \\ \text{of the contact points} \end{array} \right|}$$

EXAMPLE 8.14

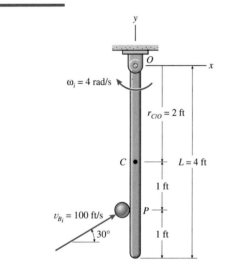

The 40-lb slender rod (length $= 4$ ft) swinging about hinge O at the vertical position shown has an angular velocity of 4 rad/s clockwise. At this position, the bar is struck by a 4-lb ball thrown in the direction shown at a velocity of 100 ft/s. Determine the velocity of the ball immediately after impact, and the corresponding angular velocity of the rod. The coefficient of restitution between rod and ball is 0.75. The impact is assumed smooth.

(continued)

EXAMPLE 8.14 *(concluded)*

Solution Considering the ball and the slender rod as part of a system we see that except for the weight of the ball all other external forces are concurrent with point O and, thus, do not contribute to any angular impulse. The equation of conservation of angular momentum when expressed about the hinge O yields

$$(\mathbf{H}_O)_i = (\mathbf{H}_O)_f$$

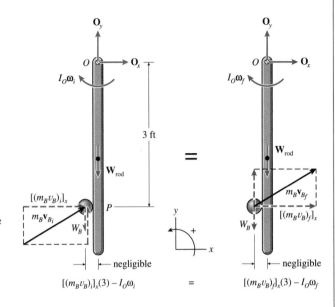

$$\begin{Bmatrix} [m_B(v_B)_i \cos 30°](3.0) \\ + \\ (-I_O\omega_i) \end{Bmatrix} = \begin{Bmatrix} [m_B(v_{Bx})_f(3.0)] \\ + \\ (+I_O\omega_f) \end{Bmatrix}$$

where $I_O = \frac{1}{3}m_r L^2$. The above expression ignores the very small impulsive moment due to the weight of the ball about the hinge at O. It can be expanded to read

$$\left(\frac{4}{32.2}\right)(100) \cos 30°(3.0) - \left[\frac{1}{3}\left(\frac{40}{32.2}\right)(4)^2\right](4)$$

$$= \frac{4}{32.2}(v_{Bx})_f(3.0) + \left[\frac{1}{3}\left(\frac{40}{32.2}\right)(4)^2\right]\omega_f$$

After collecting and rearranging terms, we get

$$17.77\omega_f + (v_{Bx})_f = 15.48 \qquad\qquad (a)$$

We also have the coefficient of restitution (e) given as 0.75, and we write

$$+v_{P_f} - (+v_{Bx})_f = e[(v_{Bx})_i - (-v_P)_i]$$

$$3\omega_f - (v_{Bx})_f = 0.75[100 \cos 30° + 3(4)]$$

$$3\omega_f - (v_{Bx})_f = 73.95 \qquad\qquad (b)$$

Here the point P is on the rod and its velocity is given by $v_P = \omega r$. Solving Equations (a) and (b) simultaneously for ω_f and $(v_{Bx})_f$, we obtain

$$\omega_f = +4.32 \text{ rad/s} \circlearrowleft \qquad (v_{Bx})_f = 61.0 \text{ ft/s} \Leftarrow$$

Assuming that both objects (ball and rod) are perfectly smooth and frictionless, the only impulse exerted on the ball during the impact is due to internal forces directed along the line of impact, that is, along the x axis. It follows that the y component of the momentum of the ball is conserved and $(v_B)_y$ remains unchanged.

$$(v_{By})_f = (v_{By})_i = 100 \sin 30° = 50 \text{ ft/s} \uparrow \quad \blacktriangleleft$$

The velocity of the ball immediately after impact thus becomes

$$(v_B)_f = -61\mathbf{i} + 50\mathbf{j} \text{ (ft/s)} \; _{39.3°} \quad \blacktriangleleft$$

EXAMPLE 8.15

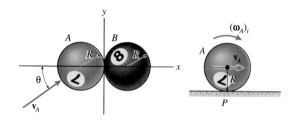

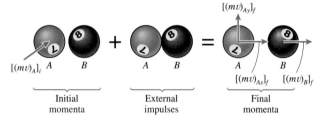

| | Initial momenta | | External impulses | | Final momenta |

Two billiard balls (radius $= R$) collide obliquely on a horizontal table as shown. Ball A rolls without slipping with a velocity $\mathbf{v}_A$. Ball B is initially at rest. Assuming the balls to be perfectly smooth (no friction between the balls) and perfectly elastic ($e =$ 1.0), determine the angular velocity of each ball and the velocities of their centers immediately after the impact. The coefficient of kinetic friction between the balls and the table is μ_k.

Solution   Considering the fact that during impact friction forces remain nonimpulsive, the equation of angular impulse–momentum can be reduced to the equation of conservation of angular momentum, and we write for each billiard ball

Ball A: $\qquad\qquad (\mathbf{H}_A)_i = (\mathbf{H}_A)_f$ $\qquad\qquad$ (a)

Ball B: $\qquad\qquad (\mathbf{H}_B)_i = (\mathbf{H}_B)_f$ $\qquad\qquad$ (b)

From Equation (a) we obtain

$$I_A(\boldsymbol{\omega}_A)_i = I_A(\boldsymbol{\omega}_A)_f \qquad (\boldsymbol{\omega}_A)_f = (\boldsymbol{\omega}_A)_i$$

However, since ball A is rolling in the direction of motion as indicated by the velocity vector $\mathbf{v}$,

$$\mathbf{v}_A = (\boldsymbol{\omega}_A)_i \times (\mathbf{R})$$
$$v(\cos\theta\,\mathbf{i} + \sin\theta\,\mathbf{j}) = [(\omega_{Ax})_i\mathbf{i} + (\omega_{Ay})_i\mathbf{j}] \times (R\mathbf{k})$$
$$v\cos\theta\,\mathbf{i} + v\sin\theta\,\mathbf{j} = -(\omega_{Ax})_iR\mathbf{j} + (\omega_{Ay})_iR\mathbf{i}$$
$$(\omega_{Ax})_i = -\frac{v\sin\theta}{R} \qquad (\omega_{Ay})_i = \frac{v\cos\theta}{R}$$

We can now write

$$(\boldsymbol{\omega}_A)_f = (\boldsymbol{\omega}_A)_i = -\frac{v\sin\theta}{R}\mathbf{i} + \frac{v\cos\theta}{R}\mathbf{j}$$

Hence the angular velocity of ball A after impact would remain

$$(\boldsymbol{\omega}_A)_f = \frac{v}{R}(-\sin\theta\,\mathbf{i} + \cos\theta\,\mathbf{j}) \blacktriangleleft$$

The angular velocity of ball B immediately after impact can, likewise, be obtained from the conservation of angular momentum theorem expressed in Equation (b). So we write

$$I_B(\boldsymbol{\omega}_B)_i = I_B(\boldsymbol{\omega}_B)_f$$

$$(\boldsymbol{\omega}_B)_f = (\boldsymbol{\omega}_B)_i = 0 \blacktriangleleft$$

since ball B is initially at rest.

(*continued*)

EXAMPLE 8.15 (*concluded*)

To find the linear velocities of the balls immediately after impact, we will appeal to the x component of the equation of linear impulse and momentum written for the system consisting of the two billiard balls, as well as to the y component of the equation of linear impulse–momentum applied to ball A. We will also make use of the coefficient of restitution.

The x component of the system momenta will be conserved, since there is no external impulse acting on the system during impact. We have

$$m_A(v_{Ax})_i + m_B[(v_{Bx})_i = 0] = m_A(v_{Ax})_f + m_B(v_{Bx})_f$$

Since $m_A = m_B$ and $(v_{Ax})_i = v \cos \theta$, we obtain

$$(v_{Ax})_f + (v_{Bx})_f = v \cos \theta \qquad (c)$$

The conservation of the y components of the linear momenta of balls A and B can also be expressed by writing

$$m_A(v_{Ay})_i = m_A(v_{Ay})_f \qquad m_B(v_{By})_i = m_B(v_{By})_f$$

and since $(v_{Ay})_i = v \sin \theta$ and $(v_{By})_i = 0$, we obtain

$$(v_{Ay})_f = v \sin \theta \qquad (v_{By})_f = 0 \qquad (d)$$

Finally, we introduce the coefficient of restitution for the impact under consideration as

$$\overset{+}{\underset{\rightarrow}{\oplus}} \qquad e = \frac{[(v_{Bx})_f - (v_{Ax})_f]}{[(v_{Ax})_i - (v_{Bx})_i]}$$

Since $(v_{Bx})_i = 0$, $(v_{Ax})_i = v \cos \theta$, and $e = 1.0$, we have

$$(v_{Bx})_f - (v_{Ax})_f = v \cos \theta \qquad (e)$$

From Equations (c) and (e) we conclude that

$$(v_{Ax})_f = 0 \quad \text{and} \quad (v_{Bx})_f = v \cos \theta$$

The velocity of each ball immediately after impact (and before ball B begins to roll without slipping) is given as

$$(\mathbf{v}_A)_f = (v \sin \theta)\mathbf{j} \, \textcircled{$\uparrow$} \; \blacktriangleleft$$
$$(\mathbf{v}_B)_f = v \cos \theta \mathbf{i} \, \textcircled{$\rightarrow$} \; \blacktriangleleft$$

8.8 SUMMARY

In this chapter, we have learned the following:

1. The work–kinetic energy relationship can be expressed as

$$T_1 + \Sigma U_{1 \to 2} = T_2 \qquad (8.1)$$

where

$$T = \frac{1}{2}mv_C^2 + \frac{1}{2}I_C\omega^2 \qquad (8.9)$$

and the work terms for various types of forces are given as

For a variable force: $\quad (U_{1 \to 2})_F = \displaystyle\int_1^2 F \cos \theta \, ds \qquad (8.2)$

For a constant force: $\quad (U_{1 \to 2})_F = FR \cos \theta \qquad (8.3)$

For the weight force: $\quad (U_{1 \to 2})_W = -W \Delta y \qquad (8.4)$

For a spring force: $\quad (U_{1 \to 2})_{Sp} = -\dfrac{1}{2}k(x_2^2 - x_1^2) \qquad (8.5)$

For a couple moment: $\quad (U_{1 \to 2})_M = \displaystyle\int_{\theta_1}^{\theta_2} M \, d\theta \qquad (8.6)$

2.   If only conservative forces act on a body, the mechanical energy of the system is conserved. The governing relationship is

$$T_1 + V_1 = T_2 + V_2 \tag{8.12}$$

where V represents the potential energy of the system. The various potential energy terms are

For gravitational potential energy:

$$V_g = Wy \tag{8.13}$$

For elastic potential energy:

$$V_e = \frac{1}{2}kx^2 \tag{8.14}$$

3.   The linear impulse–momentum relationship is expressed as

$$\mathbf{G}_1 + \sum \int_{t_1}^{t_2} \mathbf{F}\, dt = \mathbf{G}_2 \tag{8.15}$$

where $\mathbf{G} = m\mathbf{v}_C$ is the linear momentum of the body having a mass center moving with a velocity $\mathbf{v}_C$.

The angular impulse–momentum relationship is expressed in the form

$$(\mathbf{H}_O)_1 + \sum \int \mathbf{M}_O\, dt = (\mathbf{H}_O)_2 \tag{8.25}$$

where $\mathbf{H}_O = I_O\boldsymbol{\omega}$
I_O = mass moment of inertia of the body about an arbitrary fixed point O
$\boldsymbol{\omega}$ = angular velocity of the body.

4.   The angular impulse–momentum relationship can also be expressed as

$$(\mathbf{H}_C)_1 + \sum \int \mathbf{M}_C\, dt = (\mathbf{H}_C)_2 \tag{8.26}$$

where $\mathbf{H}_C = I_C\boldsymbol{\omega}$
I_C = mass moment of inertia of the body about its mass center

5.   If the forces acting on a body are such that their impulses are zero in one or more coordinate directions, the linear momentum of the body will be conserved in the corresponding directions. The conservation of linear momentum equation is written

$$m(\mathbf{v}_C)_1 = m(\mathbf{v}_C)_2 \tag{8.29}$$

6.   If the angular impulse–momentum equation is written along a direction for which the impulsive forces cause zero angular impulse, then the angular momentum of the body would be conserved

$$I_O\boldsymbol{\omega}_1 = I_O\boldsymbol{\omega}_2 \qquad \text{or} \qquad I_C(\boldsymbol{\omega})_1 = I_C(\boldsymbol{\omega})_2 \tag{8.31}$$

7. The coefficient of restitution e for eccentric impact is the ratio of the relative velocity of *separation* of the *points of contact* just after impact to the relative velocity of *approach* of the *points of contact* immediately prior to impact.

$$e = \frac{\left| \begin{array}{c} \text{relative velocity of separation} \\ \text{between contact points} \end{array} \right|}{\left| \begin{array}{c} \text{relative velocity of approach} \\ \text{between contact points} \end{array} \right|}$$

KEY TERMS

conservation of mechanical
  energy *353*
    of angular momentum *368*
    of linear momentum *367*
couple *344*
eccentric impact *371*
impulse
  angular impulse *360*
  linear impulse *360*
kinetic energy *345*
  rotational kinetic energy *346*
  translational kinetic energy *346*

momentum
  angular momentum *360*
  linear momentum *360*
potential energy
  elastic potential energy *354*
  gravitational potential energy *353*
power *354*
rolling without sliding *345*
work *342*

PROBLEMS

SECTIONS 8.2, 8.3, AND 8.4

8.1 A 20-lb uniform slender bar (length = 7 ft) is released from rest at the position shown. Determine the velocity of the end point of the bar when $\theta = 90°$.

8.2 The bar in Problem 8.1, at the position shown, is rotating clockwise at the rate of $\omega_1 = 2$ rad/s. Determine the velocity of the end point of the bar when $\theta = 135°$.

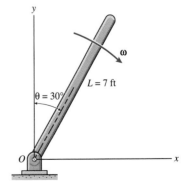

Figure P8.1 and P8.2

8.3   A 20-kg uniform slender bar ($L = 2$ m) is released from rest at the position shown. Determine the bar's angular velocity when $\theta = 90°$.

8.4   The bar in Problem 8.3, at the position shown, has an initial angular velocity $\omega_1 = 3$ rad/s. Determine the bar's final angular velocity when $\theta = 90°$.

8.5   The rod assembly shown is released from rest when $\theta = 45°$. The 20-lb slender rod *OA* is linked to the 30-lb rod *AB* through a hinge at *A*. The *B* end of rod *AB* slides on the smooth surface until *A* strikes the surface. Determine the final angular velocity of *AB* just before it comes to rest on the floor.

8.6   The rods of the assembly given in Problem 8.5, at the position ($\theta = 45°$) shown, are released with an angular velocity $\omega = 1.0$ rad/s, *OA* clockwise and *AB* counterclockwise. Determine the final angular velocity of the bar *AB* when $\theta = 90°$.

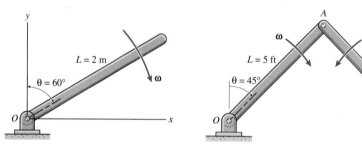

Figure P8.3 and P8.4   Figure P8.5 and P8.6

8.7   The 40-kg wheel shown has a 50-cm radius and a mass radius of gyration of 350 mm. The wheel is subjected to a torque *M* of 100 N · m and at the position shown has an angular velocity of 150 rpm clockwise. Determine the velocity and acceleration of point *A* after the wheel has completed one full revolution.

8.8   The 100-lb wheel shown is starting from rest and rotating counterclockwise under the action of a torque $M = 400$ lb · ft. Determine the velocity of a point *P* along the rim of the wheel after two full revolutions.

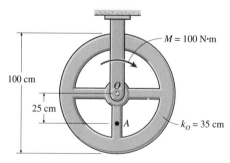

Figure P8.7

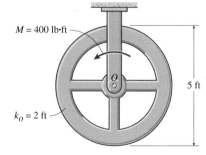

Figure P8.8

8.9 The 10-kg block A is suspended from a cord that is wrapped around the inner core of the 100-kg spool pinned at O. The mass radius of gyration of the spool about O is 500 mm. Neglecting the mass of the cord, determine the spool's angular velocity after the block A has moved 1.0 m down from rest.

8.10 The 5-lb uniform slender rod (length $L = 5$ ft) is subjected to the force $P = 25$ lb and torque $M = 60$ lb · ft as shown. If, in the position shown ($\theta = 0°$), the rod rotates counterclockwise in the vertical plane about O with an angular velocity of 8 rad/s, determine its angular velocity when $\theta = 90°$.

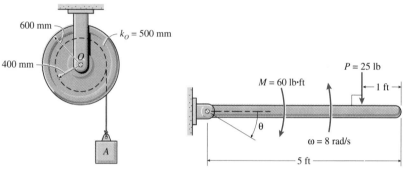

Figure P8.9   **Figure P8.10**

8.11 A pendulum consists of a 5-kg slender rod (length $L = 2$ m) at the end of which is attached a 25-kg sphere (radius $R = 250$ mm). If the pendulum is released from rest at the position shown and rotates clockwise in the vertical plane under the action of a moment $M = 75$ N · m, determine its angular velocity when $\theta = 90°$.

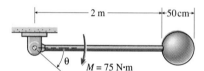

Figure P8.11

8.12 The two ends of a 50-lb rod (length $L = 5$ ft) move in the horizontal plane along the grooved and frictionless slots shown. The rod, which is initially at rest

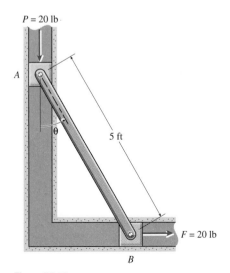

Figure P8.12

when $\theta = 30°$, is moved under the influence of a force $P = 20$ lb acting on block A and a force $F = 20$ lb acting on block B. Neglecting the mass of blocks A and B, determine the angular velocity of the rod when $\theta = 60°$.

8.13   A linkage consists of two 10-kg rods AB and CD (each of length $L = 1$ m) and a 20-kg bar BD ($L = 2$ m). In the position shown ($\theta = 0°$) the angular velocity of rod AB is 4 rad/s counterclockwise. If under the action of a horizontal force F, the angular velocity of the rod AB becomes 8 rad/s when $\theta = 90°$, determine the magnitude of the horizontal force F.

8.14   A linkage consists of two 10-lb rods AB ($L = 2$ ft) and CD ($L = 2$ ft) and a 20-lb bar BD ($L = 5$ ft). In the position shown ($\theta = 0°$) the angular velocity of rod AB is 4 rad/s counterclockwise. If under the action of a moment M, the angular velocity of the rod AB becomes 8 rad/s when $\theta = 90°$, determine the magnitude of the moment M.

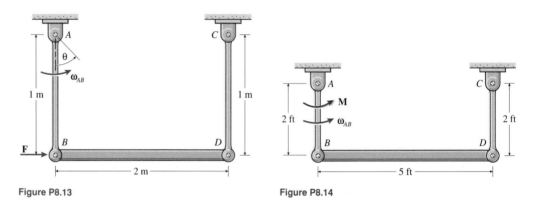

Figure P8.13   Figure P8.14

8.15   At a given instant the 25-kg block A shown is located at a distance of 2 m from a spring ($k_s = 100$ N/m) when its velocity along the incline is 5 m/s. If the coefficient of kinetic friction between the block and the inclined plane is 0.20, determine the total distance traveled down the plane by the block before coming to rest.

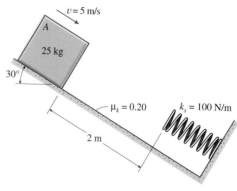

Figure P8.15

8.16 A 25-lb disk with a radius of 1.0 ft is initially maintained in equilibrium by a spring (k_s = 10 lb/ft) as shown. When a moment M = 20 lb · ft is applied to the disk and assuming that the disk rolls without slipping, determine the total distance traveled down the incline by the mass center of the disk before it comes to rest.

8.17 A uniform 50-kg spool (centroidal radius of gyration k_c = 0.5 m) is released from rest as shown. Determine the angular velocity of the spool after its mass center has moved 1 m down along the incline. The coefficient of kinetic friction between the spool and the inclined surface is 0.25. Neglect the mass of the cable.

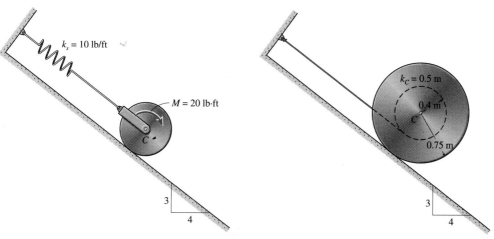

Figure P8.16   Figure P8.17

8.18 Two 10-kg bars of equal length (2 m) form a linkage as shown. The assembly is released from rest when θ = 60°. Determine the angular velocity of bar OA when θ = 0°.

8.19 The bar OA of the linkage shown in Problem 8.18 has, at the position given (θ = 60°), an initial angular velocity of 4 rad/s clockwise. Determine the angular velocity of the bar OA when θ = 30°.

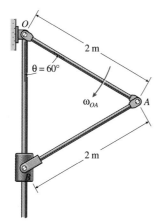

Figure P8.18 and P8.19

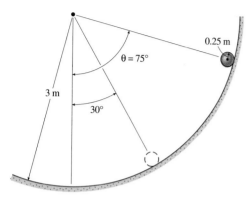

Figure P8.20

8.20   The 25-kg sphere (radius 0.25 m) is released from rest at the position shown ($\theta = 75°$) and rolls without slipping along a cylindrical surface of 3 m radius. Determine the reaction exerted by the surface on the sphere when $\theta = 30°$.

8.21   The 20-lb unbalanced wheel (radius $R = 2$ ft) has a centroidal radius of gyration $k_c = 1.25$ ft as it rolls without sliding. At the position shown, the angular velocity of the wheel is 10 rad/s counterclockwise. Determine the wheel's angular velocity after it has rolled one quarter of a revolution.

8.22   A 5-kg pendulum with a cord length of 1 m is released from rest in the position shown and strikes a spring that has a spring constant $k_s = 50$ N/cm. Determine the maximum compression of the spring.

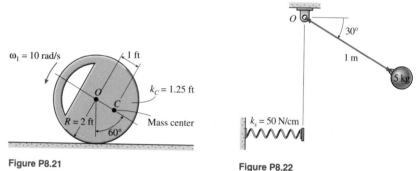

Figure P8.21

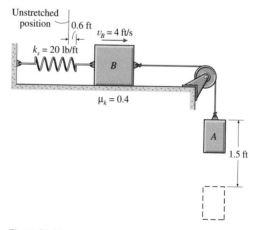

Figure P8.22

8.23   A 100-lb block B and a 50-lb block A are linked by a cable passing over a smooth pulley. Block B is attached to a spring that has a spring constant $k_s = 20$ lb/ft. The coefficient of kinetic friction between block B and the horizontal surface is 0.4. At the instant shown, the spring is stretched 0.6 ft and block B has a velocity of 4 ft/s to the right. The mass of the pulley is negligible. Determine the velocity of the block A after it has descended 1.5 ft.

Figure P8.23

8.24 A 40-kg block A is suspended by a cord that passes around a frictionless pulley as shown and is wrapped around the drum (radius $R_d = 1.2$ m) of a 200-kg wheel (radius $R_w = 1.5$ m), which is released from rest. The wheel-drum assembly has a centroidal radius of gyration $k_O = 0.75$ m. Assuming that the wheel rolls without slipping, determine the velocity of the block A after it has descended 4 m.

8.25 The 200-lb flywheel (radius $R = 2.5$ ft, centroidal radius of gyration $k_O = 2.0$ ft) is initially at rest as shown. Determine the angular velocity of the flywheel after it has rotated two full revolutions under the action of an 80-lb force.

8.26 The drum of a 250-lb flywheel (radius $R = 2.5$ ft, centroidal radius of gyration $k_O = 2.0$ ft) holds a 40-lb box B. If the system is released from rest, determine the angular velocity of the flywheel-drum assembly after it has rotated by 180°. (Use the equation of conservation of mechanical energy.)

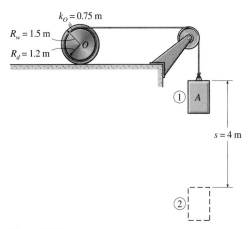

Figure P8.24

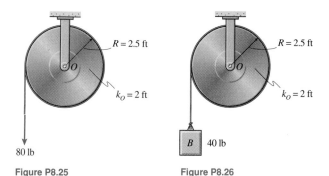

Figure P8.25   Figure P8.26

8.27 A car and its driver have a combined weight of 2000 lb, excluding the four wheels. Each wheel has a radius of 1.0 ft, a weight of 45 lb, and a centroidal radius of gyration of $k_0 = 0.8$ ft. Assuming that the wheels roll without slipping and neglecting all frictional effects, determine the speed of the car after it has traveled 250 ft starting from rest. (Use the equation of conservation of mechanical energy.)

Figure P8.27

8.28 Using the conservation of mechanical energy, solve Problem 8.1.

8.29 Using the conservation of mechanical energy, solve Problem 8.2.

8.30 The four-panel revolving door shown is initially rotating with $\omega = 2$ rad/s. The mass of each panel is 40 kg. Neglecting the friction at the axle of the revolving door, determine its angular velocity after it has rotated through 90°. (Use the equation of conservation of mechanical energy.)

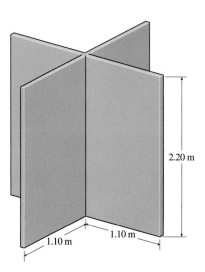

Figure P8.30

8.31   Using the equation of conservation of mechanical energy, solve Problem 8.3.

8.32   Using the equation of conservation of mechanical energy, solve Problem 8.4.

8.33   Using the equation of conservation of mechanical energy, solve Problem 8.5.

8.34   Using the equation of conservation of mechanical energy, solve Problem 8.6.

8.35   The gear assembly shown consists of two gears A and B weighing 10 and 15 lb, respectively. The system is initially at rest. Their centroidal radii of gyration are 0.75 ft and 1.2 ft, respectively. A constant clockwise moment $M = 20$ lb · ft is applied on the gear A. Determine the angular velocity of gear B after gear A has executed five full revolutions.

8.36   Using the equation of conservation of mechanical energy, solve Problem 8.19.

8.37   Using the equation of conservation of mechanical energy, solve Problem 8.20.

8.38   Using the equation of conservation of mechanical energy, solve Problem 8.21.

8.39   Using the equation of conservation of mechanical energy, solve Problem 8.22.

8.40   The double pulley shown has a mass of 30 kg and a centroidal mass radius of gyration of 2 m. If the masses attached to the pulley are 100 kg and 150 kg and the system is released from rest, determine the speeds of the blocks A and B, after the pulley has gone through two revolutions.

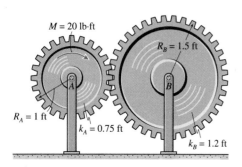

Figure P8.35

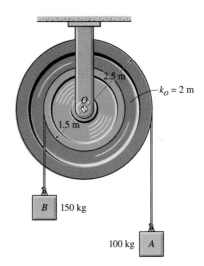

Figure P8.40

8.41   Frictionless gears A ($m_A = 20$ kg, $R_A = 0.3$ m) and B ($m_B = 5$ kg, $R_B = 0.10$ m) are initially at rest. Suddenly a couple $M = 10$ N · m is applied to gear B as shown. Determine the angular velocity of gear B after it has executed 10 revolutions. The radii of gyration of gears A and B are 0.25 m and 0.075 m, respectively.

8.42   In Problem 8.41, determine the tangential force exerted by gear B on gear A and the number of revolutions executed by gear A when gear B has reached 500 rpm.

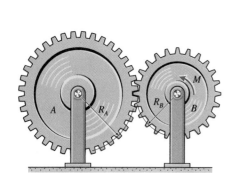

Figure P8.41 and P8.42

8.43 A sphere of radius R and mass m is released from rest on an incline as shown. Determine the velocity of its center after it has rolled without slipping through a distance L.

8.44 Solve Problem 8.43, assuming that the sphere is replaced by a cylinder of equal mass and radius.

8.45 A hydraulic cylinder is used to exert the force necessary to bring to stop the rotation of a 1-ft-radius brake drum as shown. The total mass moment of inertia of the brake drum and the attached flywheel is 25 lb · ft · s² and the coefficient of kinetic friction between the brake shoe and the drum is 0.35. If the initial angular speed of the drum is 360 rpm counterclockwise, find the force F necessary to stop the drum after 100 revolutions.

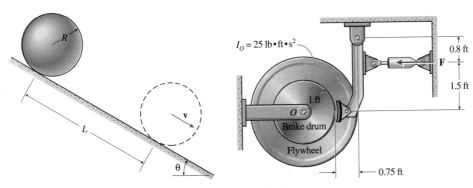

Figure P8.43 and P8.44 **Figure P8.45**

8.46 The 200-lb unbalanced wheel A with a centroidal radius of gyration $k_c = 1$ ft rolls along the horizontal plane shown without slipping and is connected to a 75-lb weight B by means of an inextensible cord that passes over a smooth pulley of negligible mass and is wrapped around the wheel. A spring ($k_s = 25$ lb/ft) of negligible mass is attached to the wheel at O. In the position indicated, the tension in the spring is 50 lb, and the velocity of the center O of the wheel is 5 ft/s to the left. Determine the velocity of O after the wheel has rolled 90° counterclockwise.

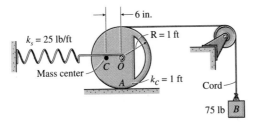

Figure P8.46

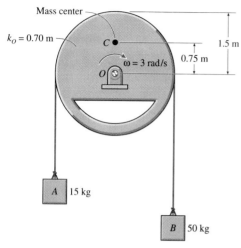

Mass center

$k_O = 0.70$ m

C

$\omega = 3$ rad/s

O

1.5 m

0.75 m

A | 15 kg

B | 50 kg

Figure P8.47 and P8.48

8.47 Two blocks A ($m_A = 15$ kg) and B ($m_B = 50$ kg) are connected through an inextensible cord, which is wrapped around an unbalanced drum with a radius of 1.5 m, a 25-kg mass, and a radius of gyration of 0.7 m about O. In the position shown, the drum rotates clockwise with an angular speed of 3 rad/s. Determine the angular speed of the drum when the mass center C of the drum reaches the point directly below the rotation center O.

8.48 Solve Problem 8.47, if, initially, in the position shown the system is released from rest.

8.49 A 50-lb slender bar OA is in the vertical position when supported by an unstretched spring that has a spring constant $k_s = 10$ lb/in. Determine the initial angular speed ω of the bar necessary for it to reach the horizontal position with zero velocity. Compare the results for clockwise and counterclockwise rotations.

8.50 A 2-kg toggle having a radius of gyration about pin O of 0.05 m is initially in its null position ($\theta = 0°$) in the horizontal plane. A spring ($k_s = 300$ kN/m) is attached to the toggle as shown. If the toggle is slightly displaced from its null position it moves under the pull of the spring and impacts point A. Determine the minimum unstretched length of the spring necessary to limit the velocity of the toggle at impact to 0.3 m/s.

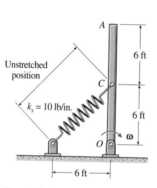

A

Unstretched position

$k_s = 10$ lb/in.

C

O

ω

6 ft

6 ft

6 ft

Figure P8.49

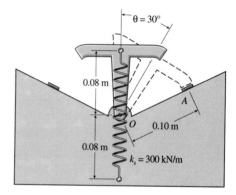

$\theta = 30°$

0.08 m

O 0.10 m

A

0.08 m

$k_s = 300$ kN/m

Figure P8.50

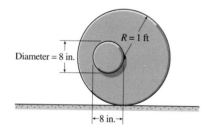

$R = 1$ ft

Diameter = 8 in.

8 in.

Figure P8.51

8.51 The unbalanced 200-lb disk of 1-ft radius is released from rest on a horizontal surface from the position shown. The disk rolls without slipping under the influence of its own weight. Determine the maximum angular velocity reached by the wheel.

8.52 The 100-kg horizontal bar is freely pinned to the two identical 75-kg disks. The bar, at the position shown, has an initial velocity of 1 m/s as shown. If the disks roll without slipping, determine the angular velocity of the disks after they have rotated $\theta = 180°$.

8.53 A 100-lb plate is attached to the 20-lb slender rod (length $L = 8$ ft), which is pinned from O as shown. In the position shown ($\theta = 25°$), the pendulum system rotates counterclockwise with an angular velocity of 0.75 rad/s. Determine the largest angle θ to which the pendulum swings before it stops and begins its clockwise rotation.

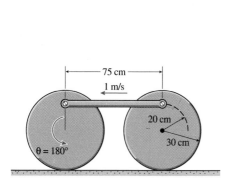

75 cm

1 m/s

20 cm

30 cm

θ = 180°

Figure P8.52

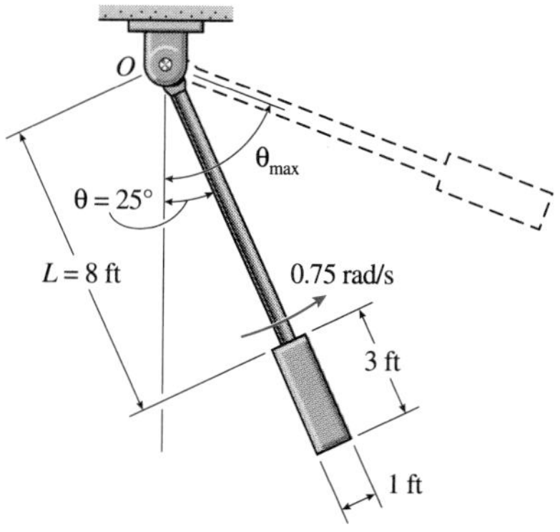

O

θ_max

θ = 25°

$L = 8$ ft

0.75 rad/s

3 ft

1 ft

Figure P8.53

8.54 Solve Problem 8.53 assuming that the plate is replaced by a 100-lb cylinder having a 1-ft diameter and 1-ft height.

8.55 A garage door is operated by two spring-and-cable assemblies, one on each side of the door, as shown. The 500-lb door is an 8-ft by 12-ft panel and the two springs' $k_s = 10$ lb/in. If the springs are unstretched when the door is fully open (i.e., horizontal), determine its angular velocity when under its own weight the door is closed and the panel touches the floor. Ignore the masses of the struts OA and OB.

8.56 A 10-kg pulley is attached to the ceiling by a spring as shown. The pulley, which can be approximated as a disk with a 250-mm radius, is suddenly pulled downward by a force F. Assuming that the disk is initially at rest supported by the spring, determine the magnitude of the constant force F required to give the center of the pulley a velocity of 1.0 m/s, 2 m from its position of rest.

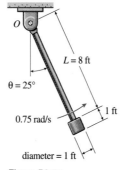

O

$L = 8$ ft

θ = 25°

0.75 rad/s

1 ft

diameter = 1 ft

Figure P8.54

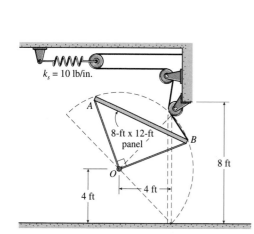

$k_s = 10$ lb/in.

A

8-ft x 12-ft panel

B

O

4 ft

4 ft

8 ft

Figure P8.55

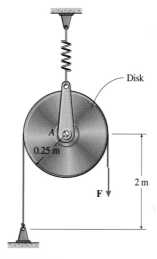

Disk

A

0.25 m

F

2 m

Figure P8.56

8.57 A gearbox used in the transmission of power is shown. If a power of 20 hp is applied at one end of shaft A and the angular speed of the shaft is 200 rpm, determine the magnitude of the torque delivered to shaft C.

8.58 The power output of a motor is determined by measuring the forces exerted at the two spring scales shown. If the motor is operating at 300 rpm and the forces exerted at A and B are 20 and 30 lb respectively, determine the power developed by the motor.

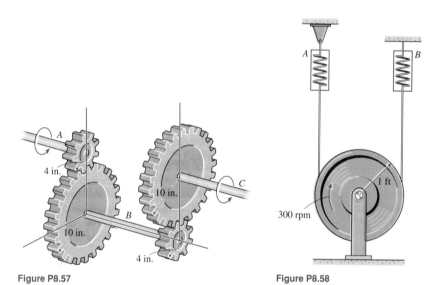

Figure P8.57   Figure P8.58

8.59 A motor develops 2 hp when running at a speed of 4000 rpm. Determine the torque exerted on the shaft.

8.60 A motor developing 10 kW is connected to a machine through a belt linking two pulleys A and B as shown. The motor runs at a constant angular speed of 1000 rpm. Determine the torques delivered along shafts A and B.

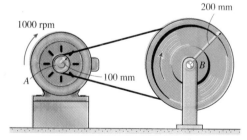

Figure P8.60

SECTIONS 8.5, 8.6, AND 8.7

8.61 A 200-kg flywheel-pulley system (radius $R = 1.2$ m, centroidal radius of gyration $k_O = 0.85$ m) is released from rest when a force $F = 400$ N is acting on the cord wrapped around the pulley as shown. Determine the angular velocity of the system 5 s after its release.

8.62 A 200-kg flywheel-pulley system (pulley radius $R = 1.2$ m, centroidal radius of gyration $k_o = 0.85$ m) is released from rest as shown under the action of a force $F = 40t$ (N), where t is in s. Determine the angular velocity of the system 10 s after its release.

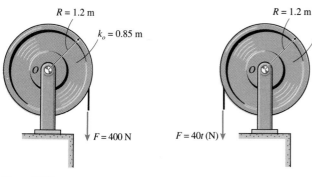

Figure P8.61

Figure P8.62

8.63 A 400-kg flywheel-pulley system (radius $R = 3$ m, centroidal radius of gyration $k_o = 2.3$ m) is at rest while supporting a 400-N weight as shown. Determine the angular velocity of the system 5 s after its release.

8.64 The 35-kg disk (radius $R = 0.35$ m) is initially rotating with an angular velocity of 8 rad/s as shown. If suddenly a counterclockwise torque $M = 25$ N · m is applied to the disk for $\Delta t = 1$ s, determine its final angular velocity. The coefficient of kinetic friction between the disk and the side walls is 0.25.

8.65 The 100-lb disk (radius $R = 1.5$ ft) is initially rotating with an angular velocity of 5 rad/s as shown. If suddenly a counterclockwise torque $M = 5t$ (lb · ft), where t is in s, is applied to the disk, determine the time required to bring the disk to rest. Will the disk reverse direction and continue rotating? The coefficient of kinetic friction between the disk and the side walls is 0.15.

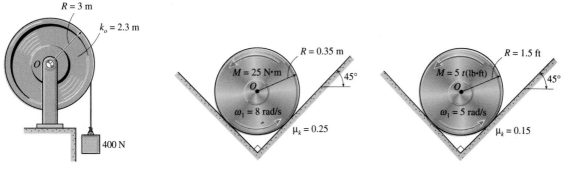

Figure P8.63

Figure P8.64

Figure P8.65

8.66 The 20-kg disk (radius $R = 0.5$ m) is released from rest and rolls along the inclined plane shown. If the coefficient of *static* friction between disk and inclined plane is 0.35, determine the maximum angle θ for which the disk would roll without slipping.

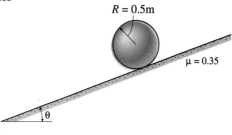

Figure P8.66

8.67   The 50-lb triangular plate is at rest on a smooth horizontal surface. For a duration of 7 s, it is acted upon by the horizontal forces shown. Determine the velocity of the mass center of the plate and its angular velocity after 7 s.

8.68   The 50-kg double spool shown (centroidal radius of gyration $k_O = 0.4$ m) is released from rest. Neglecting the masses of the ropes, determine the speeds of blocks A ($m_A = 50$ kg) and B ($m_B = 30$ kg), 5 s into the motion.

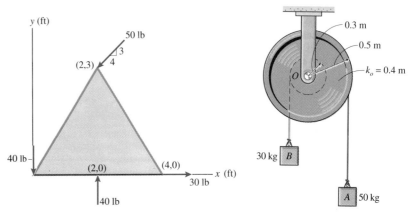

Figure P8.67   **Figure P8.68**

8.69   The 40-lb spool shown (centroidal radius of gyration $k_O = 0.6$ ft) when subjected to a horizontal force $F = 10$ lb starts rolling without slipping. Determine its angular velocity 10 s into the motion.

8.70   The 80-kg double pulley (centroidal radius of gyration $k_O = 0.7$ m) is released from rest under the action of a force $F = 100$ N and the weight of a 50-kg block as shown. Neglecting the mass of the cord, determine the speed of the 50-kg block 6 s after the release.

8.71   Solve Problem 8.70 when the force $F = 3t^2 + 50$ (N) where t is in s.

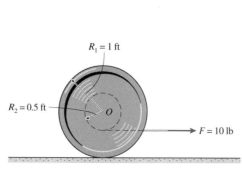

Figure P8.69

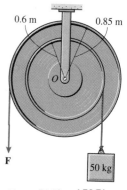

Figure P8.70 and P8.71

8.72 Two 25-lb double pulleys (centroidal radius of gyration k_o = 1.2 ft) are released from rest when a 100-lb block is allowed to descend. Neglecting any bearing friction, determine the velocity of the block 5 s after its release. Also find the tension in the cord connecting the two double pulleys.

8.73 The 60-lb double pulley (centroidal radius of gyration k_o = 0.5 ft) has, at a given instant (t = 0), an angular velocity ω = 15 rad/s counterclockwise as it pulls a 30-lb block B. The pulley is subjected to a force $F = 6t^3 + 2t^2$ (lb) where t is in s. If the coefficient of kinetic friction between the block and the surface is 0.40, determine the velocity of the block when t = 4 s.

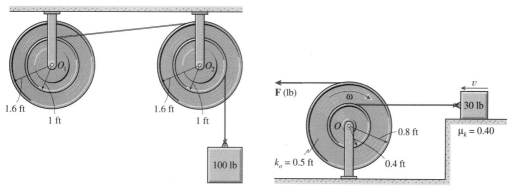

Figure P8.72   Figure P8.73

8.74 The mass center of the 30-kg double pulley (centroidal radius of gyration k_o = 0.25 m) has, at a given instant (t = 0), a downard velocity of 2 m/s. A variable force $F = t^2 + 20$ (N), where t is in s, acts on the cable, as shown. Determine the velocity of the double pulley's mass center when t = 3 s.

8.75 A uniform 10-lb bar (length L = 3 ft) is released from rest when θ = 75°. Determine the angular velocity of the bar after Δt = 0.06 s, assuming that the hinge at O is frictionless and the variation of the position angle θ during the impulse period Δt is negligible. The motion is in the vertical plane.

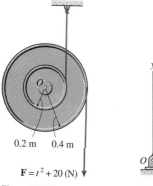

Figure P8.74   Figure P8.75

8.76 A uniform 10-kg bar (length 2 m) has an initial clockwise angular velocity $\omega = 2$ rad/s when the bar's position is at $\theta = 75°$. Determine the bar's angular velocity after $\Delta t = 0.006$ s, assuming that the hinge at O is frictionless and the variation of the bar's position angle θ during the impulse period Δt is negligible. The motion is in the vertical plane.

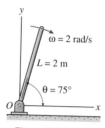

Figure P8.76

8.77 The two 20-lb rod system (rod length $= 4$ ft) is released from rest as shown when $\theta = 45°$. The rod OA is hinged and supported at O. The rod AB is hinged to OA at A and slides on the smooth surface at B. Determine the vertical velocity of the hinge at A after a period of $\Delta t = 0.01$ s has elapsed.

8.78 The two 20-kg rod system (rod length $= 2$ m) is released from rest as shown when $\theta = 60°$. At the instant of release ($t = 0$) a constant force $F = 10$ N is applied on bar AB at point B. Determine the vertical velocity of the hinge at A after the end B has slid on the smooth surface for a period of $\Delta t = 0.02$ s.

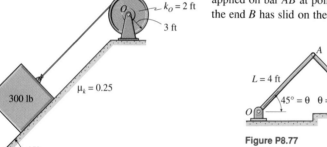

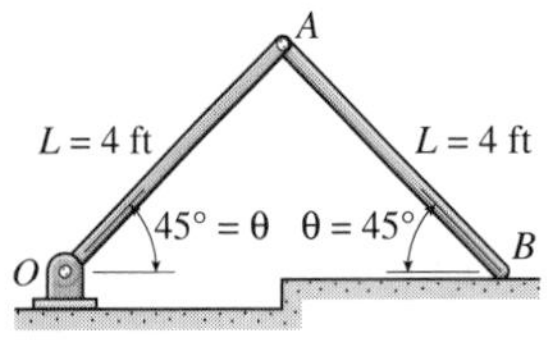

Figure P8.77

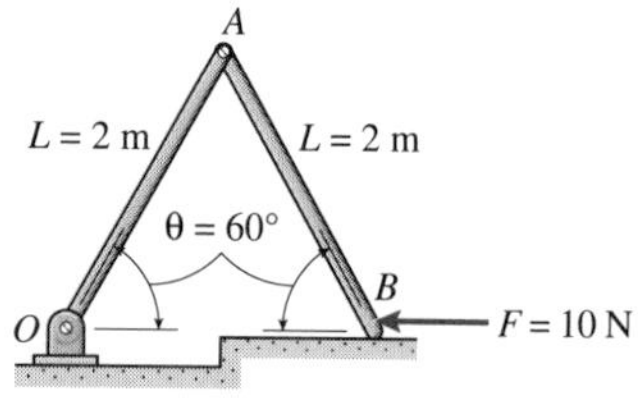

Figure P8.78

8.79 The 300-lb crate is being pulled up an inclined surface (coefficient of kinetic friction between crate and surface $\mu_k = 0.25$) by an 80-lb rotating drum (centroidal radius of gyration $k_o = 2.0$ ft) as shown. The drum's movement at any given instant (t) is caused by a clockwise couple moment $M = 500 + 30\,t$ (lb · ft), where t is in s. If initially ($t = 0$) the crate has an uphill velocity of 2 ft/s, determine the velocity of the crate at $t = 6$ s.

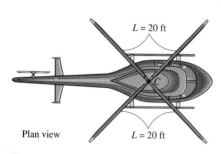

Figure P8.79

8.80 The centroidal mass moment of inertia I_C of the helicopter cabin shown is 1500 lb · ft s². Each of the four main blades is approximated as a 60-lb slender uniform rod (length $L = 20$ ft). The cabin initially has zero angular velocity, its rotation being prevented by a vertical tail propeller. If the vertical tail propeller fails to operate, the cabin will suffer rotational motion every time the rotational speeds of the main blades are changed. Determine the final angular velocity of the cabin if the rotational speed of the main blades, measured relative to the cabin, is changed from 20 rad/s to 40 rad/s. Air friction on the blades is ignored.

Figure P8.80

8.81 The 10-kg uniform slender bar (length $L = 2.0$ m) is hinged at O and is impacted as shown by a 50-gram bullet that becomes embedded in the bar. Determine the final angular speed of the bullet-bar system right at the end of the impact period, ($\Delta t = 0.02$ s) assuming that the bar has not moved significantly from its initial position.

8.82 Solve Problem 8.81 for the case when the bullet's direction is as indicated. Also determine the reaction O_x and O_y at the pin support O caused by the impact of the bullet.

8.83 A slender uniform rod has a mass of 10 kg and a length of 1.0 m. It rotates in the horizontal plane about a vertical axis located at O as shown. The rod has an angular velocity of 5 rad/s clockwise when it is struck by a particle B that has a mass of 100 g and a velocity of 200 m/s in the same direction as the motion of the point of contact on the rod. If the coefficient of restitution is zero and after impact the angular velocity of the rod is 10 rad/s, determine the location x_P relative to the hinge at O of the point of impact P.

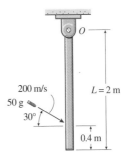

200 m/s
50 g
30°
0.4 m
$L = 2$ m

Figure P8.81

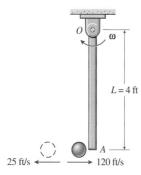

ω
$L = 4$ ft
25 ft/s ← A → 120 ft/s

Figure P8.84

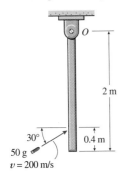

2 m
30°
50 g
$v = 200$ m/s
0.4 m

Figure P8.82

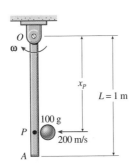

ω
x_P
$L = 1$ m
100 g
P
200 m/s
A

Figure P8.83

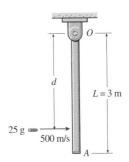

d
$L = 3$ m
25 g
500 m/s
A

Figure P8.85

8.84 The 5-lb uniform slender bar OA (length $L = 4$ ft) is at rest suspended from a pin support at O in the vertical position shown. A 0.20-lb small ball hits the bar horizontally with a velocity of 120 ft/s at the tip A of the bar. After impact the ball rebounds with a velocity of 25 ft/s in the opposite direction. Determine the angular velocity of the bar just after the collision.

8.85 The 10-kg uniform slender bar OA (length $L = 3$ m) is at rest suspended from a pin support at O in the vertical position shown. A 25-g bullet is fired horizontally with a velocity of 500 m/s into the bar. The bullet becomes embedded in the bar in 0.001 s. Determine the required distance (d) in order for the impulsive reactions at O to be zero. (Use a trial and error method of solution.)

8.86 The 2-lb uniform rod OA (length $L = 1$ ft) is at rest as shown and suspended from a pin support O, which moves freely along a horizontal guide. If, for a brief duration ($\Delta t = 0.001$ s), a force $F = 100$ lb is applied at A, in the direction normal to the rod, determine the maximum angle θ_{max} through which the rod will rotate during its motion.

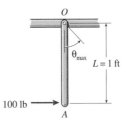

O
θ_{max}
$L = 1$ ft
100 lb →
A

Figure P8.86

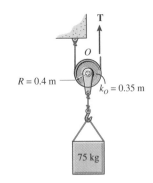

8.87 The 10-kg pulley (radius $R = 0.4$ m, centroidal radius of gyration $k_O = 0.35$ m) is used to support a 75-kg load while at rest. Determine the tension force T in the cord required to start the system shown from rest and bring it to an upward velocity of 10 m/s within a period of 3 s.

Figure P8.87

8.88 The 5-lb turntable (radius $R = 1$ ft, centroidal radius of gyration $k_O = 0.3$ ft) is rotating at a speed of 45 rpm when a 0.10-lb disk (radius $= 1$ ft) is dropped on it. Initially the disk slips on the turntable for a period of 0.3 s. After this time, disk and turntable are expected to rotate at the original angular speed of 45 rpm. Determine the additional torque that the drive motor must apply to the shaft of the turntable during the initial 0.3 s period to bring the speed up to the desired value.

Figure P8.88

8.89 The pendulum shown consists of a 5-kg sphere and a 2-kg rod. When it is released from rest at the horizontal position shown, the pendulum rotates counterclockwise 90°, strikes the wall, and rebounds. Assuming a coefficient of restitution $e = 0.75$, determine the maximum angle (θ_{max}) reached by the pendulum during its rebound.

8.90 A 5-lb sphere A is dropped from a height of 10 ft onto the end of the uniform slender 15-lb rod (length $L = 8$ ft), which is pinned at O as shown. A 3-lb sphere B, placed at the other end of the rod, is lifted upward when sphere A impacts on the rod. Assuming the impact of the sphere A onto the rod is perfectly plastic, determine the height to which the sphere B will rise.

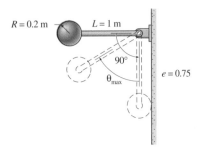

Figure P8.89

8.91 The 20-kg rod OA (length $L = 1.5$ m) rotates counterclockwise with an angular velocity of 5 rad/s when it strikes the point P as shown. If the coefficient of restitution between the rod and the point P is $e = 0.6$, determine the angular velocity of the rod immediately after the impact.

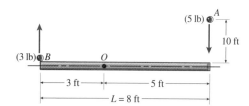

Figure P8.90

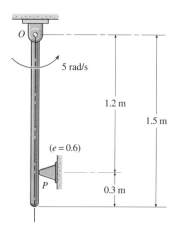

Figure P8.91

8.92 The 60-lb pulley (radius $R = 1.2$ ft, centroidal radius of gyration $k_o = 1.0$ ft) supports a 100-lb load which, initially, is moving downward with a velocity of 3 ft/s. At the instant shown a clockwise moment is applied to the hoisting rig in order to maintain a constant force $T = 85$ lb in the cable between the pulley and the hoisting drum. Determine the angular velocity of the pulley 10 s after the torque is applied to the hoisting drum. Also determine the tension in the cable AB.

8.93 The 5-kg gear B starts from rest and rotates in the horizontal plane about the stationary gear A, to which it is fastened through the 3-kg arm AB as shown. The arm AB and gear B have radii of gyration $k_A = 1.0$ m and $k_B = 0.3$ m, respectively. If a constant counterclockwise torque $M = 2$ N $\cdot$ m is applied to the arm AB, determine the absolute angular velocity of the arm after 5 s.

8.94 A 2000-lb flywheel initially rotating at a speed of 360 rpm coasts to rest after 20 minutes. Determine the average magnitude of the torque caused by friction in the bearings of the shaft supporting the flywheel. The radius of gyration of the flywheel is 5 ft.

8.95 A 300-kg flywheel with a radius of gyration of 500 mm rotates at a rate of 10,000 rpm when it begins to coast and eventually comes to rest after 20 days. Neglecting the friction due to air, determine the average moment due to friction in the bearings.

8.96 A driver is changing the tire on his car. The tire is free to rotate and is initially at rest. A clockwise torque of magnitude 40 N $\cdot$ m is applied as shown to one bolt for a duration of 0.2 s. The bolt is located 5 cm from the center of the tire, which has a weight of 160 N and a radius of gyration of 0.3 m. Determine the angular velocity of the tire immediately after 0.2 s.

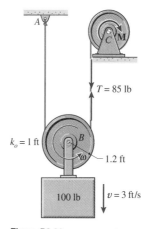

$T = 85$ lb

$k_o = 1$ ft

B

ω 1.2 ft

100 lb $v = 3$ ft/s

Figure P8.92

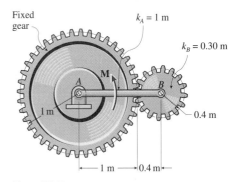

Fixed gear

$k_A = 1$ m

$k_B = 0.30$ m

M

A B

1 m 0.4 m

1 m 0.4 m

Figure P8.93

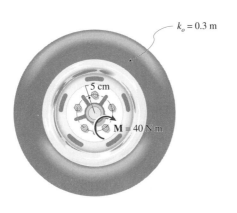

$k_o = 0.3$ m

5 cm

$M = 40$ N·m

Figure P8.96

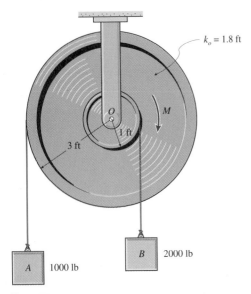

$k_o = 1.8$ ft

M

1 ft

3 ft

B 2000 lb

A 1000 lb

Figure P8.97

8.97 The system shown consists of a 100-lb double pulley and two weights A and B ($W_A = 1000$ lb, $W_B = 2000$ lb) connected by a cord having negligible mass. Initially the system is held at rest. If upon release a constant torque M is applied to the shaft of the double pulley at O, the weight A reaches an upward velocity of 12 ft/s in 3 s. Determine the magnitude of the torque M. The radius of gyration of the double pulley is 1.8 ft.

8.98 The wheel shown rolls without slipping on inclined rails. The two side hubs of the wheel are 0.10 m in radius. If initially the wheel rotates counterclockwise with an angular velocity of 10 rad/s, determine its angular velocity after $t = 10$ s. The radius of gyration of the wheel about its center is 0.20 m.

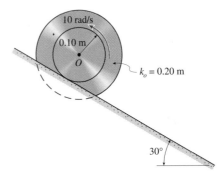

10 rad/s

0.10 m

O

$k_o = 0.20$ m

30°

Figure P8.98

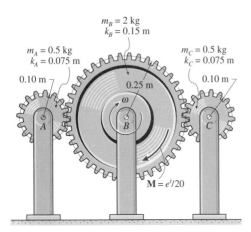

$m_B = 2$ kg
$k_B = 0.15$ m

$m_A = 0.5$ kg
$k_A = 0.075$ m

$m_C = 0.5$ kg
$k_C = 0.075$ m

0.10 m

0.25 m

0.10 m

A ω B C

$M = e^t/20$

Figure P8.99

8.99 Two small identical gears A and C are placed at diametrically opposite ends of a large gear B as shown. The central gear is initially rotating clockwise at a rate of $\omega = 10$ rad/s when a clockwise torque $M = [(e^t)/20]$ (N $\cdot$ m), where t is in s, is applied to it. Determine the angular velocity ω of the central gear after $t = 3$ s.

8.100 Two identical 50-kg disks A and B (radius $R = 200$ mm) are connected by a cord of negligible mass wrapped around their rims as shown. Disk A is pinned at its center. If disk B is released from rest, determine the angular velocity of disk A after 2 s.

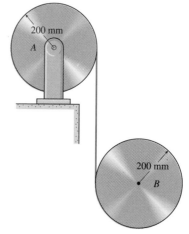

200 mm

A

200 mm

B

Figure P8.100

SPATIAL DYNAMICS*

9.1 INTRODUCTION

In Chapters 7 and 8, the focus of our attention was the kinetics of the planar motion of rigid bodies. In Chapter 6, we studied the velocity and acceleration fields of rigid-body motion. The constraints brought about by the planar nature of the motion allowed us to simplify and considerably reduce the complexity of the expressions describing the velocity and acceleration vectors. However, the initial analysis of the problem was not limited to slabs and the results obtained were, in general, valid for the case of spatial motion of a three-dimensional rigid body. We studied the three-dimensional motion of a rigid body in greater detail in Sections 6.9, 6.10, and 6.11. Furthermore, in Chapter 7 we developed the governing relationships, as expressed by Equations (7.1) through (7.9), for the most general three-dimensional rigid-body motion.

The present chapter will be devoted to the development of the computational methods necessary for the determination of the inertial terms appearing in the equations of motion of a three-dimensional body subjected to a spatial motion. This we will achieve by developing the relevant impulse-momentum principle (Section 9.2) or the work–kinetic energy principle (Section 9.3) applicable to the spatial motion of a rigid body. In Section 9.4, we will develop the fundamental equations of motion of a three-dimensional rigid body. The chapter will also apply the above equations to a very useful and interesting case called *gyroscopic motion*.

9.2 LINEAR AND ANGULAR MOMENTA OF A THREE–DIMENSIONAL RIGID BODY

Linear Momentum

In Chapter 8, during the analysis of the planar motion of rigid bodies, we extended the results of Chapter 5 to derive the linear momentum **G** of a three-dimensional rigid body of constant mass. Equation (8.17) expressed this in the form $\mathbf{G} = m\mathbf{v}_C$, where $m = \int_m dm$ is the total mass of the rigid body and $\mathbf{v}_C$ the velocity of its mass center measured relative to the inertial frame of reference XYZ (Figure 9.1).

Angular Momentum

In Chapter 8, we developed the angular momentum $\mathbf{H}_A$ of a three-dimensional rigid body about an arbitrary point A (Figure 9.1) for the most general (spatial) motion and expressed it as

$$\mathbf{H}_A = \left(\int_m \mathbf{r}_{P/A}\, dm \right) \times \dot{\mathbf{r}}_{A/O} + \int_m \mathbf{r}_{P/A} \times (\boldsymbol{\omega} \times \mathbf{r}_{P/A})\, dm$$

where $\dot{\mathbf{r}}_{A/O} = \mathbf{v}_A$ is the absolute velocity of point A—that is, relative to the inertial frame of reference XYZ.

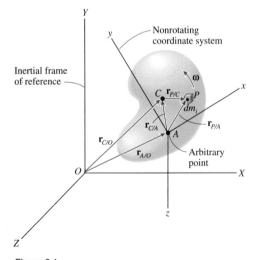

Figure 9.1

Upon introducing the definition of the mass center as

$$\int_m \mathbf{r}_P\, dm = \mathbf{r}_C \int_m dm = m\mathbf{r}_C$$

we can rewrite the above expression for $\mathbf{H}_A$ as

$$\mathbf{H}_A = m\mathbf{r}_{C/A} \times \mathbf{v}_A + \int_m \mathbf{r}_{P/A} \times (\boldsymbol{\omega} \times \mathbf{r}_{P/A})dm \qquad (9.1)$$

Two special cases will now be considered.

1.   If the mass center C of the rigid body is chosen as the arbitrary point A, then $\mathbf{r}_{C/A} = \mathbf{0}$ and Equation (9.1) is reduced to

$$\mathbf{H}_C = \int_m \mathbf{r}_{P/C} \times (\boldsymbol{\omega} \times \mathbf{r}_{P/C})dm \qquad (9.2)$$

since position vectors measured from C are now indicated by $\mathbf{r}_{P/C}$ (Figure 9.2).

2.   If the body has a *fixed* point O as in Figure 9.3, it is advantageous to locate point A at the fixed point; thus, $\mathbf{v}_A = \mathbf{0}$, which will then reduce Equation (9.1) to

$$\mathbf{H}_O = \int_m \mathbf{r}_{P/O} \times (\boldsymbol{\omega} \times \mathbf{r}_{P/O})dm \qquad (9.3)$$

Next, we will develop the analytical techniques necessary to evaluate $\mathbf{H}_C$ via Equation (9.2), and $\mathbf{H}_O$ via Equation (9.3). Considering the noninertial coordinate system xyz as in Figure 9.2, we will express $H_C = \int_m \mathbf{r}_{P/C} \times (\boldsymbol{\omega} \times \mathbf{r}_{P/C})dm$ in terms of the Cartesian components of $\mathbf{r}_{P/C}$ and $\boldsymbol{\omega}$. Thus, we write

$$\begin{bmatrix} (H_C)_x\mathbf{i} \\ + \\ (H_C)_y\mathbf{j} \\ + \\ (H_C)_z\mathbf{k} \end{bmatrix} = \int_m (x_P\mathbf{i} + y_P\mathbf{j} + z_P\mathbf{k})$$

$$\times\, [(\omega_x\mathbf{i} + \omega_y\mathbf{j} + \omega_z\mathbf{k}) \times (x_P\mathbf{i} + y_P\mathbf{j} + z_P\mathbf{k})]dm$$

Since the angular velocity $\boldsymbol{\omega}$ is not dependent on position (x, y, z) the above expression can be expanded by carrying out the vector operations and by rearranging terms to yield

$$\begin{bmatrix} (H_C)_x\mathbf{i} \\ + \\ (H_C)_y\mathbf{j} \\ + \\ (H_C)_z\mathbf{k} \end{bmatrix} = \begin{bmatrix} [\omega_x\int_m(y_P^2 + z_P^2)dm - \omega_y\int_m x_P y_P\, dm - \omega_z\int_m x_P z_P\, dm]\mathbf{i} \\ + \\ [-\omega_x\int_m x_P y_P\, dm + \omega_y\int_m(x_P^2 + z_P^2)dm - \omega_z\int_m y_P z_P\, dm]\mathbf{j} \\ + \\ [-\omega_x\int_m z_P x_P\, dm - \omega_y\int_m y_P z_P\, dm + \omega_z\int_m(x_P^2 + y_P^2)dm]\mathbf{k} \end{bmatrix}$$

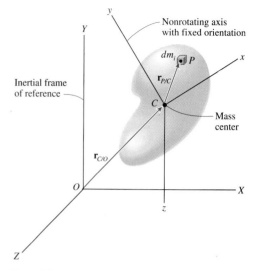

Figure 9.2

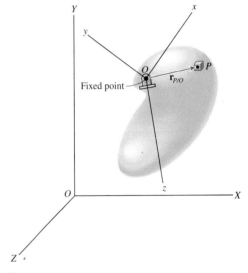

Figure 9.3

The corresponding scalar equations become

$$(H_C)_x = \omega_x \underbrace{\int_m (y_P^2 + z_P^2)dm}_{I_{xx}} - \omega_y \underbrace{\int_m x_P y_P\, dm}_{I_{xy}} - \omega_z \underbrace{\int_m x_P z_P\, dm}_{I_{xz}}$$

$$(H_C)_y = -\omega_x \underbrace{\int_m x_P y_P\, dm}_{I_{xy}} + \omega_y \underbrace{\int_m (x_P^2 + z_P^2)dm}_{I_{yy}} - \omega_z \underbrace{\int_m y_P z_P\, dm}_{I_{yz}}$$

$$(H_C)_z = -\omega_x \underbrace{\int_m z_P x_P\, dm}_{I_{xz}} - \omega_y \underbrace{\int_m y_P z_P\, dm}_{I_{yz}} + \omega_z \underbrace{\int_m (x_P^2 + y_P^2)dm}_{I_{zz}}$$

or

$$(H_C)_x = I_{xx}\omega_x - I_{xy}\omega_y - I_{xz}\omega_z$$
$$(H_C)_y = -I_{yz}\omega_x + I_{yy}\omega_y - I_{yz}\omega_z \qquad (9.4)$$
$$(H_C)_z = -I_{zx}\omega_x - I_{zy}\omega_y + I_{zz}\omega_z$$

When the rigid body moves about a fixed point O, by placing the noninertial frame of reference at O as in Figure 9.3, we can write expressions similar to the above:

$$(H_O)_{x'} = I_{x'x'}\omega_{x'} - I_{x'y'}\omega_{y'} - I_{x'z'}\omega_{z'}$$
$$(H_O)_{y'} = -I_{y'x'}\omega_{x'} + I_{y'y'}\omega_{y'} - I_{y'z'}\omega_{z'} \qquad (9.5)$$
$$(H_O)_{z'} = -I_{z'x'}\omega_{x'} - I_{z'y'}\omega_{y'} + I_{z'z'}\omega_{z'}$$

A concise way of expressing Equations (9.4) and (9.5) is by adopting the matrix notation to obtain

$$\underbrace{\begin{bmatrix} (H_C)_x \\ (H_C)_y \\ (H_C)_z \end{bmatrix}}_{[H_C]} = \underbrace{\begin{bmatrix} I_{xx} & -I_{xy} & -I_{xz} \\ -I_{yx} & +I_{yy} & -I_{yz} \\ -I_{zx} & -I_{zy} & +I_{zz} \end{bmatrix}}_{[I]} \underbrace{\begin{bmatrix} \omega_x \\ \omega_y \\ \omega_z \end{bmatrix}}_{[\omega]} \qquad (9.6)$$

$$\underbrace{\begin{bmatrix} (H_O)_{x'} \\ (H_O)_{y'} \\ (H_O)_{z'} \end{bmatrix}}_{[H_O]} = \underbrace{\begin{bmatrix} I_{x'x'} & -I_{x'y'} & -I_{x'z'} \\ -I_{y'x'} & +I_{y'y'} & -I_{y'z'} \\ -I_{z'x'} & -I_{z'y'} & +I_{z'z'} \end{bmatrix}}_{[I]} \underbrace{\begin{bmatrix} \omega_{x'} \\ \omega_{y'} \\ \omega_{z'} \end{bmatrix}}_{[\omega]} \qquad (9.7)$$

In dealing with Equations (9.4) or (9.6), the mass moments of inertia (I_{xx}, I_{yy}, and I_{zz}) and the mass products of inertia (I_{xy}, I_{xz}, and I_{yz}) are measured with respect to the noninertial frame of reference xyz. Similarly, in dealing with Equations (9.5) or (9.7), the corresponding terms are measured with respect to $x'y'z'$. By a judicious selection of these coordinate axes it is possible to further simplify the above equations. If the *principal axes of inertia* (when $I_{xy} = I_{yz} = I_{zx} = 0$ and $I_{xx} = \bar{I}_x, I_{yy} = \bar{I}_y, I_{zz} = \bar{I}_z$) are chosen as the xyz axes, then Equations (9.4) are reduced to

$$(H_C)_x = \bar{I}_x\omega_x \qquad (H_C)_y = \bar{I}_y\omega_y \qquad (H_C)_z = \bar{I}_z\omega_z \qquad (9.8)$$

Similarly, if $x'y'z'$ are the principal axes of inertia ($I_{x'y'} = I_{y'z'} = I_{z'x'} = 0$ and $I_{x'x'} = \bar{I}_{x'}, I_{y'y'} = \bar{I}_{y'}, I_{z'z'} = \bar{I}_{z'}$), Equations (9.5) become

$$(H_O)_{x'} = \bar{I}_{x'}\omega_{x'} \qquad (H_O)_{y'} = \bar{I}_{y'}\omega_{y'} \qquad (H_O)_{z'} = \bar{I}_{z'}\omega_{z'} \qquad (9.9)$$

In general, the angular momentum vector $\mathbf{H}_C$ and the angular velocity vector $\boldsymbol{\omega}$ are not collinear. However, if the angular velocity vector $\boldsymbol{\omega}$ is aligned with any one of the principal axes of inertia, the motion is *planar*. If the body is symmetrical with respect to a plane normal to the principal axis—that is, a slab—we obtain the results developed in Chapters 7 and 8. Also, in the special case when the *principal centroidal moments of inertia* of the body are identical to each other ($\bar{I}_x = \bar{I}_y = \bar{I}_z$), any centroidal axis becomes a principal axis of inertia including the axis collinear with $\boldsymbol{\omega}$, and it follows that $\mathbf{H}_C$ and $\boldsymbol{\omega}$ will remain collinear.

The angular momentum $\mathbf{H}_A$ of a rigid body about an arbitrary point A that may be neither the mass center of the body nor a fixed point, as in Figure 9.1, was evaluated in Chapter 7 [Equation (7.8)] and expressed as

$$\mathbf{H}_A = [\mathbf{r}_{C/A} \times (m\mathbf{v}_C)] + \mathbf{H}_C \qquad (9.10)$$

where $\mathbf{v}_C = \dot{\mathbf{r}}_{C/O}$, measured relative to the inertial frame of reference. The equation can be reduced into

$$\mathbf{H}_A = \mathbf{r}_{C/A} \times \mathbf{G} + \mathbf{H}_C \qquad (9.11)$$

where $\mathbf{G} = m\mathbf{v}_C$ is the linear momentum of the rigid body. The moment of the linear momentum is taken about the arbitrary point A. Equation (9.11) states that the angular momentum of a rigid body about an arbitrary point A is equal to the vectorial sum of the moment of its linear momentum and the angular momentum of the body about its mass center.

Equation of Linear Impulse and Momentum

The *linear impulse–momentum equation* for a system of particles of constant mass was established in Chapter 5, Equation (5.16). Considering a rigid body as a finite but large number of particles with constant relative positions, in Chapter 8 we extended the results of Chapter 5 to the case of a rigid body in planar motion [Equation (8.15)]. The above analysis was also applicable to three-dimensional bodies. Thus we write

$$\mathbf{G}_1 + \sum \int_{t_1}^{t_2} \mathbf{F}\,dt = \mathbf{G}_2 \qquad (9.12)$$

where $\mathbf{G} = m\mathbf{v}_C$ is the linear momentum of the body, and the integral term represents the total linear impulse exerted on the body by all external forces during the interval t_1 to t_2. Note that Equation (9.12) is a vector expression and therefore can be represented by three scalar component equations.

Conservation of Linear Momentum

If the resultant of all the external forces or their linear impulse $\Sigma \int_{t_1}^{t_2} \mathbf{F}\, dt$ is zero, the initial and final linear momenta are equal and we have

$$\mathbf{G}_1 = \mathbf{G}_2 \qquad (9.13)$$

The above equation is a restatement of the relationship developed in Chapter 5, Equation (5.18), and represents the *conservation of linear momentum* equation for a three-dimensional rigid body in spatial motion.

Equation of Angular Impulse and Momentum

The *angular impulse–momentum equation* for a system of particles of constant mass was established in Chapter 5. By integrating the equations of moment and time rate of change of angular momentum [Equation (5.20) or Equation (5.24)] over the interval t_1 to t_2, we obtain

$$(\mathbf{H}_O)_1 + \Sigma \int_{t_1}^{t_2} \mathbf{M}_O\, dt = (\mathbf{H}_O)_2 \qquad (9.14)$$

or

$$(\mathbf{H}_C)_1 + \Sigma \int_{t_1}^{t_2} \mathbf{M}_C\, dt = (\mathbf{H}_C)_2 \qquad (9.15)$$

In Equation (9.14), $\mathbf{H}_O$ represents the angular momentum of the rigid body about an arbitrary and *fixed* reference point O and $\Sigma \mathbf{M}_O$ is the resultant moment due to all the external forces and moments acting on the body, taken about O. Equation (9.15) represents the same principle, except that moments of linear momenta and of external forces are all taken about the mass center C of the rigid body. They can both be represented by three scalar component equations.

Conservation of Angular Momentum

If the resultant moment $\Sigma \mathbf{M}_O$ or $\Sigma \mathbf{M}_C$ of all the external forces and moments acting on the body is zero or if the angular impulse term $\Sigma \int_{t_1}^{t_2} \mathbf{M}_O\, dt$ or $\Sigma \int_{t_1}^{t_2} \mathbf{M}_C\, dt$ is zero, the initial and final angular momenta are equal and we have

$$(\mathbf{H}_O)_1 = (\mathbf{H}_O)_2 \qquad (9.16)$$

or

$$(\mathbf{H}_C)_1 = (\mathbf{H}_C)_2 \qquad (9.17)$$

The above vector equations represent the ***conservation of angular momentum*** for a three-dimensional rigid body in spatial motion. As before, each equation will yield three scalar component equations. It must be emphasized that the principle of conservation of angular momentum may hold true about O without being valid about C or vice versa.

The reason for the efforts made earlier in this chapter to develop the computational procedures necessary to evaluate the angular momentum of a three-dimensional rigid body must now become apparent to the reader. To apply the equation of angular impulse–momentum or of conservation of angular momentum, one must compute the angular momentum of a three-dimensional rigid body with reference to its inertial properties, that is, its centroidal axes, its mass moments and products of inertia, and its angular velocity at the instant considered. The computation of $\mathbf{H}_O$ or $\mathbf{H}_C$ will thus require the application of one of the appropriate equations (9.6) through (9.9).

In conclusion, we note that the impulse–momentum relationship applied to a rigid body's spatial motion will involve two vector equations: Equation (9.12), dealing with the system's linear momentum in lb · s or N · s, and Equation (9.15), dealing with the system's angular momentum in lb · ft · s or N · m · s. These equations will remain valid for as long as the quantities are measured with respect to translating (at constant velocity) but nonrotating coordinate axes, that is reference frames with fixed orientations.

Conservation of Momentum

To sum up the principles of conservation of momentum, considering Equation (9.12) or (9.15) we observe that if the respective impulse terms—linear ($\Sigma \int \mathbf{F} \, dt$) or angular ($\Sigma \int \mathbf{M} \, dt$)—are zero, then we have $\mathbf{G}_1 = \mathbf{G}_2$ or $(\mathbf{H}_C)_1 = (\mathbf{H}_C)_2$, stated in Equations (9.13) and (9.17). These equations restate what was already established in Chapter 8 for the planar motion of a rigid body: that if the sum of all linear impulses caused by the external forces acting on a rigid body, over a period of time, is zero, the linear momentum of the body is conserved and that likewise, if the sum of all angular impulses caused by the external forces and moments acting on a rigid body, over a period of time, is zero, the angular momentum of the body is conserved. The reader is once again reminded that either of the above momentum equations may be satisfied, without the other momentum being conserved.

EXAMPLE   9.1

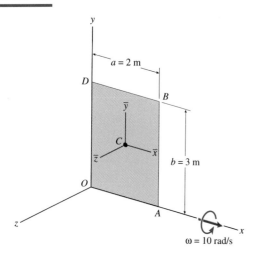

A thin rectangular plate of 20-kg mass rotates about its horizontal edge OA with a constant angular speed $\omega = 10$ rad/s. Determine the angular momentum of the plate about (a) point O, and about (b) the mass center C of the plate.

Solution

Part a. The angular velocity $\boldsymbol{\omega}$ can be expressed in the form

$$\boldsymbol{\omega} = \omega\mathbf{i} = \omega_x\mathbf{i} + \omega_y\mathbf{j} + \omega_z\mathbf{k}$$

and from this we conclude that

$$\omega_x = \omega \qquad \omega_y = 0 \qquad \omega_z = 0$$

The above can now be used to determine the $\mathbf{i}$, $\mathbf{j}$, and $\mathbf{k}$ components of the angular momentum from Equation (9.5); thus,

$$(H_O)_x = I_{xx}\omega \qquad (H_O)_y = -I_{yx}\omega$$
$$(H_O)_z = -I_{zx}\omega$$

where

$$I_{xx} = \frac{1}{3}mb^2 = \frac{1}{3}(20)(3)^2 = 60 \text{ kg} \cdot \text{m}^2$$

$$I_{yx} = m\frac{a}{2}\frac{b}{2} = (20)\frac{(2)(3)}{4} = 30 \text{ kg} \cdot \text{m}^2$$

$$I_{zx} = 0$$

The angular momentum vector $\mathbf{H}_O$ becomes

$$\mathbf{H}_O = (H_O)_x\mathbf{i} + (H_O)_y\mathbf{j} + (H_O)_z\mathbf{k}$$
$$= (I_{xx}\omega)\mathbf{i} - (I_{yx}\omega)\mathbf{j} = 60(10)\mathbf{i} - 30(10)\mathbf{j}$$
$$\mathbf{H}_O = 600\mathbf{i} - 300\mathbf{j} \text{ (kg} \cdot \text{m}^2/\text{s)} \blacktriangleleft$$

Part b. The angular momentum of the plate about its mass center will require the use of the centroidal mass moments of inertia about the plate's principal axes $\bar{x}, \bar{y}, \bar{z}$. From Equation (9.8) we have

$$\mathbf{H}_C = (H_C)_x\mathbf{i} + (H_C)_y\mathbf{j} + (H_C)_z\mathbf{k} = (\bar{I}_x\omega)\mathbf{i}$$

where

$$\bar{I}_x = \frac{1}{12}mb^2 = \frac{1}{12}(20)(3)^2 = 15 \text{ kg} \cdot \text{m}^2$$

and the angular momentum vector becomes

$$\mathbf{H}_C = 15(10)\mathbf{i}$$
$$\mathbf{H}_C = 150\mathbf{i} \text{ (kg} \cdot \text{m}^2/\text{s)} \blacktriangleleft$$

EXAMPLE 9.2

A 3-m-long slender rod of 5-kg mass is attached rigidly to a vertical shaft rotating as shown with an angular speed $\omega_z = 10$ rad/s about the z axis. At the instant shown, the rod lies within the plane yz and is inclined at $\theta = 60°$ to the horizontal. Determine the angular momentum of the rod about its end point O.

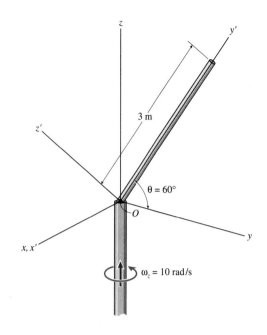

Solution In order to align one of the axes along the rod, we will make a transformation of coordinates, bringing Oy' in line with the longitudinal principal axis of the rod as shown. The angular velocity vector $\boldsymbol{\omega}$ can be expressed as

$$\boldsymbol{\omega} = \omega_x \mathbf{i} + \omega_y \mathbf{j} + \omega_z \mathbf{k}$$

where $\omega_x = \omega_y = 0$, or in the new coordinate system as

$$\boldsymbol{\omega} = \omega_x \mathbf{i} + \omega_{y'} \mathbf{j}' + \omega_{z'} \mathbf{k}'$$

where $\omega_{x'} = \omega_x = 0$
$\omega_{y'} = \omega_z \sin 60° = 10 \sin 60°$
$\omega_{z'} = \omega_z \cos 60° = 10 \cos 60°$

The pertinent mass moments and products of inertia are

$$I_{y'y'} = I_{y'z'} = I_{y'x'} = I_{z'x'} = 0$$

$$I_{z'z'} = I_{x'x'} = \frac{1}{3} ml^2 = \frac{1}{3}(5)(3)^2 = 15 \text{ kg} \cdot \text{m}^2$$

We can now write the angular momentum vector $\mathbf{H}_O$ about the point O as

$$\mathbf{H}_O = (H_O)_{x'}\mathbf{i} + (H_O)_{y'}\mathbf{j}' + (H_O)_{z'}\mathbf{k}'$$
$$= (I_{x'x'})\omega_{x'}\mathbf{i} + (I_{y'y'})\omega_{y'}\mathbf{j}' + (I_{z'z'})\omega_{z'}\mathbf{k}'$$
$$= 15(0)\mathbf{i} + (0)(10 \sin 60°)\mathbf{j}' + (15)(10 \cos 60°)\mathbf{k}'$$
$$\mathbf{H}_O = 150(\cos 60°)\mathbf{k}' = 75\mathbf{k}'$$

where $\mathbf{k}' = -\sin 60°\mathbf{j} + \cos 60°\mathbf{k}$. Hence we find

$$\mathbf{H}_O = -64.95\mathbf{j} + 37.5\mathbf{k} \text{ (kg} \cdot \text{m}^2/\text{s)} \blacktriangleleft$$

EXAMPLE 9.3

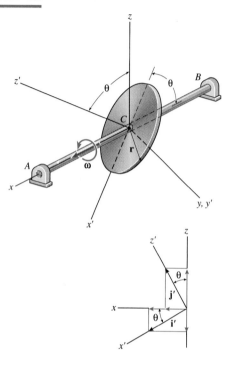

A thin uniform disk of radius r and mass m is mounted rigidly on a horizontal shaft AB as shown. The plane of the disk forms an angle θ with the axis of the shaft. If the shaft rotates with an angular velocity ω as shown, determine the angular momentum of the disk about its center of mass.

Solution Selection of the coordinate system $x'y'z'$ aligned with the principal axes of the disk will allow us to write the angular velocity $\boldsymbol{\omega}$ as

$$\boldsymbol{\omega} = \omega_{x'}\mathbf{i'} + \omega_{y'}\mathbf{j'} + \omega_{z'}\mathbf{k'}$$

where $\omega_{x'} = \omega \cos \theta$
$\omega_{y'} = 0$
$\omega_{z'} = \omega \sin \theta$

The centroidal mass moments of inertia of the disk about its principal axes are

$$\bar{I}_{x'} = \bar{I}_{y'} = \frac{1}{4}mr^2 \qquad \bar{I}_{z'} = \frac{1}{2}mr^2$$

Hence, the angular momentum of the disk about its center of mass becomes

$$\mathbf{H}_C = (H_C)_{x'}\mathbf{i'} + (H_C)_{y'}\mathbf{j'} + (H_C)_{z'}\mathbf{k'}$$

where $(H_C)_{x'} = I_{x'}\omega_{x'} = \left(\frac{1}{4}mr^2\right)(\omega \cos \theta)$

$(H_C)_{y'} = I_{y'}\omega_{y'} = \left(\frac{1}{4}mr^2\right)(0) = 0$

$(H_C)_{z'} = I_{z'}\omega_{z'} = \left(\frac{1}{2}mr^2\right)(\omega \sin \theta)$

We write

$$\mathbf{H}_C = \frac{1}{4}mr^2\omega \cos \theta\mathbf{i'} + \frac{1}{2}mr^2\omega \sin \theta\mathbf{k'}$$

Since $\mathbf{i'} = \cos \theta\mathbf{i} - \sin \theta\mathbf{k}$

$$\mathbf{k'} = \sin \theta\mathbf{i} + \cos \theta\mathbf{k}$$

We find

$$\mathbf{H}_C = \frac{1}{4}mr^2\omega \cos \theta(\cos \theta\mathbf{i} - \sin \theta\mathbf{k})$$

$$+ \frac{1}{2}mr^2\omega \sin \theta(\sin \theta\mathbf{i} + \cos \theta\mathbf{k})$$

$$\mathbf{H}_C = \frac{1}{4}mr^2\omega[(\cos^2 \theta + 2 \sin^2 \theta)\mathbf{i} + (\sin \theta \cos \theta)\mathbf{k}] \quad \blacktriangleleft$$

EXAMPLE 9.4

A 50-g bullet is fired with a velocity of $\mathbf{v}_B = -1200\mathbf{i} + 1000\mathbf{k}$ (m/s) into a 20-kg thin uniform plate (6 m × 6 m), and becomes embedded in the plate at point P, as shown. Determine the angular momentum and the angular velocity of the plate about the ball-and-socket joint O from which it is suspended.

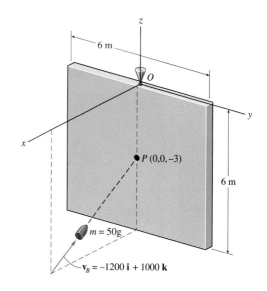

Solution Since all the external forces, the reactions and the weight of the plate, except for the weight of the bullet, are concurrent through the joint O, we conclude that the impulse term in Equation (9.14) can be neglected, and the angular momentum of the system about O is conserved: $(\mathbf{H}_O)_1 = (\mathbf{H}_O)_2$. The initial momentum of the bullet and plate can be expressed as

$$(\mathbf{H}_O)_1 = (\mathbf{H}_O)_{1(\text{bullet})} + (\mathbf{H}_O)_{1(\text{plate})}$$

where

$$(\mathbf{H}_O)_{1(\text{bullet})} = \mathbf{r}_{P/O} \times m_B \mathbf{v}_B$$
$$= (-3\mathbf{k}) \times (0.050)(-1200\mathbf{i} + 1000\mathbf{k})$$
$$= +180\mathbf{j}$$

and

$$(\mathbf{H}_O)_{1(\text{plate})} = \mathbf{0}$$
$$(\mathbf{H}_O)_1 = +180\mathbf{j} \ (\text{kg} \cdot \text{m}^2/\text{s})$$

Hence, the final angular momentum of the system will be identical to the initial value, and we write

$$(\mathbf{H}_O)_2 = +180\mathbf{j} \ (\text{kg} \cdot \text{m}^2/\text{s}) \ \blacktriangleleft$$

To evaluate the instantaneous angular velocity of the plate right after the bullet becomes embedded in it, we write

$$(\mathbf{H}_O)_2 = (H_O)_x\mathbf{i} + (H_O)_y\mathbf{j} + (H_O)_z\mathbf{k} = +180\mathbf{j} \quad (a)$$

From Equation (9.9), we have

$$(H_O)_x = \bar{I}_x \omega_x \qquad (H_O)_y = \bar{I}_y \omega_y \qquad (H_O)_z = \bar{I}_z \omega_z \quad (b)$$

The pertinent mass moments of inertia are

$$\bar{I}_x = \frac{1}{12}(m)(a^2 + b^2) + m(OP)^2$$

$$= \frac{1}{12}(20)(6^2 + 6^2) + (20)(3)^2 = 300 \ \text{kg} \cdot \text{m}^2$$

$$\bar{I}_y = \frac{1}{12}ma^2 + m(OP)^2 = \frac{1}{12}(20)(6)^2 + (20)(3)^2 = 240 \ \text{kg} \cdot \text{m}^2$$

$$\bar{I}_z = \frac{1}{12}ma^2 = \frac{1}{12}(20)(6)^2 = 60 \ \text{kg} \cdot \text{m}^2$$

Substituting $\bar{I}_x$, $\bar{I}_y$, and $\bar{I}_z$ into Equations (b), we have

$$(H_O)_x = 300\omega_x \qquad (H_O)_y = 240\omega_y \qquad (H_O)_z = 60\omega_z \quad (c)$$

Now, introduction of (c) into (a) yields

$$300\omega_x\mathbf{i} + 240\omega_y\mathbf{j} + 60\omega_z\mathbf{k} = 180\mathbf{j}$$

and we conclude $\omega_x = 0$, $\omega_y = 0.75$ rad/s, $\omega_z = 0$; thus,

$$\omega = 0.75\mathbf{j} \ (\text{rad/s}) \ \blacktriangleleft$$

EXAMPLE 9.5

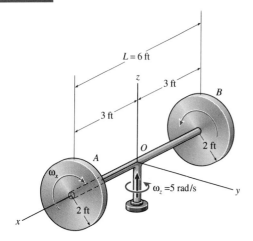

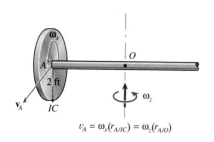

$$v_A = \omega_x(r_{A/IC}) = \omega_z(r_{A/O})$$

Two 25-lb disks (radius = 2 ft) are linked by a 5-lb axle (length = 6 ft) and roll without slipping on a horizontal surface by rotating counterclockwise about a vertical axis with an angular speed of 5 rad/s, as shown. Determine the angular momentum of the disks-axle system.

Solution The total angular momentum of the disks-axle system about the fixed point O is

$$\mathbf{H}_O = (\mathbf{H}_O)_{\text{disk }A} + (\mathbf{H}_O)_{\text{disk }B} + (\mathbf{H}_O)_{\text{axle}}$$

Both disks rotate about a fixed point O, which we can assume to be part of their extended yet massless bodies. Hence

$$(\mathbf{H}_O)_A = \bar{I}_x(\omega_x)_A\mathbf{i} + \bar{I}_y(\omega_y)_A\mathbf{j} + \bar{I}_z(\omega_z)_A\mathbf{k}$$

Considering the disk's instantaneous center of rotation (IC), we write

$$(\omega_x)_A = \omega_z\frac{r_{A/O}}{r_{A/IC}} \quad \text{and} \quad (\omega_x)_A\mathbf{i} = -(5)\frac{3}{2}\mathbf{i} = -7.5\mathbf{i}\ (\text{rad/s})$$

$$(\omega_y)_A = 0$$

$$(\omega_z)_A = 5\ \text{rad/s} \quad \text{and} \quad (\omega_z)_A\mathbf{k} = 5\mathbf{k}\ (\text{rad/s})$$

and

$$\bar{I}_x = \frac{1}{2}mr^2 = \frac{1}{2}\left(\frac{25}{32.2}\right)(2)^2 = 1.55\ \text{lb}\cdot\text{ft}\cdot\text{s}^2$$

$$\bar{I}_z = \frac{1}{4}mr^2 + m\left(\frac{L}{2}\right)^2$$

$$= \frac{1}{4}\left(\frac{25}{32.2}\right)(2)^2 + \left(\frac{25}{32.2}\right)(3)^2 = 7.76\ \text{lb}\cdot\text{ft}\cdot\text{s}^2$$

Substituting the angular velocities and mass moments of inertia into $(\mathbf{H}_O)_A$, we obtain

$$(\mathbf{H}_O)_A = -1.55(7.5)\mathbf{i} + 7.76(5)\mathbf{k}$$

$$(\mathbf{H}_O)_A = -11.63\mathbf{i} + 38.8\mathbf{k}\ (\text{lb}\cdot\text{ft}\cdot\text{s})$$

The angular momentum of disk B about O becomes

$$(\mathbf{H}_O)_B = \bar{I}_x(\omega_x)_B\mathbf{i} + \bar{I}_z(\omega_z)_B\mathbf{k}$$

where

$$(\omega_x)_B\mathbf{i} = -(\omega_x)_A\mathbf{i} = +7.5\mathbf{i}\ (\text{rad/s})$$

$$(\boldsymbol{\omega}_z)_B = (\boldsymbol{\omega}_z)_A = 5\mathbf{k}\ (\text{rad/s})$$

(continued)

EXAMPLE 9.5   (*concluded*)

Thus,

$$(\mathbf{H}_O)_B = +1.55(7.5)\mathbf{i} + 7.76(5)\mathbf{k}$$

$$(\mathbf{H}_O)_B = +11.63\mathbf{i} + 38.8\mathbf{k}\,(\text{lb}\cdot\text{ft}\cdot\text{s})$$

The angular momentum of the axle is given by

$$(\mathbf{H}_O)_{\text{axle}} = \bar{I}_x\omega_x\mathbf{i} + \bar{I}_y\omega_y\mathbf{j} + \bar{I}_z\omega_z\mathbf{k}$$

where $\bar{I}_x \approx 0$, $(\omega_y) = 0$, $\bar{I}_z = \frac{1}{12}(m)_{\text{axle}}L^2$, and $\omega_z = 5\,\text{rad/s}$.

Hence

$$(\mathbf{H}_O)_{\text{axle}} = \left[\frac{1}{12}\left(\frac{5}{32.2}\right)(6)^2\right]5\mathbf{k}$$

$$(\mathbf{H}_O)_{\text{axle}} = 2.33\mathbf{k}\,(\text{lb}\cdot\text{ft}\cdot\text{s})$$

The total angular momentum of the system becomes

$$\mathbf{H}_O = (-11.63\mathbf{i} + 38.8\mathbf{k}) + (11.63\mathbf{i} + 38.8\mathbf{k}) + (2.33)\mathbf{k}$$

$$\mathbf{H}_O = +79.9\mathbf{k}\,(\text{lb}\cdot\text{ft}\cdot\text{s}) \blacktriangleleft$$

9.3 KINETIC ENERGY OF A THREE–DIMENSIONAL RIGID BODY

The kinetic energy of a three-dimensional rigid body system in general (spatial) motion can be derived by extending the result obtained in Chapter 5 for a system of particles of constant mass. From Equation (5.11) we can state that

$$T = \frac{1}{2}mv_C^2 + \frac{1}{2}\int_m dm\, v_{P/C}'^2 \qquad (9.18)$$

which means that the total kinetic energy of the system is the sum of the kinetic energy of the total mass, assumed to be concentrated at the mass center of the system and measured relative to a fixed frame of reference, and the kinetic energies, relative to the mass center, of all the particles of the system. The *nonrotating* frame of reference attached to the mass center we will assume to be translating with the mass center, as in Figure 9.4. The term $\frac{1}{2}mv_C^2$ represents the translational kinetic energy of the body. The term $\frac{1}{2}\int_m v_{P/C}'^2\,dm$ expresses the rotational motion of the particles of the system about the mass center of the body.

Since, in a rigid body, particles maintain their positions relative to each other, the velocity of each particle about the mass center is related to the angular velocity of the rigid body and we write

$$\mathbf{v}_P'/C = \boldsymbol{\omega} \times \mathbf{r}_{P/C}$$

This expression for $\mathbf{v}'$, when introduced into the integral expression below, yields

$$\frac{1}{2}\int_m v_{P/C}'^2\,dm = \frac{1}{2}\int_m (\mathbf{v}_P'/_C \cdot \mathbf{v}_P'/_C)dm$$

$$= \frac{1}{2}\int_m (\boldsymbol{\omega} \times \mathbf{r}_{P/C}) \cdot (\boldsymbol{\omega} \times \mathbf{r}_{P/C})dm$$

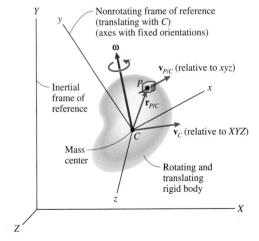

Figure 9.4

Since, from vector calculus, we have

$$(\boldsymbol{\omega} \times \mathbf{r}_{P/C}) \cdot (\boldsymbol{\omega} \times \mathbf{r}_{P/C}) = \boldsymbol{\omega} \cdot [\mathbf{r}_{P/C} \times (\boldsymbol{\omega} \times \mathbf{r}_{P/C})]$$

the rotational kinetic energy of the body becomes

$$\frac{1}{2} \int_m v'^2_{P/C}\, dm = \frac{1}{2} \int_m \boldsymbol{\omega} \cdot [\mathbf{r}_{P/C} \times (\boldsymbol{\omega} \times \mathbf{r}_{P/C})]\, dm \qquad (9.19)$$

At any given instant, the angular velocity $\boldsymbol{\omega}$ is a kinetic parameter of the body and can be factored out to yield

$$\frac{1}{2} \int_m v'^2_{P/C}\, dm = \frac{1}{2} \boldsymbol{\omega} \cdot \int_m \mathbf{r}_{P/C} \times (\boldsymbol{\omega} \times \mathbf{r}_{P/C})\, dm \qquad (9.20)$$

The integral appearing on the right-hand side of Equation (9.20) represents the angular momentum $\mathbf{H}_C$ of the rigid body about its mass center as given in Equation (9.2). Thus, Equation (9.20) becomes

$$\frac{1}{2} \int_m v'^2_{P/C}\, dm = \frac{1}{2} \boldsymbol{\omega} \cdot \mathbf{H}_C \qquad (9.21)$$

Substituting Equation (9.21) into Equation (9.18) yields

$$T = \frac{1}{2} m v_C^2 + \frac{1}{2} \boldsymbol{\omega} \cdot \mathbf{H}_C \qquad (9.22)$$

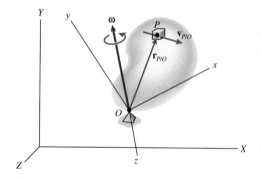

Figure 9.5

When the rigid body pivots about a fixed point O, the translational kinetic energy becomes zero and the body's kinetic energy is reduced to its rotational energy about the fixed point O (Figure 9.5). We write

$$T = \frac{1}{2} \int_m dm\, v_{P/O}^2 \qquad (9.23)$$

where $v_{P/O}^2 = (\boldsymbol{\omega} \times \mathbf{r}_{P/O}) \cdot (\boldsymbol{\omega} \times \mathbf{r}_{P/O}) = \boldsymbol{\omega} \cdot [\mathbf{r}_{P/O} \times (\boldsymbol{\omega} \times \mathbf{r}_{P/O})]$

Equation (9.23), upon substitution, yields

$$T = \frac{1}{2} \boldsymbol{\omega} \cdot \int_m \mathbf{r}_{P/O} \times (\boldsymbol{\omega} \times \mathbf{r}_{P/O})\, dm$$

or

$$T = \frac{1}{2} \boldsymbol{\omega} \cdot \mathbf{H}_O \qquad (9.24)$$

We can now determine the kinetic energy of a rigid body by substituting the expression for $\mathbf{H}_C$ [Equation (9.4)] into Equation (9.22):

$$T = \frac{1}{2} m v_C^2 + \frac{1}{2} [(\omega_x \mathbf{i} + \omega_y \mathbf{j} + \omega_z \mathbf{k})] \cdot [I_{xx}\omega_x - I_{xy}\omega_y - I_{xz}\omega_z)\mathbf{i}$$
$$+ (-I_{xy}\omega_x + I_{yy}\omega_y - I_{yz}\omega_z)\mathbf{j} + (-I_{xz}\omega_x - I_{yz}\omega_y + I_{zz}\omega_z)\mathbf{k}]$$

The above equation when expanded and rearranged yields

$$T = \frac{1}{2}mv_C^2 + \frac{1}{2}(I_{xx}\omega_x^2 + I_{yy}\omega_y^2 + I_{zz}\omega_z^2 - 2I_{xy}\omega_x\omega_y$$
$$- 2I_{yz}\omega_y\omega_z - 2I_{zx}\omega_z\omega_x) \qquad (9.25)$$

and if we choose a frame of reference system where the coordinate axes coincide with the principal axes of inertia of the rigid body, the kinetic energy term is reduced to

$$T = \frac{1}{2}mv_C^2 + \frac{1}{2}(\bar{I}_x\omega_x^2 + \bar{I}_y\omega_y^2 + \bar{I}_z\omega_z^2) \qquad (9.26)$$

The kinetic energy of a rigid body pivoting about a fixed point O can be expressed by substituting the term for $\mathbf{H}_O$ from Equations (9.5) or (9.9) into Equation (9.24):

$$T = \frac{1}{2}(I_{xx}\omega_x^2 + I_{yy}\omega_y^2 + I_{zz}\omega_z^2 - 2I_{xy}\omega_x\omega_y - 2I_{yz}\omega_y\omega_z - 2I_{zx}\omega_z\omega_x) \qquad (9.27)$$

The kinetic energy of the same rigid body, when measured with respect to a frame of reference $x'y'z'$ with origin at O and coordinate axes oriented along the principal axes of the rigid body, would reduce Equation (9.27) into

$$T = \frac{1}{2}(I_{x'x'}\omega_{x'}^2 + I_{y'y'}\omega_{y'}^2 + I_{z'z'}\omega_{z'}^2) \qquad (9.28)$$

Principle of Work and Kinetic Energy

The principle of work and kinetic energy was developed in Chapter 5 for the general motion of a system of particles and the pertinent relationship, Equation (5.6), was used later for the planar motion of rigid bodies. Since the development of the equation was not limited to two-dimensional bodies or planar motion, it is equally valid for rigid-body motion in three dimensions. The applicable equation can be written as *equation of work and kinetic energy*

$$T_1 + \Sigma U_{1 \to 2} = T_2 \qquad (9.29)$$

where T_1 and T_2 represent, respectively, the initial and final kinetic energies of the rigid body in spatial motion. They can be evaluated through the use of Equation (9.27) or (9.28). The term $\Sigma U_{1 \to 2}$ is the algebraic sum of the works done by all of the external forces and moments acting upon the rigid body. The work done by variable or constant forces, by the weight of the body, a spring, or friction forces, and finally, by a moment couple acting on the body during its translational and rotational motion have all been developed in Chapter 8 for planar motion. However, the results are equally applicable to three-dimensional rigid-body motion.

Conservation of Mechanical Energy

When a three-dimensional rigid body is acted upon by a force system consisting only of *conservative forces*, the work–kinetic energy equation is reduced to the form developed in Chapters 5 [Equation (5.12)] and 8 [Equation (8.12)].

$$T_1 + V_1 = T_2 + V_2 \qquad\qquad (9.30)$$

where V_1 and V_2 represent, respectively, the body's initial and final potential energies.

EXAMPLE 9.6

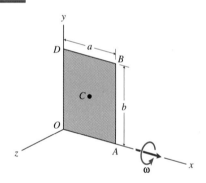

A thin rectangular plate of mass m rotates about its horizontal edge OA, as shown, with a constant angular speed ω rad/s. Determine the kinetic energy of the plate at the instant shown.

Solution   Since the plate rotates about the edge OA without being subjected to a translational motion, we can express the kinetic energy T of the plate from Equation (9.24) as $T = \frac{1}{2}\boldsymbol{\omega} \cdot \mathbf{H}_O$, where

$$\boldsymbol{\omega} = \omega\mathbf{i} \qquad\qquad (a)$$

or $\omega_x = \omega$ and $\omega_y = \omega_z = 0$. Also,

$$\mathbf{H}_O = (H_O)_x\mathbf{i} + (H_O)_y\mathbf{j} + (H_O)_z\mathbf{k}$$

where
$$(H_O)_x = I_{xx}\omega$$
$$(H_O)_y = -I_{yx}\omega$$
$$(H_O)_z = -I_{zx}\omega$$

and we have $I_{xx} = \frac{1}{3}mb^2$, $I_{yx} = \frac{1}{4}mab$, and $I_{zx} = 0$. The angular momentum $\mathbf{H}_O$ is written as

$$\mathbf{H}_O = (I_{xx}\omega)\mathbf{i} - (I_{yx}\omega)\mathbf{j}$$

$$\mathbf{H}_O = \left(\frac{1}{3}mb^2\omega\right)\mathbf{i} - \left(\frac{1}{4}mab\omega\right)\mathbf{j} \qquad (b)$$

Thus, introducing Equations (a) and (b) into Equation (9.24) for the kinetic energy, we obtain

$$T = \frac{1}{2}(\omega\mathbf{i}) \cdot \left[\left(\frac{1}{3}mb^2\omega\right)\mathbf{i} - \left(\frac{1}{4}mab\omega\right)\mathbf{j}\right]$$

$$T = \frac{1}{6}mb^2\omega^2 \quad \blacktriangleleft$$

EXAMPLE 9.7

Determine the kinetic energy of the disks-axle system of Example 9.5.

Solution Considering that the system rotates about a fixed point O, from Equation (9.28) we express the kinetic energy of the system as $T_{system} = 2T_{disk} + T_{axle}$. Hence,

$$T_{disk\ A} = \frac{1}{2}m_{disk}v_A^2 + \frac{1}{2}(I_x\omega_x^2 + I_y\omega_y^2 + I_z\omega_z^2)_{disk}$$

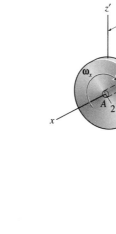

where $\quad m_{disk} = \dfrac{25}{32.2} \qquad v_A = \omega_z(r_{A/O}) = 5(3) = 15$ ft/s

$$\omega_x = \omega_z\frac{r_{A/O}}{r_{A/IC}} = 5\left(\frac{3}{2}\right) = 7.5 \text{ rad/s}$$

$$\omega_y = 0$$

$$\omega_z = 5 \text{ rad/s}$$

$$[I_x]_{disk} = [I_{x'}]_{disk} = \frac{1}{2}m_{disk}r^2 = \frac{1}{2}\left(\frac{25}{32.2}\right)(2)^2$$

$$= 1.55 \text{ ft} \cdot \text{lb} \cdot \text{s}^2$$

$$[I_y]_{disk} = [I_z]_{disk}$$

$$= [I_{z'}]_{disk} = \frac{1}{4}m_{disk}r^2 + m_{disk}\left(\frac{L}{2}\right)^2$$

$$= \frac{1}{4}\left(\frac{25}{32.2}\right)(2)^2 + \frac{25}{32.2}(3)^2 = 7.76 \text{ ft} \cdot \text{lb} \cdot \text{s}^2$$

Upon substitution,

$$T_{disk} = \frac{1}{2}\left(\frac{25}{32.2}\right)(15)^2 + \frac{1}{2}[1.55(7.5)^2$$

$$+ 7.76(0)^2 + 7.76(5)^2] = 228 \text{ lb} \cdot \text{ft}$$

Next, we evaluate the kinetic energy of the axle.

$$T_{axle} = \frac{1}{2}(I_x\omega_x^2 + I_y\omega_y^2 + I_z\omega_z^2)_{axle}$$

where $\quad (I_x)_{axle} = 0$

$$(I_y)_{axle} = (I_z)_{axle} = \frac{1}{12}m_{axle}L^2 = \frac{1}{12}\left(\frac{5}{32.2}\right)(6)^2$$

$$= 0.47 \text{ ft} \cdot \text{lb} \cdot \text{s}^2$$

Upon substitution,

$$T_{axle} = \frac{1}{2}[0(7.5)^2 + (0.47)(0)^2 + (0.47)(5)^2] = \frac{1}{2}(0.47)(5)^2$$

$$T_{axle} = 5.9 \text{ lb} \cdot \text{ft}$$

The total kinetic energy of the system thus becomes

$$T_{system} = 2(228) + 5.9$$

$$T_{system} = 461.9 \text{ lb} \cdot \text{ft} \blacktriangleleft$$

EXAMPLE 9.8

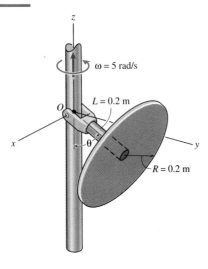

An assembly consisting of a 20-kg disk (radius $= 0.2$ m) and a 3-kg rod (length $= 0.2$ m) is rotating as shown about the vertical z axis at a rate of 5 rad/s. Determine the kinetic energy of the assembly.

Solution   The disk-rod assembly rotates about a fixed point O. By adopting $x'y'z'$ as the principal axes coordinate system, we write from Equation (9.28)

$$T = \frac{1}{2}(I_{x'}\omega_{x'}^2 + I_{y'}\omega_{y'}^2 + I_{z'}\omega_{z'}^2) \qquad \text{(a)}$$

where

$$I_{x'} = \overbrace{(I_{x'})_{\text{disk}}}^{} + \overbrace{(I_{x'})_{\text{rod}}}^{}$$

$$I_{x'} = \left(\frac{1}{4}m_{\text{disk}}R^2 + m_{\text{disk}}L^2\right) + \left(\frac{1}{3}m_{\text{rod}}L^2\right)$$

$$= \left[\frac{1}{4}(20)(0.2)^2 + (20)(0.2)^2\right] + \left[\frac{1}{3}(3)(0.2)^2\right]$$

$$= [0.2 + 0.8 + 0.04]\ (\text{kg} \cdot \text{m}^2)$$

$$I_{y'} = I_{x'} = 1.04\ \text{kg} \cdot \text{m}^2 \qquad \text{(b)}$$

$$I_{z'} = (I_{z'})_{\text{disk}} = \frac{1}{2}mR^2 = \frac{1}{2}(20)(0.2)^2$$

$$I_{z'} = 0.40\ \text{kg} \cdot \text{m}^2 \qquad \text{(c)}$$

The angular rotation was initially given as

$$\boldsymbol{\omega} = 5\mathbf{k} = 5(\sin\theta\mathbf{i}' + \cos\theta\mathbf{j}')$$

Now, we have

$$\boldsymbol{\omega} = \omega_{x'}\mathbf{i}' + \omega_{y'}\mathbf{j}' + \omega_{z'}\mathbf{k}' = 5\sin\theta\mathbf{i}' + 5\cos\theta\mathbf{j}'$$

Thus,

$$\left.\begin{array}{l} \omega_{x'} = 0 \\ \omega_{y'} = 5\sin\theta = 5\sin 45° = 3.54\ \text{rad/s} \\ \omega_{z'} = 5\cos\theta = 5\cos 45° = 3.54\ \text{rad/s} \end{array}\right\} \qquad \text{(d)}$$

Substituting (b), (c), and (d) into (a) yields

$$T = \frac{1}{2}[(1.04)(0)^2 + (1.04)(3.54)^2 + (0.4)(3.54)^2]$$

$$T = \frac{1}{2}[0 + 13.03 + 5.01] = \frac{1}{2}(18.04)$$

$$T = 9.02\ \text{J} \quad \blacktriangleleft$$

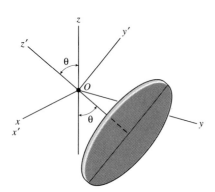

9.4 FUNDAMENTAL EQUATIONS OF MOTION OF A THREE–DIMENSIONAL RIGID BODY

The two fundamental equations upon which the most general spatial motion of a three-dimensional rigid body is based are natural extensions of the relationships developed in Chapter 5 for the general motion of a system of particles. Equation (5.4) or (5.14) and Equation (5.20) or (5.24) can now be applied to the three-dimensional rigid body to yield

$$\Sigma \mathbf{F} = m\mathbf{a}_C \qquad (9.31)$$

and

$$\Sigma \mathbf{M}_C = \dot{\mathbf{H}}_C \qquad (9.32a)$$

or

$$\Sigma \mathbf{M}_O = \dot{\mathbf{H}}_O \qquad (9.32b)$$

where $\Sigma \mathbf{F}$ = the resultant of all external forces
$\mathbf{a}_C$ = the acceleration of the mass center
$\Sigma \mathbf{M}_C$ = the resultant moment about the mass center C of all the external forces and moments acting on the body
$\mathbf{H}_C$ = the resultant moment about the body's mass center C of all linear momenta of the system (the angular momentum of the rigid body about its mass center)
$\Sigma \mathbf{M}_O$ = the resultant moment about the fixed point O of all the external forces and moments acting on the body
$\mathbf{H}_O$ = the resultant moment about the fixed point O of all the linear momenta of the system (the angular momentum of the rigid body about the fixed point O)

Having established in Section 9.2 the functional relationship at a given instant between the centroidal angular momentum $\mathbf{H}_C$ and the inertial properties of the rigid body and its angular velocity $\boldsymbol{\omega}$, our task is now to develop an expression for the time derivative $\dot{\mathbf{H}}_C$ of the angular momentum vector which will then be substituted into Equation (9.32a). A similar development can be carried out to secure the time derivative $\dot{\mathbf{H}}_O$ of the angular momentum $\mathbf{H}_O$ measured about a fixed point O. $\dot{\mathbf{H}}_O$ will then be substituted into Equation (9.32b).

We defined the angular momentum $\mathbf{H}_C$ with respect to a *nonrotating* frame of reference and developed it for a given angular velocity $\boldsymbol{\omega}$, that is, for a given position of the body at a particular instant t. If the orientation of the axes are maintained the same (nonrotating), at another instant when the position of the body is different, the rigid body's mass moments and products of inertia may acquire different values, which would present an almost intractable problem when time differentiating the angular momentum vector. In order to investigate the variations of the inertial properties of the body with time, we will attach a rotating coordinate frame (*xyz*) to the rigid body at its mass center

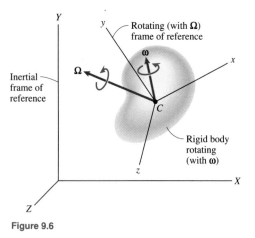

Figure 9.6

C. The reference axes will rotate with an absolute angular velocity $\mathbf{\Omega}$, which may be different from the absolute angular velocity $\mathbf{\omega}$ of the rigid body (see Figure 9.6).

In Chapter 6, Section 6.8, the relationship between the time rate of change of a vector measured with respect to the rotating—with $\mathbf{\Omega}$—frame of reference *xyz* and the time rate of change of the same vector with respect to the inertial (fixed) frame *XYZ* was developed for the most general three-dimensional motion. The relationship [Equation (6.29)], when applied to the vector $\mathbf{H}_C$, yields

$$(\dot{\mathbf{H}}_C)_{XYZ} = (\dot{\mathbf{H}}_C)_{xyz} + \mathbf{\Omega} \times \mathbf{H}_C \tag{9.33a}$$

where $(\dot{\mathbf{H}}_C)_{XYZ}$ = the time derivative of the rigid body's centroidal angular momentum, measured from a *fixed* (absolute) frame of reference

$(\dot{\mathbf{H}}_C)_{xyz}$ = the time derivative of the rigid body's centroidal angular momentum, measured from a *moving* (relative) frame of reference

$\mathbf{\Omega}$ = the angular velocity of the moving (rotating) frame of reference

A similar development for the time derivative of the angular momentum about an arbitrary *fixed* point *O* measured from an inertial (*XYZ*) frame yields

$$(\dot{\mathbf{H}}_O)_{XYZ} = (\dot{\mathbf{H}}_O)_{xyz} + \mathbf{\Omega} \times \mathbf{H}_O \tag{9.33b}$$

From Equations (9.33) we conclude that when the moving coordinate axes are translating but nonrotating ($\mathbf{\Omega} = \mathbf{0}$), then the relative and absolute angular momentum vectors are equal and we write

$$(\dot{\mathbf{H}}_C)_{abs} = (\dot{\mathbf{H}}_C)_{rel} \qquad (\dot{\mathbf{H}}_O)_{abs} = (\dot{\mathbf{H}}_O)_{rel}$$

Substituting Equations (9.33) into the corresponding Equations (9.32), we obtain

$$\Sigma \mathbf{M}_C = (\dot{\mathbf{H}}_C)_{xyz} + \mathbf{\Omega} \times \mathbf{H}_C \tag{9.34a}$$

and

$$\Sigma \mathbf{M}_O = (\dot{\mathbf{H}}_O)_{xyz} + \mathbf{\Omega} \times \mathbf{H}_O \tag{9.34b}$$

where $\Sigma \mathbf{M}_C = (\Sigma M_C)_x \mathbf{i} + (\Sigma M_C)_y \mathbf{j} + (\Sigma M_C)_z \mathbf{k}$
$\mathbf{\Omega} = \Omega_x \mathbf{i} + \Omega_y \mathbf{j} + \Omega_z \mathbf{k}$
$\mathbf{H}_C = (H_C)_x \mathbf{i} + (H_C)_y \mathbf{j} + (H_C)_z \mathbf{k}$
$(\dot{\mathbf{H}}_C)_{xyz} = (\dot{H}_C)_x \mathbf{i} + (\dot{H}_C)_y \mathbf{j} + (\dot{H}_C)_z \mathbf{k}$

Similar expressions can be written for the terms appearing in Equation (9.34b) by replacing the subscript *C* with *O*. In what follows we will limit our analysis to the further expansion of Equation (9.34a). Substituting from Equations (9.4) for $(H_C)_x$, $(H_C)_y$, and $(H_C)_z$ and upon differentiating with respect to time, we write

$$\begin{bmatrix} (\Sigma M_C)_x\mathbf{i} \\ + \\ (\Sigma M_C)_y\mathbf{j} \\ + \\ (\Sigma M_C)_z\mathbf{k} \end{bmatrix} = \begin{bmatrix} (I_{xx}\dot\omega_x - I_{xy}\dot\omega_y - I_{xz}\dot\omega_z)\mathbf{i} \\ + \\ (-I_{yx}\dot\omega_x + I_{yy}\dot\omega_y - I_{yz}\dot\omega_z)\mathbf{j} \\ + \\ (-I_{zx}\dot\omega_x - I_{zy}\dot\omega_y + I_{zz}\dot\omega_z)\mathbf{k} \end{bmatrix} + \begin{vmatrix} \mathbf{i} & \mathbf{j} & \mathbf{k} \\ \Omega_x & \Omega_y & \Omega_z \\ (H_C)_x & (H_C)_y & (H_C)_z \end{vmatrix} \qquad (9.35)$$

where
$$(H_C)_x = I_{xx}\omega_x - I_{xy}\omega_y - I_{xz}\omega_z$$
$$(H_C)_y = -I_{yx}\omega_x + I_{yy}\omega_y - I_{yz}\omega_z$$
$$(H_C)_z = -I_{zx}\omega_x - I_{zy}\omega_y + I_{zz}\omega_z$$

However, if the *xyz* axes are chosen to coincide with the *principle axes of inertia* of the rigid body, then we have

$$I_{xx} = \bar I_x \qquad I_{yy} = \bar I_y \qquad I_{zz} = \bar I_z$$

and

$$I_{xy} = I_{yx} = 0 \qquad I_{xz} = I_{zx} = 0 \qquad I_{yz} = I_{zy} = 0$$

Now, substituting Equation (9.8) into Equation (9.33) yields

$$(\dot{\mathbf{H}}_C)_{xyz} = (\bar I_x\dot\omega_x)\mathbf{i} + (\bar I_y\dot\omega_y)\mathbf{j} + (\bar I_z\dot\omega_z)\mathbf{k} \qquad (9.36)$$

And Equation (9.36) when substituted into Equation (9.34) will give

$$\begin{Bmatrix} (\Sigma M_C)_x\mathbf{i} \\ + \\ (\Sigma M_C)_y\mathbf{j} \\ + \\ (\Sigma M_C)_z\mathbf{k} \end{Bmatrix} = \begin{Bmatrix} (\bar I_x\dot\omega_x)\mathbf{i} \\ + \\ (\bar I_y\dot\omega_y)\mathbf{j} \\ + \\ (\bar I_z\dot\omega_z)\mathbf{k} \end{Bmatrix} + \begin{vmatrix} \mathbf{i} & \mathbf{j} & \mathbf{k} \\ \Omega_x & \Omega_y & \Omega_z \\ \bar I_x\omega_x & \bar I_y\omega_y & \bar I_z\omega_z \end{vmatrix} \qquad (9.37)$$

This vector relationship, when expressed in terms of its scalar components and complemented by the scalar components of Equation (9.31), yields

$$\left.\begin{aligned} (\Sigma M_C)_x &= \bar I_x\dot\omega_x - \bar I_y\Omega_z\omega_y + \bar I_z\Omega_y\omega_z \\ (\Sigma M_C)_y &= \bar I_y\dot\omega_y - \bar I_z\Omega_x\omega_z + \bar I_x\Omega_z\omega_x \\ (\Sigma M_C)_z &= \bar I_z\dot\omega_z - \bar I_x\Omega_y\omega_x + \bar I_y\Omega_x\omega_y \\ \Sigma F_x &= m(a_C)_x \\ \Sigma F_y &= m(a_C)_y \\ \Sigma F_z &= m(a_C)_z \end{aligned}\right\} \qquad (9.38)$$

Further simplification of Equations (9.38) will result if we choose a frame of reference *xyz* rotating with the same angular velocity as the rigid body (i.e., $\Omega = \omega$). Equation (9.38) is then reduced to

$$
\left.
\begin{aligned}
(\Sigma M_C)_x &= \bar{I}_x \dot{\omega}_x - (\bar{I}_y - \bar{I}_z)\omega_y\omega_z \\
(\Sigma M_C)_y &= \bar{I}_y \dot{\omega}_y - (\bar{I}_z - \bar{I}_x)\omega_z\omega_x \\
(\Sigma M_C)_z &= \bar{I}_z \dot{\omega}_z - (\bar{I}_x - \bar{I}_y)\omega_x\omega_y \\
\Sigma F_x &= m(a_C)_x \\
\Sigma F_y &= m(a_C)_y \\
\Sigma F_z &= m(a_C)_z
\end{aligned}
\right\}
\qquad (9.39)
$$

Equations (9.39) are known as *Euler's equations of motion*, after the eighteenth century Swiss mathematician Leonhard Euler (1707–1783).

If a body rotates about a fixed point O, it is preferable to evaluate the moments, moments of inertia, and angular velocities about the point O, and apply them to Euler's equations of motion developed for a coordinate system $(x'y'z')$ attached to the body and rotating along with it. The Euler's equations of motion can then be expressed as

$$
\left.
\begin{aligned}
(\Sigma M_O)_{x'} &= \bar{I}_{x'} \dot{\omega}_{x'} - (\bar{I}_{y'} - \bar{I}_{z'})\omega_{y'}\omega_{z'} \\
(\Sigma M_O)_{y'} &= \bar{I}_{y'} \dot{\omega}_{y'} - (\bar{I}_{z'} - \bar{I}_{x'})\omega_{z'}\omega_{x'} \\
(\Sigma M_O)_{z'} &= \bar{I}_{z'} \dot{\omega}_{z'} - (\bar{I}_{x'} - \bar{I}_{y'})\omega_{x'}\omega_{y'} \\
\Sigma F_{x'} &= m(a_C)_{x'} \\
\Sigma F_{y'} &= m(a_C)_{y'} \\
\Sigma F_{z'} &= m(a_C)_{z'}
\end{aligned}
\right\}
\qquad (9.40)
$$

Special Case: Rotation about a Fixed Axis   A further constraint to the motion of a rigid body can occur when the body is forced to rotate about a *fixed axis*. All points within the body will describe circular paths located within parallel planes (planar motion). In Chapter 8, we studied the motion of a rigid body with a plane of symmetry (slab) and rotating about a fixed axis perpendicular to its plane of symmetry. We shall now extend the study to unsymmetrical bodies rotating about a fixed axis that is not necessarily centroidal. The moving frame of reference $x'y'z'$ is attached to the body at O and rotating with it. Observe that by aligning the Oz' axis with the axis of rotation, as in Figure 9.7, we have

$$\mathbf{\Omega} = \boldsymbol{\omega} = \omega_z\mathbf{k}$$

and

$$\omega_x = \omega_y = 0$$

Since the axis of rotation will not usually be a principal axis of inertia, Equa-

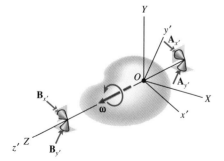

Figure 9.7

tions (9.40) will not be applicable to this case. Instead, we will use Equation (9.35) after introducing the relationships $\omega_x = \Omega_x = \omega_y = \Omega_y = 0$ and $\Omega_z = \omega_z$ and substituting the subscript O for C and x',y',z' for x,y,z, respectively. We obtain

$$
\left.
\begin{aligned}
(\Sigma M_O)_{x'} &= -\bar{I}_{x'z'}\dot{\omega}_{z'} + \bar{I}_{y'z'}\omega_{z'}^2 \\
(\Sigma M_O)_{y'} &= -\bar{I}_{y'z'}\dot{\omega}_{z'} - \bar{I}_{x'z'}\omega_{z'}^2 \\
(\Sigma M_O)_{z'} &= \bar{I}_{z'}\dot{\omega}_{z'} \\
\Sigma F_{x'} &= m(a_C)_{x'} \\
\Sigma F_{y'} &= m(a_C)_{y'} \\
\Sigma F_{z'} &= 0
\end{aligned}
\right\}
\qquad (9.41)
$$

where $\omega_{z'} = \omega$, the angular velocity of the body, and $\dot{\omega}_z = \alpha_{z'}$, the angular acceleration of the body about the fixed axis Oz'.

Special Case: Constant-Angular-Speed Rotation about a Fixed Axis   If a rigid body rotates about a fixed axis Oz' with a constant angular velocity ω (Figure 9.7), the moment equations (9.41) can be further simplified by writing $\dot{\omega}_{z'} = 0$ and $\omega_{z'} = \omega$ to yield

$$
\left.
\begin{aligned}
(\Sigma M_O)_{x'} &= \bar{I}_{y'z'}\omega^2 \\
(\Sigma M_O)_{y'} &= -\bar{I}_{x'z'}\omega^2 \\
(\Sigma M_O)_{z'} &= 0 \\
\Sigma F_{x'} &= m(a_C)_{x'} \\
\Sigma F_{y'} &= m(a_C)_{y'} \\
\Sigma F_{z'} &= 0
\end{aligned}
\right\}
\qquad (9.42)
$$

Some significant conclusions can be drawn from the above equations. If the mass products of inertia $I_{y'z'}$, and $I_{x'z'}$ are not zero, then it follows that, at any given instant, the dynamic balance of the body (i.e., the moment equations) will necessitate the presence of moments—nonvanishing $(\Sigma M_O)_{x'}$ and $(\Sigma M_O)_{y'}$—in the plane normal to the axis of rotation. These moments will, in turn, indicate the presence of transverse reaction forces $(A_{x'}, A_{y'}, B_{x'}, B_{y'})$ acting normal to the axis of rotation at the supports A and B. With the rotation of the body and of the $x'y'z'$ frame, such transverse reactions will rotate too (with the shaft) and cause undesirable vibrations within the support structure of the body. In order to avoid these vibrations, the mass of the body is usually rearranged and distributed in a way that yields

$$
I_{y'z'} = 0 \quad \text{and} \quad I_{x'z'} = 0
$$

and the moment equations for a body rotating about a fixed axis with a constant ω are finally reduced to

$$
\left.
\begin{aligned}
(\Sigma M_O)_{x'} &= 0 \\
(\Sigma M_O)_{y'} &= 0 \\
(\Sigma M_O)_{z'} &= 0 \\
\Sigma F_{x'} &= m(a_C)_{x'} \\
\Sigma F_{y'} &= m(a_C)_{y'} \\
\Sigma F_{z'} &= 0
\end{aligned}
\right\}
\tag{9.43}
$$

Equations (9.42) represented the motion, about a fixed axis, of a body said to be *dynamically unbalanced*. When the body's mass distribution is symmetrical with respect to x' and y' axes (symmetrical about the xy plane) we write $I_{x'z'} = I_{y'z'} = 0$ and obtain the moment equations, given in Equation (9.43), for a *dynamically balanced* body rotating about a fixed axis.

EXAMPLE   9.9

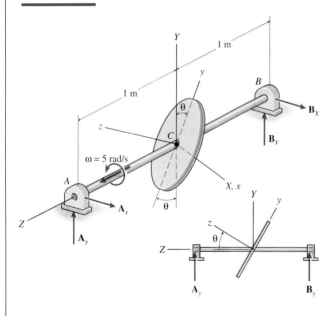

A thin uniform 30-kg disk (radius = 0.2 m) is rigidly mounted as shown on a 2-m-long horizontal shaft AB of negligible mass. The direction normal to the plane of the disk forms an angle $\theta = 30°$ with the axis of the shaft. The shaft rotates with a constant angular velocity $\omega = 5$ rad/s as shown. Determine the reactions at A and B when the disk is in the position shown.

Solution   The origins of the inertial and rotating coordinate systems are both located at the mass center O of the disk and shaft, which is a fixed point. The xyz axes are fixed in and rotate with the disk at $\omega = 5$ rad/s about the shaft.

The angular velocity vector $\boldsymbol{\omega}$ of the disk is constant in magnitude and direction along the shaft axis. In the xyz system $\boldsymbol{\omega}$ becomes

$$
\boldsymbol{\omega} = \omega_x \mathbf{i} + \omega_y \mathbf{j} + \omega_z \mathbf{k}
$$

where
$$
\begin{aligned}
\omega_x &= 0 \\
\omega_y &= -\omega \sin\theta = -5 \sin 30° = -2.5 \text{ rad/s} \\
\omega_z &= \omega \cos\theta = 5 \cos 30° = +4.33 \text{ rad/s} \\
\boldsymbol{\omega} &= -2.5\mathbf{j} + 4.33\mathbf{k} \text{ (rad/s)}
\end{aligned}
$$

The pertinent mass moments of inertia $\bar{I}_x$, $\bar{I}_y$, and $\bar{I}_z$ of the disk about the principal axes of inertia are

(continued)

EXAMPLE 9.9 (*concluded*)

$$\bar{I}_x = \bar{I}_y = \frac{1}{4}mR^2 = \frac{1}{4}(30)(0.2)^2 = 0.3 \text{ kg} \cdot \text{m}^2$$

$$\bar{I}_z = \frac{1}{2}mR^2 = \frac{1}{2}(30)(0.2)^2 = 0.6 \text{ kg} \cdot \text{m}^2$$

Now we can apply the Euler's equations in the three coordinate directions. After considering the fact that $\dot{\omega}_x = \dot{\omega}_y = \dot{\omega}_z = 0$, we write Equations (9.39) as

$$\Sigma M_x = \bar{I}_x\dot{\omega}_x - (\bar{I}_y - \bar{I}_z)\omega_y\omega_z$$

$$-A_y\left(\frac{L}{2}\right) + B_y\left(\frac{L}{2}\right) = \bar{I}_x(0) - (\bar{I}_y - \bar{I}_z)(\omega_y)(\omega_z)$$

$$-A_y + B_y = -(0.3 - 0.6)(-2.5)(+4.33)$$

$$-A_y + B_y = -3.25 \qquad (a)$$

$$\Sigma M_y = \bar{I}_y\dot{\omega}_y - (\bar{I}_z - \bar{I}_x)\omega_z\omega_x$$

$$A_x\left(\frac{L}{2}\cos\theta\right) - B_x\left(\frac{L}{2}\cos\theta\right) = \bar{I}_y(0) - (\bar{I}_z - \bar{I}_x)(\omega_z)(0)$$

$$A_x\cos 30° - B_x\cos 30° = 0$$

$$A_x - B_x = 0 \qquad (b)$$

$$\Sigma M_z = \bar{I}_z\dot{\omega}_z - (\bar{I}_x - \bar{I}_y)\omega_x\omega_y$$

$$A_x\left(\frac{L}{2}\sin\theta\right) - B_x\left(\frac{L}{2}\sin\theta\right) = \bar{I}_z(0) - (\bar{I}_x - \bar{I}_y)(0)\omega_y$$

$$A_x - B_x = 0$$

In addition, the three components of the vector equation $\Sigma \mathbf{F} = m\mathbf{a}_C$ are further reduced, since C is a fixed point, and we obtain

$$\Sigma F_x = m(a_C)_x = 0 \qquad A_x + B_x = 0 \qquad (c)$$

$$\Sigma F_y = m(a_C)_y = 0 \qquad A_y + B_y - m_{\text{disk}}g = 0$$

$$A_y + B_y - 294.3 = 0 \qquad (d)$$

$$\Sigma F_z = m(a_C)_z = 0 \qquad 0 = 0$$

The simultaneous solution of Equations (a) through (d) yields

$$A_x = B_x = 0 \qquad A_y = 145.5 \text{ N} \qquad B_y = 148.8 \text{ N} \blacktriangleleft$$

EXAMPLE 9.10

The rod assembly shown is supported by journal bearings at A and B. All rods have equal diameter and weigh 2 lb/ft. At a given instant the shaft AB is rotating counterclockwise at a rate of $\omega = 8$ rad/s. At this instant, determine the shaft's angular acceleration, and the reactions at A and B.

Solution At the instant shown, the rotational motion of the rod assembly is defined by the angular velocity $\boldsymbol{\omega}$ of the assembly as

$$\boldsymbol{\omega} = \omega_x\mathbf{i} + \omega_y\mathbf{j} + \omega_z\mathbf{k}$$

where $\omega_x = 0$, $\omega_y = 8$ rad/s, and $\omega_z = 0$. And since the shaft rotates about the y axis only, we also have $\dot{\omega}_x = 0$ and $\dot{\omega}_z = 0$. We note that the chosen coordinate axes x,y,z are embedded in the rod assembly and rotate with it ($\boldsymbol{\Omega} = \boldsymbol{\omega}$). Furthermore, the xyz axes are not the principal axes of inertia and therefore the applicable equations of motion are Equations (9.34b) or their scalar counterparts (Euler's Equations) and the three scalar components of the Equation $\Sigma \mathbf{F} = m\mathbf{a}_C$. Considering that $\omega_x = \omega_z = \dot{\omega}_x = \dot{\omega}_z = 0$, the Euler's Equations given by Equation (9.35) (modified by taking the

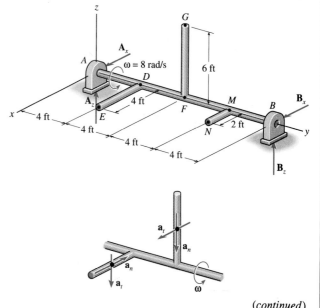

(*continued*)

EXAMPLE 9.10 (*concluded*)

moments about the origin at A instead of the mass center of the assembly) will yield

$$\Sigma M_x = -I_{xy}\dot{\omega}_y - I_{yz}\omega_y^2 \tag{a}$$

$$\Sigma M_y = I_{yy}\dot{\omega}_y \tag{b}$$

$$\Sigma M_z = I_{xy}\omega_y^2 - I_{yz}\dot{\omega}_y \tag{c}$$

$$\Sigma F_x = m(a_C)_x \tag{d}$$

$$\Sigma F_y = m(a_C)_y \tag{e}$$

$$\Sigma F_z = m(a_C)_z \tag{f}$$

where, from $I_{xy} = (I_{xy})_C + mx_Cy_C$ we can write

$$I_{xy} = [(I_{xy})_{AB} + (I_{xy})_{DE} + (I_{xy})_{FG} + (I_{xy})_{MN}]$$

$$= 0 + \frac{2(4)2(4)}{32.2} + 0 + \frac{2(2)1(12)}{32.2} = 3.48 \text{ slug} \cdot \text{ft}^2$$

$$I_{yz} = [(I_{yz})_{AB} + (I_{yz})_{DE} + (I_{yz})_{FG} + (I_{yx})_{MN}]$$

$$= 0 + 0 + \frac{2(6)8(3)}{32.2} + 0 = 8.94 \text{ slug} \cdot \text{ft}^2$$

and

$$I_{yy} = [(I_{yy})_{AB} + (I_{yy})_{DE} + (I_{yy})_{FG} + (I_{yy})_{MN}]$$

$$= 0 + \frac{1}{3}\frac{(2)(4)(4)^2}{32.2} + \frac{1}{3}\frac{(2)(6)(6)^2}{32.2} + \frac{1}{3}\frac{(2)(2)(2)^2}{32.2}$$

$$= \frac{42.67 + 144 + 5.33}{32.2}$$

$$= 5.96 \text{ slug} \cdot \text{ft}^2$$

Next, we calculate the weights of the various components of the rod assembly. We have

$$W_{AB} = wL_{AB} = 2(16) = 32 \text{ lb, acting at point } (0,8,0)$$

$$W_{DE} = wL_{DE} = 2(4) = 8 \text{ lb, acting at point } (2,4,0)$$

$$W_{FG} = wL_{FG} = 2(6) = 12 \text{ lb, acting at point } (0,8,3)$$

$$W_{MN} = wL_{MN} = 2(2) = 4 \text{ lb, acting at point } (1,12,0)$$

Equations (a), (b), and (c) can now be expressed in the form

$$-8(4) - 32(8) - 12(8) - 4(12) + B_z(16)$$

$$= -3.48\dot{\omega}_y - 8.94(8)$$

$$16B_z + 3.48\dot{\omega}_y = 360.48 \tag{a}$$

$$8(2) + 4(1) = 5.96\dot{\omega}_y$$

$$5.96\dot{\omega}_y = 20 \tag{b}$$

$$-B_x(16) = 3.48(8)^2 - 8.94\dot{\omega}_y$$

$$-16B_x + 8.94\dot{\omega}_y = 222.72 \tag{c}$$

Equation (b) yields the angular acceleration of the shaft at the given instant:

$$\alpha = \dot{\omega}_y = 3.3 \text{ rad/s}^2 \blacktriangleleft$$

Substituting this into Equations (a) and (c) gives

$$B_z = 21.23 \text{ lb} (\uparrow) \qquad B_x = -10.59 \text{ lb} \blacktriangleleft$$

We evaluate the reactions at the journal bearings at A through Equations (d), (e), and (f). Since the shaft AB is not subject to translation, we have

$$\Sigma F_x = [m(a_C)_x]_{DE} + [m(a_C)_x]_{FG} + [m(a_C)_x]_{MN}$$

$$A_x + B_x = \underbrace{[m(a_C)_n]_{DE}}_{r\omega^2} + \underbrace{[m(a_C)_t]_{FG}}_{r\alpha} + \underbrace{[m(a_C)_n]_{MN}}_{r\omega^2}$$

$$A_x - 18 = \frac{-(2)(4)2(8)^2}{32.2} + \frac{2(6)3(3.42)^2}{32.2} - \frac{(2)(4)1(8)^2}{32.2}$$

$$A_x = 18 + \frac{-1024 + 421.1 - 512}{32.2}$$

$$A_x = -34.62 \text{ lb} \blacktriangleleft$$

$$\Sigma F_z = [m(a_C)_z]_{DE} + [m(a_C)_z]_{FG} + [m(a_C)_z]_{MN}$$

$$A_z + B_z - W_{AB} - W_{DE} - W_{FG} - W_{MN}$$

$$= [m(a_C)_z]_{DE} + [m(a_C)_z]_{FG} + [m(a_C)_z]_{MN}$$

$$A_z + 21.23 - 32 - 8 - 12 - 4$$

$$= \underbrace{[m(a_C)_t]_{DE}}_{r\alpha} + \underbrace{[m(a_C)_n]_{FG}}_{r\omega^2} + \underbrace{[m(a_C)_t]_{MN}}_{r\alpha}$$

$$A_z - 34.77 = \frac{-2(4)2(3.42)}{32.2} - \frac{(2)(6)3(8)^2}{32.2} - \frac{2(2)1(3.42)}{32.2}$$

$$A_z = 34.77 - \frac{54.72 + 2304 + 13.68}{32.2}$$

$$A_z = -38.91 \text{ lb} \blacktriangleleft$$

9.5 GYROSCOPIC MOTION

In the previous sections we examined the general spatial motion of a rigid body and developed equations that permitted the analysis of certain special cases: the motion of a body rotating about a fixed axis, and planar motion. There is another special case, one that is essential for the development and examination of an important device: the gyroscope. The motion pertinent for this special case is called **gyroscopic motion**—that of a rigid body rotating about a *fixed* point. The axis of rotation will always pass through the fixed point but its orientation will not remain fixed. The kinematics of the motion was studied in Section 6.9 and the velocity and deceleration vector fields developed.

Defining the location, in space, of a rigid body that has a fixed point attached to an inertial frame of reference *XYZ*, as in Figure 9.8, will now be the focus

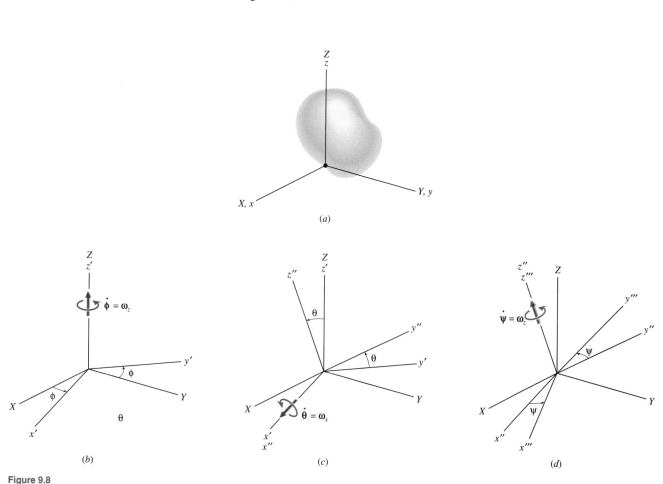

Figure 9.8

of our attention. By selecting the fixed point as the origin of both the inertial frame *XYZ* and the rotating coordinate axes *xyz* attached to the body, the body's instantaneous orientation could be inferred from the position of the *xyz* system relative to the inertial frame. An effective way of describing the position of the *xyz* system relative to the inertial system *XYZ* is by specifying three successive rotations, in a given sequence, that enable us to bring the *xyz* frame from an initial orientation coincident with the *XYZ* frame, to the desired orientation. The three successive rotations are specified by three angles ϕ, θ, and ψ, called the *Eulerian* angles. The angle ϕ, called the **angle of precession**, specifies the counterclockwise rotation of the *xyz* system about the *Z* axis. It brings (Figure 9.8*b*) the *x* axis to a new position x' and the frame becomes $x'y'Z$. Next, the $x'y'Z$ frame is rotated counterclockwise about the x' axis by an angle θ, called the **angle of nutation** (Figure 9.8*c*). It brings the *Z* or z' axis to a new position z'' and the relative frame becomes $x''y''z''$. The third and counterclockwise rotation will be about the z'' axis. The angle ψ, called the **angle of spin**, will bring the frame into its final orientation $x'''y'''z'''$ (Figure 9.8*d*).

The above angles are not vector quantities and therefore the sequence of the above rotations will uniquely define the final orientation of the body attached to the *xyz* frame of reference. However, the variation of the angles ϕ, θ, and ψ with respect to time will give rise to three corresponding angular velocity vectors ($\dot{\phi}$, $\dot{\theta}$, and $\dot{\psi}$) as shown in Figure 9.8. These are referred to as the *rate of precession*, the *rate of nutation*, and the *rate of spin* of the body at any given instant. They are vectors, as they obey the addition properties of vector calculus.

The angular velocities introduced above will now be related to the angular velocity components ω_x, ω_y, and ω_z appearing in the Euler's equations. In Section 9.4 the pertinent relationships were developed and given as Equation (9.34b) or as Equations (9.38).

For the special case under consideration here, we will apply Equations (9.38) to a rigid body spinning about its axis of rotational symmetry. Specifically, we will examine the motion of bodies such as a spinning top (Figure 9.9*a*), the gyroscope (Figure 9.9*b*), or an axially symmetric and spinning space vehicle (Figure 9.9*c*). In each case, the *z* axis is taken as the rotating axis of the body and the origin of the reference frame is either the fixed point *O* along the axis of rotational symmetry of the top, or the gyroscope's mass center, which must remain fixed in space. It follows that the *x*, *y*, and *z* axes are the *principal axes of inertia* of the body regardless of its rate of spin and the moments of inertia about the *x*, *y*, and *z* axes will remain constant with time: $\bar{I}_z = I_z$ and $\bar{I}_x = \bar{I}_y = I$.

The absolute angular velocity $\boldsymbol{\omega}$ of the spinning body can now be expressed in the *xyz* frame by considering Figures 9.10*a,b,c*. Thus we write, from Figure 9.10*a*,

$$\omega_{z'} = \dot{\phi}$$

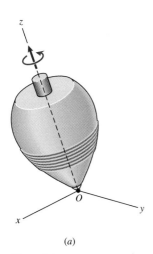

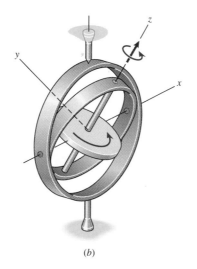

(a) (b) (c)

Figure 9.9

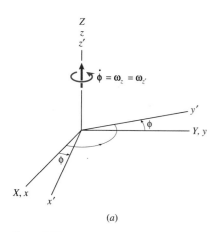

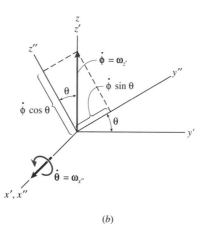

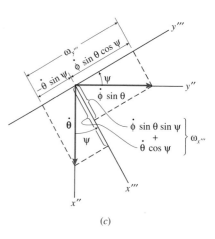

(a) (b) (c)

Figure 9.10

From Figure 9.10*b* we can write

$$\omega_{x''} = \dot{\theta}$$
$$\omega_{y''} = \omega_{z'} \sin \theta = \dot{\phi} \sin \theta$$
$$\omega_{z''} = \omega_{z'} \cos \theta = \dot{\phi} \cos \theta$$

and from Figure 9.10*c* we obtain

$$\omega_{z'''} = \omega_{x''} \cos \psi + \omega_{y''} \sin \psi$$

Substituting for $\omega_{x''}$ and $\omega_{y''}$ from above we write

$$\omega_{x'''} = \dot\theta \cos\psi + \dot\phi \sin\theta \sin\psi$$

$$\omega_{y'''} = -\dot\theta \sin\psi + \dot\phi \sin\theta \cos\psi$$

$$\omega_{z'''} = \dot\psi + \dot\phi \cos\theta$$

Hence the angular velocity components relative to the rotating frame of reference xyz are

$$\left.\begin{array}{l} \omega_x = \dot\theta \cos\psi + \dot\phi \sin\theta \sin\psi \\[4pt] \omega_y = -\dot\theta \sin\psi + \dot\phi \sin\theta \cos\psi \\[4pt] \omega_z = \dot\phi \cos\theta + \dot\psi \end{array}\right\} \qquad (9.44)$$

Equations (9.44) represent the angular velocity components of a body rotating about a fixed point in terms of the time derivatives of the Euler's angles. The coordinate axes are embedded in the body and therefore $\boldsymbol{\Omega} = \boldsymbol{\omega}$, where $\boldsymbol{\Omega}$ is the angular velocity vector of the coordinate system.

However, a significant amount of simplification can be achieved if we choose a reference frame that follows the motion of the body only in precession and nutation but has a zero rate of spin ($\dot\psi = 0$). By a judicious selection of the x and y axes, we can elect to have the spin angle $\psi = 0$, and Equations (9.44) become

$$\begin{array}{ll} \omega_x = \dot\theta & \Omega_x = \dot\theta \\[4pt] \omega_y = \dot\phi \sin\theta & \Omega_y = \dot\phi \sin\theta \\[4pt] \omega_z = \dot\phi \cos\theta + \dot\psi & \Omega_z = \dot\phi \cos\theta \end{array}$$

or

$$\left.\begin{array}{l} \boldsymbol{\omega} = (\dot\theta)\mathbf{i} + (\dot\phi \sin\theta)\mathbf{j} + (\dot\phi \cos\theta + \dot\psi)\mathbf{k} \\[4pt] \boldsymbol{\Omega} = (\dot\theta)\mathbf{i} + (\dot\phi \sin\theta)\mathbf{j} + (\dot\phi \cos\theta)\mathbf{k} \end{array}\right\} \qquad (9.45)$$

Since the angular velocities of the body and of the reference frame are not identical ($\boldsymbol{\omega} \neq \boldsymbol{\Omega}$) we will now introduce Equations (9.45) into the Euler's equations developed and given in Equations (9.38). The substitution will yield

$$\left.\begin{array}{l} (\Sigma M_C)_x = I(\ddot\theta - \dot\phi^2 \sin\theta \cos\theta) + I_z\dot\phi \sin\theta(\dot\phi \cos\theta + \dot\psi) \\[4pt] (\Sigma M_C)_y = I(\ddot\phi \sin\theta + 2\dot\phi\dot\theta \cos\theta) - I_z\dot\theta(\dot\phi \cos\theta + \dot\psi) \\[4pt] (\Sigma M_C)_z = I(\ddot\psi + \ddot\phi \cos\theta - \dot\phi\dot\theta \sin\theta) \end{array}\right\} \qquad (9.46)$$

The reader is reminded that just as Equations (9.38) were developed from Equation (9.34a), identical relationships are obtained for the Euler's equations from Equation (9.34b) where all moment summations are taken about an arbitrary *fixed* point O. Equations (9.46) permit us to analyze the motion of a *body of revolution* about its mass center C or about an arbitrary fixed point that lies on its rotational axis of symmetry.

A very useful device satisfying the definition given above of a body of revolution spinning about its geometric axis of symmetry is the *gyroscope*. As shown in Figure 9.11, the gyroscope consists of a *rotor*, an *inner gimbal*, and an *outer gimbal*. The gyroscope's rotor can spin freely about its geometric axis while its mass center always remains fixed in space. In analyzing the gyroscopic motion, the inertial frame of reference has its origin at the mass center C of the gyroscope. The relative reference frame xyz is attached to the inner gimbal, with the z axis directed along the spin axis of the rotor and the y axis directed along the axis of rotation of the inner gimbal. This will satisfy the condition of zero spin angle and allow the Z, z, and y axes to be always coplanar.

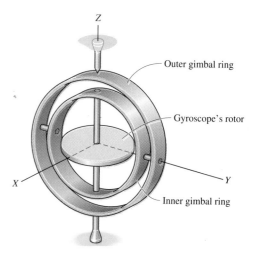

Figure 9.11

Steady Precession

Unfortunately, the Equations (9.46) require the solution of a simultaneous set of nonlinear differential equations for which a closed-form solution may not be obtainable. However, the Equations (9.46) can be further reduced and solved for a special case occurring when the rates of precession $\dot{\phi}$ and spin $\dot{\psi}$ and the nutation angle θ will all remain constant. The equations become

$$\left.\begin{aligned}(\Sigma M)_x &= -I\dot{\phi}^2 \sin\theta \cos\theta + I_z\dot{\phi} \sin\theta(\dot{\phi}\cos\theta + \dot{\psi})\\ (\Sigma M)_y &= 0 \qquad (\Sigma M)_z = 0\end{aligned}\right\} \qquad (9.47)$$

The term within parentheses in the first equation is ω_z, from Equation (9.45). We write

$$(\Sigma M)_x = -I\dot{\phi}^2 \sin\theta \cos\theta + I_z\dot{\phi} \sin\theta(\omega_z)$$

$$\boxed{\begin{aligned}(\Sigma M)_x &= \dot{\phi} \sin\theta(I_z\omega_z - I\dot{\phi}\cos\theta)\\ (\Sigma M)_y &= 0 \qquad (\Sigma M_z) = 0\end{aligned}} \qquad (9.48)$$

The motion described by Equations (9.48) is known as the **steady precession** of a gyroscope. We know that the translational motion of a rigid body is expressed as $\Sigma \mathbf{F} = m\mathbf{a}_C$. Since, during the gyroscopic motion, the mass center of the device remains fixed in space, we have $\mathbf{a}_C = 0$ and $\Sigma \mathbf{F} = 0$. We conclude that the *steady precession of a gyroscope requires the application of a torque, the magnitude of which can be evaluated from Equations (9.48)*. The torque vector must be applied about the x axis, which was chosen as the nutation axis. The overturning moment vector caused by the weight of a spinning top can only be balanced if the moment axis is normal to the spin and precession axes (Figure 9.12).

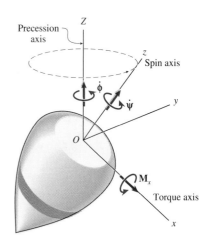

Figure 9.12

Steady Precession When Nutation Angle $\theta = 90°$

In certain engineering devices, the gyroscope is required to process steadily about an axis perpendicular to both the spin axis and the nutation axis. When the precession axis is normal to the spin axis as in Figure 9.13, we have $\theta =$

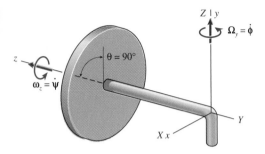

Figure 9.13

90° and the Equation (9.47) becomes

$$(\Sigma M)_x = I_z \dot{\phi} \dot{\psi} \qquad (9.49)$$

The case defined by this equation represents a gyroscopic motion in which the spin, the nutation—or moment—and the precession axes form a right-handed triad. In the case illustrated in Figure 9.13, we see that the overturning moment caused by the weight of the rotor can be counterbalanced by a judicious selection of the rate of precession $\dot{\phi} = \Omega_y$. Equation (9.49) is thus reduced to $Wr_g = I_z\omega_z\Omega_y$, which would yield $\Omega_y = Wr_g/I_z\omega_z$. The spinning rigid body's ability to remain within its horizontal plane of motion against the effect of gravity is referred to as the *gyroscopic effect*.

Steady Precession with No External Moment

A special type of gyroscopic motion characteristic of the flight of spacecrafts, projectiles, and satellites—and even a spinning football—is the movement of a body of revolution taking place in the absence of any external moment about the body's mass center. The only external force acting on such a body is caused by the gravity field and acts through the body's mass center, thus causing no torque about any of its centroidal axes. Such a movement is often referred to as *torque-free motion*.

If the summation $(\Sigma \mathbf{M}_C)$ of all external moments about the mass center C of a rigid body is zero, from Equation (9.32b) it follows that $\dot{\mathbf{H}}_C = \mathbf{0}$ and $\mathbf{H}_C = $ constant.

A judicious choice of the frames of reference (XYZ and xyz) can significantly simplify the expression for the angular momentum vector $\mathbf{H}_C$ (see Figure 9.14). By selecting the Z axis of the inertial system to be collinear with $\mathbf{H}_C$ and to have the same direction as $\mathbf{H}_C$, and by securing that the y, z, and Z axes are all coplanar, the nutation angle θ will suffice to define the $\mathbf{j}$ and $\mathbf{k}$ components of $\mathbf{H}_C$, which will have no $\mathbf{i}$ component. Thus,

$$\mathbf{H}_C = H_C \sin \theta \mathbf{j} + H_C \cos \theta \mathbf{k} \qquad (9.50)$$

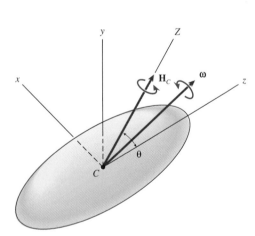

Figure 9.14

Considering the fact that the x,y,z coordinate axes are the principal axes of inertia for the body of revolution, we can write the components of the angular momentum of the body in terms of the three principal moments of inertia $\bar{I}_x = \bar{I}_y = I, \bar{I}_z = I_z$, and the three components ω_x, ω_y, and ω_z of the angular velocity of the body. From Equation (9.8) we write

$$\mathbf{H}_C = I\omega_x \mathbf{i} + I\omega_y \mathbf{j} + I_z\omega_z \mathbf{k} \qquad (9.51)$$

By equating the right-hand sides of Equations (9.50) and (9.51) and collecting the respective $\mathbf{i}$, $\mathbf{j}$, and $\mathbf{k}$ components, we obtain

$$\omega_x = 0 \qquad \omega_y = \frac{H_C \sin \theta}{I} \qquad \omega_z = \frac{H_C \cos \theta}{I_z} \qquad (9.52)$$

and the angular velocity vector $\boldsymbol{\omega}$ becomes

$$\boldsymbol{\omega} = \frac{H_C \sin \theta}{I}\mathbf{j} + \frac{H_C \cos \theta}{I_z}\mathbf{k} \tag{9.53}$$

We can now compare Equation (9.53) to Equations (9.45) to obtain

$$\dot{\theta} = 0 \qquad \dot{\phi}\sin\theta = \frac{H_C \sin\theta}{I} \qquad \dot{\phi}\cos\theta + \dot{\psi} = \frac{H_C \cos\theta}{I_z}$$

The first equation ($\dot{\theta} = 0$) yields $\theta = $ constant. Eliminating $\sin\theta$ from the second gives $\dot{\phi} = H_C/I$. Solving the third equation simultaneously with the second will finally give

$$\theta = \text{constant} \qquad \dot{\phi} = \frac{H_C}{I}$$
$$\dot{\psi} = \frac{I - I_z}{I \; I_z}H_C \cos\theta \tag{9.54}$$

We conclude that during the torque-free motion of a body in revolution, the nutation angle θ formed between the angular-momentum vector (or Z axis) and the spin axis (or z axis) of the body remains constant. Also, the angular momentum $\mathbf{H}_C$ (torque-free motion), and the rates of precession $\dot{\phi}$ and of spin $\dot{\psi}$ for the body remain constant at all times during the motion. Thus the body will *precess steadily about the Z axis*, as defined earlier.

We can now obtain a functional relationship between the precession and spin of the body from Equations (9.54) by eliminating the centroidal angular momentum H_C, and solve for the spin rate $\dot{\psi}$ as

$$\dot{\psi} = \frac{I - I_z}{I_z}\dot{\phi}\cos\theta \tag{9.55}$$

Equation (9.55) describes the angular motion of a body of revolution in terms of its two component motions: its precession and its spin. The angular velocity vector $\boldsymbol{\omega}$ has been developed and expressed in Equation (9.53). As the line specifying the direction of the angular velocity vector—the instantaneous axis of rotation—rotates about the axis of precession, it generates a fixed surface called a *space cone* as discussed and defined in Section 6.9. The cone defines the precession of the body and since the rate of precession $\dot{\phi}$ is constant the space cone is fixed in space. As for the *body cone*, generated by the line of action of the angular velocity vector $\boldsymbol{\omega}$ when the line is observed relative to the rotating body, it always rolls on the space cone (see Figure 9.15).

From Figure 9.16 and Equations (9.52), we write

$$\frac{\omega_y}{\omega_z} = \tan\beta = \frac{I_z}{I}\tan\theta \tag{9.56}$$

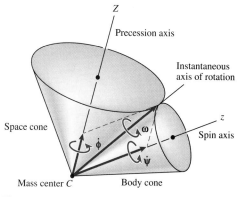

Figure 9.15

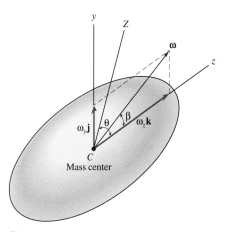

Figure 9.16

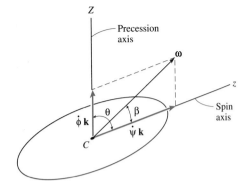

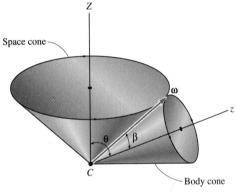

Figure 9.17

where β is the angle formed by the vector **ω** with the axis of symmetry (z) of the body. Since the problem involves steady precession and θ is constant, we conclude that the cones (space and body) are circular. Furthermore, we can make the following observations:

1.   If $I_z < I$, the body's mass moment of inertia about its rotational axis of symmetry is less than its mass moment of inertia about any transverse axis through the mass center, and the body has an elongated shape, as in Figure 9.17. By Equation (9.56) we have β < θ, the angular velocity vector **ω** lies inside the angle ZCz, and the space and body cones are tangent to each other externally. The precession is called *direct*.

2.   If $I < I_z$, the body's mass moment of inertia about a transverse axis through C is greater than its mass moment of inertia about its rotational axis of symmetry, and the body has a pancake-like shape, as in Figure 9.18. By Equation (9.56) we have θ < β, the angular velocity vector **ω** lies outside the angle ZCz, and the space and body cones are tangent to each other internally, the space cone being inside the body cone. Furthermore, since $(I - I_z)$ becomes negative, from Equation (9.55) we conclude that the rate of spin ($\dot\phi$) must be negative and hence opposite to the rate of precession ($\dot\phi$), which remains positive and equal to H_C/I [Equations (9.54)]. This particular case of precession is called *retrograde*.

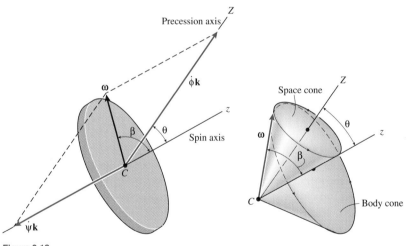

Figure 9.18

EXAMPLE 9.11

A uniform circular disk of mass 50 kg and radius 0.5 m is mounted on a shaft of negligible mass, which is pivoted about the vertical drive shaft as shown. The vertical drive shaft is turning at 5 rad/s, and the disk is rolling without slipping over the horizontal surface. Determine the normal reaction between the disk and the surface.

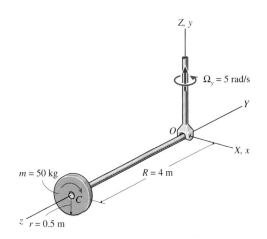

Solution The case represents a gyroscopic motion with steady precession when the nutation angle $\theta = 90°$. The precession occurs about an axis y perpendicular to both the spin axis z and the nutation axis x. The applicable equation, Equation (9.49), is

$$(\Sigma M)_x = I_z \dot{\phi} \dot{\psi} \qquad (a)$$

where $\Sigma M_x = (mg)R - NR = (50)(9.81)4 - N(4)$

$$= 1962 - 4N$$

$$I_z = \frac{1}{2}mR^2 = \frac{1}{2}(50)(0.5)^2 = 6.25 \text{ kg} \cdot \text{m}^2$$

$$\dot{\phi} = \Omega_y = 5 \text{ rad/s}$$

$$\dot{\psi} = \omega_z = \frac{-v_C}{r} = \frac{-\Omega R}{r} = \frac{-5(4)}{0.5} = -40 \text{ rad/s}$$

After substitution of the above values into Equation (a), we obtain

$$1962 - 4N = (6.25)5(-40)$$

$$N = 803 \text{ N} \blacktriangleleft$$

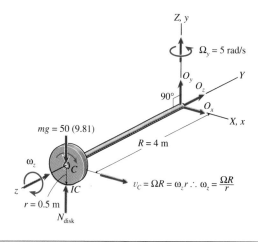

EXAMPLE 9.12

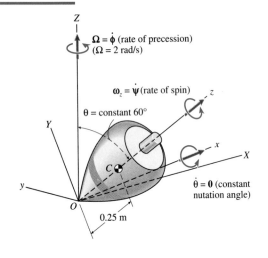

The 2-kg top shown has its mass center at C and radius of gyration of $r_g = 0.05$ m about its axis of symmetry and of $r_t = 0.10$ m about any transverse axes passing through the ball joint at O. If the top has a constant rate of precession of $\dot{\phi} = 2$ rad/s and the nutation angle is 60°, determine the rate of spin $\dot{\psi}$.

Solution   The motion represents the special case of gyroscopic motion called *steady precession*. The rate of precession is constant at $\dot{\phi} = \omega_1 = 2$ rad/s and the nutation angle is constant at $\theta = 60°$. The rate of spin must also be constant. The pertinent relationship applicable to the present situation is Equations (9.47). Thus we write

$$\Sigma M_x = -I\dot{\phi}^2 \sin\theta \cos\theta + I_z \dot{\phi} \sin\theta (\dot{\phi} \cos\theta + \dot{\psi}) \qquad \text{(a)}$$

where $\Sigma M_x = W(0.25 \sin 60°) = mg(0.25 \sin 60°)$

$$= 2(9.81)(0.25 \sin 60°) = 4.25 \,\text{N} \cdot \text{m}$$

$$I = mr_t^2 = 2(0.10)^2 = 0.02 \,\text{kg} \cdot \text{m}^2$$

$$I_z = mr_g^2 = 2(0.05)^2 = 0.005 \,\text{kg} \cdot \text{m}^2$$

Equation (a) now becomes

$$4.25 = -(0.02)(2)^2 \sin 60° \cos 60°$$

$$+ (0.005)(2) \sin 60°(2 \cos 60° + \dot{\psi})$$

$$4.25 = -0.035 + 0.0087(1 + \dot{\psi})$$

And the rate of spin is $\dot{\psi} = 491.5 \,\text{rad/s}$ ◄

9.6 SUMMARY

In this chapter, we have learned the following:

1.   The linear momentum **G** of a three-dimensional rigid body in spatial motion can be expressed by the same equation as we developed in Chapter 8 for planar motion; that is,

$$\mathbf{G} = m\mathbf{v}_C$$

where m is the total mass of the body, and $\mathbf{v}_C$ the velocity of its mass center measured relative to an inertial frame of reference XYZ.

2.   We can write the expression for the angular momentum $\mathbf{H}_A$ of a three-dimensional rigid body about an arbitrary point A as

$$\mathbf{H}_A = m\mathbf{r}_{C/A} \times \mathbf{v}_A + \int_m \mathbf{r}_{P/A} \times (\boldsymbol{\omega} \times \mathbf{r}_{P/A})dm \qquad (9.1)$$

where $\mathbf{r}_{C/A}$ and $\mathbf{r}_{P/A}$ are the position vectors of the mass center C and any point P of the body, respectively, measured relative to a reference frame xyz of fixed orientation (nonrotating) and attached to the body at A. The velocity $\mathbf{v}_A$ is measured relative to an inertial frame XYZ.

Two special cases are these: If the mass center C is chosen as the point A ($\mathbf{r}_{C/A} = \mathbf{0}$), then

$$\mathbf{H}_C = \int_m \mathbf{r}_{P/C} \times (\boldsymbol{\omega} \times \mathbf{r}_{P/C}) dm \qquad (9.2)$$

And, if the body has a *fixed* point O which is chosen as the arbitrary point A ($\mathbf{v}_A = \mathbf{0}$), then

$$\mathbf{H}_O = \int_m \mathbf{r}_{P/O} \times (\boldsymbol{\omega} \times \mathbf{r}_{P/O}) dm \qquad (9.3)$$

3. The rectangular components of the angular momentum vector $\mathbf{H}_C$ are

$$\left.\begin{aligned}
(H_C)_x &= I_{xx}\omega_x - I_{xy}\omega_y - I_{xz}\omega_z \\
(H_C)_y &= -I_{yx}\omega_x + I_{yy}\omega_y - I_{yz}\omega_z \\
(H_C)_z &= -I_{zx}\omega_x - I_{zy}\omega_y + I_{zz}\omega_z
\end{aligned}\right\} \qquad (9.4)$$

where I_{xx}, I_{yy}, and I_{zz} are the mass moments of inertia and I_{xy}, I_{xz}, and I_{yz} are the mass products of inertia, measured with respect to the noninertial frame of reference xyz.

4. We express the relationship between $\mathbf{H}_A$ and $\mathbf{H}_C$ as

$$\mathbf{H}_A = (\mathbf{r}_{C/A} \times m\mathbf{v}_C) + \mathbf{H}_C \qquad (9.10)$$

5. The equation of linear impulse and momentum is written

$$\mathbf{G}_1 + \sum \int_{t_1}^{t_2} \mathbf{F} \, dt = \mathbf{G}_2 \qquad (9.12)$$

where $\mathbf{G}_1$ and $\mathbf{G}_2$ are the initial and final linear momenta of the body, respectively, and the integral term is the total linear impulse exerted by all external forces on the body during the interval t_1 to t_2.

If the resultant force or the linear impulse $\sum \int \mathbf{F} \, dt$ is zero, *linear momentum is conserved*: $\mathbf{G}_1 = \mathbf{G}_2$.

6. For the equation of angular impulse and momentum about the mass center C of the body,

$$(\mathbf{H}_C)_1 + \sum \int_{t_1}^{t_2} \mathbf{M}_C \, dt = (\mathbf{H}_C)_2 \qquad (9.15)$$

where $(\mathbf{H}_C)_1$ and $(\mathbf{H}_C)_2$ are the initial and final angular momenta of the body (about its mass center C), respectively, and $\sum\mathbf{M}_C$ is the resultant moment of all the external forces and moments acting on the body and taken about C.

If the resultant moment $\Sigma \mathbf{M}_C$ or $\Sigma \mathbf{M}_O$ of all the external forces and moments acting on the body is zero or if the angular impulse term is zero, *angular momentum* is conserved: $(\mathbf{H}_C)_1 = (\mathbf{H}_C)_2$.

7.   The kinetic energy T of a three-dimensional rigid body in spatial motion can be written

$$T = \frac{1}{2}mv_C^2 + \frac{1}{2}\boldsymbol{\omega} \cdot \mathbf{H}_C \qquad (9.22)$$

where $\boldsymbol{\omega}$ is the angular velocity vector describing the rotational motion of the body.

In terms of the rectangular components of $\boldsymbol{\omega}$ and $\mathbf{H}_C$, we have

$$T = \frac{1}{2}mv_C^2 + \frac{1}{2}[I_{xx}\omega_x^2 + I_{yy}\omega_y^2 + I_{zz}\omega_z^2 - 2I_{xy}\omega_x\omega_y$$
$$\qquad\qquad\qquad - 2I_{yz}\omega_y\omega_z - 2I_{zx}\omega_z\omega_x] \qquad (9.25)$$

When a frame of reference is chosen so that the axes coincide with the principal axes of inertia of the body,

$$T = \frac{1}{2}mv_C^2 + \frac{1}{2}(\bar{I}_x\omega_x^2 + \bar{I}_y\omega_y^2 + \bar{I}_z\omega_z^2) \qquad (9.26)$$

8.   For the special case of a body rotating about a fixed point O,

$$T = \frac{1}{2}(\boldsymbol{\omega} \cdot \mathbf{H}_O) \qquad (9.24)$$

9.   The equation of work and kinetic energy is

$$T_1 + \Sigma U_{1\to2} = T_2 \qquad (9.29)$$

where T_1 and T_2 represent, respectively, the initial and final kinetic energies of the rigid body in spatial motion. The term $\Sigma U_{1\to2}$ is the algebraic sum of the works done by all of the external forces and moments acting upon the rigid body.

When the external forces acting on the body are all *conservative* forces, then *mechanical energy* is conserved, and

$$T_1 + V_1 = T_2 + V_2 \qquad (9.30)$$

where V_1 and V_2 represent the initial and final potential energies of the body.

10.   The equations of motion of a three-dimensional rigid body are written

$$\Sigma \mathbf{F} = m\mathbf{a}_C \qquad (9.31)$$
$$\Sigma \mathbf{M}_C = \dot{\mathbf{H}}_C = (\dot{\mathbf{H}}_C)_{xyz} + \boldsymbol{\Omega} \times \mathbf{H}_C \qquad (9.34a)$$

where $\mathbf{a}_C$ is the acceleration of the mass center C of the body, $\mathbf{H}_C$ is the angular momentum of the body about its mass center, xyz is the coordinate frame attached to the body with its origin at C and rotating with angular velocity $\boldsymbol{\Omega}$ relative to the inertial frame XYZ.

In Cartesian coordinates we write this as

$$\left.\begin{aligned}
(\Sigma M_C)_x &= \bar{I}_x\dot{\omega}_x - \bar{I}_y\Omega_z\omega_y + \bar{I}_z\Omega_y\omega_z \\
(\Sigma M_C)_y &= \bar{I}_y\dot{\omega}_y - \bar{I}_z\Omega_x\omega_z + \bar{I}_x\Omega_z\omega_z \\
(\Sigma M_C)_z &= \bar{I}_z\dot{\omega}_z - \bar{I}_x\Omega_y\omega_x + \bar{I}_y\Omega_x\omega_y \\
\Sigma F_x = m(a_C)_x \quad \Sigma F_y &= m(a_C)_y \quad \Sigma F_z = m(a_C)_z
\end{aligned}\right\} \quad (9.38)$$

11. Gyroscopic motion is the motion of a rigid body rotating about a fixed point, and is described by the equations

$$\left.\begin{aligned}
(\Sigma M_C)_x &= I(\ddot{\theta} - \dot{\phi}^2 \sin\theta\cos\theta) + I_z\dot{\phi}\sin\theta(\dot{\phi}\cos\theta + \dot{\psi}) \\
(\Sigma M_C)_y &= I(\ddot{\phi}\sin\theta + 2\dot{\phi}\dot{\theta}\cos\theta) - I_z\dot{\theta}(\dot{\phi}\cos\theta + \dot{\psi}) \\
(\Sigma M_C)_z &= I_z(\ddot{\psi} + \ddot{\phi}\cos\theta - \dot{\phi}\dot{\theta}\sin\theta)
\end{aligned}\right\} \quad (9.46)$$

where $I = I_x = I_y$.

Steady precession is the case when the rate of precession $\dot{\phi}$ is constant, the rate of spin $\dot{\psi}$ is constant, and the nutation angle θ is constant. The equations become

$$\left.\begin{aligned}
(\Sigma M)_x &= \dot{\phi}\sin\theta(I_z\omega_z - I\dot{\phi}\cos\theta) \\
(\Sigma M)_y &= 0 \quad (\Sigma M)_z = 0
\end{aligned}\right\} \quad (9.48)$$

A special case of steady precession occurs when $\theta = 90°$, and

$$(\Sigma M)_x = I_z\dot{\phi}\dot{\psi} \quad (9.49)$$

representing a gyroscopic motion in which the spin, the precession, and the nutation axes form a right-handed triad.

KEY TERMS

PROBLEMS

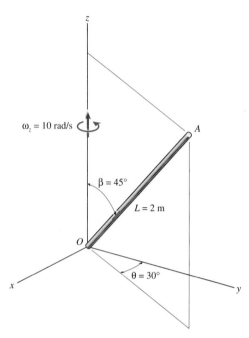

Figure P9.1

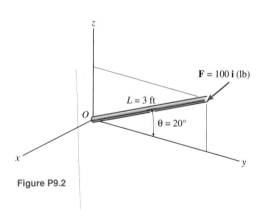

Figure P9.2

SECTIONS 9.1 and 9.2

9.1 A 2-kg slender rod OA (length $= 2$ m) is rotating about the z-axis of a shaft at the rate $\omega_z = 10$ rad/s. At the instant shown ($\theta = 30°$, $\beta = 45°$) determine the angular momentum of the rod about the origin O.

9.2 A 5-lb slender rod AO (length $= 3$ ft) fastened to a ball-and-socket joint at O is at rest in the yz plane as shown. A force $\mathbf{F} = 100\mathbf{i}$ (lb) is acting for 0.02 s at the tip A of the rod. Determine the angular momentum of the rod about the joint O immediately after the action of the force.

9.3 A 10-kg disk (radius $= 0.2$ m) rolls without slipping over a horizontal surface and is linked to a 1-kg rod (length $= 1$ m) which is rigidly fastened to the shaft AB. The shaft AB is rotating at 5 rad/s as shown. Determine the angular momentum of the disk only about point O at the position shown, when the rod is along the y-axis.

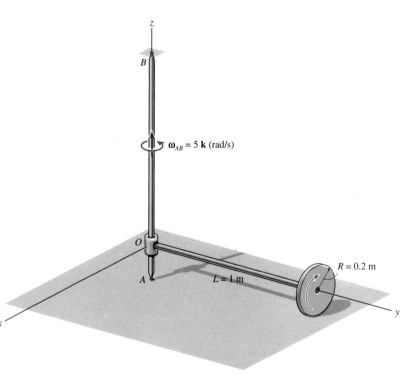

Figure P9.3

9.4 The shaft AB is rotating at $\omega_z = 5$ rad/s as shown. A 20-lb disk (diameter = 1 ft) and 2-lb rod (length = 2 ft) assembly is rigidly fastened to the sleeve of the shaft AB. Determine the angular momentum of the disk-rod assembly about point O.

9.5 A uniform thin plate of mass m is rotating about the axis OA at an angular speed ω as shown. Calculate the angular momentum of the plate about the origin O at the instant shown ($\theta = 60°$).

9.6 A uniform thin plate of mass m is at rest in the position shown. The plate is hinged about the axis OA. If the impulse of magnitude $(F\,\Delta t)$ is applied at B perpendicularly to the plane of the plate, determine the velocities of points B and C immediately after the impact.

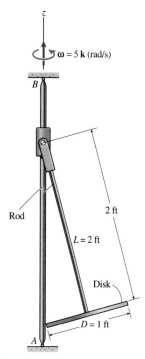

Figure P9.4

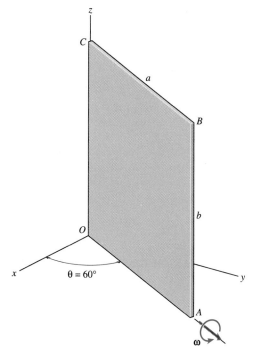

Figure P9.5

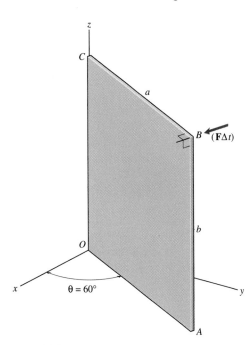

Figure P9.6

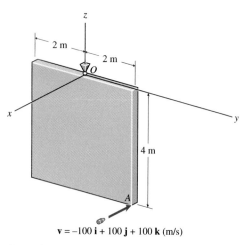

9.7   A uniform 50-kg thin plate rotates freely about a ball-and-socket joint O as shown. At the instant when the plate is at rest in the plane yz, a 60-g bullet is fired with a velocity of $\mathbf{v} = -100\mathbf{i} + 100\mathbf{j} + 100\mathbf{k}$ (m/s) into the plate. The bullet impacts the corner A of the plate and becomes embedded in it. Determine the angular momentum of the plate about O immediately after impact.

9.8   A uniform 10-lb thin disk (radius = 1 ft) rotates about its axle AB (length $L_1 = 1$ ft) at the angular speed $\omega_1 = 10$ rad/s as shown. The axle AB itself is rigidly fastened to an arm (length $L_2 = 2$ ft) that rotates at the constant angular speed $\omega_2 = 5$ rad/s, about the vertical axis z. Determine the angular momentum of the disk about its center B at the instant shown.

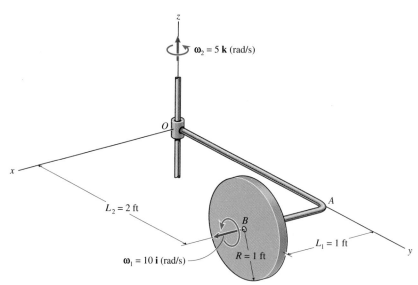

Figure P9.8 and P9.9

9.9   Determine the angular momentum of the disk of Problem 9.8, about the origin O.

9.10   Determine the angular momentum about O, of the disk of Problem 9.8, if the axle AB is parallel to the z axis, as shown.

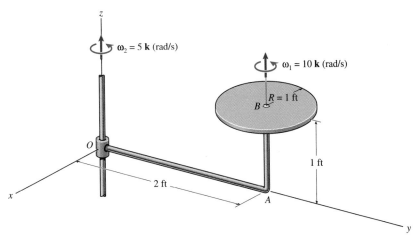

Figure P9.10

9.11 A uniform 20-kg thin disk (diameter = 0.5 m) rotates about an axis parallel to the x axis at the constant rate $\omega_1 = 10$ rad/s as shown. The disk is supported by a bent axle OAB which itself rotates at the constant rate $\omega_2 = 2$ rad/s about the z axis. Determine the angular momentum of the disk about the origin O.

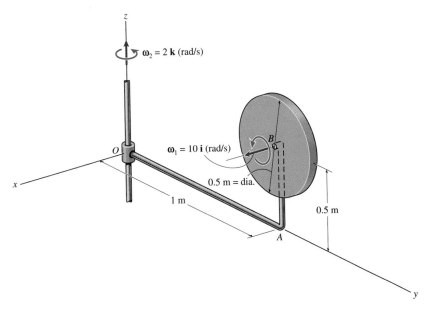

Figure P9.11

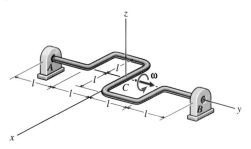

Figure P9.12

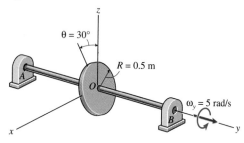

Figure P9.13

9.12 A uniform rod weighs w lb per linear foot and is used to manufacture the shaft shown. If the shaft is designed to rotate at a constant angular velocity $\boldsymbol{\omega}$ as shown, determine the angular momentum of the shaft about the origin C which is also the shaft's mass center.

9.13 A thin uniform 20-kg disk (radius = 0.5 m) is welded to the horizontal axle AB and rotates with it at the rate $\omega_y = 5$ rad/s. The plane of the disk forms an angle $\theta = 30°$ with the vertical z axis as shown. Determine the angular momentum of the disk about its mass center at O and the angle formed by the axle and the angular momentum vector of the disk.

9.14 A thin uniform square plate ($a \times a$ ft^2), weighing w lb/ft^2, is welded to a vertical shaft Oz and rotates with it at the rate of ω rad/s. The plane of the plate forms an angle $\theta = 30°$ with the z axis as shown. Determine the angular momentum of the plate about its mass center.

9.15 The rod assembly shown is formed by using a rod weighing 1 lb/linear ft and is supported at its mass center C by a ball-and-socket joint. The assembly is originally at rest in the xy plane and is symmetric with respect to C. Determine the angular velocity of the assembly immediately after an impulse of $(\mathbf{F}\,\Delta t) = 10\mathbf{k}$ (lb · s) is applied at E. The length of the rod connecting AB to DE is 1 ft.

9.16 Two 20-kg disks (radius = 0.2 m) are linked by a 5-kg axle AB. The disks-axle assembly is rotating about the z axis at $\omega_z = 5$ rad/s. Determine the angular momentum of the assembly about the z axis.

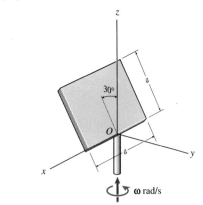

Figure P9.14

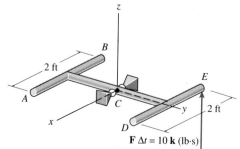

Figure P9.15

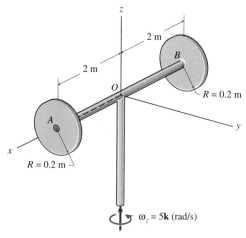

Figure P9.16

9.17 Two equilateral plates are welded to a vertical shaft AB and are within the yz plane as shown. The plates are made of a material weighing 10 lb/ft². If the vertical shaft is in rotation at a constant rate of $\omega = 4$ rad/s, determine the angular momentum of the plate assembly about its mass center O.

9.18 A solid cube with sides of length (l) and a mass (m) rotates with an angular speed ω about its diagonal OC as shown. Determine the angular momentum of the cube about the origin O of the coordinate system.

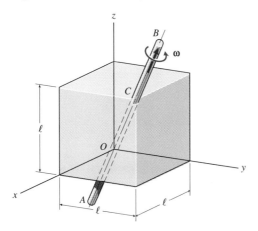

Figure P9.18

9.19 The bent shaft shown is made of a rod weighing w lb/linear ft and rotates about the z axis with an angular speed ω. Determine for the instant shown the angular momentum of the shaft about the origin O of the coordinate system xyz.

9.20 The bent shaft shown is made of a rod weighing w lb/linear ft and is at rest over a ball-and-socket joint at its mass center O. Determine the angular velocity of the bent shaft immediately after the application of an impulse $\mathbf{F}\,\Delta t$ at A in the negative x direction.

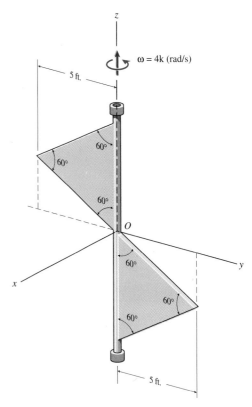

Figure P9.17

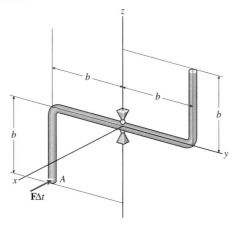

Figure P9.20 and P9.21

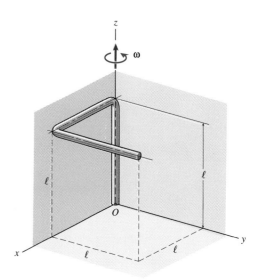

Figure P9.19

9.21 Solve Problem 9.20, assuming that the bent shaft is impacted by an impulse $\mathbf{F}\,\Delta t$ at A in the positive x direction.

9.22 A half-circular cylinder (radius $= 1$ m) with a mass of 20 kg rotates about the z axis with an angular velocity $\omega = 5$ rad/s as shown. Determine the angular momentum of the body with respect to the xyz coordinate axes.

9.23 The slender bar OA of mass m revolves about the z axis with an angular velocity of ω_1 as shown. Simultaneously it rotates about the x axis at an angular velocity of ω_2. Determine the x component of the bar's angular momentum about O when A is at $(a,0,b)$.

9.24 In Problem 9.23, solve for the z component of the bar's angular momentum for the position indicated, when A is at $(a,0,b)$.

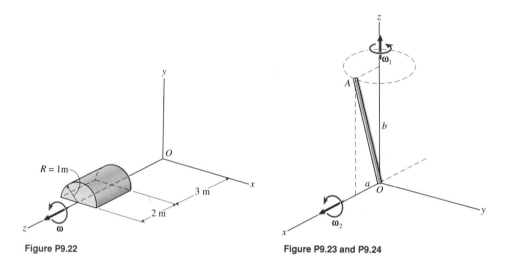

Figure P9.22   Figure P9.23 and P9.24

9.25 A solid circular cylinder of radius R, length L and mass m rotates at an angular speed ω_1 about its geometric axis as shown. Simultaneously it revolves about the x axis at an angular velocity ω_2. Determine the x, y, and z components of the cylinder's angular momentum about the origin O.

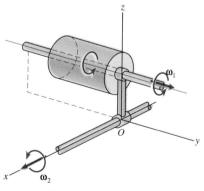

Figure P9.25

9.26 The slender rod OA of mass m revolves about the z axis with an angular velocity ω_1 as shown. Simultaneously it rotates about the y axis at an angular velocity ω_2. Determine the rod's angular momentum with respect to xyz coordinate axes.

9.27 A thin uniform plate of mass m revolves about the z axis with an angular velocity ω. Determine its angular momentum about its mass center C and about the origin O for the position indicated.

9.28 A 3000-lb spacecraft is spinning about its longitudinal axis at a rate of 120 rpm. For a short duration ($\Delta t = 0.20$ s) an attitude control jet is activated and a force F of 40 lb is applied to the spacecraft in the direction shown. Determine the angular momentum of the spacecraft about O immediately following the impulse. The spacecraft can be modeled as a cylinder.

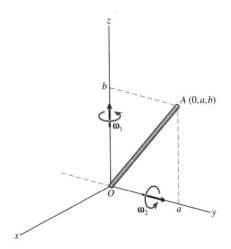

Figure P9.26

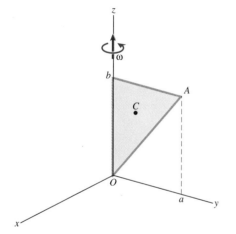

Figure P9.27

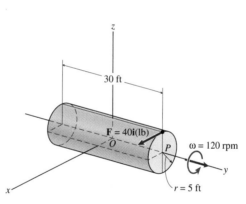

Figure P9.28 and P9.29

9.29 If the spacecraft of Problem 9.28, in the position shown, has an angular velocity vector given as $\omega = 2\mathbf{i} - 3\mathbf{j} + 2\mathbf{k}$ (rad/s), determine its angular momentum about point P located at $(0,15,0)$.

9.30 A 5000-lb spacecraft is translating without rotation along its longitudinal axis x with a velocity $(\mathbf{v_S})_1 = 2000\mathbf{i}$ (ft/s) when it is hit as shown by a 2-lb object moving with a velocity $(\mathbf{v_0})_1 = -400\mathbf{k}$ (ft/s). If the small body becomes embedded in the spacecraft determine its angular velocity immediately following the impact. The spacecraft's radii of gyration are $k_x = 1$ ft, $k_y = k_z = 4$ ft. (Assume x-, y-, z-axes are principal axes.)

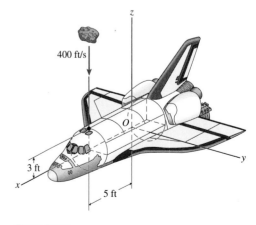

Figure P9.30

9.31   A rod assembly is rotating about its vertical arm with a constant angular velocity of ω = 5 rad/s when the horizontal arm is impacted by the introduction of a stopper at *B* as shown. If the rod assembly is made of a material weighing 5 lb/linear ft, determine the angular velocity of the assembly just after impact.

9.32   The homogeneous rectangular block translates downward with a velocity of 2 m/s just prior to striking the smooth stop shown. The coefficient of restitution between the block and stop is 0.80. Determine the angular velocity of the block immediately after impact.

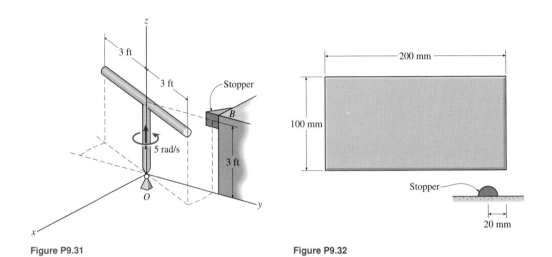

Figure P9.31   **Figure P9.32**

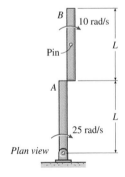

Figure P9.33

9.33   The ends of two identical slender bars collide while the bars spin on a smooth horizontal plane as shown. Just prior to their collision, the angular velocities of the bars *A* and *B* were 25 and 10 rad/s clockwise, respectively. Assuming the coefficient of restitution between the bars to be 0.60, determine the angular velocity of each bar just after impact.

9.34   Determine the angular momentum of the disk of Problem 9.3 about point *B*. (*OB* = 2 m.)

SECTION 9.3

9.35   Determine the kinetic energy of the disk of Problem 9.3.

9.36   Determine the kinetic energy of the disk-rod assembly of Problem 9.4.

9.37   Determine the kinetic energy of the plate of Problem 9.5.

9.38   Determine the kinetic energy of the plate of Problem 9.6 immediately after impact.

9.39   Determine the kinetic energy of the disk of Problem 9.8.

9.40   Determine the kinetic energy of the disk of Problem 9.10.

9.41   Determine the kinetic energy of the disk of Problem 9.11.

9.42   Determine the kinetic energy of the disk of Problem 9.13.

9.43   Determine the kinetic energy of the plate of Problem 9.14.

9.44   Determine the kinetic energy of the disks-axle assembly of Problem 9.16.

9.45   Determine the kinetic energy of the rod of Problem 9.19.

9.46   The 5-kg uniform thin disk (radius = 1 m) starts from rest and rolls without slipping over the horizontal surface xy under the action of a constant moment $M = 10 \text{ N} \cdot \text{m}$ acting about the bent axle OA which has a negligible mass. Determine the angular velocity of the bent axle OA after it rotates one revolution about the z axis. ($AB = 2$ m.)

9.47   A 20-lb rectangular plate is supported by ball-and-socket joints at A and B along one of its diagonal axes. It is subjected to a force F of magnitude 10 lb and always directed perpendicular to the plane of the plate. Determine the angular velocity of the plate after it has rotated one full revolution about AB starting from rest.

9.48   The 10-kg uniform thin plate is supported by a ball-and-socket joint at point O and is rotating counterclockwise about the z-axis with a constant angular velocity $\omega = 3$ rad/s. At the instant shown, the plate strikes a stop at P located at $(0,2,-2.5)$. Assuming the impact at P to be perfectly plastic, determine the angular velocity of the plate immediately after impact.

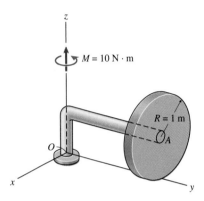

Figure P9.46

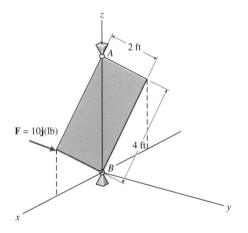

Figure P9.47

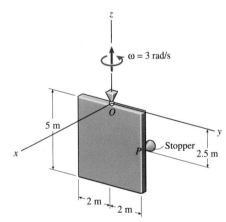

Figure P9.48 and P9.49

9.49   Determine the kinetic energy lost during the collision of the plate of Problem 9.48 with the stop at P.

9.50   Determine the kinetic energy of the plate in Problem 9.27.

9.51   Determine the final kinetic energy of the spacecraft in Problem 9.28.

9.52 The crankshaft assembly shown is manufactured by using a rod having a mass of 5 kg per linear meter. It rotates freely in the bearings at O and A with a constant angular velocity $\omega = 80$ rad/s. Determine the kinetic energy of the crankshaft.

9.53 A 2000-kg spacecraft is revolving with an angular velocity $\boldsymbol{\omega} = 0.05\mathbf{i} + 0.05\mathbf{j}$ (rad/s). Suddenly two control jets are activated at A (2,1,0) and B ($-1,1,0$) in the z direction as shown. The radii of gyration of the vehicle, with respect to its principal centroidal axes, are $k_x = 0.75$ m, $k_y = 1$ m, $k_z = 1.5$ m. If each jet applies a thrust of 25 N, determine the operating time for each jet in order to bring the angular velocity of the spacecraft to zero. (The origin O is at the center of mass and the coordinate axes are principal centroidal axes.)

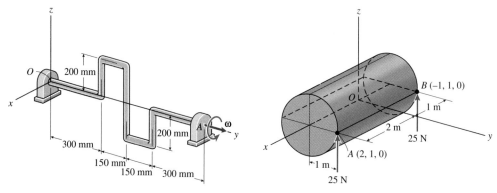

Figure P9.52

Figure P9.53 and P9.54

9.54 In Problem 9.53, determine the kinetic energy of the spacecraft in its motion about its mass center before and after the operations of the jets.

9.55 Show that the kinetic energy T of a rigid body having a fixed point O may be expressed in the form $T = \frac{1}{2}\mathbf{H}_O \cdot \boldsymbol{\omega}$, where $\boldsymbol{\omega}$ is the instantaneous angular velocity of the body and $\mathbf{H}_O$ its angular momentum about O.

9.56 Show that the kinetic energy T of a rigid body having a fixed point O may be expressed in the form $T = \frac{1}{2}I_{OO'}\omega^2$, where ω is the instantaneous angular velocity of the body and $I_{OO'}$ its moments of inertia about the line of action of ω.

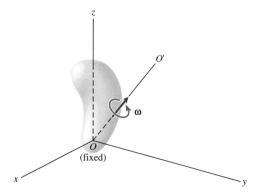

Figure P9.55 and P9.56

9.57 Two 5-kg disks are attached to a 2-kg axle as shown and the whole assembly is rotating about the vertical shaft (z axis) at an angular velocity $\omega_z = 5$ rad/s. Assuming that the disks roll without slipping on a smooth horizontal surface, determine the angular momentum of the assembly about the z axis. Also calculate the kinetic energy of the system.

9.58 A 10-lb wheel (radius = 1 ft) spins at angular speed $\omega_{y'} = 10$ rad/s about its y' axis. The wheel is supported by the arm OC shown which has negligible mass and rotates at angular speed $\omega_x = 2$ rad/s about the x axis at O. Determine the angular momentum of the disk about the origin O.

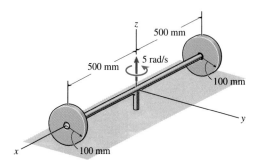

Figure P9.57

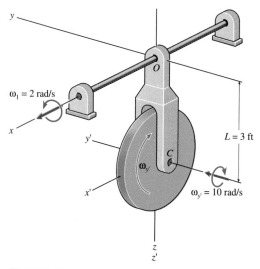

Figure P9.58

9.59 Show that if the mass center of a rigid body is located on a fixed axis about which the body rotates, the angular momentum about any point located on the fixed axis is the same.

SECTION 9.4

9.60 A slender 60-kg rod (length = 5 m) is pinned at O to a vertical shaft OB and supported at A by means of a horizontal wire BA as shown. The shaft rotates counterclockwise with a constant angular velocity ω of 20 rad/s. Determine the tension in the wire and the reaction at the pin O.

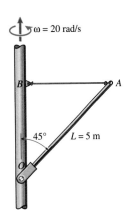

Figure P9.60

9.61   Two 20-lb thin uniform disks (radius = 1 ft) rotate in opposite directions about the axle AB at a rate of 200 rad/s as shown. The axle AB is welded to the shaft CD, which rotates counterclockwise at Ω = 100 rad/s and is supported in place by collars at C and D. Determine the dynamic reactions at the collars C and D at the instant shown.

9.62   The rod-shaft assembly shown is manufactured by using a rod weighing 5 lb/linear ft. The shaft is subjected to a moment M of magnitude 20 lb · ft, in the direction indicated. Determine the dynamic reactions at A and B at the instant when the shaft's angular speed reaches 200 rad/s.

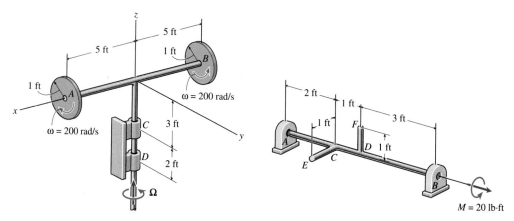

Figure P9.61   Figure P9.62

9.63   A thin uniform 5-kg triangular plate is rigidly attached to a vertical shaft OA of negligible mass and supported by ball-and-sockets at O and A. If the shaft rotates about its own axis at a constant angular speed of ω = 15 rad/s, as shown, determine the dynamic reactions at O and A.

9.64   The shaft AOB shown is formed by the use of a slender uniform rod weighing w per unit length. The shaft rotates about the y axis at the constant angular speed ω. Determine the dynamic reactions at A and B.

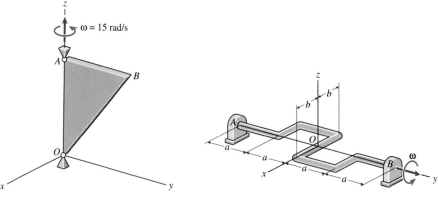

Figure P9.63   Figure P9.64, P9.65, and P9.66

9.65 The rod assembly *AOB* of Problem 9.64 is initially at rest when a moment **M** = *M***j** is applied to the shaft. Determine the dynamic reactions at *A* and *B* immediately after the moment has been applied.

9.66 The thin plate of Problem 9.63 is initially at rest when a moment **M** = 2**k** (N · m) is applied to it. Determine the resulting angular acceleration of the plate and the dynamic reactions at *O* and *A*.

9.67 The thin 15-kg disk (radius = 0.6 m) is welded to a vertical slender shaft (length = 3 m) of negligible mass. If the shaft-disk assembly rotates at a constant angular speed ω = 5 rad/s about the vertical *z* axis and pivots freely about the pin *O*, determine the constant angle θ the shaft will make with the vertical.

9.68 A thin rectangular uniform plate is made of a metal weighing *w* per unit area. It rotates at a constant angular speed ω about a shaft of negligible mass and to which it is welded. The shaft bearings are located at *A* and *B*, as shown. Determine the dynamic reactions at *A* and *B* at the instant shown.

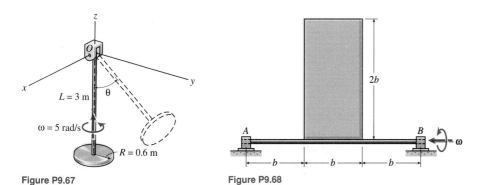

Figure P9.67   Figure P9.68

9.69 If the thin rectangular uniform plate of Problem 9.68 has a hole of radius *b*/8 drilled as shown, determine the reactions at *A* and *B* at the instant shown.

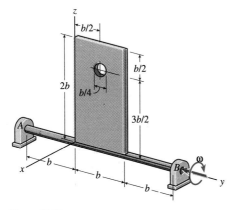

Figure P9.69

9.70 A 75-kg uniform flywheel is mounted 0.3 m off center as shown. The shaft of the flywheel rotates at a constant angular speed $\omega = 10$ rad/s. Determine the maximum reactions exerted on the journal bearings at A and B.

9.71 A 50-lb disk (radius $= 0.75$ ft) is welded to a bent rod ABC of negligible mass. The rod is, in turn, welded to a vertical shaft as shown. Determine the moment M necessary to apply to the vertical shaft in order for it to have an angular acceleration $\alpha = 5$ rad/s².

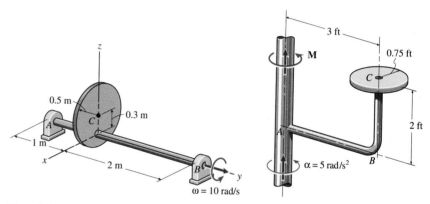

Figure P9.70   Figure P9.71

9.72 A 10-kg disk (diameter $= 1.0$ m) is fastened to a horizontal shaft AB rotating with an angular speed of 5 rad/s as shown. The plane of the disk forms an angle of 20° with the vertical to the shaft at C. Determine, for the position shown, the reactions exerted on the journal bearings at A and B.

9.73 The rod assembly shown consists of cylindrical elements weighing 3 lb per unit length. The assembly rotates about the horizontal y axis with an angular speed $\omega = 10$ rad/s. For the position shown, determine the angular acceleration of the shaft $OABC$, and the reactions developed at the journal bearings at O and C.

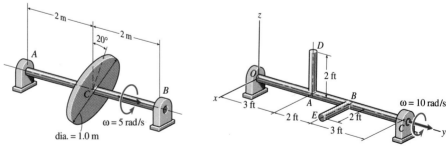

Figure P9.72   Figure P9.73

9.74 The 20-kg sphere (diameter $= 0.2$ m) is supported by a slender rod (length $= 1.5$ m) of negligible mass, which is pin-supported at A on the vertical shaft. If the shaft rotates counterclockwise with a constant angular speed of $\omega = 4$ rad/s as shown, determine the angle θ of the rod with the vertical shaft.

SECTION 9.5

9.75 The 2-kg top shown spins about its axis of symmetry z with an angular speed $\omega = 100$ rad/s. The mass center C of the top is located at a distance 0.15 m from the fixed origin O and its radii of gyration with respect to Oz and with respect to any transverse axis through O are 0.04 m and 0.07 m, respectively. If the angle of nutation $\theta = 45°$, determine the corresponding rates of precession.

9.76 A 5-lb thin uniform disk (radius $= 1$ ft) welded to a slender axle (length $= 0.25$ ft) of negligible mass is spinning about the axle OC at the rate of $\dot{\psi} = 100$ rad/s. At the instant shown OC is in the YOZ plane and $\theta = 60°$. Determine the rate of precession $\dot{\phi}$ of the disk.

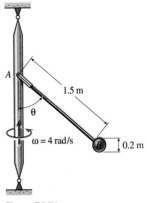

Figure P9.74

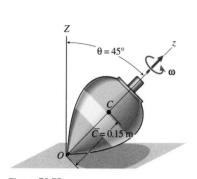

Figure P9.75

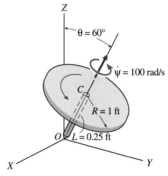

Figure P9.76 and P9.77

9.77 If the disk of Problem 9.76 has a precession rate of $\dot{\phi} = -25\mathbf{k}$ (rad/s), determine the rate of spin $\dot{\psi}$ of the disk.

9.78 The 4-kg thin uniform disk (radius $= 100$ mm) is welded to a slender axle (length $= 500$ mm) of negligible mass which freely rotates about the ball-and-socket joint at O as shown. The disk spins about the axle OC, which is in the plane OXY, at the rate $\dot{\psi} = 200$ rad/s. Determine the rate of precession of the disk for the position shown.

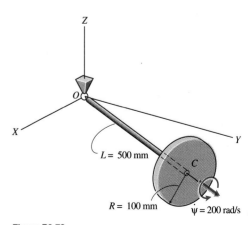

Figure P9.78

9.79 The 2-lb thin uniform disk (radius = 1 ft) is welded to a slender axle (length L = 2 ft) of negligible mass, which is spinning in the upright position at the rate of $\dot{\psi}$ = 2000 rad/s. For a brief duration (Δt = 0.05 s), the disk is subjected to a force **F** = 30**i** (lb). If the disk's rate of spin remains unchanged, determine its rate of precession.

9.80 Soon after take-off, the landing gear of an aircraft is retracted at the rate of ω_x = 1 rad/s about the point O. At the moment of take-off, the wheels freely spin at the rate of ω_y = 200 rad/s. If each wheel weighs 50 lb and has a radius of 2.5 ft and a radius of gyration of 1.2 ft about its axle, determine the torque developed on the main strut by gyroscopic effect.

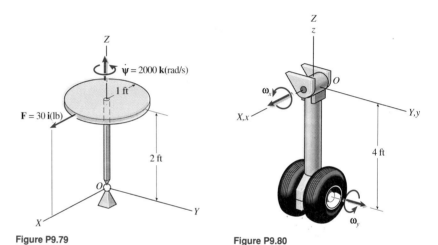

Figure P9.79   Figure P9.80

INTRODUCTION TO VIBRATION*

10

OUTLINE

10.1 INTRODUCTION

Vibration is simply defined as the *oscillating motion of a body, in alternately opposite directions, about the position of static equilibrium.* Examples of vibratory motion include the swaying of buildings in earthquakes, the shaking of bridges due to moving traffic, the motions of unbalanced rotating machines, the swaying of offshore platforms under the action of ocean waves, the fluttering of airplane wings, and the wind-induced oscillations of transmission towers and wires. Most engineering structures and machines experience vibration to some degree, and their design generally requires consideration of their vibratory characteristics.

The subject of the vibrations of structures and machines is extensive, and many textbooks have been devoted exclusively to the subject. In this chapter, we will study the analysis of vibration of bodies, or systems of bodies, whose positions can be completely described by only one displacement variable, or coordinate. These are called the ***single degree of freedom systems***. A thorough understanding of the vibration analysis of single degree of freedom systems is essential for further study of vibration of more complex multidegree of freedom and continuous systems.

There are two general types of vibration: ***free vibration*** and ***forced vibration***. In the case of free vibration, the system oscillates under the action of elastic and/or gravitational restoring forces only, without any external forces acting on the system. As an example, consider the simple pendulum shown in Figure 10.1. The bob of the pendulum is displaced from its equilibrium position A, to another position B, and released. Under the action of gravitational restoring force, the bob will in general return to the equilibrium position A with some nonzero velocity and will proceed toward a new position C. In the absence of any air resistance or other frictional forces, the bob will continue oscillating indefinitely about its position of static equilibrium. Since the motion of the pendulum is maintained by the gravitational restoring force only (no external forces are acting on the system), the vibration is a free vibration. When the vibration is caused by an external force acting on a system, it is said to be a forced vibration.

All vibrations are ***damped*** by frictional forces that diminish the motion by dissipating the mechanical energy of the system. However, in some engineering applications where damping is small, its effect on the vibration of a system can be neglected in the analysis. Such an ideal vibration is referred to as *undamped*.

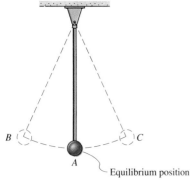

Figure 10.1

B   *C*

A

Equilibrium position

10.2 UNDAMPED FREE VIBRATION

Consider a simple system consisting of a block of mass m supported by a spring of stiffness k, as shown in Figure 10.2. We assume the mass of the spring to be negligible, and its unstretched length is shown in Figure 10.2a. The static equilibrium position of the spring-mass system is shown in Figure

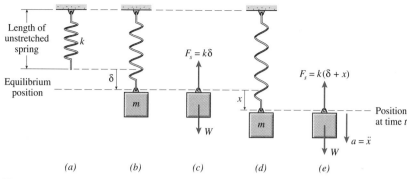

Figure 10.2

10.2*b*, where δ represents the elongation of the spring at the equilibrium position. As the free-body diagram of the block (Figure 10.2*c*) indicates, the block is in equilibrium under the action of two forces: its weight W and the spring force $F_s = k\delta$. By applying the equation of equilibrium, $\Sigma F_x = 0$, we obtain

$$W - k\delta = 0 \quad \text{or} \quad W = k\delta \qquad (10.1)$$

Next, let us assume that the block is displaced in the downward direction from its equilibrium position, and released. Since the spring pulls on the block, it will return to the equilibrium position with a nonzero velocity and then proceed toward a position above the equilibrium position. In the absence of any damping forces, the block will continue oscillating indefinitely about its static equilibrium position. Let the displacement of the oscillating block from the equilibrium position, at any instant of time t, be defined by the coordinate x (Figure 10.2*d*), which is measured positive in the downward direction. Since only one coordinate x is required to describe the motion of the block, the spring-mass system under consideration is a single degree of freedom system. The free-body diagram of the block at the displaced position x is shown in Figure 10.2*e*. The acceleration $a = \ddot{x}$ is considered to be positive in the direction of the positive displacement x. Applying Newton's second law of motion, $\Sigma F = ma$, we obtain

$$W - k(\delta + x) = ma = m\ddot{x}$$

Since from Equation (10.1) $W = k\delta$, the above equation becomes $-kx = m\ddot{x}$, or

$$m\ddot{x} + kx = 0 \qquad (10.2)$$

By measuring the displacement x from the equilibrium position instead of from an arbitrarily chosen position, we are able to eliminate the equal and opposite forces W and $-k\delta$ from Equation (10.2). This approach considerably simplifies the analysis, as will become apparent.

Equation (10.2) is a linear second-order differential equation, which is homogeneous and has constant coefficients. It is usually written in the form

$$\ddot{x} + \omega_n^2 x = 0 \tag{10.3}$$

in which

$$\omega_n = \sqrt{\frac{k}{m}} \tag{10.4}$$

The constant ω_n is called the *natural circular frequency* of the vibration and is expressed in units of radians/second. The general solution of the differential equation of motion [Equation (10.3)] is of the form

$$x = C_1 \sin \omega_n t + C_2 \cos \omega_n t \tag{10.5}$$

in which the constants C_1 and C_2 are determined from the initial displacement x_0 and initial velocity v_0 of the system. By differentiating Equation (10.5) successively with respect to time t, we obtain the equations of the velocity and acceleration as

$$v = \dot{x} = C_1 \omega_n \cos \omega_n t - C_2 \omega_n \sin \omega_n t \tag{10.6}$$

$$a = \ddot{x} = -C_1 \omega_n^2 \sin \omega_n t - C_2 \omega_n^2 \cos \omega_n t \tag{10.7}$$

To verify that Equation (10.5) is indeed a solution of Equation (10.3), we substitute the expressions for x from Equation (10.5) and $\ddot{x}$ from Equation (10.7) into Equation (10.3) to obtain

$$-C_1 \omega_n^2 \sin \omega_n t - C_2 \omega_n^2 \cos \omega_n t + \omega_n^2 (C_1 \sin \omega_n t + C_2 \cos \omega_n t) = 0$$

As all terms on the left side of the equation cancel, the equation is satisfied.

By substituting $x = x_0$ and $v = v_0$ into Equations (10.5) and (10.6), respectively, at $t = 0$, we obtain the constants C_1 and C_2 as

$$C_1 = v_0/\omega_n \qquad \text{and} \qquad C_2 = x_0 \tag{10.8}$$

We then find the expression for the displacement x in terms of the initial conditions by substituting Equations (10.8) into Equation (10.5). Thus,

$$x = \frac{v_0}{\omega_n} \sin \omega_n t + x_0 \cos \omega_n t \tag{10.9}$$

The expressions for the velocity and the acceleration in terms of the initial conditions can similarly be obtained by substituting Equations (10.8) into Equations (10.6) and (10.7), respectively.

The expressions for the displacement, velocity, and acceleration—Equations (10.5) to (10.7)—can more conveniently be written as single trigonometric functions by using different constants A and ϕ, which are related to the constants C_1 and C_2 by the equations

$$C_1 = A \cos \phi \qquad \text{and} \qquad C_2 = A \sin \phi \qquad (10.10)$$

Substituting Equations (10.10) into Equation (10.5), we write

$$x = A \cos \phi \sin \omega_n t + A \sin \phi \cos \omega_n t$$

or

$$x = A \sin(\omega_n t + \phi) \qquad (10.11)$$

By differentiating Equation (10.11) successively with respect to time, we obtain the expressions for the velocity and acceleration in the alternate form as

$$v = \dot{x} = A\omega_n \cos(\omega_n t + \phi) \qquad (10.12)$$

$$a = \ddot{x} = -A\omega_n^2 \sin(\omega_n t + \phi) \qquad (10.13)$$

The reader should verify that Equation (10.11) also represents a solution of the differential equation [Equation (10.3)] by substituting Equations (10.11) and (10.13) into Equation (10.3).

We can determine the constants A and ϕ by substituting the initial conditions $x = x_0$ and $v = v_0$ into Equations (10.11) and (10.12), respectively, at $t = 0$, and solving the resulting equations for A and ϕ. Thus,

$$x_0 = A \sin \phi \qquad (10.14)$$

and

$$v_0 = A\omega_n \cos \phi$$

or

$$\frac{v_0}{\omega_n} = A \cos \phi \qquad (10.15)$$

By squaring and adding the two equations, we obtain

$$A^2 = x_0^2 + (v_0/\omega_n)^2$$

$$A = \sqrt{x_0^2 + \left(\frac{v_0}{\omega_n}\right)^2} \qquad (10.16)$$

We can then divide Equation (10.14) by Equation (10.15) and write

$$\tan \phi = \frac{x_0}{(v_0/\omega_n)}$$

$$\phi = \tan^{-1}\left(\frac{\omega_n x_0}{v_0}\right) \tag{10.17}$$

The relationships between the two sets of constants, A and ϕ, and C_1 and C_2, are obtained from Equations (10.10) as

$$A = \sqrt{C_1^2 + C_2^2} \quad \text{and} \quad \phi = \tan^{-1}(C_2/C_1) \tag{10.18}$$

Note that the substitution of Equations (10.8) into Equations (10.18) yields Equations (10.16) and (10.17) for A and ϕ in terms of the initial conditions.

The motion of the block as expressed by Equation (10.11) is depicted graphically in Figure 10.3a. This motion is referred to as **simple harmonic motion**. From the figure, we see that the motion is oscillatory and repeats itself after the angle $\omega_n t$ has increased by 2π radians. In other words, it takes $2\pi/\omega_n$ seconds from the instant the block passes through a position moving in a direction, until it next passes through the same position moving in the same direction. This interval of time required to complete one cycle of the motion is called the **natural period** of the vibration and is given by

$$T_n = \frac{2\pi}{\omega_n} = 2\pi\sqrt{\frac{m}{k}} \tag{10.19}$$

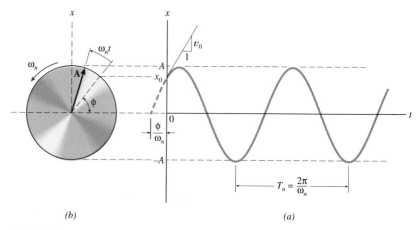

(b)   (a)

Figure 10.3

The natural period T_n is commonly expressed in seconds. The number of cycles completed per unit of time is called the ***natural frequency*** of the vibration and is given by

$$f_n = \frac{1}{T_n} = \frac{\omega_n}{2\pi} = \frac{1}{2\pi}\sqrt{\frac{k}{m}} \qquad (10.20)$$

The natural frequency f_n is usually expressed in cycles per second or *hertz* with 1 Hz = 1 cycle/s.

We can also see from Figure 10.3*a* that the maximum displacement of the block from its equilibrium position is equal to A, which is called the ***amplitude of vibration***. The angle ϕ is referred to as the ***phase angle***.

Another useful graphical representation of the simple harmonic motion of the block is presented in Figure 10.3*b*. This figure shows a vector **A** of magnitude A, initially at an angle ϕ with the horizontal axis at $t = 0$, rotating counterclockwise at a constant angular velocity ω_n rad/s. At any time t, the projection of **A** on the vertical axis is equal to $A\sin(\omega_n t + \phi)$, which, according to Equation (10.11), is the displacement x of the block at time t.

The method for the analysis of a simple spring-mass system developed in this section is general in the sense that it can be applied to any single degree of freedom system undergoing translational undamped free vibration, provided the restoring force that acts on the particle or body is linearly proportional to the displacement. In the general case of systems containing multiple springs, it becomes necessary to use an equivalent stiffness, usually called the *effective stiffness*, k_{eff}, of the system in the analysis. The effective stiffness is the stiffness of a single spring equivalent to the multiple springs of the system. While in most cases the k_{eff} can be directly determined by inspection, in some cases it is necessary to first determine the deflection of the system Δ under a static load F and then to compute the effective stiffness by using the relationship $k_{eff} = F/\Delta$. Moreover, the following section will show that the undamped free small-amplitude *rotational* vibrations of single degree of freedom systems are also described by the differential equations of the same form as Equation (10.3). Therefore, the motion of such a system is also of the simple harmonic type with the same basic characteristics as that of the spring-mass system considered herein.

EXAMPLE 10.1

A 400-lb machine is supported by four springs each of stiffness 1200 lb/ft. The machine is pushed 2 in. downward from its equilibrium position and then released with an upward velocity of 2 ft/s. For the ensuing vibration, determine the natural circular frequency, the natural period, the natural frequency, the amplitude of the motion as measured from the position of static equilibrium, the maximum velocity of the machine, and the maximum acceleration of the machine.

Solution As the machine is supported by four springs that are parallel to each other, the effective (total) stiffness of the system is

$$k_{\text{eff}} = 4k = 4(1200) = 4800 \text{ lb/ft}$$

The mass of the machine is

$$m = \frac{W}{g} = \frac{400}{32.2} = 12.42 \text{ lb} \cdot \text{s}^2/\text{ft} = 12.42 \text{ slug}$$

The equation of motion of the machine can now be written as

$$m\ddot{x} + k_{\text{eff}}x = 0$$

$$12.42\ddot{x} + 4800x = 0$$

in which x is measured positive downward from the static equilibrium position of the machine as shown in the figure.

Natural circular frequency. Using Equation (10.4), we obtain

$$\omega_n = \sqrt{\frac{k_{\text{eff}}}{m}} = \sqrt{\frac{4800}{12.42}}$$

$$\omega_n = 19.66 \text{ rad/s} \blacktriangleleft$$

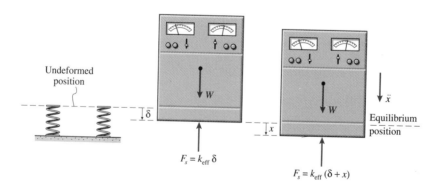

Undeformed position

δ

W

$F_s = k_{\text{eff}} \delta$

W

x

$\ddot{x}$

Equilibrium position

$F_s = k_{\text{eff}} (\delta + x)$

(continued)

EXAMPLE 10.1 *(concluded)*

Natural period. From Equation (10.19),

$$T_n = \frac{2\pi}{\omega_n} = \frac{2\pi}{19.66} \qquad T_n = 0.32 \text{ s} \blacktriangleleft$$

Natural frequency. From Equation (10.20),

$$f_n = \frac{1}{T_n} = \frac{1}{0.32}$$

$$f_n = 3.13 \text{ cycles/s} \blacktriangleleft$$

Amplitude of motion. By substituting the initial displacement $x_0 = 2$ in. $= 0.167$ ft and the initial velocity $v_0 = -2$ ft/s into Equation (10.16), we obtain

$$A = \sqrt{x_0^2 + (v_0/\omega_n)^2} = \sqrt{(0.167)^2 + (-2/19.66)^2} = \pm 0.196 \text{ ft}$$

$$A = \pm 0.196 \text{ ft} = \pm 2.35 \text{ in.} \blacktriangleleft$$

Maximum velocity. From the expression for velocity as given by Equation (10.12),

$$v = \dot{x} = A\omega_n \cos(\omega_n t + \phi)$$

we note that the velocity becomes maximum when the cosine function is equal to $+1$. Thus,

$$v_{max} = A\omega_n = 0.196(19.66)$$

$$v_{max} = 3.85 \text{ ft/s} \blacktriangleleft$$

Maximum acceleration. From Equation (10.13),

$$a = \ddot{x} = -A\omega_n^2 \sin(\omega_n t + \phi)$$

we see that the acceleration becomes maximum when the sine function is equal to -1. Thus,

$$a_{max} = A\omega_n^2 \qquad a_{max} = 75.8 \text{ ft/s}^2 \blacktriangleleft$$

10.3 ROTATIONAL VIBRATION

The analysis of small-amplitude rotational vibrations of single degree of freedom systems is essentially similar to that of the translational vibrations of such systems discussed in the preceding section. In the rotational motion, the displaced position of the body with respect to its equilibrium position at any time t is usually defined by an angle θ (although in some problems it may be convenient to use the translation x of a certain point on the body as the variable). A free-body diagram of the body displaced from its equilibrium position by an arbitrary positive value of the chosen displacement variable (e.g., θ or x) is drawn, and if necessary, kinematic relationships are employed to express the accelerations in terms of the chosen variable. An appropriate equation of motion ($\Sigma M = I\ddot{\theta}$ or $\Sigma F = m\ddot{x}$) is then written, relating the restoring (spring and gravitational) forces and couples acting on the body to its acceleration. If necessary, equilibrium equations may be used to eliminate forces and moments associated with the equilibrium position from the equation of motion, which is then simplified and/or rearranged into the form of Equation (10.3); that is, $\ddot{\theta} + \omega_n^2\theta = 0$ or $\ddot{x} + \omega_n^2 x = 0$. Once the equation of motion has been established in this form, all the equations developed in the preceding section pertaining to the solution of this differential equation [Equations (10.4) to (10.20)] can be used to determine the desired characteristics of vibratory motion of the rotating system. This method of analysis is illustrated by the following examples.

EXAMPLE   10.2

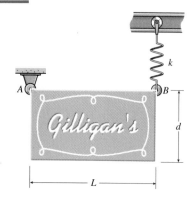

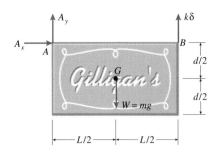

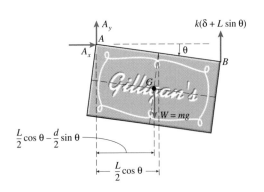

A signboard of mass m is supported by a hinged support at the corner A, and a spring of stiffness k at the corner B, as shown in the figure. Derive the equation of motion for small oscillations of the board, and determine the natural period of vibration of the board if $m = 1500$ kg, $k = 200$ N/m, $L = 3$ m, and $d = 1.5$ m. The board is in equilibrium in the position shown.

Solution The free-body diagram of the board at the static-equilibrium position is shown, where δ represents the elongation of the spring at the equilibrium position. To establish the relationship between the spring force $k\delta$ and the weight of the board $W = mg$, we apply the equation of equilibrium, $\Sigma M_A = 0$. Thus,

$$mg\left(\frac{L}{2}\right) - k\delta(L) = 0$$

$$k\delta = \frac{mg}{2} \tag{a}$$

Note that the moments are summed about point A to eliminate the reactions at support A from the equation.

Equation of motion. The free-body diagram of the body displaced from the equilibrium position by an angle θ, which is measured positive clockwise, is shown. By applying the rotational equation of motion about point A, $\Sigma M_A = I_A\ddot{\theta}$, we can eliminate the reactions at support A from the analysis. The mass moment of inertia of the board about A is determined by using the parallel axis theorem as follows:

$$I_A = I_G + mr^2 = \frac{m}{12}(L^2 + d^2) + m\left[\left(\frac{L}{2}\right)^2 + \left(\frac{d}{2}\right)^2\right]$$

$$= \frac{m}{3}(L^2 + d^2)$$

Applying the equation of motion $\Sigma M_A = I_A\ddot{\theta}$, we obtain

$$-k(\delta + L \sin \theta)L \cos \theta + mg\left(\frac{L}{2}\cos \theta - \frac{d}{2}\sin \theta\right)$$

$$= \frac{m}{3}(L^2 + d^2)\ddot{\theta}$$

By substituting $k\delta = mg/2$ from Equation (a), the equation of motion becomes

$$-kL^2 \sin \theta \cos \theta - mg\frac{d}{2}\sin \theta = \frac{m}{3}(L^2 + d^2)\ddot{\theta}$$

(continued)

EXAMPLE 10.2 (*concluded*)

For oscillations of small amplitude, we use the approximations $\sin\theta \approx \theta$ and $\cos\theta \approx 1$, in which case

$$\frac{m}{3}(L^2 + d^2)\ddot{\theta} + \left(kL^2 + \frac{1}{2}mgd\right)\theta = 0$$

or the equation of motion can be written as

$$\ddot{\theta} + \frac{3}{2}\left[\frac{2kL^2 + mgd}{m(L^2 + d^2)}\right]\theta = 0 \quad \blacktriangleleft$$

Note that this equation of motion is in the form of Equation (10.3), with the natural circular frequency of vibration,

$$\omega_n = \sqrt{\frac{3}{2}\left[\frac{2kL^2 + mgd}{m(L^2 + d^2)}\right]}$$

Natural period. From Equation (10.19),

$$T_n = \frac{2\pi}{\omega_n} = 2\pi\sqrt{\frac{2}{3}\left[\frac{m(L^2 + d^2)}{2kL^2 + mgd}\right]}$$

Substituting the numerical values, we obtain

$$T_n = 2\pi\sqrt{\frac{2}{3}\left[\frac{1500\{(3)^2 + (1.5)^2\}}{\{2(200)(3)^2\} + \{(1500)(9.81)(1.5)\}}\right]}$$

$$T_n = 4.16\text{ s} \quad \blacktriangleleft$$

EXAMPLE 10.3

Determine the natural period, and the natural frequency, of the small-amplitude vibration of the spring-supported pendulum shown in the figure. Neglect the mass of the rod and the size of the bob. The pendulum is in equilibrium in the vertical position shown, and the spring is undeformed at this position.

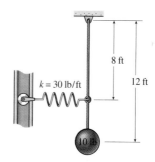

Solution The free-body diagram of the pendulum displaced from the equilibrium position by an angle θ, which is measured positive counterclockwise, is shown. Applying the rotational equation of motion $\Sigma M_A = I_A\ddot{\theta}$, we obtain

$$-10(12\sin\theta) - 30(8\sin\theta)(8\cos\theta) = \frac{10}{32.2}(12)^2\ddot{\theta}$$

For oscillations of small amplitude, we approximate $\sin\theta \approx \theta$ and $\cos\theta \approx 1$. Thus, the equation of motion can be written as

$$44.72\ddot{\theta} + 2040\theta = 0$$

or

$$\ddot{\theta} + 45.62\theta = 0$$

which is in the same form as Equation (10.3), with the natural circular frequency of vibration,

$$\omega_n = \sqrt{45.62} = 6.75\text{ rad/s}$$

Natural period. From Equation (10.19),

$$T_n = \frac{2\pi}{\omega_n} = \frac{2\pi}{6.75} \qquad T_n = 0.93\text{ s} \quad \blacktriangleleft$$

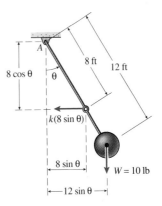

Natural frequency. From Equation (10.20),

$$f_n = \frac{1}{T_n} = \frac{1}{0.93}$$

$$f_n = 1.07\text{ cycles/s} \quad \blacktriangleleft$$

10.4 ENERGY METHOD

In the preceding sections, we derived the differential equation of motion of undamped free vibration by the direct application of Newton's second law of motion. Since a system that vibrates freely without frictional damping forces is a conservative system, the differential equation of motion for such a system can also be established by using the principle of conservation of energy. The energy method is especially convenient in determining the natural frequencies of vibration for systems undergoing simple harmonic motions.

Consider the motion of a spring-mass system shown in Figure 10.4. The position of the mass at any time is defined by the displacement x, which is measured from the equilibrium position, as shown in Figure 10.4c. As the velocity of the mass at position x is $\dot{x}$, its kinetic energy is

$$T = \frac{1}{2}m\dot{x}^2 \tag{10.21}$$

Considering the equilibrium position as the reference for potential energy (i.e., the potential energy of the system is zero in the equilibrium position $x = 0$), the potential energy of the system at a position x is

$$V = -Wx + \tfrac{1}{2}k(\delta + x)^2 - \tfrac{1}{2}k\delta^2 = -Wx + \tfrac{1}{2}k(\delta^2 + 2\delta x + x^2) - \tfrac{1}{2}k\delta^2$$

$$= -Wx + k\delta x + \tfrac{1}{2}kx^2$$

Since $W = k\delta$ from the condition of static equilibrium, the expression for potential energy of the system becomes

$$V = \tfrac{1}{2}kx^2 \tag{10.22}$$

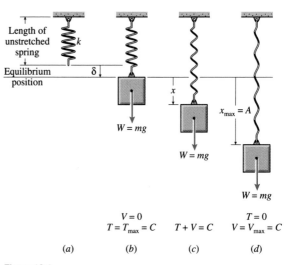

Figure 10.4

As the system is conservative, its total mechanical energy, which is the sum of its kinetic and potential energies, is always constant:

$$T + V = C \qquad (10.23)$$

where C = constant. Substituting the expressions for the kinetic and potential energies into Equation (10.23), we write

$$\tfrac{1}{2}m\dot{x}^2 + \tfrac{1}{2}kx^2 = C \qquad (10.24)$$

Differentating Equation (10.24) with respect to time t, we obtain

$$\tfrac{1}{2}m(2\dot{x})\ddot{x} + \tfrac{1}{2}k(2x)\dot{x} = 0 \quad \text{or} \quad (m\ddot{x} + kx)\dot{x} = 0$$

As the velocity $\dot{x}$ is not zero at all times, we have

$$m\ddot{x} + kx = 0$$

which is the same differential equation of motion as Equation (10.2), derived previously by the direct application of Newton's second law of motion.

The application of the principle of conservation of energy considerably expedites the determination of natural frequencies of systems oscillating with simple harmonic motions. Section 10.2 showed that the displacement and velocity of such a system are given by the equations

$$x = A \sin(\omega_n t + \phi)$$
$$v = \dot{x} = A\omega_n \cos(\omega_n t + \phi)$$

from which we can see that the magnitudes of the maximum displacement and the maximum velocity of the mass are, respectively,

$$x_{max} = A \qquad \text{and} \qquad v_{max} = \dot{x}_{max} = \omega_n x_{max} = \omega_n A \qquad (10.25)$$

When a system is passing through the equilibrium position, which is also the reference for potential energy, the potential energy of the system is zero. As the total mechanical energy of the system must remain constant ($T + V = C$) at all times, its kinetic energy must be maximum, and equal to the total mechanical energy of the system at the equilibrium position. Thus we can write, at the equilibrium position,

$$V = 0 \qquad \text{and} \qquad T = T_{max} = C \qquad (10.26)$$

Next, we consider the position of the maximum displacement of the mass. At this position, the velocity of the mass is zero as the direction of the system's motion is reversing, so that the kinetic energy of the system is zero. Since the total mechanical energy of the system must remain constant at all times, its potential energy is maximum and equal to the total mechanical energy of the system at the position of maximum displacement. Thus, at the position of maximum displacement,

$$T = 0 \qquad \text{and} \qquad V = V_{max} = C \qquad (10.27)$$

Equating Equations (10.26) and (10.27), we obtain

$$T_{max} = V_{max} \tag{10.28}$$

Equation (10.28) can be used to determine the natural frequency of any system vibrating freely with simple harmonic motion. The procedure essentially involves establishing the expressions for the maximum kinetic and the maximum potential energies of the system in terms of a displacement variable (e.g., x or θ) measured from the equilibrium position. The two energy expressions are then equated according to Equation (10.28) yielding an equation which, upon substitution of the relationships $x_{max} = A$ and $v_{max} = \omega_n A$ [Equations (10.25)], can be solved directly for the natural circular frequency, ω_n.

To illustrate this procedure, consider again the simple spring-mass system of Figure 10.4. The maximum kinetic energy occurs at the equilibrium position ($x = 0$) as shown in Figure 10.4b, and is

$$T_{max} = \tfrac{1}{2}m\dot{x}_{max}^2$$

The maximum potential energy of the system occurs when the displacement of the mass is maximum ($x = x_{max} = A$) as shown in Figure 10.4d, and is given by

$$V_{max} = \tfrac{1}{2}kx_{max}^2$$

Equating the expression for the maximum kinetic energy to the expression for the maximum potential energy [Equation (10.28)], we write

$$\tfrac{1}{2}m\dot{x}_{max}^2 = \tfrac{1}{2}kx_{max}^2$$

From Equations (10.25), we have $x_{max} = A$ and $\dot{x}_{max} = \omega_n A$. Substituting these relationships into the above equation, we write

$$\tfrac{1}{2}m\omega_n^2 A^2 = \tfrac{1}{2}kA^2 \qquad \text{or} \qquad m\omega_n^2 = k$$

from which we obtain the natural circular frequency of the spring-mass system as

$$\omega_n = \sqrt{k/m}$$

which is the same as Equation (10.4).

EXAMPLE 10.4

An 8-kg block is attached to a stepped disk as shown in the figure. The disk is supported by a hinged support at A and a spring of stiffness 500 N/m as shown. If the mass moment of inertia of the disk about its mass center A is 0.5 kg · m², determine the natural period of vibration of the system. The system is in equilibrium in the position shown. Neglect the size of the block.

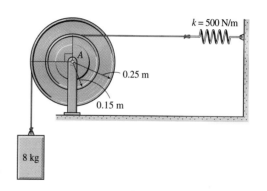

Solution The free-body diagram of the system at the static equilibrium position is shown, where δ represents the elongation of the spring at the equilibrium position. Applying the equation of equilibrium, $\Sigma M_A = 0$, we obtain

$$78.48(0.25) - 500\delta(0.15) = 0$$

$$\delta = 0.262 \text{ m}$$

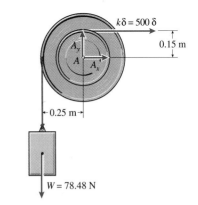

The displaced position of the system from the equilibrium position is defined by an angle θ, which is measured positive counterclockwise as shown. It can be seen that a rotation θ of the disk causes the spring to elongate by a distance 0.15θ m, and the block to displace downward by 0.25θ m.

The maximum kinetic energy of the system occurs at the equilibrium position ($\theta = 0$) and can be written as

$$T_{max} = \tfrac{1}{2}mv_{max}^2 + \tfrac{1}{2}I_A\dot{\theta}_{max}^2$$
$$= \tfrac{1}{2}(8)(0.25\dot{\theta}_{max})^2 + \tfrac{1}{2}(0.5)\dot{\theta}_{max}^2 = 0.5\dot{\theta}_{max}^2$$

The maximum potential energy of the system occurs when $\theta = \theta_{max}$, and can be written as

$$V_{max} = -W(0.25\theta_{max}) + \tfrac{1}{2}k(\delta + 0.15\theta_{max})^2 - \tfrac{1}{2}k\delta^2$$
$$= -78.48(0.25\theta_{max}) + \tfrac{1}{2}(500)(0.262 + 0.15\theta_{max})^2$$
$$- \tfrac{1}{2}(500)(0.262)^2$$
$$= 5.625\theta_{max}^2$$

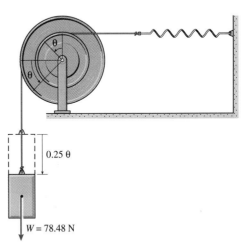

To find the natural circular frequency, we equate the expression for T_{max} to the expression for V_{max} according to Equation (10.28):

$$0.5\dot{\theta}_{max}^2 = 5.625\theta_{max}^2$$

From Equations (10.25), $\theta_{max} = A$ and $\dot{\theta}_{max} = \omega_n A$. Substitution of these relationships into the above equation yields

$$0.5\omega_n^2 A^2 = 5.625A^2$$

from which we obtain the natural circular frequency as

$$\omega_n = \sqrt{\frac{5.625}{0.5}} = 3.35 \text{ rad/s}$$

For the natural period, then,

$$T_n = \frac{2\pi}{\omega_n} = \frac{2\pi}{3.35} \qquad T_n = 1.87 \text{ s} \blacktriangleleft$$

10.5 UNDAMPED FORCED VIBRATION

Many engineering structures and machines are subjected to time-varying loads and displacements that cause them to vibrate—for example, support motion during an earthquake. Such vibrations caused by time-varying excitations are called *forced vibrations*. The analysis of forced vibration plays an important role in the design of many types of structures and machines.

In this section, we will confine our attention to the analysis of undamped vibrations caused by harmonic excitations: the forces or displacements that can be represented by sine or cosine functions of time. The effect of damping on the harmonically excited vibrations will be considered in Section 10.7. Harmonic excitations are encountered quite frequently in engineering practice; structures supporting rotating machines are often subjected to harmonic excitations due to imbalance in the rotating parts of the machine. Moreover, the analysis of harmonically excited vibrations forms the basis of the analysis for more general types of excitation.

Consider a block of mass m, supported by a spring of stiffness k as shown in Figure 10.5a. The block is subjected to a harmonic force $F = F_o \sin \overline{\omega} t$, in which F_o is the maximum magnitude of the force or the *force amplitude* (Figure 10.5b) and $\overline{\omega}$ is the *circular frequency of excitation* in radians/second. The displacement x of the block is measured positive downward from its equilibrium position as shown in Figure 10.5a, which also shows the free-body diagram of the block at a displacement x. By applying Newton's second law of motion, $\Sigma F = ma$, we obtain

$$F_o \sin \overline{\omega} t + W - k(\delta + x) = m\ddot{x}$$

Since $W = k\delta$, the equation of motion becomes

$$F_o \sin \overline{\omega} t - kx = m\ddot{x}$$

or

$$m\ddot{x} + kx = F_o \sin \overline{\omega} t \qquad (10.29)$$

As the right-hand side of Equation (10.29) is not zero, the equation is called a nonhomogeneous differential equation. It is usually expressed in the form

$$\ddot{x} + \omega_n^2 x = \frac{F_o}{m} \sin \overline{\omega} t \qquad (10.30)$$

The solution of this differential equation of motion can be expressed as

$$x = x_c + x_p \qquad (10.31)$$

where x_c represents the complementary solution of the corresponding homogeneous differential equation (i.e., the term on the right-hand side of Equa-

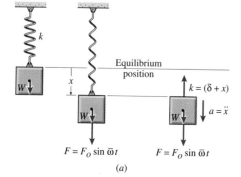

Equilibrium position

$k = (\delta + x)$

$a = \ddot{x}$

$F = F_0 \sin \overline{\omega} t$ $F = F_0 \sin \overline{\omega} t$

(a)

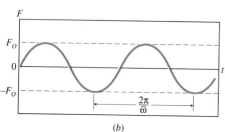

$\dfrac{2\pi}{\overline{\omega}}$

(b)

Figure 10.5

tion (10.30) is set equal to zero), and x_p represents a particular solution satisfying the nonhomogeneous equation [Equation (10.30)]. As discussed in the case of undamped free vibration (Section 10.2), the complementary solution is given by Equation (10.5),

$$x_c = C_1 \sin \omega_n t + C_2 \cos \omega_n t \qquad (10.32)$$

A particular solution of the form of the forcing function is assumed as

$$x_p = X \sin \overline{\omega} t \qquad (10.33)$$

in which X represents the maximum magnitude, or the amplitude, of x_p. Differentiating Equation (10.33) twice with respect to time t, we write

$$\ddot{x}_p = -X\overline{\omega}^2 \sin \overline{\omega} t \qquad (10.34)$$

Substituting Equations (10.33) and (10.34) into Equation (10.30), we obtain

$$-X\overline{\omega}^2 \sin \overline{\omega} t + \omega_n^2 X \sin \overline{\omega} t = \frac{F_o}{m} \sin \overline{\omega} t$$

or

$$X = \frac{F_o/m}{\omega_n^2[1 - (\overline{\omega}/\omega_n)^2]}$$

Substituting $m\omega_n^2 = k$ [from Equation (10.4)] into the above equation, we obtain

$$X = \frac{F_o/k}{1 - (\overline{\omega}/\omega_n)^2} \qquad (10.35)$$

The particular solution can therefore be written as

$$x_p = \frac{F_o/k}{1 - (\overline{\omega}/\omega_n)^2} \sin \overline{\omega} t \qquad (10.36)$$

By adding the complementary and the particular solutions, we obtain the complete solution of the differential equation of motion for undamped forced vibration as

$$x = \underbrace{C_1 \sin \omega_n t + C_2 \cos \omega_n t}_{\text{Transient vibration}} + \underbrace{\frac{F_o/k}{1 - (\overline{\omega}/\omega_n)^2} \sin \overline{\omega} t}_{\text{Steady-state vibration}} \qquad (10.37)$$

From Equation (10.37) we can see that the vibration of the system consists of two harmonic motions of different frequencies, ω_n and $\overline{\omega}$, superimposed on each other. The first two terms represent the harmonic motion of frequency $\omega_n = \sqrt{k/m}$, which depends on the mass and the stiffness characteristics of the system. It should be realized that the constants C_1 and C_2 must be determined by applying the initial conditions ($x = x_o$ and $v = v_o$ when $t = 0$) to the entire Equation (10.37), not just the complementary part of it. Thus, the expressions for C_1 and C_2 determined for the case of free vibration [Equations (10.8)] cannot be used here for forced vibration. This part of the vibration is termed the *transient vibration* because in real systems damping forces due to friction cause it to vanish with time, as we will see in the following section.

The last term of Equation (10.37) represents the harmonic motion of the same frequency $\overline{\omega}$ as that of the force function. As it will be shown in Section 10.7, the amplitude of this part of the vibration diminishes in the presence of damping; nonetheless, the motion persists as long as the force F continues to act on the system. This part of the vibration, which is referred to as the *steady-state vibration*, is of primary interest in engineering applications as it is the only motion that remains after the transient vibration dies out.

Considering the steady-state vibration, we can see from Equation (10.35) that the amplitude X of this vibration depends on the frequency ratio $\overline{\omega}/\omega_n$. Note that the numerator F_o/k of Equation (10.35) represents the static deflection of the mass under the force amplitude F_o. The dimensionless ratio of the steady-state amplitude X to the static deflection F_o/k is defined as the **dynamic magnification factor**, and is given by

$$\text{DMF} = \frac{X}{F_o/k} = \frac{1}{1 - (\overline{\omega}/\omega_n)^2} \qquad (10.38)$$

A plot of the dynamic magnification factor as a function of the frequency ratio $\overline{\omega}/\omega_n$ is shown in Figure 10.6. From this figure we see that for very small frequency ratios, the dynamic magnification factor is almost equal to 1. This is because the force varies so slowly that the amplitude of vibration X is nearly equal to the static deflection F_o/k. On the other hand, for very large frequency ratios, the DMF is almost zero because the force varies so rapidly that the system does not have time to respond, and the mass remains essentially stationary. From this figure we can also see that when the excitation frequency $\overline{\omega}$ becomes equal to the natural frequency ω_n of the system (i.e., $\overline{\omega}/\omega_n = 1$), the dynamic magnification factor, and thus the amplitude of vibration, becomes infinite. This condition is called the **resonance**. Section 10.7 will show that in real systems, because of damping, the amplitude of vibration remains finite. However, even in damped systems, when the excitation frequency is close to the natural frequency, large-amplitude vibrations may occur causing failure of the structural or mechanical systems. Therefore, it is essential that such conditions of resonance be avoided in engineering designs. Finally, from Figure 10.6 we can see that for $\overline{\omega}/\omega_n < 1$ the DMF is positive, indicating that the vibration is in phase with the force; whereas for $\overline{\omega}/\omega_n > 1$ the DMF is negative, indicating that the vibration is out of phase with the force; that is, when the force is acting downward, the block is moving upward, and vice versa.

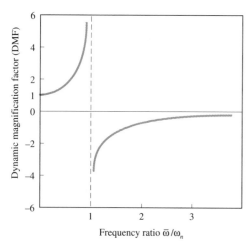

Figure 10.6

Support Motion

Next, we consider the case of forced vibration of a system caused by **support motion**. Consider a block of mass m attached to support A by a spring of stiffness k as shown in Figure 10.7. The displacement of support A is described by the equation $x_s = X_s \sin \overline{\omega} t$, where X_s is the maximum magnitude, or the amplitude, of the support displacement, and $\overline{\omega}$ is the circular frequency of excitation in radians/second. Both the displacement of the support x_s as well as the displacement of the block x are measured positive to the right from the equilibrium position of the system at $t = 0$, as shown in the figure. The elongation of the spring at any time t is equal to the difference between the displacement of the mass x and that of the support x_s. The free-body diagram of the mass in the displaced position is also shown in Figure 10.7. By applying Newton's second law of motion, $\Sigma F = ma$, we obtain

$$-k(x - x_s) = m\ddot{x}$$

$$m\ddot{x} + kx = kX_s \sin \overline{\omega} t \qquad (10.39)$$

Comparing Equations (10.39) and (10.29), we observe that the two equations would be identical if F_o in Equation (10.29) is replaced by kX_s. Therefore, the vibration of the system due to the support motion $x_s = X_s \sin \overline{\omega} t$ is described by the same equations—Equations (10.31) to (10.38)—that we developed previously for the case of the force $F = F_o \sin \overline{\omega} t$; provided that F_o is replaced by kX_s in the equations.

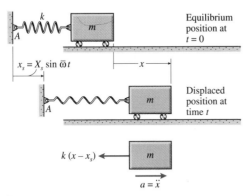

Figure 10.7

EXAMPLE   10.5

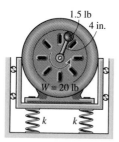

1.5 lb
4 in.
$W = 20$ lb
k k

n

F_o $\overline{\omega}t$

A 200-lb electric motor mounted on four springs, each of stiffness 500 lb/ft, is constrained to move only in the vertical direction as shown. The unbalance in the rotor is represented by an eccentric weight of 1.5 lb with the eccentricity of 4 in. from the axis of rotation. If the motor is rotating at a speed of 800 rpm, determine the amplitude of its vibration. Also, determine the speed of the motor that will cause resonance. Neglect damping.

Solution   The force exerted by the unbalanced 1.5-lb weight on the motor is

$$F_o = ma_n = mr\overline{\omega}^2 = \left(\frac{1.5}{32.2}\right)\left(\frac{4}{12}\right)\left[\frac{800}{60}(2\pi)\right]^2 = 109 \text{ lb}$$

This force F_o acts at angle $\overline{\omega}t$ with the horizontal axis as shown. The vibration of the system is caused by the vertical component of the centrifugal force F_o. Thus,

$$F = F_o \sin \overline{\omega}t$$

Substitution of $F_o = 109$ lb and $\overline{\omega} = 800$ rpm $= 83.8$ rad/s into the above expression yields

$$F = 109 \sin 83.8t \text{ lb}$$

The total mass is

$$m = \frac{200}{32.2} = 6.2 \text{ lb} \cdot \text{s}^2/\text{ft} = 6.2 \text{ slug}$$

and the total stiffness of the four springs is

$$k = 4(500) = 2000 \text{ lb/ft}$$

Therefore, the natural circular frequency of the system is

$$\omega_n = \sqrt{\frac{k}{m}} = \sqrt{\frac{2000}{6.2}} = 18 \text{ rad/s}$$

Using Equation (10.35), we obtain the desired amplitude of the vibration of the motor as

$$X = \frac{F_o/k}{1 - (\overline{\omega}/\omega_n)^2} = \frac{109/2000}{1 - (83.8/18)^2} = -0.00264 \text{ ft}$$

$$X = -0.032 \text{ in. } \blacktriangleleft$$

The resonance will occur when the excitation frequency is equal to the natural frequency of the system; thus,

$$\overline{\omega} = \omega_n = 18 \text{ rad/s} = 171.9 \text{ rpm } \blacktriangleleft$$

10.6 DAMPED FREE VIBRATION

In the analysis presented in the preceding sections, we have neglected the effect of the frictional forces that are present in a vibrating system. All vibrations are affected by frictional forces that tend to diminish the motion by dissipating the mechanical energy of the system.

The frictional or damping forces commonly encountered in engineering systems are categorized as (*a*) *Coulomb damping* (dry friction), (*b*) *viscous damping* (fluid friction), and (*c*) *structural damping* (internal friction). A frictional force due to dry friction between two sliding surfaces is equal to the product of the normal force and the coefficient of friction, and is opposed to the direction of motion. The viscous damping forces arise due to the resistance offered by the medium (air, water, etc.) in which the system vibrates. Such resisting forces are considered to be proportional to the magnitude of the velocity, and are expressed as

$$F_D = cv = c\dot{x} \tag{10.40}$$

in which the constant of proportionality c is called the *coefficient of viscous damping* and is measured in units of lb $\cdot$ s/ft or N $\cdot$ s/m. The structural damping forces are caused by the internal friction within the material of the system. The magnitudes of such damping forces have been found to be proportional to the amplitudes of vibrations.

The process by which these damping forces dissipate the mechanical (kinetic and potential) energy of a vibrating system by converting it into heat is quite complex, and is still not clearly understood. In many mechanical systems, specially designed damping devices are added to control vibrations. For example, shock absorbers are used in automobiles to provide the damping forces necessary to reduce vibrations.

In the remainder of this section, we will focus our attention on viscous damping forces. This type of damping, quite common in engineering systems, is amenable to relatively simple mathematical analysis. The presence of viscous damping in a system is usually indicated by a *dashpot*, which consists of a piston moving in a cylinder filled with a viscous fluid as in Figure 10.8. The motion of the piston is impeded by the fluid flowing around the piston or through the holes in it. The resultant force exerted by the fluid on the piston is directed opposite to the piston's motion, and has a magnitude equal to the product of the coefficient of viscous damping of the dashpot and the velocity of the piston, Equation (10.40).

To develop the analysis of free vibration of a system with viscous damping, consider the simple system shown in Figure 10.9. The system consists of a block of mass m, attached to a spring of stiffness k and a dashpot of coefficient of viscous damping c. By applying Newton's second law of motion, we obtain

$$W - k(\delta + x) - c\dot{x} = m\ddot{x}$$

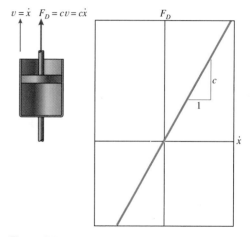

Figure 10.8

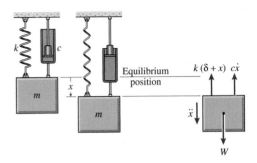

Figure 10.9

Substituting $W = k\delta$, we obtain the equation of motion as

$$m\ddot{x} + c\dot{x} + kx = 0 \qquad (10.41)$$

The solution of this homogeneous differential equation is of the form

$$x = e^{\lambda t} \qquad (10.42)$$

Substituting Equation (10.42) and its first and second derivatives with respect to time t into Equation (10.41), we write

$$m\lambda^2 e^{\lambda t} + c\lambda e^{\lambda t} + k e^{\lambda t} = 0$$
$$e^{\lambda t}(m\lambda^2 + c\lambda + k) = 0$$

from which we obtain the *characteristic equation*

$$m\lambda^2 + c\lambda + k = 0 \qquad (10.43)$$

By using the quadratic formula, we determine the two roots of this equation as

$$\lambda_{1,2} = -\frac{c}{2m} \pm \sqrt{\left(\frac{c}{2m}\right)^2 - \frac{k}{m}} \qquad (10.44)$$

The nature of the damped motion depends on whether the term under the radical in Equation (10.44) is positive, zero, or negative. The value of the damping coefficient c, which makes the term under the radical in Equation (10.44) equal to zero, is defined as the *critical damping coefficient*, c_c. Thus, the critical damping coefficient can be expressed as

$$\left(\frac{c_c}{2m}\right)^2 - \frac{k}{m} = 0$$

or

$$c_c = 2m\sqrt{\frac{k}{m}} = 2m\omega_n \qquad (10.45)$$

in which $\omega_n = \sqrt{k/m}$ is the natural circular frequency of the undamped free vibration defined in Equation (10.4).

As the term under the radical in Equation (10.44) may be positive, zero, or negative, depending on the value of the damping coefficient c, three types of damped motion may occur. These are:

Overdamped motion ($c > c_c$).   The roots λ_1 and λ_2 are both real and negative, and distinct. In this case, the general solution of the differential equation of motion [Equation (10.41)] is given by

$$x = C_1 e^{\lambda_1 t} + C_2 e^{\lambda_2 t} \qquad (10.46)$$

in which the constants C_1 and C_2 are determined from the initial conditions. As λ_1 and λ_2 are both negative, the displacement x of the system decreases exponentially from its initial value x_0 toward zero as time t increases. The motion is nonoscillatory as shown in Figure 10.10a.

Critically damped motion $(c = c_c)$.   As the term under the radical in Equation (10.44) is zero, the roots λ_1 and λ_2 are both real and negative, and equal to each other $(\lambda_1 = \lambda_2 = -\omega_n)$. The general solution of the differential equation of motion, Equation (10.41), is given by

$$x = (C_1 + C_2 t)e^{-\omega_n t} \tag{10.47}$$

The motion is again nonoscillatory as shown in Figure 10.10a. However, a critically damped system approaches the equilibrium position faster than an overdamped system.

Underdamped motion $(c < c_c)$.   In this case, the term under the radical in Equation (10.44) is negative, and hence the roots λ_1 and λ_2 are complex numbers. The general solution of the differential equation of motion [Equation (10.41)] can be expressed in either of the following two forms:

$$x = e^{-(c/2m)t}(C_1 \sin \omega_d t + C_2 \cos \omega_d t) \tag{10.48}$$

or

$$x = Ae^{-(c/2m)t}\sin(\omega_d t + \phi) \tag{10.49}$$

In these equations, the constant ω_d is called the *damped natural frequency* of the system and is expressed as

$$\omega_d = \sqrt{\frac{k}{m} - \left(\frac{c}{2m}\right)^2} = \omega_n \sqrt{1 - \left(\frac{c}{c_c}\right)^2} \tag{10.50}$$

in which the ratio c/c_c is referred to as the *damping factor*. The constants C_1 and C_2 in Equation (10.48), or A and ϕ in Equation (10.49), are determined from the initial displacement x_0 and initial velocity v_0 of the system.

The motion described by Equations (10.48) and (10.49) for initial displacement x_0 with no initial velocity, is depicted graphically in Figure 10.10b. We can see from this figure that while the motion is oscillatory, it is not periodic in the sense that it does not repeat itself. The amplitude of vibration decreases for successive cycles within the bounds of the exponential curves. The time required for the displacement curve to touch one of the exponential curves at two successive points remains constant, and is referred to as the *damped natural period* of vibration and given by

$$T_d = \frac{2\pi}{\omega_d} \tag{10.51}$$

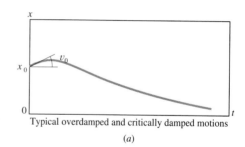

Typical overdamped and critically damped motions

(a)

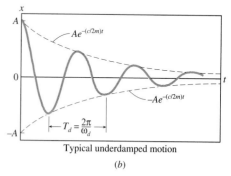

Typical underdamped motion

(b)

Figure 10.10

EXAMPLE   10.6

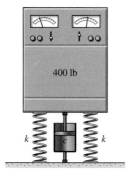

400 lb

k c k

The system of Example 10.1 is repeated here with a dashpot attached, as shown. If the coefficient of damping is 200 lb · s/ft, determine the damping factor, and the damped natural period of vibration. The vibrating system consists of a 400-lb machine supported by four springs each of stiffness 1200 lb/ft.

Solution   From Example 10.1, we have

$$k_{\text{eff}} = 4k = 4800 \text{ lb/ft}$$

$$m = 12.42 \text{ lb} \cdot \text{s}^2/\text{ft}$$

By using Equation (10.45), we obtain the critical damping coefficient as

$$c_c = 2m\sqrt{\frac{k}{m}} = 2(12.42)\sqrt{\frac{4800}{12.42}} = 488.33 \text{ lb} \cdot \text{s/ft}$$

The damping factor is, then,

$$\frac{c}{c_c} = \frac{200}{488.33} \qquad\qquad \frac{c}{c_c} = 0.41 \blacktriangleleft$$

By using Equation (10.50), we obtain the damped natural frequency as

$$\omega_d = \sqrt{\frac{k}{m} - \left(\frac{c}{2m}\right)^2} = \sqrt{\frac{4800}{12.42} - \left[\frac{200}{2(12.42)}\right]^2} = 17.93 \text{ rad/s}$$

and from Equation (10.51), we can determine the damped natural period of vibration as

$$T_d = \frac{2\pi}{\omega_d} = \frac{2\pi}{17.93} \qquad\qquad T_d = 0.35 \text{ s} \blacktriangleleft$$

Note that this period of damped vibration is about 9 percent longer than the period of undamped vibration ($T_n = 0.32$ s) of the corresponding system determined in Example 10.1.

10.7 DAMPED FORCED VIBRATION

To develop the analysis of damped vibration under harmonic excitations, we consider again the simple system consisting of a block of mass m attached to a spring of stiffness k and dashpot of coefficient of damping c, as shown in Figure 10.11. The block is subjected to a harmonic force $F = F_o \sin \overline{\omega} t$ as shown. By applying Newton's second law of motion, $\Sigma F = ma$, we obtain the differential equation of motion as

$$m\ddot{x} + c\dot{x} + kx = F_o \sin \overline{\omega} t \tag{10.52}$$

The complete solution of this nonhomogeneous differential equation consists of the sum of the *complementary* solution of the corresponding homogeneous differential equation, and a *particular* solution which would satisfy Equation (10.52). The complementary solution, which represents the transient vibration of the system, was determined in the preceding section and is given for the overdamped, critically damped, and underdamped systems, by Equations (10.46), (10.47), and (10.48) or (10.49), respectively. As stated in Section 10.5, this transient vibration vanishes with time because of damping.

The particular solution of Equation (10.52), which represents the steady-state vibration of the system, can be expressed in the following form:

$$x_p = X \sin(\overline{\omega} t - \phi) \tag{10.53}$$

in which X represents the amplitude of the steady-state vibration, and ϕ is the phase angle between the force F and the displacement x_p. Substituting Equation (10.53) and its first and second derivatives with respect to time t into Equation (10.52), we obtain

$$-m\overline{\omega}^2 X \sin(\overline{\omega} t - \phi) + c\overline{\omega} X \cos(\overline{\omega} t - \phi) + kX \sin(\overline{\omega} t - \phi) = F_o \sin \overline{\omega} t$$

which can be simplified as

$$[(k - m\overline{\omega}^2)X \cos \phi + c\overline{\omega} X \sin \phi] \sin \overline{\omega} t + [c\overline{\omega} X \cos \phi$$
$$- X(k - m\overline{\omega}^2) \sin \phi] \cos \overline{\omega} t = F_o \sin \overline{\omega} t$$

By equating the coefficients of $\sin \overline{\omega} t$ and $\cos \overline{\omega} t$, we obtain two equations:

$$(k - m\overline{\omega}^2)X \cos \phi + c\overline{\omega} X \sin \phi = F_o \tag{10.54}$$

$$c\overline{\omega} X \cos \phi - (k - m\overline{\omega}^2)X \sin \phi = 0 \tag{10.55}$$

By squaring and adding the two equations, we obtain

$$[(k - m\overline{\omega}^2)^2 + (c\overline{\omega})^2]X^2 = F_o^2$$

or

$$X = \frac{F_o}{\sqrt{(k - m\overline{\omega}^2)^2 + (c\overline{\omega})^2}} \tag{10.56}$$

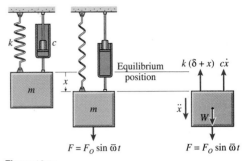

Figure 10.11

$F = F_o \sin \overline{\omega} t$

Equilibrium position

$k(\delta + x)$ $c\dot{x}$

W

$F = F_o \sin \overline{\omega} t$

and from Equation (10.55), we obtain

$$\phi = \tan^{-1}\left(\frac{c\overline{\omega}}{k - m\overline{\omega}^2}\right) \qquad (10.57)$$

Substituting $\omega_n = \sqrt{k/m}$ and $c_c = 2m\omega_n$ into Equations (10.56) and (10.57), we obtain

$$X = \frac{F_o/k}{\sqrt{[1 - (\overline{\omega}/\omega_n)^2]^2 + [2(c/c_c)(\overline{\omega}/\omega_n)]^2}} \qquad (10.58)$$

$$\phi = \tan^{-1}\left[\frac{2(c/c_c)(\overline{\omega}/\omega_n)}{1 - (\overline{\omega}/\omega_n)^2}\right] \qquad (10.59)$$

As in the case of undamped forced vibration (Section 10.5), we define the dynamic magnification factor as

$$\mathrm{DMF} = \frac{X}{F_o/k} = \frac{1}{\sqrt{[1 - (\overline{\omega}/\omega_n)^2]^2 + [2(c/c_c)(\overline{\omega}/\omega_n)]^2}} \qquad (10.60)$$

A plot of the dynamic magnification factor as a function of the frequency ratio $\overline{\omega}/\omega_n$ for various values of the damping factor c/c_c is shown in Figure 10.12. We can see from this figure that the amplitude of the steady-state vibration decreases as the coefficient of damping increases. Note that in the presence of damping, the maximum amplitude does not become infinite. However, for small damping factors, the amplitude increases substantially as the excitation frequency $\overline{\omega}$ approaches the natural frequency ω_n of the system.

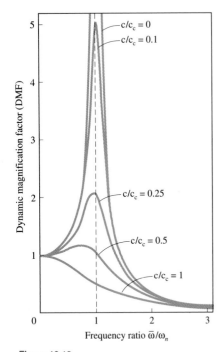

Figure 10.12

EXAMPLE   10.7

A sensitive instrument of 30-kg mass is to be installed in a laboratory, where measurements indicate that the operation of another piece of equipment causes the floor to vibrate vertically with an amplitude of 4 mm at a frequency of 0.8 Hz. The instrument is to be supported by four springs, each of stiffness 500 N/m. Determine the minimum value of the coefficient of viscous damping so that the amplitude of vibration of the instrument will not exceed 3.2 mm. The instrument is constrained to move only in the vertical direction.

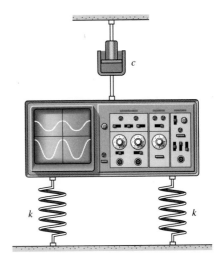

Solution As we discussed in Section 10.5, the vibration caused by the support motion is described by Equation (10.52), provided that F_o is replaced by kX_s. Thus, the equation of motion of the given system can be written as

$$m\ddot{x} + c\dot{x} + kx = kX_s \sin \overline{\omega}t$$

where $m = 30$ kg
$$k = 4(500) = 2000 \text{ N/m}$$
$$X_s = 0.004 \text{ m}$$
$$\overline{\omega} = 2\pi(0.8) = 5.03 \text{ rad/s}$$

The natural frequency of the system is

$$\omega_n = \sqrt{\frac{k}{m}} = \sqrt{\frac{2000}{30}} = 8.16 \text{ rad/s}$$

Setting $F_o = kX_s$ into Equation (10.58) for the amplitude of vibration, we write

$$X = \frac{X_s}{\sqrt{[1 - (\overline{\omega}/\omega_n)^2]^2 + [2(c/c_c)(\overline{\omega}/\omega_n)]^2}}$$

Substituting the given numerical values gives

$$0.0032 = \frac{0.004}{\sqrt{[1 - (5.03/8.16)^2]^2 + [2(c/c_c)(5.03/8.16)]^2}}$$

from which we determine the required damping factor as

$$\frac{c}{c_c} = 0.88$$

Using Equation (10.45), we obtain

$$c_c = 2m\omega_n = 489.6 \text{ N} \cdot \text{s/m}$$

Therefore, the required coefficient of viscous damping is

$$c = 0.88c_c = 0.88(489.6)$$

$$c = 431 \text{ N} \cdot \text{s/m} \blacktriangleleft$$

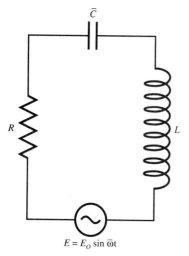

$E = E_o \sin \overline{\omega}t$

Figure 10.13

10.8 ELECTRICAL ANALOGUE

The differential equations that describe the flow of charge through oscillating electric circuits are similar in form to those we derived in this chapter for the vibrations of mechanical or structural systems. Consider, as an example, the simple series circuit shown in Figure 10.13. By applying *Kirchhoff's second law* from introductory physics, the differential equation of the circuit can be expressed as

$$L\ddot{q} + R\dot{q} + \frac{1}{C}q = E_o \sin \overline{\omega}t \qquad (10.61)$$

where $E_o \sin \overline{\omega}t$ is the applied voltage causing a current $i = dq/dt$ to flow through the circuit; q denotes the electric charge; and $L\ddot{q}$, $R\dot{q}$, and $q/\overline{C}$ are the voltage drops across the inductor L, the resistor R, and the capacitor $\overline{C}$, respectively.

Comparing Equations (10.61) and (10.52), we observe that Equation (10.61) is similar in form to the differential equation of motion of damped forced vibration ($m\ddot{x} + c\dot{x} + kx = F_o \sin \overline{\omega}t$). By comparing these two equations term-by-term, we can establish the following analogues between the mechanical/structural and electrical systems:

Mechanical/structural system		Electrical system	
Displacement	x	Charge	q
Velocity	$\dot{x}$	Current	i
Force	F	Voltage	E
Mass	m	Inductance	L
Coefficient of viscous damping	c	Resistance	R
Stiffness	k	Reciprocal of capacitance	$1/\overline{C}$

This analogy between the mechanical and electrical systems is often applied in experimental work, where electric circuits, which are easier to construct and modify than the mechanical models, are employed to simulate the behavior of complex mechanical systems.

10.9 SUMMARY

In this chapter, we have learned the following:

1. The equation of motion for the undamped free vibration of a single degree of freedom system is of the form

$$m\ddot{x} + kx = 0 \qquad (10.2)$$

in which the displacement x is measured from the equilibrium position. The solution of this equation is expressed as

$$x = A \sin(\omega_n t + \phi) \tag{10.11}$$

where A is the amplitude of vibration [Equation (10.16)], ϕ is the phase angle [Equation (10.17)], and

$$\omega_n = \sqrt{\frac{k}{m}} \tag{10.4}$$

is the natural circular frequency of vibration.

The interval of time required to complete one cycle of vibration is called the natural period of vibration, and is given by

$$T_n = \frac{2\pi}{\omega_n} = 2\pi\sqrt{\frac{m}{k}} \tag{10.19}$$

The number of cycles completed per unit of time is called the natural frequency, and is given by

$$f_n = \frac{1}{T_n} = \frac{\omega_n}{2\pi} \tag{10.20}$$

2. The differential equation of motion of a conservative system can alternately be established by applying the principle of conservation of energy ($T + V = C$). The natural frequency of vibration of such a system undergoing simple harmonic motion can be conveniently determined by equating the expressions for the maximum kinetic and the maximum potential energies of the system ($T_{max} = V_{max}$), substituting $v_{max} = \omega_n A$ into the resulting equation, and solving it for ω_n.

3. The equation of motion for the undamped vibration of a system caused by a harmonic force can be expressed as

$$m\ddot{x} + kx = F_o \sin \overline{\omega} t \tag{10.29}$$

The particular solution of this differential equation, which represents the steady-state vibration, is given by

$$x_p = X \sin \overline{\omega} t \tag{10.33}$$

in which the amplitude X is given by

$$X = \frac{F_o/k}{1 - (\overline{\omega}/\omega_n)^2} \tag{10.35}$$

As this equation indicates, when the excitation frequency is equal to the natural frequency of the system, the amplitude X becomes infinite. This condition is called the resonance.

4. The equation of motion for the damped free vibration of a system is given by

$$m\ddot{x} + c\dot{x} + kx = 0 \tag{10.41}$$

in which c is the coefficient of viscous damping. The critical damping coefficient is defined as

$$c_c = 2m\sqrt{\frac{k}{m}} = 2m\omega_n \tag{10.45}$$

Oscillatory motion occurs only when $c < c_c$. Such systems are referred to as underdamped systems.

5. The equation of motion for the damped vibration of a system caused by a harmonic force can be expressed as

$$m\ddot{x} + c\dot{x} + kx = F_o \sin \overline{\omega} t \tag{10.52}$$

The particular solution of this equation is of the form

$$x_p = X \sin(\overline{\omega} t - \phi) \tag{10.53}$$

where X is the amplitude [Equation (10.58)] and ϕ is the phase angle [Equation (10.59)].

6. The differential equations describing the flow of charge through oscillating electric circuits are similar in form to those of the vibrations of mechanical and structural systems.

KEY TERMS

amplitude of vibration *461*
damping *456*
dynamic magnification factor *472*
electrical analogue *482*
free vibrations *456*
forced vibrations *456*
natural frequency of vibration *461*
natural period of vibration *460*
phase angle *461*
resonance *472*
simple harmonic motion *460*
single degree of freedom system *456*
support motion *473*
vibration *456*

PROBLEMS

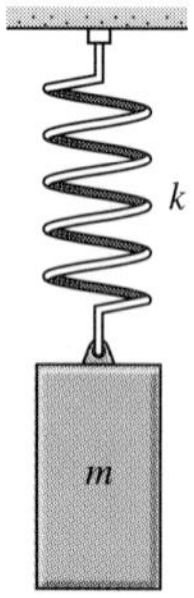

Figure P10.1 and P10.2

SECTION 10.2

10.1 A 30-lb block is supported by a spring of stiffness $k = 200$ lb/ft. Determine (*a*) the natural circular frequency, and (*b*) the natural period of vibration of the block. If the block is displaced 6 in. downward from its equilibrium position and released, determine (*c*) the amplitude of the vibration, (*d*) the maximum velocity, and (*e*) the maximum acceleration of the block.

10.2 Determine the displacement, velocity, and acceleration of the block in Problem 10.1, 0.2 s after it has been released.

10.3 A 7-kg block is attached to a spring of stiffness $k = 900$ N/m. Determine (a) the natural circular frequency, and (b) the natural period of vibration of the block. If the block is given an initial velocity of 0.2 m/s to the left when at the equilibrium position, determine (c) the amplitude of the vibration, (d) the maximum velocity, and (e) the maximum acceleration of the block.

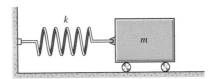

Figure P10.3 and P10.4

10.4 Determine the displacement, velocity, and acceleration of the block in Problem 10.3, 0.4 s after the vibration starts.

10.5 When a container weighing 5 lb is attached to the spring and released slowly, the spring elongates by 1.5 in. A 3-lb block is then placed in the container as shown. Determine the natural period of vibration of the system.

10.6 The natural period of vibration of the 9-kg tray supported by two springs, each of stiffness k, is measured to be 0.25 s. After the block B is placed on the tray, the natural period of the system is found to be 0.35 s. Determine (a) the mass of the block B, and (b) the spring stiffness k.

10.7 Show that the natural circular frequency of vibration of the system shown is $\omega_n = \sqrt{(k_1 + k_2)/m}$. The block is constrained to move only in the vertical direction as shown.

10.8 Show that the natural circular frequency of vibration of the system shown is
$$\omega_n = \sqrt{\frac{k_1 k_2}{m(k_1 + k_2)}}.$$

Figure P10.5

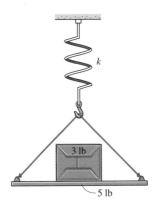

Figure P10.6

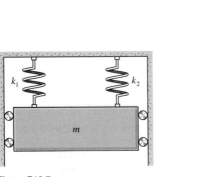

Figure P10.7

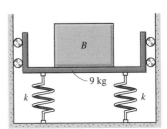

Figure P10.8

10.9 The 25-lb block is displaced 1 in. to the right from its equilibrium position, and released. For the resulting vibration, determine (a) the natural circular frequency, (b) the maximum velocity, and (c) the maximum acceleration of the block.

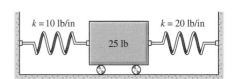

Figure P10.9

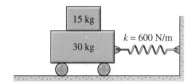

Figure P10.10

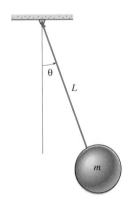

Figure P10.11 and P10.12

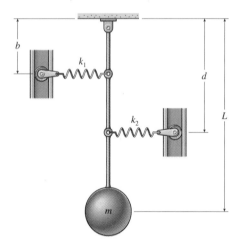

Figure P10.13 and P10.14

10.10 Determine the maximum amplitude of vibration of the system, for which no slippage will occur between the blocks. The coefficient of static friction is 0.2 between the blocks.

SECTION 10.3

10.11 Derive the differential equation for small-amplitude vibration of the simple pendulum of mass m shown. Also, determine the expression for its natural period. Neglect the size of the bob and the mass of the cord. The pendulum is in equilibrium in the vertical position.

10.12 The bob of the pendulum in Problem 10.11 weighs 2 lb, and the length of the cord is 3 ft. If the bob is displaced by an angle $\theta_o = 5°$ and released, determine the maximum velocity of the bob.

10.13 Determine the natural frequency in cycles/second of the small-amplitude vibration of the spring-supported pendulum shown, if $m = 15$ kg, $k_1 = 800$ N/m, $k_2 = 500$ N/m, $L = 1.5$ m, $b = 0.5$ m, and $d = 1$ m. Neglect the mass of the rod and the size of the bob. The pendulum is in equilibrium in the vertical position shown, and the springs are undeformed at this position.

10.14 Derive the expression for the natural circular frequency of the pendulum in Problem 10.13 in terms of m, L, k, and b, where $k = k_1 = k_2$ and $b = d$.

10.15 The natural period of small-amplitude vibration of the spring-supported pendulum is 0.25 s. If $b = 4$ ft, determine the spring stiffness k. Neglect the mass of the rod and the size of the bob. The pendulum is in equilibrium in the vertical position shown, and the spring is undeformed at this position.

10.16 For the pendulum in Problem 10.15, determine the distance b for which the spring stiffness is minimum.

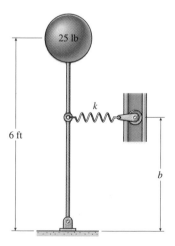

Figure P10.15 and P10.16

10.17 Determine the natural circular frequency of small-amplitude vibration of the 50-kg collar. Neglect the mass of the bent bar and the size of the collar. The system is in equilibrium in the position shown, and the spring is undeformed at this position.

10.18 Determine the expression for the natural circular frequency of small-amplitude vibration of the slender bar of length L and weight W. The bar is supported by a hinged support as shown, and is in equilibrium in the vertical position.

10.19 through 10.21 Determine the natural period of small-amplitude vibration of the plate shown. The plate is supported by a hinged support, and is in equilibrium in the position shown in the figure.

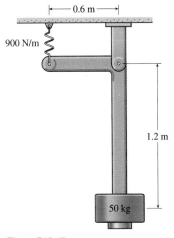

Figure P10.17

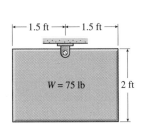

Figure P10.19

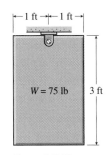

Figure P10.20

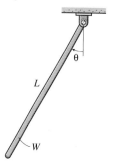

Figure P10.18

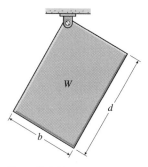

Figure P10.21

10.22 A uniform circular disk is rigidly attached to a thin shaft of torsional stiffness 30 N · m/rad as shown. When the disk is rotated (thereby twisting the shaft) and released, the period of torsional vibration is found to be 1 s. Determine the centroidal moment of inertia of the disk.

Figure P10.22

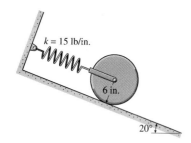

Figure P10.23

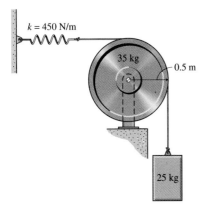

Figure P10.24

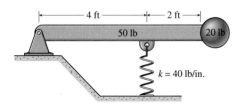

Figure P10.25

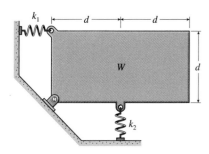

Figure P10.27

10.23 A cylinder of 6-in. radius weighing 20 lb is attached to a spring as shown. The cylinder rolls on the inclined surface without slipping. Determine the natural period of vibration of the system.

10.24 A 25-kg block is supported by a cable, which wraps over a 35-kg circular disk of 0.5 m radius and is attached to a spring as shown. The block is pulled 0.2 m downward from its equilibrium position and released. Determine (a) the natural period of vibration, and (b) the maximum velocity of the block. The system is in equilibrium in the position shown.

10.25 A 20-lb sphere is attached to a rod weighing 50 lb as shown. The sphere is pushed 3 in. downward, and released. Determine (a) the natural period of small-amplitude vibration, and (b) the maximum velocity of the sphere. The system is in equilibrium in the position shown. Neglect the size of the sphere.

10.26 A 270-kg beam is supported as shown. The end B of the beam is pushed 10 cm downward and released. Determine (a) the natural period of small-amplitude vibration, and (b) the maximum velocity of end B of the beam. The system is in equilibrium as shown.

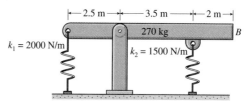

Figure P10.26

10.27 A plate is supported by a hinged support and two springs as shown. Determine the natural period of small-amplitude vibration of the system.

SECTION 10.4

10.28 Solve Problem 10.1 by the energy method.

10.29 Solve Problem 10.2 by the energy method.

10.30 Solve Problem 10.7 by the energy method.

10.31 Determine the natural period of vibration of the system shown by the energy method.

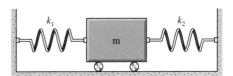

Figure P10.31

10.32   Solve Problem 10.11 by the energy method.

10.33   Solve Problem 10.14 by the energy method.

10.34   Solve Problem 10.17 by the energy method.

10.35   Solve Problem 10.18 by the energy method.

10.36   Solve Problem 10.19 by the energy method.

10.37   Solve Problem 10.20 by the energy method.

10.38   Solve Problem 10.21 by the energy method.

10.39   Solve Problem 10.23 by the energy method.

10.40   Solve Problem 10.24 by the energy method.

10.41 and 10.42   Determine the natural period of vibration of the system shown by the energy method.

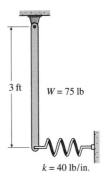

3 ft $W = 75$ lb

$k = 40$ lb/in.

Figure P10.41

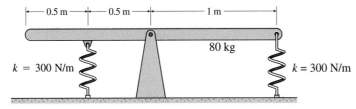

0.5 m — 0.5 m — 1 m

80 kg

$k = 300$ N/m $k = 300$ N/m

Figure P10.42

10.43   Solve Problem 10.27 by the energy method.

10.44   A cylinder of 6-in. radius is in equilibrium on a curved surface of 4-ft radius as shown. If the cylinder is displaced slightly and released, determine its natural period of vibration. Assume that the cylinder rolls on the surface without slipping. Use the energy method.

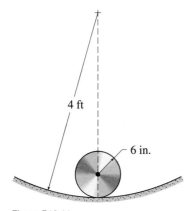

4 ft

6 in.

Figure P10.44

SECTION 10.5

10.45 A 10-kg block is attached to a spring of stiffness $k = 300$ N/m as shown. The block is subjected to an external force $F = F_o \sin \bar{\omega}t$. Determine the frequency of the force function $\bar{\omega}$ that will cause resonance.

10.46 The spring-mass system of Problem 10.45 is subjected to an external force $F = 8 \sin 3t$ N. Determine the amplitude of the steady-state vibration of the system.

10.47 The spring-mass system of Problem 10.45 is subjected to an external force $F = 30 \sin 7t$ N. If the block is given an initial displacement of 0.2 m to the right from its equilibrium position and released at $t = 0$, determine the equation of the displacement of the block. Assume positive displacement to the right from the equilibrium position.

10.48 A spring-mass system is subjected to an external force $F = F_o \cos \bar{\omega}t$ as shown. Determine (*a*) the differential equation of motion of the system, and (*b*) the equation describing the steady-state vibration of the mass. Assume positive displacement to the right from the equilibrium position as shown in the figure.

10.49 A 15-lb block is attached to a spring of stiffness 12 lb/in., and is subjected to an external force $F = 25 \sin 2t$ lb. Determine (*a*) the dynamic magnification factor, and (*b*) the amplitude of steady-state vibration of the system.

10.50 A 20-kg block is attached to a spring of stiffness 400 N/m, and is subjected to an external force $F = 35 \sin \bar{\omega}t$ N. If the amplitude of steady-state vibration is observed to be 0.12 m, determine the frequency $\bar{\omega}$ of the force function.

10.51 A 15-lb block is attached to a spring of stiffness 12 lb/in., and is subjected to an external force $F = F_o \sin \bar{\omega}t$ lb. Determine the range of values of the frequency $\bar{\omega}$ of the force function for which the amplitude of the steady-state vibration is greater than the static deflection of the block subjected to the force F_o.

10.52 For the system in Problem 10.51, determine the range of values of the frequency $\bar{\omega}$ of the force function for which the amplitude of the steady-state vibration is less than one-half of the static deflection of the block subjected to the force F_o.

10.53 A 70-kg motor mounted on four springs, each of stiffness 1500 N/m, is constrained to move only in the vertical direction as shown. The unbalance in the rotor is represented by an eccentric 0.5-kg mass with the eccentricity of 80 mm from the axis of rotation. If the motor is rotating at a speed of 400 rpm, determine the amplitude of its vibration. Also, determine the speed of the motor that will cause resonance.

10.54 Solve Problem 10.53 if the motor is rotating at a speed of 150 rpm.

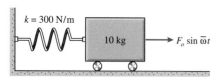

$k = 300$ N/m

10 kg $\rightarrow F_o \sin \bar{\omega}t$

Figure P10.45, P10.46, and P10.47

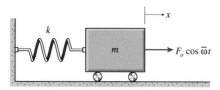

$\rightarrow x$

k

m $\rightarrow F_o \cos \bar{\omega}t$

Figure P10.48

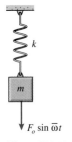

k

m

$\downarrow F_o \sin \bar{\omega}t$

Figure P10.49, P10.50, P10.51, and P10.52

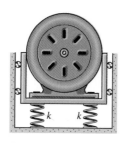

k k

Figure P10.53 and P10.54

10.55 A 5-lb block is attached to a spring of stiffness 3 lb/in. as shown. If the support is given a horizontal motion $x_s = 6 \sin 9t$ in., determine (*a*) the dynamic magnification factor, and (*b*) the amplitude of steady-state vibrat on of the system.

10.56 An 8-kg block is attached to a spring of stiffness 100 N/m as shown. If the support is given a horizontal motion $x_s = 0.25 \sin 5t$ m, determine (*a*) the dynamic magnification factor, and (*b*) the amplitude of steady-state vibration of the system.

10.57 A 50-lb instrument is supported on a floor by four springs, each of stiffness 112 lb/ft. Determine the amplitude of the steady-state vibration of the instrument if the floor vibrates in the vertical direction with an amplitude of 1 in. at a frequency of 15 rad/s.

10.58 Determine the amplitude of the steady-state vibration of end B of the rod.

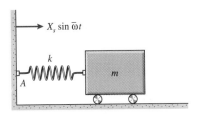

Figure P10.55 and P10.56

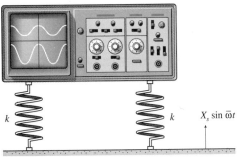

Figure P10.57

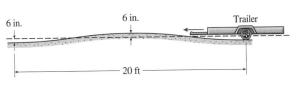

Figure P10.58

10.59 A 25-lb sphere is attached to a rod weighing 50 lb. The rod is subjected to a force $F = 100 \sin 15t$ lb as shown. Determine the amplitude of the steady-state vibration of the sphere. Neglect the size of the sphere.

10.60 A trailer weighing 400 lb is moving with a constant horizontal velocity over a rough road, whose profile can be approximated as a sinusoidal curve of amplitude 6 in. and wave length 20 ft, as shown. The trailer is attached to each of the two wheels by means of springs of stiffness 60 lb/in. each. Determine the speed of the trailer at which the resonance will occur.

10.61 For the trailer in Problem 10.60, determine the amplitude of steady-state vibration, if the trailer is moving at a constant velocity of 50 mph.

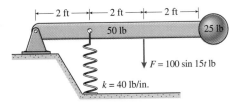

Figure P10.59

Figure P10.60 and P10.61

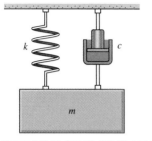

Figure P10.62, P10.63, P10.64, and P10.65

SECTION 10.6

10.62 A 50-kg block is attached to a spring of stiffness 200 N/m, and a dashpot of coefficient of viscous damping $c = 100 \text{ N} \cdot \text{s/m}$. Determine (*a*) the damping factor, and (*b*) the damped natural period of vibration if the system is underdamped.

10.63 Solve Problem 10.62 if $c = 200 \text{ N} \cdot \text{s/m}$.

10.64 Solve Problem 10.62 if $c = 225 \text{ N} \cdot \text{s/m}$.

10.65 Show that the ratio of any two successive amplitudes x_1 and x_2 of damped free vibration is constant, and can be expressed by the relationship $\ln(x_1/x_2) = (c/c_c)\omega_n T_d$. The quantity $\ln(x_1/x_2)$ is termed the *logarithmic decrement*.

10.66 and 10.67 Determine the differential equation of small-amplitude motion of the system shown. Also, determine the damping factor, and the damped natural period if the system is underdamped.

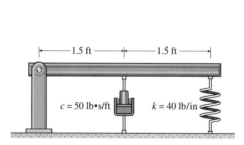

Figure P10.66

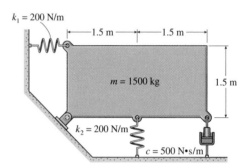

Figure P10.67

SECTION 10.7

10.68 Solve Problem 10.49 assuming that a parallel dashpot is attached to the block providing a damping factor of 0.5.

10.69 and 10.70 Solve Problems 10.51 and 10.52, respectively, assuming that a parallel dashpot with a coefficient of viscous damping $c = 6 \text{ lb} \cdot \text{s/ft}$ is attached to the block.

10.71 and 10.72 Solve Problems 10.53 and 10.54, respectively, assuming that a parallel dashpot with a coefficient of viscous damping $c = 300 \text{ N} \cdot \text{s/m}$ is attached to the machine.

10.73 Solve Problem 10.61 assuming that a parallel dashpot with a coefficient of viscous damping $c = 110 \text{ lb} \cdot \text{s/ft}$ is attached between the trailer and each of the two wheels.

10.74 A seismograph is bolted on top of a shaking table vibrating vertically with an amplitude of 8 mm at a frequency of 4 Hz. A record of the motion of mass m of the seismograph shows that the amplitude of the motion of the mass relative to the table is 12 mm. Determine the coefficient of viscous damping c, if $m = 1$ kg and $k = 300$ N/m.

SECTION 10.8

10.75 through 10.77   Construct the electrical analogue of the mechanical system shown in each of the figures.

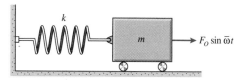

Figure P10.75

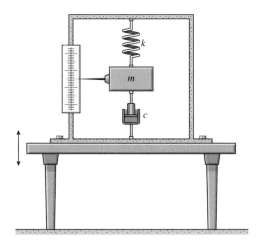

Figure P10.74

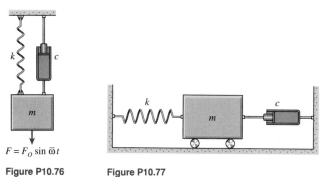

Figure P10.76   **Figure P10.77**

APPENDIX A

SI PREFIXES

Prefix	Factor	Symbol
atto	10^{-18}	a
femto	10^{-15}	f
pico	10^{-12}	p
nano	10^{-9}	n
micro	10^{-6}	μ
milli	10^{-3}	m
kilo	10^{3}	k
mega	10^{6}	M
giga	10^{9}	G
tera	10^{12}	T

APPENDIX B

CONVERSION FACTORS

Table B.1 Conversion factors from US Customary units to SI units

Length
1 ft = 0.3048 m
1 ft = 304.8 mm
1 in. = 0.0254 m
1 in. = 25.4 mm

Area
$1 \text{ ft}^2 = 0.0929 \text{ m}^2$
$1 \text{ ft}^2 = 929 \times 10^2 \text{ mm}^2$
$1 \text{ in}^2 = 6.452 \times 10^{-4} \text{ m}^2$
$1 \text{ in}^2 = 645.16 \text{ mm}^2$

Volume
$1 \text{ ft}^3 = 28.317 \times 10^{-3} \text{ m}^3$
$1 \text{ ft}^3 = 28.317 \times 10^6 \text{ mm}^3$
$1 \text{ in}^3 = 16.387 \times 10^{-6} \text{ m}^3$
$1 \text{ in}^3 = 16.387 \times 10^3 \text{ mm}^3$

Force
1 lb = 4.448 N
$1 \text{ lb} = 4.448 \times 10^{-3} \text{ kN}$
1 kip = 4.448 kN
1 lb/ft = 14.593 N/m

Speed
1 ft/sec = 0.3048 m/sec
1 mile/hr = 0.44704 m/sec
1 mile/hr = 1.6093 km/hr

Acceleration
$1 \text{ ft/sec}^2 = 0.3048 \text{ m/sec}^2$
$1 \text{ in./sec}^2 = 0.0254 \text{ m/sec}^2$

Specific weight
$1 \text{ lb/ft}^3 = 0.1572 \text{ kN/m}^3$
$1 \text{ lb/in}^3 = 271.66 \text{ kN/m}^3$

Moment
$1 \text{ lb} \cdot \text{ft} = 1.3558 \text{ N} \cdot \text{m}$
$1 \text{ lb} \cdot \text{in.} = 0.11298 \text{ N} \cdot \text{m}$

Energy
1 ft · lb = 1.3558 J (joules)

Moment of inertia of area
$1 \text{ in}^4 = 0.4162 \times 10^6 \text{ mm}^4$
$1 \text{ in}^4 = 0.4162 \times 10^{-6} \text{ m}^4$

Table B.2 Conversion factors from SI units to US Customary units

Length
1 m = 3.281 ft
$1 \text{ mm} = 3.281 \times 10^{-3} \text{ ft}$
1 m = 39.37 in.
1 mm = 0.03937 in.

Area
$1 \text{ m}^2 = 10.764 \text{ ft}^2$
$1 \text{ mm}^2 = 10.764 \times 10^{-6} \text{ ft}^2$
$1 \text{ m}^2 = 1550 \text{ in}^2$
$1 \text{ mm}^2 = 0.00155 \text{ in}^2$

Volume
$1 \text{ m}^3 = 35.32 \text{ ft}^3$
$1 \text{ cm}^3 = 35.32 \times 10^{-4} \text{ ft}^3$
$1 \text{ m}^3 = 61{,}023.4 \text{ in}^3$

Force
1 N = 0.2248 lb
1 kN = 224.8 lb
1 kN = 0.2248 kip
1 N/m = 0.0685 lb/ft

Speed
1 m/sec = 3.2808 ft/sec
1 m/sec = 2.23694 mile/hr
1 km/hr = 0.6214 mile/hr

Acceleration
$1 \text{ m/sec}^2 = 3.2808 \text{ ft/sec}^2$
$1 \text{ m/sec}^2 = 39.3701 \text{ in./sec}^2$

Specific weight
$1 \text{ kN/m}^3 = 6.361 \text{ lb/ft}^3$
$1 \text{ kN/m}^3 = 0.00368 \text{ lb/in}^3$

Moment
$1 \text{ N} \cdot \text{m} = 0.7375 \text{ lb} \cdot \text{ft}$
$1 \text{ N} \cdot \text{m} = 8.851 \text{ lb} \cdot \text{in.}$

Energy
1 J (joule) = 0.7375 ft · lb

Moment of inertia of area
$1 \text{ m}^4 = 2.402 \times 10^6 \text{ in}^4$
$1 \text{ mm}^4 = 2.402 \times 10^{-6} \text{ in}^4$

SPECIFIC WEIGHT OF COMMON MATERIALS (AVERAGE VALUES)

Material	Specific weight	
	(lb/ft^3)	(kN/m^3)
Water	62.4	9.81
Wrought iron	480	75.46
Structural steel	490	77.03
Stainless steel	495	77.82
Cast aluminum	172	27.04
Magnesium	115	18.08
Brass	545	85.68
Concrete	150	23.58
Red oak (air-dry wood)	44	6.92
Douglas fir (air-dry wood)	38	5.97

MATHEMATICAL EXPRESSIONS

A. Quadratic equation

If $ax^2 + bx + c = 0$

$$x = \frac{-b \pm \sqrt{b^2 - 4ac}}{2a}$$

B. Trigonometric relationships

1. $\sin x = \dfrac{1}{\csc x}$

2. $\cos x = \dfrac{1}{\sec x}$

3. $\tan x = \dfrac{1}{\cot x} = \dfrac{\sin x}{\cos x}$

4. $\sin x = \cos(90 - x)$

5. $\cos x = \sin(90 - x)$

6. $\tan x = \cot(90 - x)$

7. $\cot x = \tan(90 - x)$

8. $\sin 2x = 2 \sin x \cos x$

9. $\cos 2x = \cos^2 x - \sin^2 x = 2 \cos^2 x - 1 = 1 - 2 \sin^2 x$

10. $\tan 2x = \dfrac{2 \tan x}{1 - \tan^2 x}$

11. $\cot 2x = \dfrac{\cot^2 x - 1}{2 \cot x}$

12. $\sin 3x = 3 \sin x - 4 \sin^3 x$

13. $\cos 3x = 4 \cos^3 x - 3 \cos x$

14. $\tan 3x = \dfrac{3 \tan x - \tan^3 x}{1 - 3 \tan^2 x}$

15. $\sin^2 x + \cos^2 x = 1$

16. $\sec^2 x = 1 + \tan^2 x$

17. $\csc^2 x = 1 + \cot^2 x$

18. $\sin(x + y) = \sin x \cos y + \cos x \sin y$

19. $\sin(x - y) = \sin x \cos y - \cos x \sin y$

20. $\cos(x + y) = \cos x \cos y - \sin x \sin y$

21. $\cos(x - y) = \cos x \cos y + \sin x \sin y$

22. $\tan(x + y) = \dfrac{\tan x + \tan y}{1 - \tan x \tan y}$

23. $\tan(x - y) = \dfrac{\tan x - \tan y}{1 + \tan x \tan y}$

24. $\cot(x + y) = \dfrac{\cot x \cot y - 1}{\cot x + \cot y}$

25. $\cot(x - y) = \dfrac{\cot x \cot y + 1}{\cot y - \cot x}$

C. Hyperbolic functions

1. $\sinh x = \dfrac{1}{\operatorname{cosech} x}$

2. $\cosh x = \dfrac{1}{\operatorname{sech} x}$

3. $\tanh x = \dfrac{1}{\coth x}$

4. $\sinh x = \pm \sqrt{\cosh^2 x - 1}$

5. $\cosh x = \pm \sqrt{1 + \sinh^2 x}$

D. Series

1. $\sin x = x - \dfrac{x^3}{3!} + \dfrac{x^5}{5!} - \dfrac{x^7}{7!} + \cdots$ (for $x^2 < \infty$)

2. $\cos x = 1 - \dfrac{x^2}{2!} + \dfrac{x^4}{4!} - \dfrac{x^6}{6!} + \cdots$ (for $x^2 < \infty$)

3. $\sinh x = \dfrac{e^x - e^{-x}}{2} = x + \dfrac{x^3}{3!} + \dfrac{x^5}{5!} + \cdots$ (for $x^2 < \infty$)

4. $\cosh x = \dfrac{e^x + e^{-x}}{2} = 1 + \dfrac{x^2}{2!} + \dfrac{x^4}{4!} + \dfrac{x^6}{6!} + \cdots$ (for $x^2 < \infty$)

5. $(1 \pm x)^n = 1 \pm nx + \dfrac{n(n-1)}{2!} x^2 \pm \dfrac{n(n-1)(n-2)}{3!} x^3 + \cdots$ (for $x^2 < 1$)

6. $(x + y)^n = x^n + nx^{n-1}y + \dfrac{n(n-1)}{2!} x^{n-2}y^2 + \dfrac{n(n-1)(n-2)}{3!} x^{n-3}y^3 + \cdots$ (for $y^2 < x^2$)

7. $e^x = 1 + x + \dfrac{x^2}{2!} + \dfrac{x^3}{3!} + \dfrac{x^4}{4!} + \cdots$ (for all real values of x)

E. Logarithms

1. If $y = a^x$ then $x = \log_a y$
2. If $y = e^x$ then $x = \log_e y = \ln y$
3. $\log a^n = n \log a$
4. $\log \left(\dfrac{1}{n} \right) = -\log n$
5. $\log (ab) = \log a + \log b$
6. $\log \left(\dfrac{a}{b} \right) = \log a - \log b$

F. Derivatives

1. $\dfrac{d}{dx}(nu) = n \dfrac{du}{dx}$

2. $\dfrac{d}{dx}(uv) = u \dfrac{dv}{dx} + v \dfrac{du}{dx}$

3. $\dfrac{d}{dx}\left(\dfrac{u}{v} \right) = \dfrac{v \dfrac{du}{dx} - u \dfrac{dv}{dx}}{v^2} = \dfrac{1}{v} \dfrac{du}{dx} - \dfrac{u}{v^2} \dfrac{dv}{dx}$

4. $\dfrac{d}{dx}(u^n) = nu^{n-1} \dfrac{du}{dx}$

5. $\dfrac{d}{dx}\left(\dfrac{1}{u^n} \right) = -\dfrac{n}{u^{n+1}} \dfrac{du}{dx}$

6. $\dfrac{d}{dx}(u^n v^m) = u^{n-1} v^{m-1} \left(nv \dfrac{du}{dx} + mu \dfrac{dv}{dx} \right)$

7. $\dfrac{d}{dx}\left(\dfrac{u^n}{v^m} \right) = \dfrac{u^{n-1}}{v^{m+1}} \left(nv \dfrac{du}{dx} - mu \dfrac{dv}{dx} \right)$

8. $\dfrac{d}{dx}(\sin x) = \cos x$

9. $\dfrac{d}{dx}(\cos x) = -\sin x$

10. $\dfrac{d}{dx}(\tan x) = \sec^2 x$

11. $\dfrac{d}{dx}(\csc x) = -\cot x \csc x$

12. $\dfrac{d}{dx}(\sec x) = \tan x \sec x$

13. $\dfrac{d}{dx}(\cot x) = -\csc^2 x$

14. $\dfrac{d}{dx}(\sinh x) = \cosh x$

15. $\dfrac{d}{dx}(\cosh x) = \sinh x$

16. $\dfrac{d}{dx}(\tanh x) = \mathrm{sech}^2 x$

17. $\dfrac{d}{dx}(\log_a u) = (\log_a e) \dfrac{1}{u} \dfrac{du}{dx}$

18. $\dfrac{d}{dx}(\log_e u) = \dfrac{1}{u} \dfrac{du}{dx}$

G. Integrals

1. $\int a \, dx = ax$

2. $\int x^n \, dx = \dfrac{x^{n+1}}{n+1}$ (except for $n = -1$)

3. $\int \dfrac{dx}{x} = \ln x$

4. $\int e^x \, dx = e^x$

5. $\int e^{ax} \, dx = \dfrac{e^{ax}}{a}$

6. $\int \ln x \, dx = x \ln x - x$

7. $\displaystyle\int \frac{dx}{a^2 + x^2} = \frac{1}{a} \tan^{-1}\left(\frac{x}{a}\right)$

8. $\displaystyle\int \frac{dx}{a + bx^2} = \frac{1}{\sqrt{ab}} \tan^{-1}\left(\frac{x\sqrt{ab}}{a}\right) \ (ab > 0)$

9. $\displaystyle\int \sqrt{x^2 \pm a^2} = \frac{1}{2}[x\sqrt{x^2 \pm a^2} \pm a^2 \times$
$$\ln (x + \sqrt{x^2 \pm a^2})]$$

10. $\displaystyle\int \sqrt{a^2 - x^2}\, dx$
$$= \frac{1}{2}\left[x\sqrt{a^2 - x^2} + a^2 \sin^{-1}\left(\frac{x}{|a|}\right)\right]$$

11. $\displaystyle\int x\sqrt{a^2 - x^2} = -\frac{1}{3}\sqrt{(a^2 - x^2)^3}$

12. $\displaystyle\int x^2\sqrt{a^2 - x^2}\, dx = -\frac{x}{4}\sqrt{(a^2 - x^2)^3} +$
$$\frac{a^2}{8}\left[x\sqrt{a^2 - x^2} + a^2 \sin^{-1}\left(\frac{x}{|a|}\right)\right]$$

13. $\displaystyle\int x^3\sqrt{a^2 - x^2} = -\frac{1}{5}\left(x^2 + \frac{2}{3}a^2\right) \times$
$$\sqrt{(a^2 - x^2)^3}$$

14. $\displaystyle\int \sqrt{a + bx}\, dx = \frac{2}{3b}\sqrt{(a + bx)^3}$

15. $\displaystyle\int x\sqrt{a + bx}\, dx = \frac{2}{15b^2}(3bx - 2a) \times$
$$\sqrt{(a + bx)^3}$$

16. $\displaystyle\int \frac{dx}{\sqrt{a + bx}} = \frac{2\sqrt{a + bx}}{b}$

17. $\displaystyle\int \frac{dx}{\sqrt{x^2 \pm a^2}} = \ln (x + \sqrt{x^2 \pm a^2})$

18. $\displaystyle\int \frac{x\, dx}{a + bx} = \frac{1}{b^2}[a + bx - a \ln (a + bx)]$

19. $\displaystyle\int \frac{x\, dx}{a + bx^2} = \frac{1}{2b} \ln (a + bx^2)$

20. $\displaystyle\int \frac{x\, dx}{\sqrt{x^2 \pm a^2}} = \sqrt{x^2 \pm a^2}$

21. $\displaystyle\int \frac{x\, dx}{\sqrt{a^2 \pm x^2}} = \pm \sqrt{a^2 \pm x^2}$

22. $\int \sin x\, dx = -\cos x$

23. $\int \cos x\, dx = \sin x$

24. $\int \tan x\, dx = \ln (\sec x)$

25. $\int \cot x\, dx = \ln (\sin x)$

26. $\displaystyle\int \sin^2 x\, dx = \frac{x}{2} - \frac{\sin 2x}{4}$

27. $\displaystyle\int \cos^2 x\, dx = \frac{x}{2} + \frac{\sin 2x}{4}$

28. $\displaystyle\int \sin x \cos x\, dx = \frac{\sin^2 x}{2}$

29. $\displaystyle\int \sin^3 x\, dx = -\frac{\cos x}{3}(2 + \sin^2 x)$

30. $\displaystyle\int \cos^3 x\, dx = \frac{\sin x}{3}(2 + \cos^2 x)$

31. $\int \sinh x\, dx = \cosh x$

32. $\int \cosh x\, dx = \sinh x$

33. $\int \tanh x\, dx = \ln (\cosh x)$

34. $\int x \sin x\, dx = \sin x - x \cos x$

35. $\int x \cos x\, dx = \cos x + x \sin x$

36. $\int x^2 \sin x\, dx = 2x \sin x - x^2 \cos x + 2 \cos x$

37. $\int x^2 \cos x\, dx = 2x \cos x + x^2 \sin x - 2 \sin x$

PROPERTIES OF AREAS AND HOMOGENEOUS BODIES

Table E.1 Properties of areas

Shape	Area	$\bar{x}, \bar{y}$	Moment of inertia (or second moment of area)
Rectangle	bh	$\bar{x} = \dfrac{b}{2}$ $\bar{y} = \dfrac{h}{2}$	$I_x = \dfrac{1}{3} bh^3$ $I_y = \dfrac{1}{3} hb^3$ $I_{x'} = \dfrac{1}{12} bh^3$ $I_{y'} = \dfrac{1}{12} hb^3$
Triangle	$\dfrac{1}{2} bh$	$\bar{x} = \dfrac{b+c}{3}$ $\bar{y} = \dfrac{h}{3}$	$I_x = \dfrac{bh^3}{12}$ $I_y = \dfrac{bh}{12}(b^2 + bc + c^2)$ $I_{x'} = \dfrac{bh^3}{36}$ $I_{y'} = \dfrac{bh}{36}(b^2 - bc + c^2)$
Right-angle triangle	$\dfrac{1}{2} bh$	$\bar{x} = \dfrac{b}{3}$ $\bar{y} = \dfrac{h}{3}$	$I_x = \dfrac{bh^3}{12}$ $I_y = \dfrac{b^3 h}{12}$ $I_{x'} = \dfrac{bh^3}{36}$ $I_{y'} = \dfrac{b^3 h}{36}$
Circle	πr^2	$\bar{x} = 0$ $\bar{y} = r$	$I_x = \dfrac{5\pi r^4}{4}$ $I_{x'} = I_{y'} = \dfrac{\pi r^4}{4}$
Semicircle	$\dfrac{\pi r^2}{2}$	$\bar{x} = 0$ $\bar{y} = \dfrac{4r}{3\pi}$	$I_x = I_y = I_{y'} = \dfrac{\pi r^4}{8}$ $I_{x'} = \left(\dfrac{9\pi^2 - 64}{72\pi}\right) r^4$

Note: Location of centroid is O'; Ox and Oy are Cartesian coordinate axes; $O'x'$ and $O'y'$ are centroidal coordinate axes; $\bar{x}$ and $\bar{y}$ are centroidal coordinates with respect to the Ox and Oy axes.

500

Table E.1 Properties of areas (*continued*)

Shape	Area	$\bar{x}, \bar{y}$	Moment of inertia (or second moment of area)
Quarter-circle	$\dfrac{\pi r^2}{4}$	$\bar{x} = \bar{y} = \dfrac{4r}{3\pi}$	$I_x = I_y = \dfrac{\pi r^4}{16}$ $I_{x'} = I_{y'} = \left(\dfrac{9\pi^2 - 64}{144\pi}\right) r^4$
Ellipse	πab	$\bar{x} = \bar{y} = 0$	$I_x = I_{x'} = \dfrac{\pi ab^3}{4}$ $I_y = I_{y'} = \dfrac{\pi ba^3}{4}$
Circular sector	αr^2	$\bar{x} = \dfrac{2\,r \sin \alpha}{3\,\alpha}$ $\bar{y} = 0$	$I_x = I_{x'} = \dfrac{r^4}{4}(\alpha - \sin \alpha \cos \alpha)$ $I_y = \dfrac{r^4}{4}(\alpha + \sin \alpha \cos \alpha)$ $I_{y'} = \dfrac{r^4}{4}(\alpha + \sin \alpha \cos \alpha) - \dfrac{4}{9}\dfrac{r^4 \sin^2 \alpha}{\alpha}$
Circular segment	$r^2 (\alpha - \sin \alpha \cos \alpha)$	$\bar{x} = 0$ $\bar{y} = \dfrac{2r}{3}\left(\dfrac{\sin^3 \alpha}{\alpha - \sin \alpha \cos \alpha}\right)$	$I_x = \dfrac{r^4}{4}(\alpha + 2 \sin^3 \alpha \cos \alpha - \sin \alpha \cos \alpha)$ $I_y = I_{y'} = \dfrac{r^4}{12}(3\alpha - 2 \sin^3 \alpha \cos \alpha - 3 \sin \alpha \cos \alpha)$
Trapezoid	$\dfrac{h}{2}(b_1 + b_2)$	$\bar{y} = \dfrac{h(2b_1 + b_2)}{3(b_1 + b_2)}$	$I_x = \dfrac{h^3}{12}(3b_1 + b_2)$ $I_{x'} = \dfrac{h^3 (b_1^2 + 4b_1 b_2 + b_2^2)}{36(b_1 + b_2)}$

Table E.1 Properties of areas (*concluded*)

Shape	Area	$\bar{x}, \bar{y}$	Moment of inertia (or second moment of area)
Quarter-circle spandrel	$r^2 - \dfrac{\pi}{4} r^2$	$\bar{x} = \dfrac{2r}{3(4 - \pi)}$ $\bar{y} = \dfrac{(10 - 3\pi)}{3(4 - \pi)} r$	$I_x = \left(1 - \dfrac{5\pi}{16}\right) r^4$ $I_y = \left(\dfrac{1}{3} - \dfrac{\pi}{16}\right) r^4$
Parabolic semisegment $y = b\left(1 - \dfrac{x^2}{a^2}\right)$	$\dfrac{2ab}{3}$	$\bar{x} = \dfrac{3a}{8}$ $\bar{y} = \dfrac{2b}{5}$	$I_x = \dfrac{16}{105}(ab^3)$ $I_y = \dfrac{2}{15}(ba^3)$
Parabolic spandrel $y = \left(\dfrac{b}{a^2}\right) x^2$	$\dfrac{ab}{3}$	$\bar{x} = \dfrac{3a}{4}$ $\bar{y} = \dfrac{3b}{10}$	$I_x = \dfrac{ab^3}{21}$ $I_y = \dfrac{ba^3}{5}$

Table E.2 Properties of homogeneous bodies

Shape	Volume	$\bar{x}, \bar{y}, \bar{z}$	Mass moment of inertia
Uniform slender rod	AL	$0, 0, 0$	$I_{y'} = I_{z'} = \frac{1}{12} mL^2$ $I_{x'} = 0$
Circular cylinder	$\pi R^2 L$	$0, 0, 0$	$I_{x'} = \frac{1}{2} mR^2$ $I_{y'} = I_{z'} = \frac{1}{12} m(3R^2 + L^2)$
Sphere	$\frac{4}{3}\pi R^3$	$0, 0, 0$	$I_{x'} = I_{y'} = I_{z'} = \frac{2}{5} mR^2$
Hemisphere; Radius $= R$	$\frac{2}{3}\pi R^3$	$\bar{x} = 0$ $\bar{y} = \frac{3}{8} R$ $\bar{z} = 0$	$I_{x'} = I_{z'} = \frac{83}{320} mR^2$ $I_{y'} = \frac{2}{5} mR^2$

Note: Location of center of gravity is O'; Ox, Oy, Oz are Cartesian coordinate axes; $O'x'$, $O'y'$, $O'z'$ are centroidal coordinate axes; m = mass; $\bar{x}$, $\bar{y}$, $\bar{z}$ are centroidal coordinates with respect to the Ox, Oy, and Oz axes.

Table E.2 Properties of homogeneous bodies (*continued*)

Shape	Volume	$\bar{x}, \bar{y}, \bar{z}$	Mass moment of inertia
Rectangular prism	LBH	$\bar{x} = \dfrac{L}{2}$ $\bar{y} = 0$ $\bar{z} = 0$	$I_x = I_{x'} = \frac{1}{12} m(B^2 + H^2)$ $I_{y'} = \frac{1}{12} m(L^2 + B^2)$ $I_{z'} = \frac{1}{12} m(L^2 + H^2)$ $I_y = \frac{1}{12} mB^2 + \frac{1}{3} mL^2$ $I_z = \frac{1}{12} mH^2 + \frac{1}{3} mL^2$
Thin plate	AL	$\bar{x} = \dfrac{L}{2}$ $\bar{y} = 0$ $\bar{z} = 0$	$I_x = I_{x'} = \frac{1}{12} mH^2$ $I_{y'} = \frac{1}{12} mL^2$ $I_{z'} = \frac{1}{12} m(L^2 + H^2)$ $I_y = \frac{1}{3} mL^2$ $I_z = \frac{1}{12} mH^2 + \frac{1}{3} mL^2$
Cone	$\frac{1}{3} \pi R^2 H$	$\bar{x} = 0$ $\bar{y} = \dfrac{H}{4}$ $\bar{z} = 0$	$I_x = I_z = \frac{3}{20} mR^2 + \frac{1}{10} mH^2$ $I_y = I_{y'} = \frac{3}{10} mR^2$ $I_{x'} = I_{z'} = \frac{3}{20} mR^2 + \frac{3}{80} mH^2$
Half-cone	$\frac{1}{6} \pi R^2 H$	$\bar{x} = 0$ $\bar{y} = \dfrac{H}{4}$ $\bar{z} = \dfrac{R}{\pi}$	$I_x = I_z = \frac{3}{20} mR^2 + \frac{1}{10} mH^2$ $I_y = \frac{3}{10} mR^2$ $I_{x'} = \left(\frac{3}{20} - \frac{1}{\pi^2}\right) mR^2 + \frac{3}{80} mH^2$ $I_{y'} = \left(\frac{3}{10} - \frac{1}{\pi^2}\right) mR^2$ $I_{z'} = \frac{3}{20} mR^2 + \frac{3}{80} mH^2$

Table E.2 Properties of homogeneous bodies (*concluded*)

Shape	Volume	$\bar{x}, \bar{y}, \bar{z}$	Mass moment of inertia
Elliptic cylinder	πabL	$\bar{x} = \dfrac{L}{2}$ $\bar{y} = 0$ $\bar{z} = 0$	$I_x = I_{x'} = \frac{1}{4}m(a^2 + b^2)$ $I_y = \frac{1}{4}mb^2 + \frac{1}{3}mL^2$ $I_z = \frac{1}{4}ma^2 + \frac{1}{3}mL^2$ $I_{y'} = \frac{1}{4}mb^2 + \frac{1}{12}mL^2$ $I_{z'} = \frac{1}{4}ma^2 + \frac{1}{12}mL^2$
Tetrahedron		$\bar{x} = \dfrac{a}{4}$ $\bar{y} = \dfrac{b}{4}$ $\bar{z} = \dfrac{c}{4}$	$I_x = \frac{1}{10}m(b^2 + c^2)$ $I_y = \frac{1}{10}m(a^2 + c^2)$ $I_z = \frac{1}{10}m(a^2 + b^2)$ $I_{x'} = \frac{3}{80}m(b^2 + c^2)$ $I_{y'} = \frac{3}{80}m(a^2 + c^2)$ $I_{z'} = \frac{3}{80}m(a^2 + b^2)$

ANSWERS TO SELECTED ODD-NUMBERED PROBLEMS

CHAPTER 1

1.1 (a) $v = 5$ in./s, (b) $\Delta s = 5$ in.

1.3 (a) $s = -4$ mm, $v = -21$ mm/s, $a = -12$ mm/s^2, distance traveled $= 21.75$ mm
(b) $s = 14.375$ mm, $a = -12$ mm/s^2

1.5 (a) $s = -24$ m, $v = 19$ m/s, $a = 30$ m/s^2,
(b) $s = -9$m, $v = -18.5$ m/s
(c) $s = -30.66$ m, $a = 21.07$ m/s^2

1.7 (a) $s = -49$ mm, $v = 148$ mm/s, $a = 124$ mm/s^2,
(b) $s = 170.7$ mm, $v = 224.9$ mm/s

1.9 $s = 9 - 15t + (7/2)t^2$ (in.), $a = 7$ (in./s^2);
when $v = 0$, $s = -7.07$ in., $a = 7$ in./s^2

1.11 (a) $s = 2$ km, $v = 7$ km/h, $a = 10$ km/h^2, distance traveled $= 4$ km
(b) $s = -0.407$ km, $v = -1.333$ km/h
(c) $s = -1$ km, $a = 4$ km/h^2

1.13 $a = -250$ m/s^2

1.15 (a) $s = 6480$ ft, (b) $v = 72$ ft/s

1.17 $h = 19.62$ m, $v = -19.62$ m/s

1.19 $t = 4.27$ s, $v = -139$ ft/s

1.21 $v_0 = 34.595$ m/s, $t = 7.053$ s

1.23 $s = 0.354$ mi, $a = 4200$ mi/h^2

1.25 $h = 100.625$ ft, $v_0 = 80.5$ ft/s

1.27 $v_0 = 55.557$ ft/s, $v = -169.843$ ft/s

1.29 $s = 27.53$ km

1.31 $t = 3.537$ h

1.35 $v = 395$ mm/s

1.37 $t = 27.11$ s, $s = 1328.4$ ft

1.39 (a) Total distance traveled $= 3922$ m
(b) $s = 2930.7$ m, $v = 30.34$ m/s, $a = -0.341$ m/s^2

1.41 $s = 22.2$ in., $v = 1.29$ in./s, $a = -0.25$ in./s^2

1.43 $s = 1085.7$ ft, $v = 308.7$ ft/s, $a = 65$ ft/s^2

1.45 $s = 4096$ in., $v = 2048$ in./s, $a = 768$ in./s^2

1.47 $s = 8.41$ in., $v = -9.04$ in./s, $a = -17.37$ in./s^2

1.49 $v = \sqrt{g/k} \tanh(\sqrt{gk}\,t)$

1.51 $r = 323.3$ ft $\angle 70.11°$, $v = 242.6$ ft/s $\angle 76.65°$,
$a = 120.8$ ft/s^2 $\angle 83.35°$

1.53 $r = 2.69$ m $\angle 21.8°$, $v = 8.6$ m/s $\angle 54.46°$,
$a = 18.68$ m/s^2 $\angle 74.48°$

1.55 $r = 14.22$ m $\angle 79.88°$, $v = 16.12$ m/s $\angle 82.87°$,
$a = 10.63$ m/s^2 $\angle 48.81°$

1.57 $r = 27.71$ mm $\angle 19.45°$, $v = 2.18$ mm/s $\uparrow$,
$a = 29.39$ mm/s^2 $\angle 0.97°$

1.59 $r = 8$ mm $\angle 36°$, $v = 5.03$ mm/s $\angle 54.06°$,
$a = 3.16$ mm/s^2 $\angle 36°$

1.61 (a) $t = 0.917$ s, (b) $L = 7.14$ m, (c) $y_{max} = 1.03$ m

1.63 (a) $t = 1.53$ s, (b) $L = 19.87$ m, (c) $y_{max} = 2.87$ m

1.65 $\alpha = 35.38°$ with $t = 26.43$ s, $\alpha = 54.62°$ with $t = 37.22$ s

1.67 $L = 4014$ m

1.69 (a) $t = 18.43$ s, (b) $L = 921.5$ m, (c) $y_{max} = 452.2$ m

1.71 (a) $t = 27.01$ s, (b) $L = 2025.8$ m, (c) $y_{max} = 930$ m

1.73 $v_0 = 42.53$ ft/s

1.75 $v_0 = 53.51$ m/s

1.77 13.1 ft/s $\le v_0 \le 18.02$ ft/s

1.79 $v_0 = 50.17$ ft/s, $L = 83.77$ ft

1.81 $\mathbf{r} = 81.17\mathbf{i} - 85.5\mathbf{j} - 120.25\mathbf{k}$ (m),
$\mathbf{v} = 58.5\mathbf{i} - 40\mathbf{j} - 118\mathbf{k}$ (m/s),
$\mathbf{a} = 25\mathbf{i} - 9\mathbf{j} - 75\mathbf{k}$ (m/s^2)

1.83 $h = 9.154$ km, $v_0 = 208.3$ km/h

1.85 $v = 24.25$ m/s

1.87 $\rho = 8.93$ ft

1.89 $a = 14.28$ m/s^2

1.91 $v_B = 48$ mph ⟋ 60°, $a_B = 6.51$ ft/s² ⟋ 47.9°,
$v_c = 84.68$ mph (↑), $a_c = 25.79$ ft/s² ⟋ 4.4°,
$v_D = 98.32$ mph (→), $a_D = 2$ ft/s² (→)

1.93 $a_A = 13.33$ m/s², $a_B = 20$ m/s², $a_C = 10$ m/s²

1.95 $a_A = 16.4$ m/s², $a_c = 15.8$ m/s², $v_W = 1.41$ m/s,
$a_W = 15$ m/s² ⟍

1.97 $v = 889$ mph ⟍ 63.43°, $a = 32.2$ ft/s² (↓)

1.99 $\rho_0 = 2440$ m, $\rho = 2026$ m at maximum height

1.101 $v = 8000$ mm/s, $a = 80574$ mm/s²

1.103 $v = 24.3$ m/s

1.105 $v = 36.06$ mm/s, $a = 43.42$ mm/s²

1.107 $v = 2.06$ ft/s, $a = 5.13$ ft/s²

1.109 $v = 27.65$ mm/s, $a = 30.92$ mm/s²

1.111 $v = 531.5$ m/s, $a = 23.26$ m/s²

1.113 $v = 9504$ ft/s (↑), $a = 11461$ ft/s² (↑)

1.115 $v = 400$ m/s (↑), $a = 27.21$ m/s² (↓)

1.117 $v = 739.2$ ft/s (←)

1.119 $v = 140$ in./s (↓), $a = 173.2$ in./s² (↑)

1.121 $v = 2e\dot{\theta}, a = 2e\sqrt{4\dot{\theta}^4 + \ddot{\theta}^2}$

1.123 $v = 25.28$ in./s; $a = 26.46$ in./s²

1.125 $v = 0.509$ m/s, $a = 0.127$ m/s²

1.127 $v = (ct/\pi)\sqrt{4\pi^2 R^2 + h^2}$,
$a = c\sqrt{16c^2 R^2 t^4 + 4R^2 + h^2/\pi^2}$

1.129 (a) $v_{B/A} = 115$ km/h (←), (b) $v_{A/B} = 115$ km/h (→),
(c) $t = 12$ min

1.131 (a) $S_{B/A} = 0.75$ mi (→), $v_{B/A} = 75$ mph (←),
$a_{B/A} = 1$ mi/h² (←)
(b) $S_{A/B} = 0.75$ mi (←), $v_{A/B} = 75$ mph (→),
$a_{A/B} = 1$ mi/h² (→)
(c) $t = 36$ s, $s = 0.3$ mi

1.133 $v_{A/B} = 86.33$ ft/s at 20.8° with respect to the path of B,
$a_{A/B} = 6.19$ ft/s² at 48° with respect to the path of B

1.135 (a) $v_B = 41$ ft/s at 130° with respect to the path of A
(b) $v_{B/A} = 91.9$ ft/s at 20° with respect to the path of A

1.137 (a) $v_C = 4.83$ in./s ⟋ 11.94°,
(b) $v_{C/B} = 5.6$ in./s ⟍ 32.38°

1.139 $v_{B/A} = 21.11$ mph ⟋ 54.3°,
$a_{B/A} = 795.9$ mi/h² ⟍ 38.7°

1.141 (a) $v_{B/A} = -100$ mph, $a_{B/A} = 16119$ mi/h²,
(b) $v_{A/B} = 100$ mph

1.143 $v_B = 30$ m/s

1.145 $v_B = 0.058$ ft/s (↑)

1.147 $v_A + 2v_B + v_C = 0, a_A + 2a_B + a_C = 0$

1.149 $v_B = 2$ m/s (↓), $a_B = 5$ m/s² (↑)

CHAPTER 2

2.1 $W_m = 9.47$ lb

2.3 $T = 2000$ lb

2.5 $v_y = 5.58$ m/s (↑)

2.7 $v = 344$ ft/s ⟋ 38.6°, $r = 699$ ft ⟋ 50.1°

2.9 $\mathbf{v} = -12.86\mathbf{i} + 38.6\mathbf{j} + 32.1\mathbf{k}$ (m/s),
$\mathbf{r} = -12.86\mathbf{i} + 57.9\mathbf{j} + 32.2\mathbf{k}$ (m)

2.11 $v_0 = 8.02$ ft/s (→)

2.13 Distance traveled = 176.3 ft

2.15 (a) $\mu_k = 0.568$, (b) $t = 4.24$ s

2.17 (a) $t = 0.817$ s, (b) $x = 8.17$ ft ⟋ 30°

2.19 $x = 26.1$ ft ⟋ 30°, $v = 13.4$ ft/s ⟋ 30°

2.21 $x = 106.8$ m ⟋ 45°, $v = 106.1$ m/s ⟋ 45°

2.23 $\beta = -45°$ and 67.6°

2.25 $x = 1.04$ mi

2.27 $x = 25$ m

2.29 (a) $a_A = 8.78$ ft/s² (↑), $a_B = 8.78$ ft/s² (↓),
(b) $T = 127.3$ lb,
(c) $s_B = 39.5$ ft (↓),
(d) $v_B = 26.3$ ft/s (↓)

2.31 (a) $a_A = 6.78$ ft/s² (↓), $a_B = 1.7$ ft/s² (↑),
(b) $T = 236.8$ lb, (c) $s_B = 7.65$ ft (↑), (d) $v_B = 5.1$ ft/s (↑)

2.33 (a) $a_A = 17.8$ ft/s² (↓), $a_B = 16$ ft/s² (↑),
$a_C = 14.2$ ft/s² (↓), (b) $T = 22.4$ lb, (c) $s_B = 72$ ft (↑),
(d) $v_B = 48$ ft/s (↑)

2.35 (a) $a_A = 15.1$ ft/s² (↓), $a_B = 18.9$ ft/s² (↑),
$a_c = 3.77$ ft/s² (↓), (b) $T = 79.4$ lb in both cables,
(c) $s_B = 85.1$ ft (↑), (d) $v_B = 56.7$ ft/s (↑)

2.37 (a) $a = 0.765$ m/s² ⟍ 10°,
(b) $T_{AB} = 205$ N, $T_{BC} = 198.7$ N

2.39 $a_x = 23.9$ ft/s² (→)

2.41 $\mu = 0.467$

2.43 $a_A = 0.0932$ m/s² (←), $a_B = 4.83$ m/s² ⟍ 35.7°

2.45 $F_B = 563$ lb ⟋ 30°, $F_C = 751$ lb (→), $F_D = 0$

2.47 $F_A = 536$ N (↓), $F_B = 869$ N (↓)

2.49 $F = 855$ N ⟋ 76.2°

2.51 $a = 69.8$ ft/s² ⟋ 32.8°, $T = 42.6$ lb

2.53 (a) $N = 52.3$ N, (b) $N = 60.2$ N

2.55 $\propto = 48.2°$

2.57 $\propto = 31.6°$

2.59 $N = 922$ N (↑)

2.61 $v = 46$ mph

2.63 $v = 88.3$ mph

2.65 $F_R = -3.49$ lb, $F_\theta = 1.745$ lb, $F_z = 0.932$ lb

2.67 $F = 0.517$ lb

2.69 $F_1 = 5.13$ lb (↑), $F_2 = 5.39$ lb ⟍ 50°

2.71 $t = 1.04$ s

2.73 $\dot{\theta} = 2.93$ rad/s

2.75 $F_R = -4.44$ N, $F_\theta = 0$, $F_z = 23.6$ N

2.77 $F = 291$ lb $\longleftarrow$

2.79 $\dot{\theta} = \pm \sqrt{\dfrac{g}{a}\left(\dfrac{\sin \propto - \mu_s \cos \propto}{\cos \propto + \mu_s \sin \propto}\right)}$

CHAPTER 3

3.1 $U_{A \to B} = 4298.7$ lb $\cdot$ ft

3.3 $(U_{A \to B})_{\text{Fric}} = \mu WL - \mu F \int_B^A \sin \theta \, dx$;
$(U_{A \to B})_F = FL(\sin \theta_B - \sin \theta_A)/\sin(\theta_B - \theta_A)$

3.5 $\Sigma U_{A \to C} = -808.47$ N $\cdot$ m

3.7 $\Sigma U_{A \to B} = 120$ lb $\cdot$ ft

3.9 $\Sigma U_{A \to B} = -109.65$ N $\cdot$ m

3.11 $\Sigma U_{A \to B} = 52.4$ lb $\cdot$ ft

3.13 $\Sigma U_{A \to B} = 84.75$ lb $\cdot$ ft

3.15 $\Sigma U_{A \to B} = 230$ lb $\cdot$ ft

3.17 $\Sigma U_{A \to B} = -116.25$ lb $\cdot$ ft

3.19 $v_B = 6.66$ m/s

3.21 $L = 3.55$ ft

3.23 $F_T = 24.9$ N

3.25 $v_B = 11.7$ ft/s

3.27 $x = 9$ ft away from O

3.29 $H = 0.5$ m

3.31 $k = 193.7$ ton/ft

3.33 $d = 481$ ft

3.35 $v_{x=5} = 58.1$ ft/s

3.37 $v_A = 8.7$ ft/s

3.39 $s = 132$ ft

3.41 $v = 1.39$ m/s

3.43 $F_T = 4171.2$ lb

3.45 $k = 46.7$ lb/ft

3.47 $k = 8$ kN/m

3.49 $v_B = 7.75$ ft/s

3.51 $v_B = L\sqrt{gk/w}$

3.53 $v = 27.5$ ft/s

3.55 $v_A = 1.26$ m/s

3.57 $v_P = 3.79$ m/s

3.59 $v_A = (g[\sqrt{2}\,H + 2R - \sqrt{2}\,R])^{1/2}$

3.61 $v_A = 5.96$ m/s $\downarrow$, $v_B = 2.98$ m/s $\uparrow$

3.63 $v_A = 30.5$ ft/s

3.65 $\theta = 48.2°$

3.67 $v = 7.3$ m/s

3.69 $v_B = 7.3$ m/s

3.71 $V = -(x^3 + y^4)$

3.73   Power input $= 636.7$ hp

3.75   Hoist power $= 32,700$ N $\cdot$ m/s

3.77   Power $= 422.5$ N $\cdot$ m/s

3.79 $\eta = 0.47$

CHAPTER 4

4.1   (a) 7,515.8 lb $\cdot$ s, (b) 2505 lb, (c) d $= 121$ ft

4.3 7.9×10^6 N

4.5   102.1 N

4.7   (a) $\theta = 16.7°$, (b) $I_{\max} = 144$ lb $\cdot$ s

4.9 $(v_z)_{\max} = 1000$ m/s

4.11 $\mathbf{v}(t) = (25 + 1.29\,t^3)\,\mathbf{i} + (75 + 2t^2 - t)\mathbf{j} + (25 + 0.5t^4)\mathbf{k}$

4.13 $t = 7.1$ s

4.15 $t_2 = 4.6$ s

4.17   1.2 m/s

4.19   3.87 lb.s $\longleftarrow$

4.21   3.98 m/s $\longrightarrow$

4.23 1.1×10^{-25} kg

4.25   81,988 lb $\longleftarrow$

4.27   5000 m/s $\longrightarrow$

4.29 $\mathbf{F} = -1.55\mathbf{i} + 1.55\mathbf{j}$ ft/s

4.31 $\mathbf{v}_A = 75$ ft/s $\longrightarrow$, $\mathbf{v}_B = 33.3$ ft/s $\uparrow$

4.33   4671 lb $\longleftarrow$

4.35   0.67 ft/s $\longleftarrow$

4.37   500 m/s $\nearrow$

4.39   11.25 N $\cdot$ m

4.41 $(\mathbf{v}_B)_1 = 25.7$ ft/s $\longrightarrow$, $(\mathbf{v}_B)_2 = 69.7$ ft/s $\longrightarrow$

4.43   9255 lb $\uparrow$

4.45 $e = 0.12$

4.47 $\mathbf{v}_A = 23.8$ ft/s $\overset{21.6}{\underset{10}{\diagup}}$

4.49 $(v_{\text{ball}})_1 = 12.69$ ft/s, $(v_{\text{ball}})_2 = 7.33$ ft/s, $v_{\text{block}} = 4.09$ ft/s

4.51 $\theta_2 = 29°$, $\theta_2 = 14.3°$

4.55 $(\mathbf{H}_A)_O = -22\mathbf{i} - 17\mathbf{j} - 9$ (N $\cdot$ m $\cdot$ s),
$(\mathbf{H}_B)_O = 3\mathbf{i} - 4\mathbf{j} - 11\mathbf{k}$ (N $\cdot$ m $\cdot$ s)

4.57 $\mathbf{G} = 10\mathbf{i} - 19.65\mathbf{j}$ (kg $\cdot$ m/s), $\mathbf{H}_O = 29.5\mathbf{k}$ (kg $\cdot$ m^2/s)

4.59 $\mathbf{G} = 0.07\mathbf{i} + 0.03\mathbf{k}$ (lb $\cdot$ s), $\mathbf{H}_0 = 0.4\mathbf{j}$ (lb $\cdot$ ft $\cdot$ s)

4.61   180 rpm

4.63   128 N

4.65 $\omega_2 = 4\omega$

4.67   18 rpm

4.69   19,250 mph

4.71   3834 mph

4.75   (a) $v = 15,955$ mph, (b) 17,784 mi

4.77   (a) 7909 mph, (b) 6445 mph

4.79   18,720 km/h

CHAPTER 5

5.1 $\mathbf{r}_c = -(\frac{1}{6})\mathbf{i} + (\frac{2}{3})\mathbf{j} + (\frac{3}{2})\mathbf{k}(m)$

5.3 $\mathbf{v}_A = (\frac{4}{3})\mathbf{i} + (\frac{5}{3})\mathbf{j} - (\frac{2}{3})\mathbf{k}$ (m/s),
       $\mathbf{v}_B = -(\frac{2}{3})\mathbf{i} - (\frac{4}{3})\mathbf{j} + (\frac{5}{3})\mathbf{k}$ (m/s),
       $\mathbf{v}_c = -(\frac{2}{3})\mathbf{i} - (\frac{1}{3})\mathbf{j} - (\frac{7}{3})\mathbf{k}$ (m/s)

5.5 $\mathbf{v} = 0.82\mathbf{i} + 11.5\mathbf{j} + 179.10\mathbf{k}$ (ft/s),
       $\mathbf{a} = 1.07\mathbf{j} + 35.82\mathbf{k}$ (ft/s)

5.7 $10.73\mathbf{i} + 10.73\mathbf{j} + 26.83\mathbf{k}$ (ft/s²)

5.9 $\mathbf{v}_B = -\frac{2}{3}\mathbf{i} + 4\mathbf{j} - \frac{3}{2}\mathbf{k}$ (ft/s)

5.11   39.3 ft

5.13 $v_1 = 917.2$ m/s, $v_2 = 5712.5$ m/s

5.15 $3.33\mathbf{i}$ (m/s)

5.17   977.2 lb·ft

5.19   37.3 ft/s

5.21   2358.3 lb·ft

5.23 $0.75\mathbf{i} + 2\mathbf{j}$ (m/s)

5.25 $m_B = 152.7$ kg

5.27   6.54 ft/s

5.29   0.85 m/s

5.31 (a) $68.3\mathbf{i} + 60.6\mathbf{j}$ (lb·s), (b) $-20\mathbf{i} - 95\mathbf{j}$ (lb)

5.33 $\mathbf{v}_c = 50\mathbf{i} + 30\mathbf{j}$ (m/s)

5.35 $\mathbf{v}_c(t = 2s) = -3008\mathbf{i} - 250\mathbf{j}$ (ft/s),
       $\mathbf{r}_c(t = 2s) = -6016\mathbf{i} - 500\mathbf{j}$ (ft)

5.37 $\mathbf{v}_B = 0.89$ m/s $\searrow$ 30°, $\mathbf{v}_c = 1.39$ (m/s) $\triangle$ 30°

5.39   54,500 km/h

5.41 $(8t)\mathbf{i} - (141.15t)\mathbf{j}$

5.43 $1625\mathbf{i} + 1950\mathbf{j} + 2275\mathbf{k}$ (km/h)

5.45   17.7 rad/s

5.47 $28\mathbf{i} + 32\mathbf{j} - 4k$ (N·m·s)

5.49   6880.4 lb·ft $\circlearrowright$

5.51 $(M_O)_y = -99.4$ lb·ft, $(M_O)_z = -496.8$ lb·ft

5.53   40,708 N $\rightarrow$

5.55   12,500 N $\leftarrow$

5.57   33,000 N $\leftarrow$

5.59   46.3 lb/bolt

5.61   60 kN $\leftarrow$

5.63   34,920 J

5.65   7330 N $\nearrow$ 19.5°

5.67   6931 m/s

5.69   25,625 N

5.71   2943 kN

CHAPTER 6

6.1 (a) 41.9 rad/s², (b) 30 rev.

6.3 $v_A = 1164$ m/s, $a_A = 289$ m/s²

6.5 $v_B = 35$ ft/s $\downarrow$, $v_c = 25$ ft/s $\nearrow$
       $a_b = 178.5$ ft/s² $\nearrow$ 11.3°, $a_c = 127.5$ ft/s² $\searrow$ 48.2°

6.7 (a) $v_p = 37.1$ ft/s, $a_p = 276.6$ ft/s², (b) 1.74 s

6.9 $\alpha_B = 6.67$ rad/s², $\omega_B = 23.6$ rad/s after 5 rev.

6.11 (a) $\alpha = -6$ rad/s², (b) $t = 2.51$ s

6.13   0.7 rad/s²

6.15 (a) 30 rad/s, 15 rad/s², (b) 4.8 rev.

6.17   1273 rpm

6.19 (a) 20.9 min, (b) 12,566 rev.

6.21 $\mathbf{v}_A = 400\mathbf{i} + 400\mathbf{j}$ (ft/s), $\mathbf{v}_B = 800\mathbf{i}$, $\mathbf{v}_c = 683\mathbf{i} - 283\mathbf{j}$

6.23 $\omega_{AB} = 0$, $v_A = v_B = 26.2$ m/s

6.25 $\omega_{BC} = 12.6$ rad/s $\circlearrowleft$, $v_c = 116.7$ m/s $\downarrow$

6.27 (a) $\omega_{BC} = 1.2$ rad/s $\circlearrowright$, $(b) = v_D = 4.2\mathbf{i} + 2.1\mathbf{j}$ (m/s)

6.29 $\omega = 2$ rad/s $\circlearrowright$, $\mathbf{v}_A = 5\mathbf{i}$ (m/s), $\mathbf{v}_D = 15\mathbf{i}$ (m/s)

6.31 $\omega_{AB} = 10$ rad/s $\circlearrowleft$, $\omega_{BC} = 0$

6.33 $v_C = 251.3$ m/s $\rightarrow$, $\omega_{BC} = 0$

6.35 $\omega_{\text{truck}} = 0.017$ rad/s $\circlearrowleft$

6.37 $\mathbf{v}_p = 3.56\mathbf{i} - 0.127\mathbf{j}$ (ft/s)

6.39 $\mathbf{v}_A = 50\mathbf{i} - 900\mathbf{j}$ (m/s), $\mathbf{v}_B = 950\mathbf{i}$ (m/s) $\rightarrow$,
       $\mathbf{v}_c = -850\mathbf{i}$ (m/s) $\leftarrow$

6.41 $\omega_B = \omega_A(r_A^2 + L^2)^{1/2}/r_B$

6.43 $\omega_{BC} = 3.49$ rad/s, $v_c = 14.28$ ft/s

6.45 $\mathbf{v}_A = 50.3$ ft/s $\downarrow$, $v_B = 35.5$ $\nearrow$ ft/s

6.47 $(\mathbf{v}_A)_{\text{abs}} = 740.66$ m/s $\leftarrow$, $(\mathbf{v}_B)_{\text{abs}} = 830.14$ m/s $\rightarrow$

6.49 $\omega_{BC} = 0$

6.51 $\alpha_{AB} = 0.85$ rad/s² $\circlearrowright$, $a_A = 19.2$ ft/s² $\downarrow$

6.53 (a) $\omega_{AB} = 9.0$ rad/s $\circlearrowright$, (b) $\alpha_{AB} = 134.1$ rad/s² $\uparrow$,
       $a_B = 386.3$ in./s² $\leftarrow$

6.55 $a_p = 20.6$ m/s² $\triangle$ 29.1°

6.57 $\alpha_A = 8.75$ rad/s² $\circlearrowright$

6.59 $a_p = -65.5\mathbf{i} - 35.4\mathbf{j}$ (ft/s²)

6.61 (a) $\omega_{BC} = 10$ rad/s $\circlearrowright$, (b) $\alpha_{BC} = 100$ rad/s² $\circlearrowright$,
       (c) $\mathbf{a}_G = -150\mathbf{i} + 175\mathbf{j}$ (ft/s)

6.63 $\mathbf{v}_c = 10\mathbf{i} + 50\mathbf{j}$ (m/s), $\mathbf{a}_c = -504\mathbf{i} + 100\mathbf{j}$ (m/s²)

6.65 $\omega_{O'C} = 6$ rad/s $\circlearrowleft$, $\alpha_{O'C} = 20$ rad/s² $\circlearrowleft$

6.67 $\omega_{OC} = 0.333$ rad/s $\circlearrowleft$, $\alpha_{OC} = 4.61$ rad/s² $\circlearrowleft$

6.69 $\mathbf{v}_p = 2.1\mathbf{i} - 34.1\mathbf{j}$ (ft/s), $\mathbf{a}_p = -66.1\mathbf{i} - 2.12\mathbf{j}$ (ft/s²)

6.71 $\omega'_{O'p} = 7.32$ rad/s $\circlearrowleft$, $\alpha'_{O'p} = 41.6$ rad/s² $\circlearrowright$

6.73 $\mathbf{v}_p = -0.2\mathbf{i} - 7.5\mathbf{j} + 7.5\mathbf{k}$ (m/s),
       $\mathbf{a}_p = -2\mathbf{i} - 6\mathbf{j} - 5.6\mathbf{k}$ (m/s²)

6.75 $\mathbf{v}_B = -5.0\mathbf{i} - 13\mathbf{j} + 7.5\mathbf{k}$ (ft/s),
       $\mathbf{a}_B = 0\mathbf{i} - 3.25\mathbf{j} - 3.90\mathbf{k}$ (ft/s²)

6.77 $\mathbf{v}_D = -22.5\mathbf{i}$ (ft/s), $\mathbf{a}_D = -3\mathbf{i} - 113\mathbf{j} + 130\mathbf{k}$ (m/s²)

6.79 $\mathbf{a}_A = 40\mathbf{i} - 32\mathbf{j} - 50\mathbf{k}$ (m/s²), $\mathbf{a}_B = -90\mathbf{j}$ (m/s²),
       $\mathbf{a}_c = -40\mathbf{i} - 30\mathbf{j} + 50\mathbf{k}$ (m/s²)

6.81 $\boldsymbol{\alpha} = 4520\mathbf{i}$ (rad/s²)

6.83 $v_D = -3.5i - 2j + 8.7k$ (m/s),
$a_A = -9.2i + 47.2j + 26.9k$ (m/s²)

6.85 $\Omega = 5i + 2k$ (rad/s), $\dot{\Omega} = 10j$ (rad/s²),
$v_p = -24i - 50j$ (in./s)

6.87 $\dot{\Omega} = 13.73i$ (rad/s²)

6.89 $v_c = -15.9i + 51.6j - 2.4k$ (m/s),
$a_c = -552.4i - 68.8j - 0.97k$ (m/s²)

CHAPTER 7

7.1 7.06 m/s² (→)

7.3 8310 N

7.5 67.2 m/s² △ $\theta = 22.7°$

7.7 2.87 m/s²

7.9 $a = 2.16$ m/s², $N_B = 202$ N, $N_A = 484$ N

7.11 $N_A = 400$ lb, $a = 3.58$ ft/s²

7.13 25.4°

7.15 $T_A = 59.3$ N, $T_B = 193$ N

7.17 $a = 8.57$ m/s² (←), $A = 105.5$ kN, $B = 291$ kN

7.19 27.5 m/s

7.21 3.22 rad/s² (↻)

7.23 21.1 rad/s (↻)

7.25 5.05 rad/s (↺)

7.27 $O_t = 4.33$ lb ↘ 30°, $O_n = 28.8$ lb ∠ 30°

7.29 $\omega = 1.86$ rad/s (↻), $O_n = 948$ N, $O_t = 0$

7.31 $A_x = 0$, $A_y = 122.8$ N

7.33 $a_c = 0.78$ m/s² (↑), $O_x = 1039$ N (←), $O_y = 5822$ N (↑)

7.35 7143 rad/s² (↻)

7.37 $F = 534.8$ lb (↓), $O_x = 621$ lb (←), $O_y = 709$ lb (↑)

7.39 $\alpha = 53.7$ rad/s² (↻), $d = 4$ ft

7.41 6.95 m/s² (↘)

7.43 0.67 m/s² (→)

7.45 $\alpha = 3.33$ rad/s² (↻), $F_\mu = 99.9$ N (→), $N_A = 252$ N (↑)

7.47 $\alpha = 8.59$ rad/s² (↻), $N_A = 736$ N (↑), $F = 22.2$ N (→)

7.49 $\alpha = 0.50$ rad/s² (↺), $N_A = 105$ N (→), $N_B = 351$ N (↑)

7.51 $\alpha = 14.7$ rad/s² (↻), $C_x = 0$, $C_y = 24.5$ (↓)

7.53 $T_A = 279$ N, $T_B = 299$ N

7.55 $a_A = 7.23$ ft/s² (←), $\alpha = 6.70$ rad/s² (↺)

7.57 $B_x = 686$ lb (←), $B_y = 7.0$ lb (↑), $N_c = 268.5$ lb (↓)

7.59 9.4 lb (←)

7.61 $a_c = 5.1$ m/s² (↑), $\alpha = 0.22$ rad/s² (↺)

7.63 $\alpha = 1.2$ rad/s² (↻), $a_B = 4$ ft/s² (→)

7.67 $\alpha = 0.64$ rad/s² (↻), $a_c = 24.4i + 6.81j$ (ft/s²)

7.69 $\omega = \dfrac{1}{k_o}\sqrt{2a_ob(1 - \cos\theta)}$ (↻),

$$O_x = ma_o\left[1 - \frac{b^2}{k_o^2}(1 + 2\cos\theta - 3\cos^2\theta)\right] \text{(→)}$$

$$O_y = \frac{ma_ob^2}{k_o^2}(3\cos\theta - 2)\sin\theta \text{ (↓)}$$

7.71 $(a_c)_{\text{front}} = 10.35$ ft/s², $(a_c)_{\text{rear}} = 8.78$ ft/s²

7.73 $\alpha_B = 216$ rad/s² (↻)

7.75 $O_x = 23$ lb (→), $O_y = 14.7$ lb (↑)

7.77 $T = 490.5$ N

7.79 $A_x = 293$ lb (←), $A_y = 30$ lb (↑)

CHAPTER 8

8.1 24.2 ft/s (↓)

8.3 2.71 rad/s

8.5 3.70 rad/s (↺)

8.7 $v_A = 5.6$ m/s, $(a_A)_n = 126$ m/s², $(a_A)_t = 5.10$ m/s²

8.9 2.7 rad/s (↻)

8.11 3.28 rad/s (↻)

8.13 934 N

8.15 5.98 m

8.17 4.5 rad/s (↻)

8.19 5.99 rad/s (↻)

8.21 5.5 rad/s (↺)

8.23 2.25 ft/s

8.25 14.2 rad/s (↺)

8.27 36.5 ft/s

8.29 35.5 ft/s ∠ 45°

8.31 2.72 rad/s

8.33 3.70 rad/s (↺)

8.35 34.3 rad/s (↺)

8.37 426 N

8.39 99 mm

8.41 86.7 rad/s (↺)

8.43 $v_c = \sqrt{\frac{10}{7}gL\sin\theta}$

8.45 232 lb

8.47 5.83 rad/s (↻)

8.49 3.44 rad/s (↻)

8.51 1.36 rad/s (↻)

8.53 34.3°

8.55 0.695 rad/s (↻)

8.57 3283 lb·ft

8.59 2.63 lb·ft

8.61 16.6 rad/s (↻)

8.63 2.42 rad/s (↻)

8.65 0.54 s; disk will remain at rest

8.67 $v_c = 143$ ft/s ↗ 18°, $\omega = 309$ rad/s (↺)

8.69 29.6 rad/s (↻)

8.71 13.9 m/s (↓)

8.73 216 ft/s (←)

8.75 0.25 rad/s (↻)

8.77   0.1 ft/s $\downarrow$

8.79   194 ft/s

8.81   1.03 rad/s $\circlearrowleft$

8.83 $x_p = 0.80$ m

8.85 $d = 2$ m

8.87   571 N

8.89   64.1°

8.91   3 rad/s $\circlearrowright$

8.93   1.83 rad/s $\circlearrowleft$

8.95   0.0455 N·m

8.97   1469 lb·ft $\circlearrowright$

8.99   21.9 rad/s $\circlearrowright$

CHAPTER 9

9.1 $\mathbf{H}_O = -6.67\mathbf{i} - 11.55\mathbf{j} + 11.34\mathbf{k}$ (kg·m²/s)

9.3 $\mathbf{H}_O = -5\mathbf{j} + 50.5\mathbf{k}$ (kg·m²/s)

9.5 $\mathbf{H}_O = \frac{1}{6}mb^2\omega\mathbf{i} + \frac{\sqrt{3}}{6}mb^2\omega\mathbf{j} - \frac{1}{4}mab\omega\mathbf{k}$

9.7 $(\mathbf{H}_O)_2 = 12(3\mathbf{i} + 2\mathbf{j} + \mathbf{k})$(kg·m²/s); $\boldsymbol{\omega} = 0.108\mathbf{i} + 0.090\mathbf{j} + 0.179\mathbf{k}$ (rad/s)

9.9 $\mathbf{H}_O = 1.553\mathbf{i} + 8.152\mathbf{k}$ (slug·ft²/s)

9.11 $\mathbf{H}_O = 6.25\mathbf{i} - 20\mathbf{j} + 40.625\mathbf{k}$ (kg·m²/s)

9.13 $\mathbf{H}_O = 10.94\mathbf{j} + 2.706\mathbf{k}$ (kg·m²/s), 13.9°

9.15 $\boldsymbol{\omega} = 148.6\mathbf{i} + 241.5\mathbf{j}$ (rad/s)

9.17 $\mathbf{H}_O = 172.56\mathbf{j} + 298.86\mathbf{k}$ (slug·ft²/s)

9.19 $\mathbf{H}_O = \frac{w\ell^3}{6g}\omega[-9\mathbf{i} - 3\mathbf{j} + 10\mathbf{k}]$ (slug·ft²/s)

9.21 $\boldsymbol{\omega} = 3g(F\,\Delta t)(-5\mathbf{j} - \mathbf{k})/7wb$

9.23 $(H_O)_x = \frac{1}{3}m(a^2 + b^2)(\omega_2 \cos\theta - \omega_1 \sin\theta)\cos\theta$

9.25 $(H_O)_x = \frac{1}{12}m(3R^2 + 4L^2 + 12b^2)\omega_2$, $(H_O)_y = \frac{1}{2}m(R^2 + 2b^2)\omega_1$, $(H_O)_z = \frac{1}{2}mbL\omega_1$

9.27 $\mathbf{H}_O = \frac{ma}{12}\omega(-3b\mathbf{j} + 2a\mathbf{k})$; $\mathbf{H}_c = \frac{m\omega}{36}a(-b\mathbf{j} + 2a\mathbf{k})$

9.29 $\mathbf{H}_p = 57{,}065\mathbf{i} - 3{,}494\mathbf{j} + 57{,}065\mathbf{k}$ (slug·ft²/s)

9.31 $\boldsymbol{\omega}_2 = 1.11(\mathbf{j} + \mathbf{k})$ (rad/s)

9.33 $(\omega_A)_2 = 1$ rad/s $\circlearrowright$, $(\omega_B)_2 = 38$ rad/s $\circlearrowleft$

9.35 $T = 189$ J

9.37 $T = \frac{1}{6}mb^2\omega^2$

9.39 $T = 28.14$ lb·ft

9.41 $T = 167.5$ J

9.43 $T = \frac{1}{12g}wa^4\omega^2$ lb·ft

9.45 $T = \frac{5}{6g}w\ell^3\omega^2$ lb·ft

9.47 $\omega = 26.05$ rad/s

9.49 $\Delta T = 45.98$ J

9.51 $T_2 = 92{,}479.3$ lb·ft

9.53 $\Delta t_A = 6.25$ s, $\Delta t_B = 8.50$ s

9.57 $H_z = 3.99$ kg·m²/s, $T = 49.26$ J

9.61 $C = D = 0$

9.63 $\mathbf{A} = -178.56\mathbf{j}$ (N), $\mathbf{O} = -46.44\mathbf{j}$ (N)

9.65 $\mathbf{A} = \frac{3M(a + b)}{8b(2b + 3a)}\mathbf{k}$, $\mathbf{B} = -\frac{3M(a + b)}{8b(2b + 3a)}\mathbf{k}$

9.67 $\theta = 82.4°$

9.69 $\mathbf{A} = \mathbf{B} = -\left(0.963\frac{w}{g}b^3\omega^2\right)\mathbf{k}$

9.71 $M = 72.1$ lb·ft

9.73 $\mathbf{O} = -5.57\mathbf{i} + 38.70\mathbf{k}$ (lb), $\mathbf{c} = -10.81\mathbf{i} - 23.58\mathbf{k}$ (lb), $\dot{\omega} = 12.07$ rad/s²

9.75 $\dot{\phi} = 57.65$ rad/s or 10.93 rad/s

9.77 $\dot{\psi} = 4.04$ rad/s

9.79 $\dot{\phi} = 11.34$ rad/s

CHAPTER 10

10.1   (a) $\omega_n = 14.65$ rad/s, (b) $T_n = 0.429$ s, (c) $A = \pm 0.5$ ft, (d) $v_{max} = 7.33$ ft/s, (e) $a_{max} = 107.3$ ft/s²

10.3   (a) $\omega_n = 11.34$ rad/s, (b) $T_n = 0.554$ s, (c) $A = \pm 0.0176$ m, (d) $v_{max} = 0.2$ m/s, (e) $a_{max} = 2.26$ m/s²

10.5 $T_n = 0.495$ s

10.9   (a) $\omega_n = 21.5$ rad/s, (b) $v_{max} = 1.79$ ft/s, (c) $a_{max} = 38.5$ ft/s²

10.11 $\ddot{\theta} + (g/L)\theta = 0$, $T_n = 2\pi\sqrt{L/g}$

10.13 $f_n = 0.831$ cycles/s

10.15 $k = 92.9$ lb/in.

10.17 $\omega_n = 3.56$ rad/s

10.19 $T_n = 1.6$ s

10.21 $T_n = 2\pi\left[\dfrac{\sqrt{b^2 + d^2}}{3g/2}\right]^{1/2}$

10.23 $T_n = 0.452$ s

10.25   (a) $T_n = 0.46$ s, (b) $v_{S\,max} = 3.42$ ft/s

10.27 $T_n = 2\pi\sqrt{\dfrac{5m}{3(k_1 + k_2)}}$

10.29 $x = 0.489$ ft $\uparrow$, $v = 1.539$ ft/s $\uparrow$, $a = 104.9$ ft/s² $\downarrow$

10.31 $T_n = 2\pi\sqrt{m/(k_1 + k_2)}$

10.33 $\omega_n = \sqrt{g/L + 2kb^2/mL^2}$

10.35 $\omega_n = \sqrt{3g/2L}$

10.37 $T_n = 1.65$ s

10.39 $T_n = 0.452$ s

10.41 $T_n = 0.249$ s

10.43 $T_n = 2\pi\sqrt{\dfrac{5m}{3(k_1 + k_2)}}$

10.45 $\bar{\omega} = 5.48$ rad/s

10.47 $x = 0.2 \cos (5.48t) - 0.158 [\sin (7t) - 1.28 \sin (5.48t)]$ m

10.49 (a) $DMF = 1.013$, (b) $X = 2.11$ in.

10.51 $0 < \bar{\omega} < 24.9$ rad/s

10.53 $X = 0.601$ mm, $\bar{\omega}_{res} = 88.4$ rpm

10.55 (a) $DMF = 1.537$, (b) $X = 9.22$ in.

10.57 $X = 4.52$ in.

10.59 $X_S = 3.36$ in.

10.61 $X = 1.68$ in.

10.63 (a) $c/c_c = 1$, (b) critically damped system

10.67 $5625\ddot{\theta} + 4500\dot{\theta} + 9000\theta = 0$, $c/c_c = 1$, critically damped system

10.69 $0 < \bar{\omega} < 21.3$ rad/s

10.71 $X = 0.597$ mm

10.73 $X = 1.51$ in.

10.75 $L\ddot{q} + (1/\overline{C})q = E_o \sin \bar{\omega}t$

10.77 $L\ddot{q} + R\dot{q} + (1/\overline{C})q = 0$

INDEX

U.S. Customary Units and Their SI Equivalents

Quantity	U.S. Customary Unit	SI Equivalent
Acceleration	ft/s^2	0.3048 m/s^2
Angular acceleration	rad/s^2	1.0 rad/s^2
Angular velocity	rad/s	1.0 rad/s
Area	ft^2	0.0929 m^2
Energy	ft · lb	1.356 J
Force	kip	4.448 kN
	lb	4.448 N
Impulse	lb · s	4.448 N · s
Length	ft	0.3048 m
	in	25.4 mm
Mass	lb mass	0.4536 kg
	oz mass	28.35 g
	slug (lb-s^2/ft)	14.594 kg
	ton (2000lbs)	907.18 kg
Moment	lb · ft	1.356 N · m
Moment of inertia of an area	in^4	0.4162 x 10^{6}mm^4 = 0.4162 x 10^{-6}m^4
Moment of inertia of a mass	lb · ft · s^2	1.356 kg · m^2
Power	lb · ft/s	1.356 W
Pressure	lb/ft^2	47.88 Pa
	lb/in^2	6.895 kPa
Velocity	ft/s	0.3048 m/s
Volume (liquid)	gal	3.785 L
Volume (solid)	ft^3	0.02832 m^3
	in^3	16.39 cm^3
Work	ft · lb	1.3558 J
	kw-h	3.60 x 10^6 J